THE HISTORY OF

HENRY ESMOND, Esq.

WRITTEN BY HIMSELF

THE ENGLISH HUMOURISTS OF THE EIGHTEENTH CENTURY

THE FOUR GEORGES

AND

CHARITY AND HUMOUR

BY

WILLIAM MAKEPEACE THACKERAY

WITH ILLUSTRATIONS BY GEORGE DU MAURIER
F. BARNARD, AND FRANK DICKSEE, R.A.

HARPER & BROTHERS PUBLISHERS
NEW YORK AND LONDON
1902

THE BIOGRAPHICAL EDITION

THE WORKS OF

WILLIAM MAKEPEACE THACKERAY

WITH BIOGRAPHICAL INTRODUCTIONS BY
HIS DAUGHTER, ANNE RITCHIE

IN THIRTEEN VOLUMES

VOLUME VII.

THE HISTORY OF HENRY ESMOND, ESQ.

AND

THE LECTURES

THE DUEL IN LEICESTER FIELD.

CONTENTS

BOOK II

CONTAINS MR. ESMOND'S MILITARY LIFE, AND OTHER MATTERS APPERTAINING TO THE ESMOND FAMILY

BOOK III

CONTAINING THE END OF MR. ESMOND'S ADVENTURES IN ENGLAND

THE LECTURES

THE ENGLISH HUMOURISTS

THE FOUR GEORGES

LIST OF ILLUSTRATIONS

THE HISTORY OF HENRY ESMOND, ESQ.

THE ENGLISH HUMOURISTS

THE FOUR GEORGES

INTRODUCTION

TO

ESMOND AND TO THE LECTURES

1851–1853

Part I.

"My dear Smith," my father once wrote, "how would the lectures do with no end of illustrations?—T. O.—I was drawing these, and that made me write to you,—Yours,

"W. M. T."

Here are the sketches over the page in this book as they are in my father's letter—Captain Steele with his cane and periwig, Mr. Sterne in his bands and buckles, Dr. Johnson pacing the street with Boswell by his side.

As one reads the Lectures on the Humourists, one feels how much my father was at ease with all these people, whom he loved and admired. He trod in the actual footsteps of Johnson and Goldsmith, and Steele and Addison. He saw the things they had seen, heard the echoes to which they had listened, he walked up the very streets where they had walked. He was one of them, and happy in their good company. Sir Walter also wrote of these times, also admired and appreciated all these personalities, but he belonged to a different and more romantic world of chivalry and adventure. As for my father—so he says in one of his letters—"the eighteenth century occupies him to the exclusion almost of the nineteenth," and he carried its traditions along with him.

The first lecture was given on the 21st of May 1851. Charlotte Brontë has described it, and Mrs. Kemble has described it and Willis's Rooms, the assembled company, the undoubted

JOHNSON AND BOSWELL.

STERNE.

CAPTAIN STEELE.

success of the venture. Mrs. Kemble's friendly, funny story is well known, of the lecturer's nervousness and of her trying to encourage him, and in her confusion and sympathy letting his manuscript fall from the desk; and there is that saying of my father's which she records—"that she had just given him occupation and distraction in sorting the manuscript, during the ten minutes he had still to wait." I was scarcely in my teens at the time, and it is so long ago, that the facts are somewhat confused, so that I have no details to add, except that we all drove home together, and I do remember his comfortable look of relief as we settled down in the family brougham and started away from Willis's Rooms to homelike Young Street. Very soon the lectures ceased to alarm; they became an integral part of his daily life. He used to make a little joke of his own reading, and describe "Mr. Thackeray as having recited with unusual pathos the poem of 'How doth the little busy bee' to a large and enthusiastic audience." We give a page from the "Orphan of Pimlico," which is too much to the point to be overlooked. The original drawing belongs to Mr. Leslie Stephen.

Requisitions and invitations came from every part of the country, written in neat copperplate handwriting, from various young men's associations and literary clubs. As time went on, there arose a great deal of discussion over the lecturing. Friends remonstrated; some said it was not proper work for him (our old friend Sir Edward Hamley was among these); others applauded; others asked him to give private readings at their own houses—not for payment, but for their pleasure. It was certainly not for my father's pleasure. Before long he began to get dreadfully tired of "the business," as he used to call it. But he was glad to get a rest from quill-driving, and to earn so much money—very much more than he ever earned in the same time by writing. The plans were maturing for the American journey, and meanwhile the lectures were being repeated in London, and continued at Oxford and Cambridge, and all over the country.

Mrs. Shaen has given me the following letters, which were addressed to her father at Cambridge in the November of 1851:—

"Dear Dr. Thackeray,—I want very much to get the University opinion about some lectures which I delivered in June and July last to a great audience in London, as you may have heard. . . . What pleased me most and best, Mr. Macaulay and Mr. Hallam came almost every time. I am going to take these lectures to America, and to make a little fortune out of them, I hope, for my little people. If I ever get *another* fortune, I will keep it. I must have the Vice-Chancellor's authority. . . . My man, S. James, is the bearer of this, and destined to be my confidential man in America. He has a commission to find his way to Mr. Macmillan's Library to see the person who arranges Mrs. Kemble's readings for her, and settle about bills, tickets, and announcements. I hope he will bring me the news that you are very well, and have got my leave from the Vice-Chancellor." *

"KENSINGTON, *November* 13, 1851.

"MY DEAR DR. THACKERAY,—A sudden panic has seized me lest, in your good nature and desire to serve one of our race, you should think of purchasing tickets for you or any of my cousins for those lectures which begin to-morrow. Don't you remember coming to prescribe for me when I was ill at Cambridge, and asking me 'if I thought you were a cannibal,' when I made some little proposition regarding a fee? In like manner it would shock me to see my cousins bleed. . . . I did not ask your ladies the other day, because of my natural blushing bashfulness, and because I did not know whether ladies could attend; but at Oxford there were dons and their donnas on Thursday, and I hope there may be some ladies at Cambridge too, and that my cousins and Mrs. Thackeray will favour me, if they are so inclined."

"Old Stoddart is my host at Oxford," he writes to his mother. (It may be remembered that in one of his schoolboy letters he speaks of "a friend of mine called Stoddart.") "It is curious, isn't it, to be arrived actually at the date when some money will be put by for the young ones? They will probably be worth £30 apiece to-night."

* My father had to obtain leave from the University before lecturing, and when he went to Oxford, he was advised to apply in the proper quarters himself. He was somewhat taken aback to find that his name was not known to the dignitary to whom he had to apply, nor had this gentleman ever heard of "Vanity Fair." Some one happily was found to vouch for the lecturer's respectability.

A LECTURE.

"The Lecturer's humour convulsed the audience with laughter. Mr. Thackeray's manner of reading 'How doth the little Busy Bee' was highly impressive; and his vivid yet delicate description of the Author of 'Robinson Crusoe' in the Pillory, drew tears from every eye. Among the company present we remarked Messrs. McHuffie, McDuffie. McGuffie. Revd. Messrs. McMinn and McMie, Mrs. Col. McGaspie (of Glenbogie), Miss McCraw, in a word all the Notabilities of our town."—*Kildrummle Warder.*

Here is a note about one of those early ventures:—

"My dear Nan,—Your dear papa had a hundred subscribers and about two hundred more people at the first lecture, which was very successful on the whole. And he begins to think America is farther off than it was, and that it will be a pity to leave England. . . .

"And he sends his gals his blessing, which they are a hundred pounds richer to-day than yesterday at this time."

FIGURE OF A LADY.

In December he went to Scotland for three weeks, and wrote to his friends Dr. and Mrs. John Brown, with whom he had been staying:—

2

"WESTBURY, *January* 5, 1852.

"MY DEAR MRS. BROWN,—The children write me from afar off that you have written them a kind letter, and though I think it is twenty years ago since I left Edinburgh, I have not forgotten you, and write a stupid line to say how do you do, and the Doctor and Jock and Helen.

"Since I came away I have been out a-visiting, and write this on this grand, thick official paper from a grand house, where I am treated very hospitably as usual, and propose to pass two or three days more, very possibly to try and work a little. All this pleasuring has unfitted me for it, and I begin to fancy I am a gentleman of £5000 a year. . . . I have no earthly news to send you, only the most stupid good wishes. But I wish, instead of waiting in my room up here for dinner and three courses and silver and champagne, I was looking forward to 23 and that dear old small beer, and then we would have a cab and go to the Music Hall and hear Mrs. Kemble. I sometimes fancy that having been at Edinbro' is a dream, only there are the daguerreotypes, and a box of that horrid short-bread still, and the hat full of money to be sure. It was not at all cold coming to London, and the town of Berwick-on-Tweed looked beautiful, and I think my fellow-passenger must have wondered to see how cleverly I slept. He was a young Cambridge man, and knew your humble servant perfectly well. It was on the railroad I got the great news of Palmerston's going out. It didn't frighten you in Rutland Street much I dare say, but in the houses where I go we still talk about it, and I amongst the number as gravely as if I were a Minister myself. Why do we? What does it matter to me who's Minister? Depend upon it, 23 Rutland Street is the best, and good, dear, kind friends, and quiet talk, and honest beer.

"You see by the absurd foregoing paragraphs that I have nothing in the world to say, but I want to shake you and the Doctor by the hand, and say thank you, and God bless you.

"W. M. THACKERAY."

In January he says, "They make me an offer of £150 at the Portman Square Rooms—pretty well for six hours."

I have been surprised sometimes, reading the various criticisms of my father's work, to find how much—especially when he first began to lecture—people dwelt on his powers of criticism, his severe judgments, his sarcastic descriptions, whereas the other healing qualities are almost passed over.

And yet the gift of appreciation was his in no common degree, the instinct of discerning true dignity and beauty in humble things; that Christian gift of making simplicity great, of seeing what is noble and eternal in the most natural and commonplace facts. It takes a Newton to divine the secrets of nature from a hint; a Bach can create a new heaven upon earth with the tinkling wires of a spinet; working in his own line, a week-day preacher, as my father loved to call himself, takes peaceful reiteration of daily duty for his text, and preaches the supremacy of goodness.

Who will not remember the passage in which he says of great men: "They speak of common life more largely and generously than common men do; they regard the world with a manlier countenance. . . . Learn to admire rightly, try to frequent the company of your betters in books and life."

On the last day of her life Mrs. Brookfield, my father's lifelong friend and mine, quoted this sentence to me, with a smile and that bright steadfast look in her eyes, which ever seemed like an accompaniment to her voice.

Here is a quotation from a letter of these times, in which, writing to his mother concerning some people in trouble, he says, "Cowardly self-love cries out Save—save, or you may starve too. . . . So please God we will, and do that work resolutely for the next year. I am very well in health, I think, having staved off my old complaint; and the only thing that alarms me sometimes is the absurd fancy that, now the money making is actually at hand, some disaster may drop down and topple me over. But that's a fancy only. . . . The novel is getting on pretty well, . . . and now let's call a cab and go to Oxford." The novel, of course, was "Esmond."

"Esmond" did not seem to be a part of our lives, as "Pendennis" had been. Although I have seen the MSS. as it was written by Mr. Crowe to dictation, and also with pages in our own youthful handwriting, I cannot remember either the writing or the dictating, nor even hearing "Esmond" spoken of except very rarely.

My sister and I were a great deal away at this time, staying in Paris with our grandparents, who were living just out of the Champs Elysées, in the rue d'Angoulême, a street which has changed its name with succeeding dynasties. (The Champs Elysées happily remain Champs Elysées still, impartially appropriate to the various governments in turn, whether monarchical, imperial, or popular.)

"As you are to be in Paris, my dearest fambly, for the fêtes," my father writes in August 1852, "I send you a word and a good morning, and such a little history of the past week as that time affords.

"Eliza does for me, and her brother runs my errands. I have been twice to Richmond, where Mrs. F—— receives me with the greatest graciousness, and announces to all her friends that I am the most agreeable of men—that she looks upon me in the light of a son. At one of these dinners was Mr. B—— and his daughter, and if I had a daughter like that, all I can say is, that I should have a bore for a daughter. She scarce ceased speaking to me the whole of dinner-time; and told me that the summer was hot, the mountains were high, and so forth, and next me, on t'other side, was a very nice, natural, ugly girl, that was worth a hundred of her. My favour with Mrs. F—— is not yet over; she sent me a tabinet waistcoat of green and gold, such an ugly one! but I shall have it made up and sport it in America, and keep the remainder for pin-cushions. . . . I sent away the first sheets of 'Esmond' yesterday. It reads better in print; it is clever, but it is also stupid, no mistake. Other parts will be more amusing, I hope and think."

"I have been living in the last century for weeks past, in the day, that is; going at night as usual into the present age, until I get to fancy myself almost as familiar with one as with the other, and Oxford and Bolingbroke interest me as much as Russell and Palmerston—more, very likely. The present politics are behind the world, and not fit for the intelligence of the nation."

About the translation of "Esmond" into French he writes to his mother: "I was going to write on this very little sheet of paper when your letter came in. Mr. De Wailly's is the best offer, but is it possible he can give us as much as 4000 francs? There must be some mistake, I fear. I have given up, and only

These meetings ended in a marriage, and we need not say the young couple were happy ever after   Memoirs of Lt General Webb.

As he was one evening about to quit the theatre, he observed a young lady on the point of fainting. Having procured water he hastened to her support. The striking figure of the young soldier made a deep impression on the lady.

Memoirs of Lt General Webb.

He waited upon the lovely widow the next day, when that favorable impression was encreased, wh had been produced already by the Captain's elegant appearance and polite behaviour

Memoirs of Lt General Webb.

had for a day or two, the notion for the book in numbers; it is much too grave and sad for that." . . .

"The great Revolution's a-coming, and the man not here who's to head it. I wonder whether he is born, and where he lives. The present writers are all employed as by instinct in unscrewing the old framework of society and getting it ready for the smash."

To Lady Stanley he writes about the same time, "I am writing a book of cut-throat melancholy suitable to my state, and have no news of myself or anybody to give you which should not be written on black-edged paper, and sealed with a hatchment."

My father used often to go off into the country with his work for a day or two, and among other places he liked Southborough, near Tunbridge Wells, where he used to stay at an inn and write. The summer when he was busy upon "Esmond," his cousins, Mrs. Irvine and Miss Selina Shakespear, were living on Rustington Common, and he used to go over sometimes and spend the day with them. It was on one of these occasions that he drew the scenes from the life of Lieut.-General Webb here given, and which Miss Shakespear has kept all these years.

Meanwhile the Lectures continued their course. He undertook a northern tour, during which, however, he still worked at his book.

W. M. T. *to* Mrs. Carmichael-Smyth.

"Glasgow, 1852.

"*Saturday, Sunday, Monday.*—My dearest mother, I have had a working fit on me for the last many days, and have slaved away without a day's intermission; at home, at Brighton, and regularly since I have been here too. I wish I had six months more to put into the novel: now it's nearly done; its scarce more than a sketch, and it might have been made a durable history, complete in its parts and its whole. But at the end of six months it would want other six. It takes as much trouble as Macaulay's History almost, and he has the vast advantage of remembering everything he has read, whilst everything but impressions—I mean facts, dates, and so forth—slip out of my head, in which there's some great faculty lacking, depend upon it.

"I came on Tuesday night. What a comfort to journey four hundred miles in twelve hours, reading a volume of Swift, and noting it, all the way, and got up like a man next morning to my work. It's true I couldn't sleep for the infernal noise of the place. On Thursday I went off, accompanied by Mr. Jeames, to Balloch, on the brink of Loch Lomond, and passed two days there scribbling away, but in quiet and fresh air. I had a boat on the loch, and it's very pretty, but not so very pretty after all. It's nothing to the Swiss lakes or Killarney. And I'm glad I didn't bring the little women, as I had half a thought of doing. . . .

"The air is choky with the smoke of ten thousand furnaces for miles round, and the whole landscape blacked all over with Indian ink. The steamers smoke more, and there are more of them than anywhere!—and after the pure air of London I can't breathe this, nor sleep in the noisiest Babel of a place I've ever . . .

"A man interrupted me in this paragraph yesterday, and we went out a-lionizing, after which no work was done. Now my dearest old mother comes in at the fag end of a day's writing, and that's sure to be a stupid, yawning letter. Indeed, when isn't there a day's work of some sort in my life as it now is? You would have had many a letter but for that weariness which makes the sight of a pen odious, and sends me to sleep of a night at home when I don't go into the world. A man must live his life. Circumstance makes that for us partly, independent of ourselves. . . .

"The folks here don't understand in the least what I'm about, but are very cordial and willing to be pleased. One fat old merchant to whom I brought a letter mistook me, or rather took me, for an actor (and so I am), and said, 'Have the goodness to call upon me to-morrow at one o'clock.' Well, I should have gone, just for the fun of the thing, only the old boy, who had never heard of me from Adam, heard in the meantime who I was, and came puffing up my stairs yesterday and took me out sight-seeing, and to dinner afterwards at his hideous house, where he dispensed hospitality very kindly to a dozen people, and put me in mind of T——'s good-humour and jollity and want of education. The rich man had toadies about him too, just as in other places. It was good to watch them—two of them were painters anxious for commissions from him.

"I looked at Carlisle as we passed through with a queer feeling. I was offered, do you remember? to be editor of the *Car-*

lisle Patriot the first year of my marriage, and refused, I think, because it was too Tory for me (it was in the Lonsdale interest). What queer speculations the might have beens are! . . ."

"*Thursday, February* 26, 1852. I don't think I have got much good news, or otherwise, to tell you since I last wrote. But my book has got into a more cheerful vein, that's a comfort, and I am relieved from the lugubrious doubts I had about it. Miss Brontë has seen the first volume, and pronounces it 'admirable and odious.' Well, I think it is very well done, and very melancholy too; but the melancholy part ends with Vol. 1, and everybody begins to move and be more cheerful."

"I wish the new novel wasn't so grand and melancholy," he repeats elsewhere; "the hero is as stately as Sir Charles Grandison—something like Warrington—a handsome likeness of an ugly son of yours. There's a deal of pains in it that

SIR CHARLES GRANDISON-ESMOND.

goes for nothing; and my paper's full, and I am my dearest mother's affectionate son, W. M. T."

Again he writes from Birmingham, from a friend's house, "Such a nice family—nice children, a sweet, kind wife, Yorke a perfect prize parson—pious, humble, merry, orthodox to the most lucky point, liked by everybody. How I should like to be like Yorke!—not for the being liked, but for that happy orthodoxy, which is as natural with him as with Addison and other fortunate people, and which would make my dear old Granny so happy if I had it."

Part II.

It will be remembered that E. FitzGerald, writing to F. Tennyson in 1852, says, "Though I have had to march to London several times, I generally ran back again as fast as I could, much preferring the fresh air and the fields to the wilderness of monkeys in London. Thackeray I saw for ten minutes; he was just in the agony of finishing a novel, which has arisen out of the reading necessary for his lectures, and relates to those times —of Queen Anne, I mean. He will get £1000 for his novel; he was wanting to finish it and rush off to the Continent to shake off the fumes of it."

Here is another mention by my father of the new book:—

"Esmond looks very stately and handsome in print, and, bore as he is, I think will do me credit. But the printers only send me one hundred pages a week, and at this rate will be three months getting through the novel." . . .

"I have just recovered from a fine panic," he says in September 1852; "my third volume was lost at the publishers. What on earth was I to do, thinks I? That will keep me six weeks more at home, and that will enable me to have the children; but the missing volume cast up again an hour ago."

By this time the American journey was settled, and the time was getting very near for his going.

"Four more days gone, and again this is the very first minute for writing. I have been to Alderley for a day since; said adieu to Liverpool, and had plenty of audience; come to London by the night mail train, and arrived at poor dreary old Kensington yesterday, Sunday morning, and all to-day have been busy till now. I found at home my women's letters, and my dearest old mother's postscript. I am glad to have such good accounts of you all, and have just sent off positively the last sentence of the 'Esmond' dedication; and if I had three hours more on Saturday, I would have been off by that boat I think, so beautiful the weather is, and so tempting the sunshine.

"I hope to send you over 'Esmond' next week. God bless my children, and kiss everybody all round for the sake of son and father."

"Now I am going to work for three hours, and to re-read 'Vanity Fair' for a cheap edition."

One of the things I remember his saying about "Esmond" I have already put into print. It was when he exclaimed in pleasure and excitement, that a young publisher called George Smith—almost a boy, he said—had come with a liberal cheque in his pocket, to offer for the unfinished novel.

I have also written of a sort of second sight my father used sometimes to speak of. Occasionally when he described places, he said he could hardly believe he had not been there; and in one of the battles in "Esmond," he told us that the very details of the foreground were visible to him as he wrote, even to some reeds growing by a streamlet, and the curve of the bank by which it flowed. I find a sentence in one of his letters which corroborates this impression.

"I was pleased to find Blenheim," he wrote to his mother in August 1852, "was just exactly the place I had figured to myself, except that the village is larger; but I fancied I had actually been there, so like the aspect of it was to what I looked for. I saw the brook which Harry Esmond crossed, and almost the spot where he fell wounded, and walked down to the Danube, and mused mighty thoughts over it. It seems grand to walk down to the Danube; but the Thames at Putney is twice as big and handsome as the river here."

We give a version of "Malbrook" going off on his campaign which may interest my readers.

"Esmond" was the only book of my father's that was first

MALBROOK S'EN VA-T-EN GUERRE.

published in all the dignity of three volumes. It came out in periwig and embroidery, in beautiful type and handsome proportions. How well I can remember the packet arriving at Paris after he had sailed for America, and our opening it and finding the handsome books, and reading the dedication.

There are but one or two descriptions of places in the whole of "Esmond." It is by allusion rather than by statement that the impression is given of that brightly painted, crowded, eventful time, which he gives back to us. Does not one almost breathe the morning air when Esmond comes out of Newgate? "The fellow in the orange-tawny livery with blue lace and facings was in waiting when Esmond came out of prison, and taking the young gentleman's slender baggage, led the way out of that odious Newgate, and by Fleet Conduit down to the Thames, where a pair of oars was called, and they went up the river to Chelsey. Esmond thought the sun had never shone so bright; nor the air felt so fresh and exhilarating. Temple

Garden, as they rowed by, looked like the Garden of Eden to him, and the aspect of the quays, wharves, and buildings by the river, Somerset House, and Westminster (where the splendid new bridge was just beginning), Lambeth tower and palace, and that busy shining scene of the Thames swarming with boats and barges, filled his heart with pleasure and cheerfulness—as well such a beautiful scene might to one who had been a prisoner so long, and with so many dark thoughts deepening the gloom of his captivity. They rowed up at length to the pretty village of Chelsey."

It is well known that Castlewood was Clevedon Court in Somersetshire, and by the kindness of Sir Edmund Elton we are

EXTERIOR OF CLEVEDON COURT.

able to give the sketch of the interior of the old hall (page xxviii). It is Kensington that echoes through the latter part of "Esmond." Once when we were walking with him through "the Square," as Kensingtonians still call it, he pointed to No. 7 and said, "That is where Lady Castlewood lived," and I think he added something about the back windows looking across the lanes to Chelsea. I have sometimes wondered where Esmond's lodgings were. Perhaps he lived in one of those old

INTERIOR OF CLEVEDON HALL.

houses among the gardens at Brompton; for he meets Addison one night walking back to his lodgings at Fulham. We all know how Colonel Esmond from Chelsea spent one night at the "Greyhound" "over against" Lady Castlewood's house in Kensington Square, the house to which the portrait of Frank Castlewood by Rigaud was sent. There is a picture of the old Pretender, magnificent and blue-ribboned, in the gallery at Dresden, which may have suggested the Castlewood picture in very fact, for my father must have seen it when he was in Dresden about 1851.

Mr. Egg, R.A., painted a picture of Beatrix and Esmond, which is now in the National Gallery, and which my father went to look at in the artist's studio; but there is a much more striking picture painted in the pages of "Esmond," when Harry, with his terrible news, walks into the room where all the shop people and mantua-makers are crowding. The well-known epilogue will not be forgotten, when Esmond drives the crier away from under Beatrix's window, where he is proclaiming the death of the Duke of Hamilton. "The world was going to its business again, although dukes lay dead and ladies mourned for them. . . . Esmond thought of the courier, now galloping on the North road to inform him, who was Earl of Arran yesterday, that he was Duke of Hamilton to-day, and of a thousand great schemes, hopes, ambitions, that were alive in the gallant heart, beating a few hours since, and now in a little dust quiescent." . . .

A few topographical notes for "Esmond" remain in my father's writing.

"Statue of the King in *Stork's Market*, a very magnificent statue of Charles II. and Time on horseback trampling upon an enemy, all in white marble, at the sole cost of that worthy citizen and Alderman Sir R. Viner, Knt. Bart."

"*Golding Square.*—Fleet Brook.—This mighty chargeable beautiful work, rendering navigable the Fleet Brook, a ditch from the river Thames up to Holborn Bridge; the curious stone bridge over it; the many huge vaults on each side thereof to treasure up Newcastle coals for the use of the poor."

"The prisons were Newgate, Ludgate, and Queen's Bench, Fleet, Marshalsea, New Prison, Whitechapel, and Westminster Gate House."

"*Exchange.*—There be many Exchanges in London, besides markets and the Royal Exchange—as that stately building called the New Exchange and Exeter Change, both in the Strand, where all attire for ladies and gentlemen is sold."

"*St. Paul's building* in 1702 appeared, through a wood of scaffolding, the wonder and glory of the kingdom."

There are also some notes about the Duke of Marlborough. "Lord Oxford's knowledge of the Duke's misdeeds; and that Lord Oxford, making the Duke know that his life was in his hands, was the reason of Marlborough's voluntary exile in the year 1712." Also there are a few incidental notes—

"The ranks wore their wigs in bags, and all have swords."

"Plum broth at Christmas, and sillabub in May, were considered suitable dishes."

"Queen Anne had forty-eight chaplains in ordinary."

The following letter to a friend of his in Paris has remained among our papers:—

"Dear Forgues,—I have just read the article in the *Revue des deux Mondes*, and am glad to write a line of thanks and goodwill to the author, with whom, as I think Pichot has already told you, I have been angry for these three whole years.

"In 1851, *à propos* of my Lectures, you wrote in a French paper published here that I had praised Addison in order to curry favour with the English aristocracy. My honour was wounded at the idea that a friend should make such a charge against me. A critic may like or dislike my books, and of course is welcome to his opinion, but he has no right to attribute to

DRILL.

me mean motives, or at least, I have a right to be angry if he does. And now I will give you the history of Addison, whom I don't like personally, but whose humour I admire with all my heart; more than his humour, I admire his conduct through life; rich or poor, he was an upright, honest, dignified gentleman, a worthy man of letters; he underwent bad fortune with admirable serenity. I thought it was right to praise him as one of our profession, and leave the reader to make his own moral from what I said. You have seen there has been an absurd outcry here about neglected men of genius, about the excuses to be made for literary men; they are to get drunk, to bilk their tradesmen, to leave their children without bread! . . .

"I have been earning my own bread with my pen for near twenty years now, and sometimes very hardly too, but in the worst time, please God, never lost my own respect!"

DR. JOHNSON.

The picture of "another worthy man of letters" may perhaps not unfitly illustrate this correspondence.

Part III.

When we went abroad the summer before my father sailed for America, we met our grandparents on the Rhine; then we travelled on to Switzerland, where my father left us. We did not see him again after we parted from him in Switzerland. But he wrote to us very often. Here is a letter to my sister from Augsburg:—

"My dearest Min.,—This morning came a little letter, which they might as well have given to me yesterday. (You see I give you my *other* hand* as when we walk together I give one hand to Anny and one to you.) They might, I say, have given me the letter when I went to the post for it yesterday, for there it has been lying these three days. Yesterday when I arrived it was all rain and melancholy here, and to-day, Sunday, it's all sunshine and pleasure, the great streets thronged with people—such ugly women in such caps! and bands of brass-music blowing beautifully all about the town. It's full of the most extraordinary churches, pictures, statues, and gimcracks of every sort. I went into many churches yesterday—one something like the splendid St. Ambrogio at Milan, you remember, but spick and span new, and most byooootifully gilt painted and decorated with tableaux representing St. Ambrogio's life and miracles, in which latter anybody may believe who chooses. In one of the confessionals of another church, another most byoooooootifle sham-antique church, where I was at dusk, I heard whisswhisswhisspering in the confessional, and then hummummumbrum the priest talking, and all this excited my awe and curiosity, and I thought to myself, perhaps there is some lovely creature in there on her knees to a venerable friar, confessing some most tremendous crime. But presently hopped out of the confessional a little old speckled hunched-back frog of a creature in a green shawl, and plopped down on its knees and said some prayer—which it was quite right no doubt to say—but all the romance was gone at the sight of the queer

* He used his upright handwriting when he wrote to my sister, his slanting handwriting when he wrote to me.

little trot of a woman, who I am sure could have only had the most trumpery little sins to chatter about, and so I came out of the church not a bit better Catholic than I went in. Don't you see, if she had been a lovely countess who had just killed her grandmother or smothered her babby, I might have gone on being interested and awe-stricken? but Polly the cook-maid, who owns to having given a pie to the policeman, or melted the fat into the grease-pot, *I* can't go for to waste my compassion and wonder upon her. And here's the mistake about these fine churches, pictures, music, and splendid and gracious sights and sounds with which the Catholics entrap many people—their senses are delighted, and they fancy they are growing religious; it's a romantic wonder, not a religious one. We must set to work to have the truth with all our hearts and soul and strength, and take care not to be juggled by romanticalities and sentimentalities. This church of St. Louis is ornamented with the most beautiful dolls you ever saw, the size of life, and painted and tickled up in the most charming way, with pink cheeks, fresh gilt glories, white eyes, wooden lilies, and everything that's nice. And the people kneel before them in crowds and worship Madonna and her Sacred Infant, and the beautiful St. Louis of Gonzaga and the beautiful St. Francis of the Indies—that is to say, charming figures representing these holy persons, and acting them in wood. But do I believe that the souls of the blest go about with gilt cart-wheels round their heads! Fiddledee. These are but childish symbols and play—and there's the dinner bell; and as I love my children on earth, I know the Father of us all loves us."

The following letter was written to me:—

"My dearest A.,—I must and will go to America, not because I like it, but because it is right I should secure some money against my death for your poor mother and you two girls. And I think if I have luck I may secure nearly a third of the sum that I think I ought to leave behind me by a six months' tour in the States. And you children during that time must consider yourselves as at college; and work, work with all your heart. You'll never have such another opportunity; when

I come back, please God, your studies will be interrupted, as I shall want a secretary. So now please to learn French very well, and to play the piano if you can. It will be a comfort to me in future days, when we shall be in some quieter place and manner of life than here in London, and I shall like my women to make music for me. I should read all the books that granny wishes, if I were you; and you must come to your own deductions about them, as every honest man and woman must and does. When I was of your age I was accustomed to hear and read a great deal of the Evangelical (so called) doctrine, and got an extreme distaste for that sort of composition—for Newton, for Scott, for the preachers I heard and the prayer-meetings I attended. I have not looked into half-a-dozen books of the French modern reformed churchmen, but those I have seen are odious to me. D'Aubigné, I believe, is the best man of the modern French Reformers; and a worse guide to historical truth (for one who has a reputation) I don't know. If M. Gossaint argues that because our Lord quoted the Hebrew scriptures therefore the Scriptures are of direct Divine composition, you may make yourself quite easy; and the works of a reasoner who would maintain an argument so monstrous, need not, I should think, occupy a great portion of your time. Our Lord not only quoted the Hebrew writings (drawing illustrations from everything familiar to the people among whom He taught, from their books poetic and historic, from the landscape round about, from the flowers, the children, and the beautiful works of God), but He contradicted the old scriptures flatly; told the people that He brought them a new commandment—and that new commandment was not a complement, but a contradiction of the old—a repeal of a bad, unjust law in their statute books, which He would suffer to remain there no more. It has been said an eye for an eye, &c., but *I* say to you no such thing; *Love* your enemies, &c. It could not have been right to hate your enemies on Tuesday and to love them on Wednesday. What is right must always have been right, before it was practised as well as after. And if such and such a commandment delivered by Moses was wrong, depend on it it was not delivered by God, and the whole question of complete inspiration goes at once. And the misfortune of dogmatic belief is, that the first principle granted that the book called the Bible is written under the direct dictation of God; for instance, that the Catholic Church is under the direct dictation of God, and solely communicates with Him; that Quashimaboo is the direct appointed priest of God, and so forth—pain, cruelty, persecution, separation of dear relatives follow as a matter of course. What person possessing the secret of Divine truth by which she or he is assured of heaven, and which idea she or he worships as if it was God, but must pass nights of tears and days of grief and lamentation if persons naturally dear cannot be got to see this necessary truth? Smith's truth being established in Smith's mind as the Divine one, persecution follows as a matter of course—martyrs have roasted all over Europe, all over God's world, upon this dogma. To my mind, scripture only means a writing, and Bible means a book. It contains Divine truths, and the history of a Divine Character; but imperfect, but not containing a thousandth part of Him; and it would be an untruth before God were I to hide my feelings from my dearest children; as it would be a sin if, having other opinions, and believing literally in the Mosaic writings, in the six days' cosmogony, in the serpent and apple and consequent damnation of the human race, I should hide them, and not try to make those I loved best adopt opinions of such immense importance to them. And so God bless my darlings and teach us the truth.

"Every one of us in every fact, book, circumstance of life sees a different meaning and moral, and so it must be about religion. But we can all love each other and say, 'Our Father.'"

I have another letter of October 1852. It is dated Manchester, Liverpool, Alderley, Kensington, Covent Garden. "I am writing this at the station, having missed the quick train, and not sorry to have half-an-hour to myself and my dearest girls. I have just said good-bye to Manchester, and stopped this morning to hear Mr. Scott address his College, of which he is Principal. A gentleman, a Mr. Owen, left a hundred thousand pounds to found an institution for educating his townsfolk, and Scott is the first head of the College, and a very noble speech I thought he made to his boys and young men, and I wished I was a boy myself that I might learn something, but I am too old a boy to learn much now, I fear. You two must try and do so, and when you are at work, work with all your heart, and don't play with learning."

He sailed for America from Liverpool on October 30th by the *Canada*, Captain Lang. The house in Kensington was shut up. His publishers gave him a despatch-box, his mother sent him a lifebelt, and made him promise not to leave it behind. We were all very anxious and sad, but very glad he did not go alone: Mr. Eyre Crowe went with him as secretary. "Six months tumbling about the world will do you no harm," he wrote, offering the post to his young friend. As the steamer was starting, a messenger arrived on board with letters from Messrs. Smith and Elder and the first copy of "Esmond."

One of the farewell notes was addressed to Dr. John Brown* of Edinburgh.

W. M. THACKERAY *to* DR. JOHN BROWN, M.D.

"85 RENSHAW STREET, LIVERPOOL,
" *Wednesday, October* 6 (1852).

"MY DEAR BROWN,—Your constant kindness deserves, not more good will on my part, for that you have, but better marks of friendship than my laziness is inclined to show. My time is drawing near for the *ingens aequor*. I have taken places for self and Crowe, Junior, by the *Canada*, which departs on the 30th of this month, a Saturday, and all you who pray for travellers by land and water (if you do pray in your Scotch Church) are entreated to offer up supplications for me. I don't like going out at all; have dismal presentiments sometimes, but the right thing is to go; and the pleasant one will be to come back again with a little money for the young ladies. I hope to send you 'Esmond' before I sail; if not, it will follow me as a legacy. I doubt whether it will be popular, although it has cost me so much trouble.

"I wish this place were like Edinburgh, but I only get a small audience, say 300, in a hall capable of holding 3000 at least, and all the papers will cry out at the smallness of the

*It is Dr. John Brown's son who with a traditional kindness has sent me the correspondence to quote from.

attendance. At Manchester the audience isn't greater, but looks greater, or the room is small, and though pecuniarily the affair is a failure, it is not so really; I air my reputation, and the people who do come seem to like what they hear hugely.

"Carlyle is away in Germany looking after 'Frederick the Great.' I don't know what Literature is about. I heard James Martineau (the Unitarian) last Sunday, and was struck by his lofty devotional spirit, and afterwards an old schoolfellow on the Evangelical dodge—ah, what rubbish! and so is this which I am writing. I think it is partly owing to an uncomfortable pen; but with bad pen and good I am always yours and your wife's, sincerely, W. M. T."

From Liverpool he wrote to Lady Stanley, "Not above 200 people come to the lectures, and the Philharmonic Hall, the most beautiful room I've seen, is made for 2500, so that the little audience shudders in the middle, and the lecturer stands in a vast empty orchestra, where there is a place for 150 musicians. It is like a dinner for twenty and three people to eat it. They go away and say unto each other what a good dinner and so forth, but I don't think they'll have the courage to come again.

"Who would like to be one of six in a theatre with a good actor performing a good *douche* for a man's vanity?

"There is a Boston boat sails on the 30th of October, and that will be the steamer which will carry Titmarsh and his lectures."

Mr. Crowe describes the passengers on board the *Canada*. "Lowell, fresh from Italy, coming up the companion-ladder; and a burly form in a wideawake hat, Arthur Hugh Clough, the poet and Oxford Don. . . ."

And here is the welcome letter which came to us at Paris from the other side of the Atlantic.

"I try to write a little with a pencil," says my father, "now the troubles of sea-sickness are over, the appetite come back, and the sky bright overhead; the sea of a wonderful purple, except in the wake of the ship, where there quivers a long line of emerald; six sea-gulls are following after the ship, six hundred miles—think of that! Nobody really likes the sea; they go through with it with a brave heart, but the captain and all like the fireside and home a thousand times better. . . . I find the vessel pitches so I can't write, and my sentences lurch about and grasp hold of anything to support themselves, so I'll stop. . . . In that horrid little cabin below, where we are tumbling and rolling, and bumping and creaking in the roaring black midnight, you may be sure I am often thinking of you. I know you look at the sky, and G. P.* at the glass (I don't mean the looking-glass), and speculate how the *Canada* makes way. Well, we have had the wind dead against us, and got on well in spite of it, and are now some eleven hundred miles out at sea, lat. 50° 32′, lon. 27° 36′. I was trying as I lay awake last night to see if I could understand the difference between latitude and longitude. . . .

"This morning, as I was full in a dream about A. and M. eating a pot of bear's grease and mistaking it for jam, the Admiralty agent wakes me to come and see the sun rise. Such a royal apparition! To see such sights with the eyes is to pray with the heart. . . . We have had a tolerable bad passage, wind against us all the way; even against that, except in the very bad weather, running ten miles an hour. Isn't it wonderful? Instead of going over yon thundering wave, why don't we go right down and disappear? Looking at the little lifebelt and then at the ocean makes one laugh. The waves are immense; about four of them go to the horizon, but I'm disappointed in the grandeur of the prospect. It looks small somehow, not near so extensive as a hundred landscapes we have seen. And where shall we pass next November? Shall we go to Rome? Shall I make a good bit of money in America, and write a book about it? I think not. It seems impudent to write a book, and mere sketches now are somehow below my rank in the world—I mean, a grave old gentleman, father of young ladies, mustn't be comic and grinning too much. I wonder are the critics praising or abusing 'Esmond'? I have forgotten all about him, and he seems like everything else, to have happened a hundred years ago. . . ."

"How wonderful the thing is that we should be here at all,"

* This was always my father's abbreviation for "Grand Papa."

he writes in another letter. "On Tuesday evening, at about half-past five, the captain goes on deck from dinner and sends a sailor aloft to look out. Sailor comes down and says he can see nothing. The minute after captain sends him up again. Again sailor sees nothing. Captain sends him up a third time. He sees Beaver Island light; so that we come three thousand miles over the enormous pathless ocean, through storm and darkness, with many a day no sun to make observations by, and the captain knows within fifteen minutes when we shall see a particular little rock with a light on it. Seven hours afterwards the ship came close up to the quay at Halifax, as if there had been a rope pulling us all the way from Liverpool. And so the voyage ends with a *laus Deo*."

One of the first welcomes he received on landing was from Mr. Prescott, with whom he dined the first Sunday at Boston. The next host to receive him, when he reached New York, was Mr. Henry James, the father of the good friend of these present days, who has told me that he can remember going as a little boy to the hotel where our lecturer was staying in New York, and watching Mr. Crowe at work upon a portrait of his own father. All the national, well-known names follow in succession—Washington Irving and Dana and Horace Greeley and George Curtis and Bayard Taylor and others less known to the outer world, but familiarly quoted in our home, such as Mrs. Baxter and her daughters, for whom my father ever had a special affection.

The first letter from New York begins with a cheerful, "Now that I am here comfortably settled with a hundred kind people to make your papa welcome, and two thousand every night to come and hear his lectures, doesn't it seem absurd that we should all have been so gloomy, and foreboding so many evils at my going away? . . .

"We are up three pairs of stairs, in very snug rooms, at a very good hotel. The people have not turned out with flags and drums to receive me like Dickens, but the welcome is a most pleasant one. There is no speechifying or ceremony in it—everybody has read Somebody's book."

W. M. T. *to* MRS. PROCTER.

"BOSTON, *Wednesday, December* 22, 1852.

"MY DEAR FRIEND,—I should like to send you a longer letter than can be written in a quarter of an hour, when the mails close for the ship, which is on the slips to start for dear old home, but a word I know will please you to tell you how happy I am, what a many many friends I have found (I have found Beatrix Esmond and lost my heart to her), and what a fortunate venture this is likely to prove to me. Last night was the first lecture here—twelve hundred people, I should think—and I left behind me near a thousand pounds at New York, which Baring's house will invest for me, so that my girls will be very considerably the better for this journey,

And grim Death if ever he come to me,
Will find that I have the £, *s. d.*

There's a parody! I find I'm constantly talking of dying somehow, but hope to wait time enough to see the poor wife and children provided. It would have been worth while even for my books to come out here: the publishers are liberal enough, and will be still more so with any future thing I may do. As for writing about this country, about Goshen, about Canada flowing with milk and honey, about the friends I have found here, and who are helping me to procure independence for my children, if I cut jokes against them, may I choke on the instant. If I can say anything to show that my name is really Makepeace, and to increase the source of love between the two countries, then please God I will. The laugh dies out as we get old, you see, but the love and the truth don't, praised be God! and I begin to think of the responsibilities of this here pen now writing to you with a feeling of no small awe. The first name I heard in the railroad going hence to New York was my own, by a pretty child selling books, and I was touched somehow by his fresh voice and kind face, and should have liked to take him by the hand. So—here it is after fifteen years, think I, here's the fame they talk about: my impression though was one of awe and humility rather than exultation, and to pray God I might keep honest and tell truth always.

"This is nothing but Ego, but I know you like that. I was

very glad to get your letter. God bless you, and all yours, and my dear old Dicky Doyle when you see him. The success of 'Esmond' has quite surprised me, for I only looked for a few to like it.

"Write again to Appleton, New York, please, to yours affectionately, W. M. T."

The little memorandum-book for 1852–53 gives the history of these eventful days; that much of a history that can best be told by names and dates, from which, as from the notes of a music-book, the tune of the past can be played once more. There is a list of places and lectures all the way from Boston to Savannah, and from Savannah to England again, and the names of the hospitable people with whom my father chiefly spent his time, with the dates of their hospitable entertainments. All noted in their turn, with the names of our old friend Mr. Synge, and Mr. Crampton, and Governor Fish, and many others.

One of Mr. Lowell's charming little invitations has been preserved:—

"CAMBRIDGE, *30th December*.

"MY DEAR SIR,—Have you any engagement for Wednesday or Thursday evening of next week? If not, will you give me one of them? Timmins, revolving many things, has decided on a *supper*, because he can have it under his own roof, and because he can have more pleasant people at it. He will ask only *clubbable* men, and such as can't make speeches. You shall either be carried back to Boston, or spend the night with us. Crowe survived it.—Very sincerely yours, J. R. LOWELL."

"Mr. Prescott, the historian, is delightful," my father wrote from Boston; "Mr. Ticknor is a great city magnate and *littérateur*. It's like the society of a rich Cathedral-town in England—grave and decorous, and very pleasant and well read."

One of the first of the lectures was delivered in a Unitarian Chapel. My father was rather nervous when he found he was expected to mount the pulpit, and asked whether the organ would strike up when he entered. He not only gave lectures, but attended them. Bancroft was lecturing at that time; so was Theodore Parker, the eloquent anti-slavery champion; so was Mr. Home, whose rapping manifestations were then coming into vogue. We have one or two scraps pasted into an American scrap-book, with various mysterious messages like telegrams from the unseen world, "*I merely wished to say Make-peace you argue of importance.*" This oracle is dated December 1852. Here is another revelation, "*Carissima may move the table.*" One of the messages on the same page *may* be spiritual, but it rather reminds one of common life. "*Please deliver to W. M. Thackeray, Esq. a hat or a cap as he may wish, and place the same to the account of John N. Genin,* 214 *Broadway.*" A stamp in the corner with Genin, Broadway, New York, and the picture of a very tall hat, gives authority to the document.

A letter to Lady Stanley, written from Philadelphia, sums up his first impressions:—

"*January* 21, 1853.

"All those fine plans of writing letters, which my friends were to keep and restore to me, and of which I was to make a book on my return home, are of no avail. I can't see the country, I can't write any letters; the business I am on prevents the one and the other. I am making and receiving visits all day long, going out to dinner and supper prodigiously, and perfectly drunk with the number of new acquaintances poured into me. I tremble as I walk the streets here, lest every man I meet is my friend of last night, who will be offended of course if I forget him. It is like a man canvassing, but the canvass begins afresh in every new city, and goes on till I am perfectly weary of shaking hands and acting. Do you know that there are over five hundred thousand inhabitants in this town? The great impression I have got in going about is how small and dwindled the old country is, and how great and strong the new. Here I must go, Mr. M'Michael of the *North American Enquirer* is below.

"It is two hours afterwards. M'Michael and I have been to the Mint (shake hands with everybody), which is a beautiful institution, of which the Philadelphians have a right to be proud, to the Free School (shake hands with all the professors), a capital school too, seemingly, where the youngest boys know much more than I do, where it is a good thing to think small beer of oneself, comparing one's own ignorance with the knowledge of these little ones. I am making money pretty well, and have put by already nearly two thousand pounds since I have been here; and do you know that the common interest here is eight per cent., as safe as English Funds, they tell me? . . . I hope to make nearly double what I have before I bend my steps homeward, and then shall get ready some fresh lectures for a new campaign. They will bear me over again in this country, and like me, I believe. I have nothing but praise and kindness, except from some of the Boston papers, who fired into me, and said I was a humbug. But Boston is the centre of lecturing; lecturers go out thence to all quarters of the Union, lecturers who only get one dollar to my ten, and who are at least quite as good as I am, hence animosities and natural heart-burnings; and I don't care, so long as the reason is with them, and the dollars with me. I find wonderfully little difference in manners, an accent not quite like ours; but why should it be? Why should not Jordan be as good as Abana and Pharpar, rivers of Damascus? Even the dress of the New York girls, which struck me as odious at first on account of their splendaciousness, I think now quite handsome. I have found kind matrons and pretty girls everywhere, and in Boston very good, fogeyfied, literary society, with everywhere a love for the old country quite curious, nay, touching, to remark. They are great about pronunciation especially, and take down at my lectures words which this present arbiter of English pronounces differently to them. If Carlyle comes, I wonder whether they will take him as an exemplar. Crowe is my comfort and delight in life; he is worth his weight in gold. Everybody lectures in this country, and it isn't, nor any trade or calling else, for that matter, thought *infra dig.* Nor is a man thought the worse of for showing a little independence. For instance, when I came here they told me it was usual for lecturers (Mr. B. of London had done it) to call upon all the editors of all the papers, hat in hand, and ask them to puff my lectures. Says I, 'I'll see them all . . .,' here I used a strong expression, which you will find in the Athanasian Creed. Well, they were pleased rather than otherwise, and now the papers are puffing me so as to make me blush."

After Philadelphia, where Mr. Reid made the travellers at home, came Baltimore and Washington, and "an interminable succession of balls, parties, banquets at the British Embassy and elsewhere." Sir John Crampton was ambassador in those days, President Fillmore was at the White House, and for three weeks lecturing and hospitality alternated. Then they took steamer to Richmond. "I sketched the distant outline of Mr. Washington's home," says Mr. Crowe, "and we tried to spot the new Castlewood, which was raised on the beautiful banks of the Potomac."

Brief records of Richmond, Charleston, and Savannah follow in my father's little diary: "Calm passage, pleasant boat, river like the Nile. Quitted the horrible hotel for Mr. Low's pleasant house. On Tuesday the 15th of March drove to Bon Aventure and Mr. Faversham's estate. Negro houses, moss on the trees, yellow jessamine, splendid magnolia. First lecture about 360, I should think. I read in the papers of snow twelve inches thick falling in New England; here all windows open, peach-trees in most 'lubly' blossom, leaves coming out, fresh salad for dinner, balmy air blowing."

On Saturday the 19th March he wrote to us: "Yesterday your papa performed for the first time in a theatre—who would ever have thought of seeing him on a stage? The room where I generally act is engaged, and I had such a dirty little theatre instead. The proceeds for the three lectures are about the smallest I shall get in the States, but it is only a little place—a friendly, pretty little place—and Mr. Low, my host, has made me and Eyre as comfortable as mortal man could be in this hot weather. It doesn't agree with me, I think, and I am glad I am going out of these enervating damp climates. I wish you could have seen a little negrillo of five years old toddling about with the plates at dinner yesterday, and listening to the young ladies making music afterwards."

"Providence has proved rather a failure," he wrote from that place after the first lecture. "There are not above 500 auditors, and I must return half the money we agreed for. Nobody must lose money by me in America, where I have had such a welcome and hospitality."

He says in a letter to Dr. Brown:—

"CHARLESTOWN, *March* 25, 1853.

"The lectures do pretty well, and I have laid by already. This will make me easy against the day when work will be over, and then and then who knows what fate will bring. The idleness of the life is dreary and demoralising though, and the bore and humiliation of delivering these stale old lectures is growing intolerable. Why, what a superior heroism is Albert Smith's, who has ascended Mont Blanc 400 times!

"It's all exaggeration about this country—barbarism, eccentricities, nigger cruelties, and all. They are not so highly educated as individuals, but a circle of people knows more than an equal number of English (of Scotch I don't say—there, in Edinburgh you *are* educated)."

By April he was back in New York. Mr. George Smith has given me some letters dated from the Clarendon, New York. "We have had a very pleasant and not unprofitable tour in the South," my father dictates. "The words are the words of Thackeray, but the pen is the pen of Crowe. The former is boiling himself in a warm bath, and is, whether in or out of hot water, yours very faithfully always. . . ."

The following amusing little *jeu d'esprit* appeared in the *Boston Post*, and is pasted into the American scrap-book: "High Life in Boston: Literary Breakfast of a family of opulence moving in a select circle, residing in a select square.

"*Clever Daughter*. Decidedly I esteem Mr. Thackeray, the *fort esprit* of his time: strongly resembling Bussy de Rabutin, but with a more introspective cast. He reminds one constantly of the subtle companion of Faust: no moral obliquity without its palliative, no human weakness without a claim to a tender extenuation. We learn to love the vice, but hate the sinner; I would say, hate the sinner and love the vice—vice-versa.

"*Sentimental Daughter*. I'm sure I wish I had been born in Queen Anne's day, when all the gentlemen were so enthusiastic, and wore red cloaks and green stockings. They seem to have had *such* a ceaseless flow of spirits.

"*Pert Son*. Well, they didn't have anything else.

"*Gruff Papa*. A pack of d—d scamps as ever 'scaped hanging. If I'd had any idea of such characters being raked up at a lecture in Boston, no son or daughter of mine should have set foot in the hall, 'if they grew up ever so ignorant.'

"*Clever Girl*. But, dear papa, genius is *ever* eccentric: cannot be cabin'd, cribb'd, confined to ordinary limits. Their 'noble rage' will burst out, and, like the Pythian priestess, they are borne away by the afflatus of the tripod. Byron had his faults, but——

"*Silly Mamma to Gruff Papa.* I'm sure, my love, Mr. Thackeray has made a decidedly favourable impression on our most fashionable people: which could not have happened if these authors *really* were to blame in their behaviour. If it was the *fashion* to be 'gay,' and to be carried about in chairs, it was not their fault, but that of their rulers. . . .

"*Fossil Grandmother* (timidly). Mr. Thackeray ought to be spoken to—dispassionately."

A CONFERENCE.

In 1855 my father returned to America and delivered the second series of his lectures, "The Four Georges," which for convenience are bound up with the Humourists in this present volume.

The American letters which he wrote during his second visit are included in the preface to "The Virginians," and are altogether omitted here.

A. I. R.

THE HISTORY

OF

HENRY ESMOND, Esq.

A COLONEL IN THE SERVICE OF HER MAJESTY QUEEN ANNE

WRITTEN BY HIMSELF

. . . SERVETUR AD IMUM
QUALIS AB INCERTO PROCESSERIT, ET SIBI CONSTET

TO THE RIGHT HONOURABLE

WILLIAM BINGHAM, LORD ASHBURTON

MY DEAR LORD,—The writer of a book which copies the manners and language of Queen Anne's time, must not omit the Dedication to the Patron; and I ask leave to inscribe this volume to your Lordship, for the sake of the great kindness and friendship which I owe to you and yours.

My volume will reach you when the Author is on his voyage to a country where your name is as well known as here. Wherever I am, I shall gratefully regard you; and shall not be the less welcomed in America because I am

Your obliged friend and servant,

W. M. THACKERAY.

LONDON: *October* 18, 1852.

PREFACE

THE ESMONDS OF VIRGINIA

THE estate of Castlewood, in Virginia, which was given to our ancestors by King Charles the First, as some return for the sacrifices made in His Majesty's cause by the Esmond family, lies in Westmoreland county, between the rivers Potomac and Rappahannoc, and was once as great as an English Principality, though in the early times its revenues were but small. Indeed, for near eighty years after our forefathers possessed them, our plantations were in the hands of factors, who enriched themselves one after another, though a few scores of hogsheads of tobacco were all the produce that, for long after the Restoration, our family received from their Virginian estates.

My dear and honoured father, Colonel Henry Esmond, whose history, written by himself, is contained in the accompanying volume, came to Virginia in the year 1718, built his house of Castlewood, and here permanently settled. After a long stormy life in England, he passed the remainder of his many years in peace and honour in this country; how beloved and respected by all his fellow-citizens, how inexpressibly dear to his family, I need not say. His whole life was a benefit to all who were connected with him. He gave the best example, the best advice, the most bounteous hospitality to his friends; the tenderest care to his dependants; and bestowed on those of his immediate family such a blessing of fatherly love and protection as can never be thought of, by us at least, without veneration and thankfulness; and my sons' children, whether established here in our Republic, or at home in the always beloved mother country, from which our late quarrel hath separated us, may surely be proud to be descended from one who in all ways was so truly noble.

My dear mother died in 1736, soon after our return from England, whither my parents took me for my education; and where I made the acquaintance of Mr. Warrington, whom my children never saw. When it pleased Heaven, in the bloom of his youth, and after but a few months of a most happy union, to remove him from me, I owed my recovery from the grief which that calamity caused me, mainly to my dearest father's tenderness, and then to the blessing vouchsafed to me in the birth of my two beloved boys. I know the fatal differences which separated them in politics never disunited their hearts; and as I can love them both, whether wearing the King's colours or the Republic's, I am sure that they love me and one another, and him above all, my father and theirs, the dearest friend of their childhood, the noble gentleman who bred them from their infancy in the practice and knowledge of Truth, and Love, and Honour.

My children will never forget the appearance and figure of their revered grandfather; and I wish I possessed the art of drawing (which my papa had in perfection), so that I could leave to our descendants a portrait of one who was so good and so respected. My father was of a dark complexion, with a very great forehead and dark hazel eyes, overhung by eyebrows which remained black long after his hair was white. His nose was aquiline, his smile extraordinary sweet. How well I remember it, and how little any description I can write can recall his image! He was of rather low stature, not being above five feet seven inches in height; he used to laugh at my sons, whom he called his crutches, and say they were grown too tall for him to lean upon. But small as he was, he had a perfect grace and majesty of deportment, such as I have never seen in this country, except perhaps in our friend Mr. Washington, and commanded respect wherever he appeared.

In all bodily exercises he excelled, and showed an extraordinary quickness and agility. Of fencing he was especially fond, and made my two boys proficient in that art; so much so that when the French came to this country with Monsieur Rochambeau, not one of his officers was superior to my Henry, and he was not the equal of my poor George, who had taken the King's side in our lamentable but glorious War of Independence.

Neither my father nor my mother ever wore powder in their hair; both their heads were as white as silver, as I can remember them. My dear mother possessed to the last an extraordinary brightness and freshness of complexion; nor would people believe that she did not wear rouge. At sixty years of age she still looked young, and was quite agile. It was not until after that dreadful siege of our house by the Indians, which left me a widow ere I was a mother, that my dear mother's health broke. She never recovered her terror and anxiety of those days, which ended so fatally for me, then a bride scarce six months married, and died in my father's arms ere my own year of widowhood was over.

From that day, until the last of his dear and honoured life, it was my delight and consolation to remain with him as his comforter and companion; and from those little notes which my mother hath made here and there in the volume in which my father describes his adventures in Europe, I can well understand the extreme devotion with which she regarded him—a devotion so passionate and exclusive as to prevent her, I think, from loving any other person except with an inferior regard; her whole thoughts being centred on this one object of affection and worship. I know that, before her, my dear father did not show the love which he had for his daughter; and in her last and most sacred moments, this dear and tender parent owned to me her repentance that she had not loved me enough; her jealousy even that my father should give his affection to any but herself; and in the most fond and beautiful words of affection and admonition, she bade me never to leave him, and to supply the place which she was quitting. With a clear conscience, and a heart inexpressibly thankful, I think I can say that I fulfilled those dying commands, and that until his last hour my dearest father never had to complain that his daughter's love and fidelity failed him.

And it is since I knew him entirely—for during my mother's life he never quite opened himself to me—since I knew the value and splendour of that affection which he bestowed upon me, that I have come to understand and pardon what, I own, used to anger me in my mother's lifetime, her jealousy respecting her husband's love. 'Twas a gift so precious, that no wonder she who had it was for keeping it all, and could part with none of it, even to her daughter.

Though I never heard my father use a rough word, 'twas extraordinary with how much awe his people regarded him; and the servants on our plantation, both those assigned from England and the purchased negroes, obeyed him with an eagerness such as the most severe taskmasters round about us could never get from their people. He was never familiar, though perfectly simple and natural; he was the same with the meanest man as with the greatest, and as courteous to a black slave girl as to the Governor's wife. No one ever thought of taking a liberty with him (except once a tipsy gentleman from York, and I am bound to own that my papa never forgave him): he set the humblest people at once on their ease with him, and brought down the most arrogant by a grave satiric way, which made persons exceedingly afraid of him. His courtesy was not put on like a Sunday suit, and laid by when the company went away; it was always the same; as he was always dressed the same, whether for a dinner by ourselves or for a great entertainment. They say he liked to be the first in his company; but what company was there in which he would not be first? When I went to Europe for my education, and we passed a winter at London with my half-brother, my Lord Castlewood and his second lady, I saw at Her Majesty's Court some of the most famous gentlemen of those days; and I thought to myself none of these are better than my papa; and the famous Lord Bolingbroke, who came to us from Dawley, said as much and that the men of that time were not like those of his youth:—"Were your father, madam," he said, "to go into the woods, the Indians would elect him Sachem;" and his Lordship was pleased to call me Pocahontas.

I did not see our other relative, Bishop Tusher's lady, of whom so much is said in my papa's memoirs—although my mamma went to visit her in the country. I have no pride (as I showed by complying with my mother's request, and marrying a gentleman who was but the younger son of a Suffolk Baronet), yet I own to *a decent respect* for my name, and wonder how one who ever bore it should change it for that of Mrs. *Thomas Tusher*. I pass over as odious and unworthy of credit those reports (which I heard in Europe, and was then too young to understand), how this person, having *left her family* and fled to Paris, out of jealousy of the Pretender, betrayed his secrets to my Lord Stair, King George's Ambassador, and nearly caused the Prince's death there; how she came to England and married this Mr. Tusher, and became a great favourite of King George the Second, by whom Mr. Tusher was made a Dean, and then a Bishop. I did not see the lady, who chose to remain *at her palace* all the time we were in London; but after visiting her, my poor mamma said she had lost all her good looks, and warned me not to set too much store by any such gifts which nature had bestowed upon me. She grew exceedingly stout; and I remember my brother's wife, Lady Castlewood, saying: "No wonder she became a favourite, for the King likes them old and ugly, as his father did before him." On which Papa said: "All women were alike; that there was never one so beautiful as that one; and that we could forgive her everything but her beauty." And hereupon my mamma looked vexed, and my Lord Castlewood began to laugh; and I, of course, being a young creature, could not understand what was the subject of their conversation.

After the circumstances narrated in the third book of these Memoirs, my father and mother both went abroad, being advised by their friends to leave the country in consequence of the transactions which are recounted at the close of the volume of the

Memoirs. But my brother, hearing how the *future Bishop's lady* had quitted Castlewood and joined the Pretender at Paris, pursued him, and would have killed him, Prince as he was, had not the Prince managed to make his escape. On his expedition to Scotland directly after, Castlewood was so enraged against him that he asked leave to serve as a volunteer, and join the Duke of Argyle's army in Scotland, which the Pretender never had the courage to face; and thenceforth my Lord was quite reconciled to the present reigning family, from whom he hath even received promotion.

Mrs. Tusher was by this time as angry against the Pretender as any of her relations could be, and used to boast, as I have heard, that she not only brought back my Lord to the Church of England, but procured the English peerage for him, which the *junior branch* of our family at present enjoys. She was a great friend of Sir Robert Walpole, and would not rest until her husband slept at Lambeth, my papa used laughing to say. However, the Bishop died of apoplexy suddenly, and his wife erected a great monument over him; and the pair sleep under that stone, with a canopy of marble clouds and angels above them—the first Mrs. Tusher lying sixty miles off at Castlewood.

But my papa's genius and education are both greater than any a woman can be expected to have, and his adventures in Europe far more exciting than his life in this country, which was passed in the tranquil offices of love and duty; and I shall say no more by way of introduction to his Memoirs, nor keep my children from the perusal of a story which is much more interesting than that of their affectionate old mother,

RACHEL ESMOND WARRINGTON.

CASTLEWOOD, VIRGINIA:
November 3, 1778.

THE HISTORY OF

HENRY ESMOND

BOOK I

THE EARLY YOUTH OF HENRY ESMOND, UP TO THE TIME OF HIS LEAVING TRINITY COLLEGE, IN CAMBRIDGE

THE actors in the old tragedies, as we read, piped their iambics to a tune, speaking from under a mask, and wearing stilts and a great head-dress. 'Twas thought the dignity of the Tragic Muse required these appurtenances, and that she was not to move except to a measure and cadence. So Queen Medea slew her children to a slow music: and King Agamemnon perished in a dying fall (to use Mr. Dryden's words): the Chorus standing by in a set attitude, and rhythmically and decorously bewailing the fates of those great crowned persons. The Muse of History hath encumbered herself with ceremony as well as her Sister of the Theatre. She too wears the mask and the cothurnus, and speaks to measure. She too, in our age, busies herself with the affairs only of kings; waiting on them obsequiously and stately, as if she were but a mistress of court ceremonies, and had nothing to do with the registering of the affairs of the common people. I have seen in his very old age and decrepitude the old French King Lewis the Fourteenth, the type and model of kinghood—who never moved but to measure, who lived and died according to the laws of his Court-marshal, persisting in enacting through life the part of Hero; and, divested of poetry, this was but a little wrinkled old man, pock-marked, and with a great periwig and red heels to make him look tall—a hero for a book if you like, or for a brass statue or a painted ceiling, a god in a Roman shape, but what more than a man for Madame Maintenon, or the barber who shaved him, or Monsieur Fagon, his surgeon? I wonder shall History ever pull off her periwig and cease to be court-ridden? Shall we see something of France and England besides Versailles and Windsor? I saw Queen Anne at the latter place tearing down the Park slopes, after her stag-hounds, and driving her one-horse chaise—a hot, red-faced woman, not in the least resembling that statue of her which turns its stone back upon St. Paul's, and faces the coaches struggling up Ludgate Hill. She was neither better bred nor wiser than you and me, though we knelt to hand her a letter or a washhand basin. Why shall History go on kneeling to the end of time? I am for having her rise up off her knees, and take a natural posture: not to be for ever performing cringes and congees like a court-chamberlain, and shuffling backwards out of doors in the presence of the sovereign. In a word, I would have History familiar rather than heroic: and think that Mr. Hogarth and Mr. Fielding will give our children a much better idea of the manners of the present age in England, than the *Court Gazette* and the newspapers which we get thence.

There was a German officer of Webb's, with whom we used to joke, and of whom a story (whereof I myself was the author) was got to be believed in the army, that he was eldest son of the hereditary Grand Bootjack of the Empire, and the heir to that honour of which his ancestors had been very proud, having been kicked for twenty generations by one imperial foot, as they drew the boot from the other. I have heard that the old Lord Castlewood, of part of whose family these present volumes are a chronicle, though he came of quite as good blood as the Stuarts whom he served (and who as regards mere lineage are no better than a dozen English and Scottish houses I could name), was prouder of his post about the Court than of his ancestral honours, and valued his dignity (as Warden of the Butteries and Groom of the King's Posset) so highly, that he cheerfully ruined himself for the thankless and thriftless race who bestowed it. He pawned his plate for King Charles the First, mortgaged his property for the same cause, and lost the greater part of it by fines and sequestration: stood a siege of his castle by Ireton, where his brother Thomas capitulated (afterward making terms with the Commonwealth, for which the elder brother never forgave him), and where his second brother Edward, who had embraced the ecclesiastical profession, was slain on Castlewood Tower, being engaged there both as preacher and artilleryman. This resolute old loyalist, who was with the King whilst his house was thus being battered down, escaped abroad with his only son, then a boy, to return and take a part in Worcester fight. On that fatal field Eustace Esmond was killed, and Castlewood fled from it once more into exile, and henceforward, and after the Restoration, never was away from the Court of the monarch (for whose return we offer thanks in the Prayer-Book) who sold his country and who took bribes of the French king.

What spectacle is more august than that of a great king in exile? Who is more worthy of respect than a brave man in misfortune? Mr. Addison has painted such a figure in his noble piece of "Cato." But suppose fugitive Cato fuddling himself at a tavern with a wench on each knee, a dozen faithful and tipsy companions of defeat, and a landlord calling out for his bill; and the dignity of misfortune is straightway lost. The Historical Muse turns away shamefaced from the vulgar scene, and closes the door—on which the exile's unpaid drink is scored up—upon him and his pots and his pipes, and the tavern-chorus which he and his friends are singing. Such a man as Charles should have had an Ostade or Mieris to paint him. Your Knellers and Le Bruns only deal in clumsy and impossible allegories: and it hath always seemed to me blasphemy to claim Olympus for such a wine-drabbled divinity as that.

About the King's follower, the Viscount Castlewood—orphaned of his son, ruined by his fidelity, bearing many wounds and marks of bravery, old and in exile—his kinsmen I suppose should be silent; nor if this patriarch fell down in his cups, call fie upon him, and fetch passers-by to laugh at his red face and white hairs. What! does a stream rush out of a mountain free and pure, to roll through fair pastures, to feed and throw out bright tributaries, and to end in a village gutter? Lives that have noble commencements have often no better endings; it is not without a kind of awe and reverence that an observer should speculate upon such careers as he traces the course of them. I have seen too much of success in life to take off my hat and huzzah to it as it passes in its gilt coach; and would do my little part with my neighbours on foot, that they should not gape with too much wonder, nor applaud too loudly. Is it the Lord Mayor going in state to mince-pies and the Mansion House? Is it poor Jack of Newgate's procession, with the sheriff and javelin-men, conducting him on his last journey to Tyburn? I look into my heart and think that I am as good as my Lord Mayor, and know I am as bad as Tyburn Jack. Give me a chain and red gown and a pudding before me, and I could play the part of Alderman very well, and sentence Jack after dinner. Starve me, keep me from books and honest people, educate me to love dice, gin, and pleasure, and put me on Hounslow Heath, with a purse before me, and I will take it. "And I shall be deservedly hanged," say you, wishing to put an end to this prosing. I don't say No. I can't but accept the world as I find it, including a rope's end, as long as it is in fashion.

CHAPTER I

AN ACCOUNT OF THE FAMILY OF ESMOND OF CASTLEWOOD HALL

WHEN Francis, fourth Viscount Castlewood, came to his title, and presently after to take possession of his house of Castlewood, County Hants, in the year 1691, almost the only tenant of the place besides the domestics was a lad of twelve years of age, of whom no one seemed to take any note until my Lady Viscountess lighted upon him, going over the house with the housekeeper on the day of her arrival. The boy was in the room known as the Book-room, or Yellow Gallery, where the portraits of the family used to hang, that fine piece among others of Sir Antonio Van Dyck of George, second Viscount, and that by Mr. Dobson of my Lord the third Viscount, just deceased, which it seems his lady and widow did not think fit to carry away, when she sent for and carried off to her house at Chelsey, near to London, the picture of herself by Sir Peter Lely, in which her Ladyship was represented as a huntress of Diana's court.

The new and fair lady of Castlewood found the sad, lonely, little occupant of this gallery busy over his great book, which he laid down when he was aware that a stranger was at hand. And, knowing who that person must be, the lad stood up and bowed before her, performing a shy obeisance to the mistress of his house.

She stretched out her hand—indeed when was it that that hand would not stretch out to do an act of kindness, or to protect grief and ill-fortune? "And this is our kinsman," she said; "and what is your name, kinsman?"

"My name is Henry Esmond," said the lad, looking up at her in a sort of delight and wonder, for she had come upon him as a *Dea certè*, and appeared the most charming object he had ever looked on. Her golden hair was shining in the gold of the sun; her complexion was of a dazzling bloom; her lips smiling, and her eyes beaming with a kindness which made Harry Esmond's heart to beat with surprise.

"His name is Henry Esmond, sure enough, my Lady," says Mrs. Worksop, the housekeeper (an old tyrant whom Henry Esmond

HENRY ESMOND FINDS FRIENDS.

plagued more than he hated), and the old gentlewoman looked significantly towards the late lord's picture, as it now is in the family, noble and severe-looking, with his hand on his sword, and his order on his cloak, which he had from the Emperor during the war on the Danube against the Turk.

Seeing the great and undeniable likeness between this portrait and the lad, the new Viscountess, who had still hold of the boy's hand as she looked at the picture, blushed and dropped the hand quickly, and walked down the gallery, followed by Mrs. Worksop.

When the lady came back, Harry Esmond stood exactly in the same spot, and with his hand as it had fallen when he dropped it on his black coat.

Her heart melted, I suppose (indeed, she hath since owned as much), at the notion that she should do anything unkind to any mortal, great or small; for, when she returned, she had sent away the housekeeper upon an errand by the door at the farther end of the gallery; and, coming back to the lad, with a look of infinite pity and tenderness in her eyes, she took his hand again, placing her other fair hand on his head, and saying some words to him, which were so kind, and said in a voice so sweet, that the boy, who had never looked upon so much beauty before, felt as if the touch of a superior being or angel smote him down to the ground, and kissed the fair protecting hand as he knelt on one knee. To the very last hour of his life, Esmond remembered the lady as she then spoke and looked, the rings on her fair hands, the very scent of her robe, the beam of her eyes lighting up with surprise and kindness, her lips blooming in a smile, the sun making a golden halo round her hair.

As the boy was yet in this attitude of humility, enters behind him a portly gentleman, with a little girl of four years old in his hand. The gentleman burst into a great laugh at the lady and her adorer, with his little queer figure, his sallow face and long black hair. The lady blushed, and seemed to deprecate his ridicule by a look of appeal to her husband, for it was my Lord Viscount who now arrived, and whom the lad knew, having once before seen him in the late lord's lifetime.

"So this is the little priest!" says my Lord, looking down at the lad. "Welcome, kinsman!"

"He is saying his prayers to mamma," says the little girl, who came up to her papa's knees; and my Lord burst out into another great laugh at this, and kinsman Henry looked very silly. He invented a half-dozen of speeches in reply, but 'twas months afterwards when he thought of this adventure: as it was, he had never a word in answer

"Le pauvre enfant, il n'a que nous," says the lady, looking to her lord; and the boy, who understood her, though doubtless she thought otherwise, thanked her with all his heart for her kind speech.

"And he shan't want for friends here," says my Lord, in a kind voice, "shall he, little Trix?"

The little girl, whose name was Beatrix, and whom her papa called by this diminutive, looked at Henry Esmond solemnly, with a pair of large eyes, and then a smile shone over her face, which was as beautiful as that of a cherub, and she came up and put out a little hand to him. A keen and delightful pang of gratitude, happiness, affection, filled the orphan child's heart as he received from the protectors, whom Heaven had sent to him, these touching words and tokens of friendliness and kindness. But an hour since he had felt quite alone in the world; when he heard the great peal of bells from Castlewood church ringing that morning to welcome the arrival of the new lord and lady, it had rung only terror and anxiety to him, for he knew not how the new owner would deal with him; and those to whom he formerly looked for protection were forgotten or dead. Pride and doubt too had kept him within-doors, when the Vicar and the people of the village, and the servants of the house, had gone out to welcome my Lord Castlewood—for Henry Esmond was no servant, though a dependant; no relative, though he bore the name and inherited the blood of the house; and in the midst of the noise and acclamations attending the arrival of the new lord (for whom, you may be sure, a feast was got ready, and guns were fired, and tenants and domestics huzzahed when his carriage approached and rolled into the courtyard of the Hall), no one ever took any notice of young Henry Esmond, who sate unobserved and alone in the Book-room, until the afternoon of that day, when his new friends found him.

When my Lord and Lady were going away thence, the little girl, still holding her kinsman by the hand, bade him to come too. "Thou wilt always forsake an old friend for a new one, Trix," says her father to her good-naturedly; and went into the gallery, giving an arm to his lady. They passed thence through the music gallery, long since dismantled, and Queen Elizabeth's Rooms, in the clock-tower, and out into the terrace, where was a fine prospect of sunset and the great darkling woods with a cloud of rooks returning; and the plain and river with Castlewood village beyond, and purple hills beautiful to look at—and the little heir of Castlewood, a child of two years old, was already here on the terrace in his nurse's arms, from whom he ran across the grass instantly he perceived his mother, and came to her.

"If thou canst not be happy here," says my Lord, looking round at the scene, "thou art hard to please, Rachel."

"I am happy where you are," she said, "but we were happiest of all at Walcote Forest." Then my Lord began to describe what was before them to his wife, and what indeed little Harry knew better than he—viz., the history of the house: how by yonder gate the page ran away with the heiress of Castlewood, by which the estate came into the present family; how the Roundheads attacked the clock-tower, which my Lord's father was slain in defending. "I was but two years old then," says he, "but take forty-six from ninety, and how old shall I be, kinsman Harry?"

"Thirty," says his wife, with a laugh.

"A great deal too old for you, Rachel," answers my Lord, looking fondly down at her. Indeed she seemed to be a girl, and was at that time scarce twenty years old.

"You know, Frank, I will do anything to please you," says she, "and I promise you I will grow older every day."

"You mustn't call papa Frank; you must call papa my Lord now," says Miss Beatrix, with a toss of her little head; at which the mother smiled, and the good-natured father laughed, and the little trotting boy laughed, not knowing why—but because he was happy, no doubt—as every one seemed to be there. How those trivial incidents and words, the landscape and sunshine, and the group of people smiling and talking, remain fixed on the memory!

As the sun was setting, the little heir was sent in the arms of his nurse to bed, whither he went howling; but little Trix was promised to sit to supper that night—"and you will come too, kinsman, won't you?" she said.

Harry Esmond blushed: "I—I have supper with Mrs. Worksop," says he.

"D—n it," says my Lord, "thou shalt sup with us, Harry, to-night! Shan't refuse a lady, shall he, Trix?"—and they all wondered at Harry's performance as a trencherman, in which character the poor boy acquitted himself very remarkably; for the truth is he had had no dinner, nobody thinking of him in the bustle which the house was in, during the preparations antecedent to the new lord's arrival.

"No dinner! poor dear child!" says my Lady, heaping up his plate with meat, and my Lord, filling a bumper for him, bade him call a health; on which Master Harry, crying "The King," tossed off the wine. My Lord was ready to drink that, and most other toasts: indeed only too ready. He would not hear of Doctor Tusher (the Vicar of Castlewood, who came to supper) going away when the sweetmeats were brought: he had not had a chaplain long enough, he said, to be tired of him: so his reverence kept my Lord company for some hours over a pipe and a punch bowl; and went away home with rather a reeling gait, and declaring a dozen of times, that his Lordship's affability surpassed every kindness he had ever had from his Lordship's gracious family.

As for young Esmond, when he got to his little chamber, it was with a heart full of surprise and gratitude towards the new friends whom this happy day had brought him. He was up and watching long before the house was astir, longing to see that fair lady and her children—that kind protector and patron; and only fearful lest their welcome of the past night should in any way be withdrawn or altered. But presently little Beatrix came out into the garden, and her mother followed, who greeted Harry as kindly as before. He told her at greater length the histories of the house (which he had been taught in the old lord's time), and to which she listened with great interest; and then he told her, with respect to the night before, that he understood French, and thanked her for her protection.

"Do you?" says she, with a blush; "then, sir, you shall teach me and Beatrix." And she asked him many more questions regarding himself, which had best be told more fully and explicitly than in those brief replies which the lad made to his mistress's questions.

CHAPTER II

RELATES HOW FRANCIS, FOURTH VISCOUNT, ARRIVES AT CASTLEWOOD

'TIS known that the name of Esmond and the estate of Castlewood, com. Hants, came into possession of the present family through Dorothea, daughter and heiress of Edward, Earl and Marquis Esmond, and Lord of Castlewood, which lady married, 23 Eliz., Henry Poyns, gent.; the said Henry being then a page in the household of her father. Francis, son and heir of the above Henry and Dorothea, who took the maternal name, which the family hath borne subsequently, was made Knight and Baronet by King James the First; and being of a military disposition, remained long in Germany with the Elector-Palatine, in whose service Sir Francis incurred both expense and danger, lending large sums of money to that unfortunate Prince; and receiving many wounds in the battles against the Imperialists, in which Sir Francis engaged.

On his return home Sir Francis was rewarded for his services and many sacrifices, by his late Majesty James the First, who graciously conferred upon this tried servant the post of Warden of the Butteries and Groom of the King's Posset, which high and confidential office he filled in that king's and his unhappy successor's reign.

His age, and many wounds and infirmities, obliged Sir Francis to perform much of his duty by deputy; and his son, Sir George Esmond, knight and banneret, first as his father's lieutenant, and afterwards as inheritor of his father's title and dignity, performed this office during almost the whole of the reign of King Charles the First, and his two sons who succeeded him.

Sir George Esmond married, rather beneath the rank that a person of his name and honour might aspire to, the daughter of Thos. Topham, of the city of London, alderman and goldsmith, who, taking the Parliamentary side in the troubles then commencing, disappointed Sir George of the property which he expected at the demise of his father-in-law, who devised his money to his second daughter, Barbara, a spinster.

Sir George Esmond, on his part, was conspicuous for his attachment and loyalty to the royal cause and person; and the King being at Oxford in 1642, Sir George, with the consent of his father, then very aged and infirm, and residing at his house of Castlewood, melted the whole of the family plate for his Majesty's service.

For this, and other sacrifices and merits, his Majesty, by patent under the Privy Seal, dated Oxford, Jan. 1643, was pleased to advance Sir Francis Esmond to the dignity of Viscount Castlewood, of Shandon, in Ireland: and the Viscount's estate being much impoverished by loans to the King, which in those troublesome times his Majesty could not repay, a grant of land in the plantations of Virginia was given to the Lord Viscount; part of which land is in possession of descendants of his family to the present day.

The first Viscount Castlewood died full of years, and within a few months after he had been advanced to his honours. He was succeeded by his eldest son, the before-named George; and left issue besides, Thomas, a colonel in the King's army, who afterwards joined the Usurper's Government; and Francis, in holy orders, who was slain whilst defending the House of Castlewood against the Parliament, anno 1647.

George Lord Castlewood (the second Viscount), of King Charles the First's time, had no male issue save his one son, Eustace Esmond, who was killed with half of the Castlewood men beside him, at Worcester fight. The lands about Castlewood were sold and apportioned to the Commonwealth-men; Castlewood being concerned in almost all of the plots against the Protector, after the death of the King, and up to King Charles the Second's restoration. My Lord followed that King's Court about in its exile, having ruined himself in its service. He had but one daughter, who was of no great comfort to her father; for misfortune had not taught those exiles sobriety of life; and it is said that the Duke of York and his brother the King both quarrelled about Isabel Esmond. She was maid of honour to the Queen Henrietta Maria; she early joined the Roman Church; her father, a weak man, following her not long after at Breda.

On the death of Eustace Esmond at Worcester, Thomas Esmond, nephew to my Lord Castlewood, and then a stripling, became heir to the title. His father had taken the Parliament side in the quarrels, and so had been estranged from the chief of his house; and my Lord Castlewood was at first so much enraged to think that his title (albeit little more than an empty one now) should pass to a rascally Roundhead, that he would have married again, and indeed proposed to do so to a vintner's daughter at Bruges, to whom his Lordship owed a score for lodging when the King was there, but for fear of the laughter of the Court, and the anger of his daughter, of whom he stood in awe; for she was in temper as imperious and violent as my Lord, who was much enfeebled by wounds and drinking, was weak.

Lord Castlewood would have had a match between his daughter Isabel and her cousin, the son of that Francis Esmond who was killed at Castlewood siege. And the lady, it was said, took a fancy to the young man, who was her junior by several years (which circumstance she did not consider to be a fault in him); but having paid his court, and being admitted to the intimacy of the house, he suddenly flung up his suit, when it seemed to be pretty prosperous, without giving a pretext for his behaviour. His friends rallied him at what they laughingly chose to call his infidelity; Jack Churchill, Frank Esmond's lieutenant in the Royal Regiment of Foot-guards, getting the company which Esmond vacated, when he left the Court and went to Tangier in a rage at discovering that his promotion depended on the complaisance of his elderly affianced bride. He and Churchill, who had been *condiscipuli* at St. Paul's School, had words about this matter; and Frank Esmond said to him with an oath, "Jack, your sister may be so-and-so, but by Jove my wife shan't!" and swords were drawn, and blood drawn too, until friends separated them on this quarrel. Few men were so jealous about the point of honour in those days; and gentlemen of good birth and lineage thought a royal blot was an ornament to their family coat. Frank Esmond retired in the sulks, first to Tangier, whence he returned after two years' service, settling on a small property he had of his mother, near to Winchester, and became a country gentleman, and kept a pack of beagles, and never came to Court again in King Charles's time. But his uncle Castlewood was never reconciled to him; nor, for some time afterwards, his cousin whom he had refused.

By places, pensions, bounties from France, and gifts from the King, whilst his daughter was in favour, Lord Castlewood, who had spent in the Royal service his youth and fortune, did not retrieve the latter quite, and never cared to visit Castlewood, or repair it, since the death of his son, but managed to keep a good house, and figure at Court, and to save a considerable sum of ready money.

And now, his heir and nephew, Thomas Esmond, began to bid for his uncle's favour. Thomas had served with the Emperor, and with the Dutch, when King Charles was compelled to lend troops to the States, and against them, when his Majesty made an alliance with the French King. In these campaigns Thomas Esmond was more remarked for duelling, brawling, vice, and play, than for any conspicuous gallantry in the field, and came back to England, like many another English gentleman who has travelled, with a character by no means improved by his foreign experience. He had dissipated his small paternal inheritance of a younger brother's portion, and, as truth must be told, was no better than a hanger-on of ordinaries, and a brawler about Alsatia and the Friars, when he bethought him of a means of mending his fortune.

His cousin was now of more than middle age, and had nobody's word but her own for the beauty which she said she once possessed. She was lean, and yellow, and long in the tooth; all the red and white in all the toy-shops in London could not make a beauty of her—Mr. Killigrew called her the Sibyl, the death's-head put up at the King's feast as a *memento mori*, &c.—in fine, a woman who might be easy of conquest, but whom only a very bold man would think of conquering. This bold man was Thomas Esmond. He had a fancy to my Lord Castlewood's savings, the amount of which rumour had very much exaggerated. Madame Isabel was said to have Royal jewels of great value; whereas poor Tom Esmond's last coat but one was in pawn.

My Lord had at this time a fine house in Lincoln's Inn Fields, nigh to the Duke's Theatre and the Portugal ambassador's chapel. Tom Esmond, who had frequented the one, as long as he had money to spend among the actresses, now came to the church as assiduously. He looked so lean and shabby, that he passed without difficulty for a repentant sinner; and so, becoming converted, you may be sure took his uncle's priest for a director.

This charitable Father reconciled him with the old lord his uncle, who a short time before would not speak to him, as Tom passed under my Lord's coach window, his Lordship going in state to his place at Court, while his nephew slunk by with his battered hat and feather, and the point of his rapier sticking out of the scabbard —to his twopenny ordinary in Bell Yard.

Thomas Esmond, after this reconciliation with his uncle, very soon began to grow sleek, and to show signs of the benefits of good living and clean linen. He fasted rigorously twice a week, to be sure; but he made amends on the other days: and, to show how great his appetite was, Mr. Wycherley said, he ended by swallowing that fly-blown rank old morsel his cousin. There were endless jokes and lampoons about this marriage at Court: but Tom rode thither in his uncle's coach now, called him father, and having won could afford to laugh. This marriage took place very shortly before King Charles died: whom the Viscount of Castlewood speedily followed.

The issue of this marriage was one son, whom the parents watched with an intense eagerness and care; but who, in spite of nurses and physicians, had only a brief existence. His tainted blood did not run very long in his poor feeble little body. Symptoms of evil broke out early on him; and, part from flattery, part superstition, nothing would satisfy my Lord and Lady, especially the latter, but having the poor little cripple touched by his Majesty at his church. They were ready to cry out miracle at first (the doctors and quacksalvers being constantly in attendance on the child, and experimenting on his poor little body with every conceivable nostrum)—but though there seemed, from some reason, a notable amelioration in the infant's health after his Majesty touched him, in a few weeks afterward the poor thing died—causing the lampooners of the Court to say, that the King, in expelling evil out of the infant of Tom Esmond and Isabella his wife, expelled the life out of it, which was nothing but corruption.

The mother's natural pang at losing this poor little child must have been increased when she thought of her rival Frank Esmond's wife, who was a favourite of the whole Court, where my poor Lady Castlewood was neglected, and who had one child, a daughter, flourishing and beautiful, and was about to become a mother once more.

The Court, as I have heard, only laughed the more because the poor lady, who had pretty well passed the age when ladies are accustomed to have children, nevertheless determined not to give hope up, and even when she came to live at Castlewood, was constantly sending over to Hexton for the doctor, and announcing to her friends the arrival of an heir. This absurdity of hers was one amongst many others which the wags used to play upon. Indeed, to the last days of her life, my Lady Viscountess had the comfort of fancying herself beautiful, and persisted in blooming up to the very midst of winter, painting roses on her cheeks long after their natural season, and attiring herself like summer though her head was covered with snow.

Gentlemen who were about the Court of King Charles, and King James, have told the present writer a number of stories about this queer old lady, with which it's not necessary that posterity should be entertained. She is said to have had great powers of invective; and, if she fought with all her rivals in King James's favour, 'tis certain she must have had a vast number of quarrels on her hands. She was a woman of an intrepid spirit, and, it appears, pursued and rather fatigued his Majesty with her rights and her wrongs. Some say that the cause of her leaving Court was jealousy of Frank Esmond's wife; others, that she was forced to retreat after a great battle which took place at Whitehall, between her Ladyship and Lady Dorchester, Tom Killigrew's daughter, whom the King delighted to honour, and in which that ill-favoured Esther got the better of our elderly Vashti. But her Ladyship, for her part, always averred that it was her husband's quarrel, and not her own, which occasioned the banishment of the two into the country; and the cruel ingratitude of the Sovereign in giving away, out of the family, that place of Warden of the Butteries and Groom of the King's Posset, which the two last Lords Castlewood had held so honourably, and which was now conferred upon a fellow of yesterday, and a hanger-on of that odious Dorchester creature, my Lord Bergamot;* "I never," said my Lady, "could have come to see his Majesty's posset carried by any other hand than an Esmond. I should have dashed the salver out of Lord Bergamot's hand, had I met him." And those who knew her Ladyship are aware that she was a person quite capable of performing this feat, had she not wisely kept out of the way.

Holding the purse-strings in her own control, to which, indeed, she liked to bring most persons who came near her, Lady Castlewood could command her husband's obedience, and so broke up her establishment at London; she had removed from Lincoln's Inn Fields to Chelsey, to a pretty new house she bought there; and brought her establishment, her maids, lapdogs, and gentlewomen, her priest, and his Lordship her husband, to Castlewood Hall, that she had never seen since she quitted it as a child with her father during the troubles of King Charles the First's reign. The walls were still open in the old house as they had been left by the shot of the Commonwealth-men. A part of the mansion was restored and furbished up with the plate, hangings, and furniture brought from the house in London. My Lady meant to have a triumphal entry into Castlewood village, and expected the people to cheer as she drove over the Green in her great coach, my Lord beside her, her gentlewomen, lapdogs, and cockatoos on the opposite seat, six horses to her carriage, and servants armed and mounted following it and preceding it. But 'twas in the height of the No-Popery cry; the folks in the village and the neighbouring town were scared by the sight of her Ladyship's painted face and eyelids, as she bobbed her head out of the coach window, meaning, no doubt, to be very gracious; and one old woman said, "Lady Isabel! lord-a-mercy, it's Lady Jezebel!" a name by which the enemies of the

* Lionel Tipton, created Baron Bergamot, ann. 1686, Gentleman Usher of the Back Stairs, and afterwards appointed Warden of the Butteries and Groom of the King's Posset (on the decease of George, second Viscount Castlewood), accompanied his Majesty to St. Germain's, where he died without issue. No Groom of the Posset was appointed by the Prince of Orange, nor hath there been such an officer in any succeeding reign.

right honourable Viscountess were afterwards in the habit of designating her. The country was then in a great No-Popery fervour; her Ladyship's known conversion, and her husband's, the priest in her train, and the service performed at the chapel of Castlewood (though the chapel had been built for that worship before any other was heard of in the country, and though the service was performed in the most quiet manner), got her no favour at first in the county or village. By far the greater part of the estate of Castlewood had been confiscated, and been parcelled out to Commonwealth-men. One or two of these old Cromwellian soldiers were still alive in the village, and looked grimly at first upon my Lady Viscountess, when she came to dwell there.

She appeared at the Hexton Assembly, bringing her lord after her, scaring the country folks with the splendour of her diamonds, which she always wore in public. They said she wore them in private, too, and slept with them round her neck; though the writer can pledge his word that this was a calumny. "If she were to take them off," my Lady Sark said, "Tom Esmond, her husband, would run away with them and pawn them." 'Twas another calumny. My Lady Sark was also an exile from Court, and there had been war between the two ladies before.

The village people began to be reconciled presently to their lady, who was generous and kind, though fantastic and haughty, in her ways, and whose praises Doctor Tusher, the Vicar, sounded loudly amongst his flock. As for my Lord, he gave no great trouble, being considered scarce more than an appendage to my Lady, who, as daughter of the old lords of Castlewood, and possessor of vast wealth, as the country folk said (though indeed nine-tenths of it existed but in rumour), was looked upon as the real queen of the castle, and mistress of all it contained.

CHAPTER III

WHITHER IN THE TIME OF THOMAS, THIRD VISCOUNT, I HAD PRECEDED HIM AS PAGE TO ISABELLA

COMING up to London again some short time after this retreat, the Lord Castlewood despatched a retainer of his to a little cottage in the village of Ealing, near to London, where for some time had dwelt an old French refugee, by name Mr. Pastoureau, one of those whom the persecution of the Huguenots by the French king had brought over to this country. With this old man lived a little lad, who went by the name of Henry Thomas. He remembered to have lived in another place a short time before, near to London too, amongst looms and spinning-wheels, and a great deal of psalm-singing and church-going, and a whole colony of Frenchmen.

There he had a dear, dear friend, who died, and whom he called Aunt. She used to visit him in his dreams sometimes; and her face, though it was homely, was a thousand times dearer to him than that of Mrs. Pastoureau, Bon Papa Pastoureau's new wife, who came to live with him after aunt went away. And there, at Spittlefields, as it used to be called, lived Uncle George, who was a weaver too, but used to tell Harry that he was a little gentleman, and that his father was a captain, and his mother an angel.

When he said so, Bon Papa used to look up from the loom, where he was embroidering beautiful silk flowers, and say "Angel! she belongs to the Babylonish scarlet woman." Bon Papa was always talking of the scarlet woman. He had a little room where he always used to preach and sing hymns out of his great old nose. Little Harry did not like the preaching: he liked better the fine stories which aunt used to tell him. Bon Papa's wife never told him pretty stories; she quarrelled with Uncle George, and he went away.

After this, Harry's Bon Papa and his wife and two children of her own that she brought with her, came to live at Ealing. The new wife gave her children the best of everything and Harry many a whipping, he knew not why. Besides blows, he got ill names from her, which need not be set down here, for the sake of old Mr.

Pastoureau, who was still kind sometimes. The unhappiness of those days is long forgiven, though they cast a shade of melancholy over the child's youth, which will accompany him, no doubt, to the end of his days: as those tender twigs are bent the trees grow afterward; and he, at least, who has suffered as a child, and is not quite perverted in that early school of unhappiness, learns to be gentle and long-suffering with little children.

Harry was very glad when a gentleman dressed in black, on horseback, with a mounted servant behind him, came to fetch him away from Ealing. The noverca, or unjust step-mother, who had neglected him for her own two children, gave him supper enough the night before he went away, and plenty in the morning. She did not beat him once, and told the children to keep their hands off him. One was a girl, and Harry never could bear to strike a girl; and the other was a boy, whom he could easily have beat, but he always cried out, when Mrs. Pastoureau came sailing to the rescue with arms like a flail. She only washed Harry's face the day he went away; nor ever so much as once boxed his ears. She whimpered rather when the gentleman in black came for the boy; and old Mr. Pastoureau, as he gave the child his blessing, scowled over his shoulder at the strange gentleman, and grumbled out something about Babylon and the scarlet lady. He was grown quite old, like a child almost. Mrs. Pastoureau used to wipe his nose as she did to the children. She was a great, big, handsome young woman; but, though she pretended to cry, Harry thought 'twas only a sham, and sprang quite delighted upon the horse upon which the lacquey helped him.

He was a Frenchman; his name was Blaise. The child could talk to him in his own language perfectly well: he knew it better than English indeed, having lived hitherto chiefly among French people: and being called the Little Frenchman by other boys on Ealing Green. He soon learnt to speak English perfectly, and to forget some of his French: children forget easily. Some earlier and fainter recollections the child had of a different country; and a town with tall white houses; and a ship. But these were quite indistinct in the boy's mind, as indeed the memory of Ealing soon became, at least of much that he suffered there.

The lacquey before whom he rode was very lively and voluble, and informed the boy that the gentleman riding before him was my lord's chaplain, Father Holt—that he was now to be called Master Harry Esmond—that my Lord Viscount Castlewood was his *parrain*—that he was to live at the great house of Castlewood, in the province of ——shire, where he would see Madame the Viscountess, who was a grand lady. And so, seated on a cloth before Blaise's saddle, Harry Esmond was brought to London, and to a fine square called Covent Garden, near to which his patron lodged.

Mr. Holt, the priest, took the child by the hand, and brought him to this nobleman, a grand languid nobleman in a great cap and flowered morning-gown, sucking oranges. He patted Harry on the head and gave him an orange.

"C'est bien ça," he said to the priest after eyeing the child, and the gentleman in black shrugged his shoulders.

"Let Blaise take him out for a holiday," and out for a holiday the boy and the valet went. Harry went jumping along; he was glad enough to go.

He will remember to his life's end the delights of those days. He was taken to see a play by Monsieur Blaise, in a house a thousand times greater and finer than the booth at Ealing Fair—and on the next happy day they took water on the river, and Harry saw London Bridge, with the houses and booksellers' shops thereon, looking like a street, and the Tower of London, with the armour, and the great lions and bears in the moat—all under company of Monsieur Blaise.

Presently, of an early morning, all the party set forth for the country, namely, my Lord Viscount and the other gentleman; Monsieur Blaise and Harry on a pillion behind them, and two or three men with pistols leading the baggage-horses. And all along the road the Frenchman told little Harry stories of brigands, which made the child's hair stand on end, and terrified him; so that at the great gloomy inn on the road where they lay, he besought to be allowed to sleep in a room with one of the servants, and was compassionated by Mr. Holt, the gentleman who travelled with my lord, and who gave the child a little bed in his chamber.

His artless talk and answers very likely inclined this gentleman in the boy's favour, for next day Mr. Holt said Harry should ride behind him, and not with the French lacquey; and all along the journey put a thousand questions to the child—as to his foster-brother and relations at Ealing; what his old grandfather had taught him; what languages he knew; whether he could read and write, and sing, and so forth. And Mr. Holt found that Harry could read and write, and possessed the two languages of French and English very well; and when he asked Harry about singing, the lad broke out with a hymn to the tune of Dr. Martin Luther, which set Mr. Holt a-laughing; and even caused his *grand parrain* in the laced hat and periwig to laugh too when Holt told him what the child was singing. For it appeared that Dr. Martin Luther's hymns were not sung in the churches Mr. Holt preached at.

"You must never sing that song any more: do you hear, little mannikin?" says my Lord Viscount, holding up a finger.

"But we will try and teach you a better, Harry," Mr. Holt said; and the child answered, for he was a docile child, and of an affectionate nature, "that he loved pretty songs, and would try and learn anything the gentleman would tell him." That day he so pleased the gentlemen by his talk, that they had him to dine with them at the inn, and encouraged him in his prattle; and Monsieur Blaise, with whom he rode and dined the day before, waited upon him now.

"'Tis well, 'tis well!" said Blaise, that night (in his own language) when they lay again at an inn. "We are a little lord here; we are a little lord now: we shall see what we are when we come to Castlewood, where my Lady is."

"When shall we come to Castlewood, Monsieur Blaise?" says Harry.

"*Parbleu!* my Lord does not press himself," Blaise says, with a grin; and, indeed, it seemed as if his Lordship was not in a great hurry, for he spent three days on that journey, which Harry Esmond hath often since ridden in a dozen hours. For the last two of the days Harry rode with the priest, who was so kind to him, that the child had grown to be quite fond and familiar with him by the journey's end, and had scarce a thought in his little heart which by that time he had not confided to his new friend.

At length, on the third day, at evening, they came to a village standing on a green with elms round it, very pretty to look at; and the people there all took off their hats, and made curtseys to my Lord Viscount, who bowed to them all languidly; and there was one portly person that wore a cassock and a broad-leafed hat, who bowed lower than any one—and with this one both my Lord and Mr. Holt had a few words. "This, Harry, is Castlewood church," says Mr. Holt, "and this is the pillar thereof, learned Doctor Tusher. Take off your hat, sirrah, and salute Doctor Tusher!"

"Come up to supper, Doctor," says my Lord; at which the Doctor made another low bow, and the party moved on towards a grand house that was before them, with many grey towers and vanes on them, and windows flaming in the sunshine; and a great army of rooks, wheeling over their heads, made for the woods behind the house, as Harry saw; and Mr. Holt told him that they lived at Castlewood too.

They came to the house, and passed under an arch into a courtyard, with a fountain in the centre, where many men came and held my Lord's stirrup as he descended, and paid great respect to

Mr. Holt likewise. And the child thought that the servants looked at him curiously, and smiled to one another—and he recalled what Blaise had said to him when they were in London, and Harry had spoken about his godpapa, when the Frenchman said, "*Parbleu*, one sees well that my Lord is your godfather;" words whereof the poor lad did not know the meaning then, though he apprehended the truth in a very short time afterwards, and learned it, and thought of it with no small feeling of shame.

Taking Harry by the hand as soon as they were both descended from their horses, Mr. Holt led him across the court, and under a low door to rooms on a level with the ground; one of which Father Holt said was to be the boy's chamber, the other on the other side of the passage being the Father's own; and as soon as the little man's face was washed, and the Father's own dress arranged, Harry's guide took him once more to the door by which my Lord had entered the hall, and up a stair, and through an ante-room to my Lady's drawing-room—an apartment than which Harry thought he had never seen anything more grand—no, not in the Tower of London which he had just visited. Indeed, the chamber was richly ornamented in the manner of Queen Elizabeth's time, with great stained windows at either end, and hangings of tapestry, which the sun shining through the coloured glass painted of a thousand hues; and here in state, by the fire, sate a lady, to whom the priest took up Harry, who was indeed amazed by her appearance.

My Lady Viscountess's face was daubed with white and red up to the eyes, to which the paint gave an unearthly glare: she had a tower of lace on her head, under which was a bush of black curls—borrowed curls—so that no wonder little Harry Esmond was scared when he was first presented to her—the kind priest acting as master of the ceremonies at that solemn introduction—and he stared at her with eyes almost as great as her own, as he had stared at the player-woman who acted the wicked tragedy-queen, when the players came down to Ealing Fair. She sate in a great chair by the fire-corner; in her lap was a spaniel dog that barked furiously; on a little table by her was her Ladyship's snuffbox and her sugar-plum box. She wore a dress of black velvet, and a petticoat of flame-coloured brocade. She had as many rings on her fingers as the old woman of Banbury Cross; and pretty small feet which she was fond of showing, with great gold clocks to her stockings, and white pantofles with red heels; and an odour of musk was shook out of her garments whenever she moved or quitted the room, leaning on her tortoiseshell stick, little Fury barking at her heels.

Mrs. Tusher, the parson's wife, was with my Lady. She had been waiting-woman to her Ladyship in the late Lord's time, and, having her soul in that business, took naturally to it when the Viscountess of Castlewood returned to inhabit her father's house.

"I present to your Ladyship your kinsman and little page of honour, Master Henry Esmond," Mr. Holt said, bowing lowly, with a sort of comical humility. "Make a pretty bow to my Lady, Monsieur; and then another little bow, not so low, to Madame Tusher—the fair priestess of Castlewood."

"Where I have lived and hope to die, sir," says Madame Tusher, giving a hard glance at the brat, and then at my Lady.

Upon her the boy's whole attention was for a time directed. He could not keep his great eyes off from her. Since the Empress of Ealing, he had seen nothing so awful.

"Does my appearance please you, little page?" asked the lady.

"He would be very hard to please if it didn't," cried Madame Tusher.

"Have done, you silly Maria," said Lady Castlewood.

"Where I'm attached, I'm attached, Madame—and I'd die rather than not say so."

"Je meurs où je m'attache," Mr. Holt said with a polite grin. "The ivy says so in the picture, and clings to the oak like a fond parasite as it is."

"Parricide, sir!" cries Mrs. Tusher.

"Hush, Tusher—you are always bickering with Father Holt," cried my Lady. "Come and kiss my hand, child;" and the oak held out a *branch* to little Harry Esmond, who took and dutifully kissed the lean old hand, upon the gnarled knuckles of which there glittered a hundred rings.

"To kiss that hand would make many a pretty fellow happy!" cried Mrs. Tusher; on which my Lady crying out "Go, you foolish Tusher!" and tapping her with her great fan, Tusher ran forward to seize her hand and kiss it. Fury arose and barked furiously at Tusher; and Father Holt looked on at this queer scene, with arch, grave glances.

The awe exhibited by the little boy perhaps pleased the lady on whom this artless flattery was bestowed; for having gone down on his knee (as Father Holt had directed him, and the mode then was) and performed his obeisance, she said, "Page Esmond, my groom of the chamber will inform you what your duties are, when you wait upon my Lord and me; and good Father Holt will instruct you as becomes a gentleman of our name. You will pay him obedience in everything, and I pray you may grow to be as learned and as good as your tutor."

The lady seemed to have the greatest reverence for Mr. Holt, and to be more afraid of him than of anything else in the world. If she was ever so angry, a word or look from Father Holt made her calm: indeed he had a vast power of subjecting those who came near him; and, among the rest, his new pupil gave himself up with an entire confidence and attachment to the good Father, and became his willing slave almost from the first moment he saw him.

He put his small hand into the Father's as he walked away from his first presentation to his mistress, and asked many questions in his artless childless way. "Who is that other woman?" he asked. "She is fat and round; she is more pretty than my Lady Castlewood."

"She is Madame Tusher, the parson's wife of Castlewood. She has a son of your age, but bigger than you."

"Why does she like so to kiss my Lady's hand? It is not good to kiss."

"Tastes are different, little man. Madame Tusher is attached to my Lady, having been her waiting-woman before she was married, in the old lord's time. She married Doctor Tusher the chaplain. The English household divines often marry the waiting-women."

"You will not marry the Frenchwoman, will you? I saw her laughing with Blaise in the buttery."

"I belong to a Church that is older and better than the English Church," Mr. Holt said (making a sign whereof Esmond did not then understand the meaning, across his breast and forehead); "in our Church the clergy do not marry. You will understand these things better soon."

"Was not Saint Peter the head of your Church?—Dr. Rabbits of Ealing told us so."

The Father said, "Yes, he was."

"But Saint Peter was married, for we heard only last Sunday that his wife's mother lay sick of the fever." On which the Father again laughed, and said he would understand this too better soon, and talked of other things, and took away Harry Esmond, and showed him the great old house which he had come to inhabit.

It stood on a rising green hill, with woods behind it, in which were rooks' nests, where the birds at morning and returning home at evening made a great cawing. At the foot of the hill was a river, with a steep ancient bridge crossing it; and beyond that a large pleasant green flat, where the village of Castlewood stood, and stands, with the church in the midst, the parsonage hard by it, the inn with the blacksmith's forge beside it, and the sign of the "Three Castles" on the elm. The London road stretched away towards the rising sun, and to the west were swelling hills and peaks, behind which many a time Harry Esmond saw the same sun setting, that he now looks on thousands of miles away across the great ocean—in a new Castlewood, by another stream, that bears, like the new country of wandering Æneas, the fond names of the land of his youth.

The Hall of Castlewood was built with two courts, whereof one only, the fountain-court, was now inhabited, the other having been battered down in the Cromwellian wars. In the fountain-court, still in good repair, was the great hall, near to the kitchen and butteries; a dozen of living-rooms looking to the north, and communicating with the little chapel that faced eastwards and the buildings stretching from that to the main gate, and with the hall (which looked to the west) into the court now dismantled. This court had been the most magnificent of the two, until the Protector's cannon tore down one side of it before the place was taken and stormed. The besiegers entered at the terrace under the clock-tower, slaying every man of the garrison, and at their head my Lord's brother, Francis Esmond.

The Restoration did not bring enough money to the Lord Castlewood to restore this ruined part of his house; where were the morning parlours, above them the long music-gallery, and before which stretched the garden-terrace, where, however, the flowers grew again which the boots of the Roundheads had trodden in their assault, and which was restored without much cost, and only a little care, by both ladies who succeeded the second viscount in the government of this mansion. Round the terrace garden was a low wall with a wicket leading to the wooded height beyond, that is called Cromwell's Battery to this day.

Young Harry Esmond learned the domestic part of his duty, which was easy enough, from the groom of her Ladyship's chamber: serving the Countess, as the custom commonly was in his boyhood, as page, waiting at her chair, bringing her scented water and the silver basin after dinner—sitting on her carriage-step on state occasions, or on public days introducing her company to her. This was chiefly of the Catholic gentry, of whom there were a pretty many in the country and neighbouring city; and who rode not seldom to Castlewood to partake of the hospitalities there. In the second year of their residence, the company seemed especially to increase. My Lord and my Lady were seldom without visitors, in whose society it was curious to contrast the difference of behaviour between Father Holt, the director of the family, and Doctor Tusher, the rector of the parish—Mr. Holt moving amongst the very highest as quite their equal, and as commanding them all; while poor

Doctor Tusher, whose position was indeed a difficult one, having been chaplain once to the Hall, and still to the Protestant servants there, seemed more like an usher than an equal, and always rose to go away after the first course.

Also there came in these times to Father Holt many private visitors, whom, after a little, Henry Esmond had little difficulty in recognising as ecclesiastics of the Father's persuasion, whatever their dresses (and they adopted all) might be. These were closeted with the Father constantly, and often came and rode away without paying their devoirs to my Lord and Lady—to the Lady and Lord rather—his Lordship being little more than a cipher in the house, and entirely under his domineering partner. A little fowling, a little hunting, a great deal of sleep, and a long time at cards and table, carried through one day after another with his Lordship. When meetings took place in this second year, which often would happen with closed doors, the page found my Lord's sheet of paper scribbled over with dogs and horses, and 'twas said he had much ado to keep himself awake at these councils: the Countess ruling over them, and he acting as little more than her secretary.

Father Holt began speedily to be so much occupied with these meetings as rather to neglect the education of the little lad who so gladly put himself under the kind priest's orders. At first they read much and regularly, both in Latin and French; the Father not neglecting in anything to impress his faith upon his pupil, but not forcing him violently, and treating him with a delicacy and kindness which surprised and attached the child, always more easily won by these methods than by any severe exercise of authority. And his delight in their walks was to tell Harry of the glories of his order, of its martyrs and heroes, of its Brethren converting the heathen by myriads, traversing the desert, facing the stake, ruling the courts and councils, or braving the tortures of kings; so that Harry Esmond thought that to belong to the Jesuits was the greatest prize of life and bravest end of ambition; the greatest career here and in heaven the surest reward; and began to long for the day, not only when he should enter into the one church and receive his first communion, but when he might join that wonderful brotherhood, which was present throughout all the world, and which numbered the wisest, the bravest, the highest born, the most eloquent of men among its members. Father Holt bade him keep his views secret, and to hide them as a great treasure which would escape him if it was revealed; and, proud of this confidence and secret vested in him, the lad became fondly attached to the master who initiated him into a mystery so wonderful and awful. And when little Tom Tusher, his neighbour, came from school for his holiday, and said how he, too, was to be bred up for an English priest, and would get what he called an exhibition from his school, and then a college scholarship and fellowship, and then a good living—it tasked young Harry Esmond's powers of reticence not to say to his young companion, "Church! priesthood! fat living! My dear Tommy, do you call yours a church and a priesthood? What is a fat living compared to converting a hundred thousand heathens by a single sermon? What is a scholarship at Trinity by the side of a crown of martyrdom, with angels awaiting you as your head is taken off? Could your master at school sail over the Thames on his gown? Have you statues in your church that can bleed, speak, walk, and cry? My good Tommy, in dear Father Holt's church these things take place every day. You know Saint Philip of the Willows appeared to Lord Castlewood, and caused him to turn to the one true church. No saints ever come to you." And Harry Esmond, because of his promise to Father Holt, hiding away these treasures of faith from T. Tusher, delivered himself of them nevertheless simply to Father Holt; who stroked his head, smiled at him with his inscrutable look, and told him that he did well to meditate on these great things, and not to talk of them except under direction.

CHAPTER IV

I AM PLACED UNDER A POPISH PRIEST AND BRED TO THAT RELIGION—VISCOUNTESS CASTLEWOOD

HAD time enough been given, and his childish inclinations been properly nurtured, Harry Esmond had been a Jesuit priest ere he was a dozen years older, and might have finished his days a martyr in China or a victim on Tower Hill: for, in the few months they spent together at Castlewood, Mr. Holt obtained an entire mastery over the boy's intellect and affections; and had brought him to think, as indeed Father Holt thought with all his heart too, that no life was so noble, no death so desirable, as that which many brethren of his famous order were ready to undergo. By love, by a brightness of wit and good-humour that charmed all, by an authority which he knew how to assume, by a mystery and silence about him which increased the child's reverence for him, he won Harry's absolute fealty, and would have kept it, doubtless, if schemes greater and more important than a poor little boy's admission into orders had not called him away.

After being at home for a few months in tranquillity (if theirs might be called tranquillity, which was, in truth, a constant bickering), my Lord and Lady left the country for London, taking their director with them: and his little pupil scarce ever shed more bitter tears in his life than he did for nights after the first parting with his dear friend, as he lay in the lonely chamber next to that which the Father used to occupy. He and a few domestics were left as the only tenants of the great house: and, though Harry sedulously did all the tasks which the Father set him, he had many hours unoccupied, and read in the library, and bewildered his little brains with the great books he found there.

After a while, the little lad grew accustomed to the loneliness of the place; and in after days remembered this part of his life as a period not unhappy. When the family was at London the whole of the establishment travelled thither with the exception of the porter—who was, moreover, brewer, gardener, and woodman—and his wife and children. These had their lodging in the gate-house hard by, with a door into the court; and a window looking out on the green was the Chaplain's room; and next to this a small chamber where Father Holt had his books, and Harry Esmond his sleeping closet. The side of the house facing the east had escaped the guns of the Cromwellians, whose battery was on the height facing the western court; so that this eastern end bore few marks of demolition, save in the chapel, where the painted windows surviving Edward the Sixth had been broke by the Commonwealth-men. In Father Holt's time little Harry Esmond acted as his familiar, and faithful little servitor; beating his clothes, folding his vestments, fetching his water from the well long before daylight, ready to run anywhere for the service of his beloved priest. When the Father was away, he locked his private chamber; but the room where the books were was left to little Harry, who, but for the society of this gentleman, was little less solitary when Lord Castlewood was at home

The French wit saith that a hero is none to his *valet-de-chambre*, and it required less quick eyes than my Lady's little page was naturally endowed with, to see that she had many qualities by no means heroic, however much Mrs. Tusher might flatter and coax her. When Father Holt was not by, who exercised an entire authority over the pair, my Lord and my Lady quarrelled and abused each other so as to make the servants laugh, and to frighten the little page on duty. The poor boy trembled before his mistress, who called him by a hundred ugly names, who made nothing of boxing his ears, and tilting the silver basin in his face which it was his business to present to her after dinner. She hath repaired, by subsequent kindness to him, these severities, which it must be owned made his childhood very unhappy. She was but unhappy herself at this time, poor soul! and I suppose made her dependants lead her own sad life. I think my Lord was as much afraid of her as her page was, and the only person of the household who mastered her was Mr. Holt. Harry was only too glad when the Father dined at table, and to slink away and prattle with him afterwards, or read with him, or walk with him. Luckily my Lady Viscountess did not rise till noon. Heaven help the poor waiting-woman who had charge of her toilette! I have often seen the poor wretch come out with red eyes from the closet where those long and mysterious rites of her Ladyship's dress were performed, and the backgammon-box locked up with a rap on Mrs. Tusher's fingers when she played ill, or the game was going the wrong way.

Blessed be the king who introduced cards, and the kind inventors of piquet and cribbage, for they employed six hours at least of her Ladyship's day, during which her family was pretty easy. Without this occupation my Lady frequently declared she should die. Her dependants one after another relieved guard—'twas rather a dangerous post to play with her Ladyship—and took the cards turn about. Mr. Holt would sit with her at piquet during hours together, at which time she behaved herself properly; and as for Doctor Tusher, I believe he would have left a parishioner's dying bed, if summoned to play a rubber with his patroness at Castlewood. Sometimes, when they were pretty comfortable together, my Lord took a hand. Besides these my Lady had her faithful poor Tusher, and one, two, three gentlemen whom Harry Esmond could recollect in his time. They could not bear that genteel service very long; one after another tried and failed at it. These and the housekeeper, and little Harry Esmond, had a table of their own. Poor ladies! their life was far harder than the page's. He was sound asleep, tucked up in his little bed, whilst they were sitting by her Ladyship reading her to sleep, with the "News Letter," or the "Grand Cyrus." My Lady used to have boxes of new plays from London, and Harry was forbidden, under the pain of a whipping, to look into them. I am afraid he deserved the penalty pretty often, and got it sometimes. Father Holt applied it twice or thrice, when he caught the young scapegrace with a delightful wicked comedy of Mr. Shadwell's or Mr. Wycherley's under his pillow.

These, when he took any, were my Lord's favourite reading. But he was averse to much study, and, as his little page fancied, to much occupation of any sort.

It always seemed to young Harry Esmond that my Lord treated him with more kindness when his lady was not present, and Lord Castlewood would take the lad sometimes on his little journeys a-hunting or a-birding; he loved to play at cards and tric-trac with him, which games the boy learned to pleasure his lord: and was growing to like him better daily, showing a special pleasure if Father Holt gave a good report of him, patting him on the head, and promising that he would provide for the boy. However, in my Lady's presence, my Lord showed no such marks of kindness, and affected to treat the lad roughly, and rebuked him sharply for little faults, for which he in a manner asked pardon of young Esmond when they were private, saying if he did not speak roughly, she would, and his tongue was not such a bad one as his lady's—a point whereof the boy, young as he was, was very well assured.

Great public events were happening all this while, of which the simple young page took little count. But one day, riding into the neighbouring town on the step of my Lady's coach, his Lordship and she and Father Holt being inside, a great mob of people came hooting and jeering round the coach, bawling out "The Bishops for ever!" "Down with the Pope!" "No Popery! no Popery! Jezebel, Jezebel!" so that my Lord began to laugh, my Lady's eyes to roll with anger, for she was as bold as a lioness, and feared nobody; whilst Mr. Holt, as Esmond saw from his place on the step, sank back with rather an alarmed face, crying out to her Ladyship, "For God's sake, madam, do not speak or look out of window; sit still." But she did not obey this prudent injunction of the Father; she thrust her head out of the coach window, and screamed out to the coachman, "Flog your way through them, the brutes, James, and use your whip!"

The mob answered with a roaring jeer of laughter, and fresh cries of "Jezebel! Jezebel!" My Lord only laughed the more: he was a languid gentleman: nothing seemed to excite him commonly, though I have seen him cheer and halloo the hounds very briskly, and his face (which was generally very yellow and calm) grow quite red and cheerful during a burst over the Downs after a hare, and laugh, and swear, and huzzah at a cock-fight, of which sport he was very fond. And now, when the mob began to hoot his lady, he laughed with something of a mischievous look, as though he expected sport, and thought that she and they were a match.

James the coachman was more afraid of his mistress than the mob, probably, for he whipped on his horses as he was bidden, and the postboy that rode with the first pair (my Lady always rode with her coach-and-six) gave a cut of his thong over the shoulders of one fellow who put his hand out towards the leading horse's rein.

It was a market-day, and the country people were all assembled with their baskets of poultry, eggs, and such things; the postillion had no sooner lashed the man who would have taken hold of his horse, but a great cabbage came whirling like a bombshell into the carriage, at which my Lord laughed more, for it knocked my Lady's fan out of her hand, and plumped into Father Holt's stomach. Then came a shower of carrots and potatoes.

"For Heaven's sake be still!" says Mr. Holt; "we are not ten paces from the 'Bell' archway, where they can shut the gates on us, and keep out this *canaille.*"

The little page was outside the coach on the step, and a fellow in the crowd aimed a potato at him, and hit him in the eye, at which the poor little wretch set up a shout; the man laughed, a great big saddler's apprentice of the town. "Ah! you d—— little yelling Popish bastard," he said, and stooped to pick up another; the crowd had gathered quite between the horses and the inn door by this time, and the coach was brought to a dead stand-still. My Lord jumped as briskly as a boy out of the door on his side of the coach, squeezing little Harry behind it; had hold of the potato-thrower's collar in an instant, and the next moment the brute's heels were in the air, and he fell on the stones with a thump.

"You hulking coward!" says he; "you pack of screaming blackguards! how dare you attack children, and insult women? Fling another shot at that carriage, you sneaking pigskin cobbler, and by the Lord I'll send my rapier through you!"

Some of the mob cried, "Huzzah, my Lord!" for they knew him, and the saddler's man was a known bruiser, near twice as big as my Lord Viscount.

"Make way there," says he (he spoke in a high shrill voice, but with a great air of authority). "Make way, and let her Ladyship's carriage pass." The men that were between the coach and the gate of the "Bell" actually did make way, and the horses went in, my Lord walking after them with his hat on his head.

As he was going in at the gate, through which the coach had just rolled, another cry begins, of "No Popery—no Papists!" My Lord turns round and faces them once more.

"God save the King!" says he at the highest pitch of his voice. "Who dares abuse the King's religion? You, you d——d psalm-singing cobbler, as sure as I'm a magistrate of this county I'll commit you!" The fellow shrank back, and my Lord retreated with all the honours of the day. But when the little flurry caused by the scene was over, and the flush passed off his face, he relapsed into his usual languor, trifled with his little dog, and yawned when my Lady spoke to him.

This mob was one of many thousands that were going about the country at that time, huzzahing for the acquittal of the seven bishops who had been tried just then, and about whom little Harry Esmond at that time knew scarce anything. It was Assizes at Hexton, and there was a great meeting of the gentry at the "Bell"; and my Lord's people had their new liveries on, and Harry a little suit of blue-and-silver, which he wore upon occasions of state; and the gentlefolks came round and talked to my Lord; and a judge in a red gown, who seemed a very great personage, especially complimented him and my Lady, who was mighty grand. Harry remembers her train borne up by her gentlewoman. There was an assembly and ball at the great room at the "Bell," and other young gentlemen of the county families looked on as he did. One of them jeered him for his black eye, which was swelled by the potato, and another called him a bastard, on which he and Harry fell to fisticuffs. My Lord's cousin, Colonel Esmond of Walcote, was there, and separated the two lads—a great tall gentleman, with a handsome good-natured face. The boy did not know how nearly in after-life he should be allied to Colonel Esmond, and how much kindness he should have to owe him.

There was little love between the two families. My Lady used not to spare Colonel Esmond in talking of him, for reasons which have been hinted already; but about which, at his tender age, Henry Esmond could be expected to know nothing.

Very soon afterwards, my Lord and Lady went to London with Mr. Holt, leaving, however, the page behind them. The little man had the great house of Castlewood to himself; or between him and the housekeeper, Mrs. Workscp, an old lady who was a kinswoman of the family in some distant way, and a Protestant, but a staunch Tory and king's-man, as all the Esmonds were. He used to go to school to Dr. Tusher when he was at home, though the Doctor was much occupied too. There was a great stir and commotion everywhere, even in the little quiet village of Castlewood, whither a party of people came from the town, who would have broken Castlewood Chapel windows, but the village people turned out, and even old Sieveright, the republican blacksmith, along with them: for my Lady, though she was a Papist, and had many odd ways, was kind to the tenantry, and there was always a plenty of beef, and blankets, and medicine for the poor at Castlewood Hall.

A kingdom was changing hands whilst my Lord and Lady were away. King James was flying, the Dutchmen were coming; awful stories about them and the Prince of Orange used old Mrs. Worksop to tell to the idle little page.

He liked the solitude of the great house very well; he had all the play-books to read, and no Father Holt to whip him, and a hundred childish pursuits and pastimes, without doors and within, which made this time very pleasant.

CHAPTER V

MY SUPERIORS ARE ENGAGED IN PLOTS FOR THE RESTORATION OF KING JAMES THE SECOND

NOT having been able to sleep, for thinking of some lines for eels which he had placed the night before, the lad was lying in his little bed, waiting for the hour when the gate would be open, and he and his comrade, John Lockwood, the porter's son, might go to the pond and see what fortune had brought them. At daybreak, John was to awaken him, but his own eagerness for the sport had served as a *réveillez* long since—so long, that it seemed to him as if the day never would come.

It might have been four o'clock when he heard the door of the opposite chamber, the Chaplain's room, open, and the voice of a man coughing in the passage. Harry jumped up, thinking for certain it was a robber, or hoping perhaps for a ghost, and, flinging open his own door, saw before him the Chaplain's door open, and a light inside, and a figure standing in the doorway, in the midst of a great smoke which issued from the room.

"Who's there?" cried out the boy, who was of a good spirit.

"*Silentium!*" whispered the other; "'tis I, my boy!" and, holding his hand out, Harry had no difficulty in recognising his master and friend, Father Holt. A curtain was over the window of the Chaplain's room that looked to the court, and Harry saw that the smoke came from a great flame of papers which were burning in a brazier when he entered the Chaplain's room. After giving a hasty greeting and blessing to the lad, who was charmed to see his tutor, the Father continued the burning of his papers, drawing them from a cupboard over the mantelpiece wall, which Harry had never seen before.

Father Holt laughed, seeing the lad's attention fixed at once on this hole. "That is right, Harry," he said; "faithful little famuli see all and say nothing. You are faithful, I know."

"I know I would go to the stake for you," said Harry.

"I don't want your head," said the Father, patting it kindly; "all you have to do is to hold your tongue. Let us burn these papers, and say nothing to anybody. Should you like to read them?"

Harry Esmond blushed, and held down his head; he *had* looked as the fact was, and without thinking, at the paper before him; and though he had seen it, could not understand a word of it, the letters being quite clear enough, but quite without meaning. They burned the papers, beating down the ashes in a brazier, so that scarce any traces of them remained.

Harry had been accustomed to see Father Holt in more dresses than one; it not being safe, or worth the danger, for Popish ecclesiastics to wear their proper dress; and he was, in consequence, in no wise astonished that the priest should now appear before him in a riding-dress, with large buff leather boots, and a feather to his hat, plain, but such as gentlemen wore.

"You know the secret of the cupboard," said he, laughing, "and must be prepared for other mysteries;" and he opened—but not a secret cupboard this time—only a wardrobe, which he usually kept locked, and from which he now took out two or three dresses and perruques of different colours, and a couple of swords of a pretty make (Father Holt was an expert practitioner with the small-sword, and every day, whilst he was at home, he and his pupil practised this exercise, in which the lad became a very great proficient), a military coat and cloak, and a farmer's smock, and placed them in the large hole over the mantelpiece from which the papers had been taken.

"If they miss the cupboard," he said, "they will not find these; if they find them, they'll tell no tales, except that Father Holt wore more suits of clothes than one. All Jesuits do. You know what deceivers we are, Harry."

Harry was alarmed at the notion that his friend was about to leave him; but "No," the priest said, "I may very likely come back with my Lord in a few days. We are to be tolerated; we are not to be persecuted. But they may take a fancy to pay a visit at Castlewood ere our return; and, as gentlemen of my cloth are suspected, they might choose to examine my papers, which concern nobody—at least not them." And to this day, whether the papers in cipher related to politics, or to the affairs of that mysterious society whereof Father Holt was a member, his pupil, Harry Esmond, remains in entire ignorance.

The rest of his goods, his small wardrobe, &c., Holt left untouched on his shelves and in his cupboard, taking down—with a laugh, however—and flinging into the brazier, where he only half burned them, some theological treatises which he had been writing against the English divines. "And now," said he, "Henry, my son, you may testify, with a safe conscience, that you saw me burning Latin sermons the last time I was here before I went away to London; and it will be daybreak directly, and I must be away before Lockwood is stirring."

"Will not Lockwood let you out, sir?" Esmond asked. Holt laughed; he was never more gay or good-humoured than when in the midst of action or danger.

"Lockwood knows nothing of my being here, mind you," he said; "nor would you, you little wretch! had you slept better. You must forget that I have been here; and now farewell. Close the door, and go to your own room, and don't come out till—stay, why should you not know one secret more? I know you will never betray me."

In the Chaplain's room were two windows: the one looking into the court facing westwards to the fountain; the other, a small casement strongly barred, and looking on to the green in front of the Hall. This window was too high to reach from the ground: but, mounting on a buffet which stood beneath it, Father Holt showed me how, by pressing on the base of the window, the whole framework of lead, glass, and iron stanchions descended into a cavity worked below, from which it could be drawn and restored to its usual place from without; a broken pane being purposely open to admit the hand which was to work upon the spring of the machine.

"When I am gone," Father Holt said, "you may push away the buffet, so that no one may fancy that an exit has been made that way; lock the door; place the key—where shall we put the key?—under 'Chrysostom' on the bookshelf; and if any ask for it, say I keep it there, and told you where to find it, if you had need to go to my room. The descent is easy down the wall into the ditch; and so once more farewell, until I see thee again, my dear son." And with this the intrepid Father mounted the buffet with great agility and briskness, stepped across the window, lifting up the bars and framework again from the other side, and only leaving room for Harry Esmond to stand on tiptoe and kiss his hand before the casement closed, the bars fixing as firm as ever, seemingly, in the stone arch overhead. When Father Holt next arrived at Castlewood, it was by the public gate on horseback; and he never so much as alluded to the existence of the private issue to Harry, except when he had need of a private messenger from within, for which end, no doubt, he had instructed his young pupil in the means of quitting the Hall.

Esmond, young as he was, would have died sooner than betray his friend and master, as Mr. Holt well knew; for he had tried the boy more than once, putting temptations in his way, to see whether he would yield to them and confess afterwards, or whether he would resist them, as he did sometimes, or whether he would lie, which he never did. Holt instructing the boy on this point, however, that if to keep silence is not to lie, as it certainly is not, yet silence is, after all, equivalent to a negation—and therefore a downright No, in the interest of justice or your friend, and in reply to a question that may be prejudicial to either, is not criminal, but, on the contrary, praiseworthy; and as lawful a way as the other of eluding a wrongful demand. For instance (says he), suppose a good citizen, who had seen his Majesty take refuge there, had been asked, "Is King Charles up that oak tree?" his duty would have been not to say, Yes—so that the Cromwellians should seize the king and murder him like his father—but No; his Majesty being private in the tree, and therefore not to be seen there by loyal eyes: all which instruction, in religion and morals, as well as in the rudiments of the tongues and sciences, the boy took eagerly and with gratitude from his tutor. When, then, Holt was gone, and told Harry not to see him, it was as if he had never been. And he had this answer pat when he came to be questioned a few days after.

The Prince of Orange was then at Salisbury, as young Esmond learned from seeing Doctor Tusher in his best cassock (though the roads were muddy, and he never was known to wear his silk, only his stuff one, a-horseback), with a great orange cockade in his broad-leafed hat, and Nahum, his clerk, ornamented with a like decoration. The Doctor was walking up and down in front of his parsonage, when little Esmond saw him, and heard him say he was going to pay his duty to his Highness the Prince, as he mounted his pad and rode away with Nahum behind. The village people had orange cockades too, and his friend the blacksmith's laughing daughter pinned one into Harry's old hat, which he tore out indignantly when they bade him to cry "God save the Prince of Orange and the Protestant religion!" but the people only laughed, for they liked the boy in the village, where his solitary condition moved the general pity, and where he found friendly welcomes and faces in many houses. Father Holt had many friends there too, for he not only would fight the blacksmith at theology, never losing his temper, but laughing the whole time in his pleasant way; but he cured him of an ague with quinquina, and was always ready with a kind word for any man that asked it, so that they said in the village 'twas a pity the two were Papists.

The Director and the Vicar of Castlewood agreed very well; indeed, the former was a perfectly-bred gentleman, and it was the latter's business to agree with everybody. Doctor Tusher and the lady's maid, his spouse, had a boy who was about the age of little Esmond · and there was such a friendship between the lads, as propinquity and tolerable kindness and good-humour on either side would be pretty sure to occasion. Tom Tusher was sent off early, however, to a school in London, whither his father took him and a volume of sermons, in the first year of the reign of King James; and Tom returned but once a year afterwards to Castlewood for many years of his scholastic and collegiate life. Thus there was less danger to Tom of a perversion of his faith by the Director, who scarce ever saw him, than there was to Harry, who constantly was in the Vicar's company; but as long as Harry's religion was his Majesty's, and my Lord's, and my Lady's, the Doctor said gravely, it should not be for him to disturb or disquiet him: it was far from him to say that his Majesty's Church was not a branch of the Catholic Church; upon which Father Holt used, according to his custom, to laugh, and say that the Holy Church throughout all the world, and the noble Army of Martyrs, were very much obliged to the Doctor.

It was while Doctor Tusher was away at Salisbury that there came a troop of dragoons with orange scarfs, and quartered in Castlewood, and some of them came up to the Hall, where they took possession, robbing nothing however beyond the hen-house and the beer-cellar; and only insisting upon going through the house and looking for papers. The first room they asked to look at was Father Holt's room, of which Harry Esmond brought the key, and they opened the drawers and the cupboards, and tossed over the papers and clothes—but found nothing except his books and clothes, and the vestments in a box by themselves, with which the dragoons made merry, to Harry Esmond's horror. And to the questions which the gentleman put to Harry, he replied that Father Holt was a very kind man to him, and a very learned man, and Harry supposed would tell him none of his secrets, if he had any. He was about eleven years old at this time, and looked as innocent as boys of his age.

The family were away more than six months, and when they returned they were in the deepest state of dejection, for King James had been banished, the Prince of Orange was on the throne, and the direst persecutions of those of the Catholic faith were apprehended by my Lady, who said she did not believe that there was a word of truth in the promises of toleration that Dutch monster made, or in a single word the perjured wretch said. My Lord and Lady were in a manner prisoners in their own house; so her Ladyship gave the little page to know, who was by this time growing of an age to understand what was passing about him, and something of the characters of the people he lived with.

"We are prisoners," says she; "in everything but chains we

are prisoners. Let them come, let them consign me to dungeons, or strike off my head from this poor little throat" (and she clasped it in her long fingers). "The blood of the Esmonds will always flow freely for their kings. We are not like the Churchills—the Judases, who kiss their master and betray him. We know how to suffer, how even to forgive in the royal cause" (no doubt it was that fatal business of losing the place of Groom of the Posset to which her Ladyship alluded, as she did half-a-dozen times in the day). "Let the tyrant of Orange bring his rack and his odious Dutch tortures—the beast! the wretch! I spit upon him and defy him. Cheerfully will I lay this head upon the block; cheerfully will I accompany my Lord to the scaffold: we will cry 'God save King James!' with our dying breath, and smile in the face of the executioner." And she told her page, a hundred times at least, of the particulars of the last interview which she had with his Majesty.

"I flung myself before my liege's feet," she said, "at Salisbury. I devoted myself—my husband—my house, to his cause. Perhaps he remembered old times, when Isabella Esmond was young and fair; perhaps he recalled the day when 'twas not *I* that knelt—at least he spoke to me with a voice that reminded *me* of days gone by. 'Egad!' said his Majesty, 'you should go to the Prince of Orange, if you want anything.' 'No, sire,' I replied, 'I would not kneel to a Usurper; the Esmond that would have served your Majesty will never be groom to a traitor's posset.' The royal exile smiled, even in the midst of his misfortune; he deigned to raise me with words of consolation. The Viscount, my husband, himself, could not be angry at the august salute with which he honoured me!"

The public misfortune had the effect of making my Lord and his Lady better friends than they ever had been since their courtship. My Lord Viscount had shown both loyalty and spirit, when these were rare qualities in the dispirited party about the King; and the praise he got elevated him not a little in his wife's good opinion, and perhaps in his own. He wakened up from the listless and supine life which he had been leading; was always riding to and fro in consultation with this friend or that of the King's; the page of course knowing little of his doings, but remarking only his greater cheerfulness and altered demeanour.

Father Holt came to the Hall constantly, but officiated no longer openly as chaplain; he was always fetching and carrying: strangers, military and ecclesiastic (Harry knew the latter, though they came in all sorts of disguises), were continually arriving and departing. My Lord made long absences and sudden reappearances, using sometimes the means of exit which Father Holt had employed, though how often the little window in the Chaplain's room let in or let out my Lord and his friends, Harry could not tell. He stoutly kept his promise to the Father of not prying, and if at midnight from his little room he heard noises of persons stirring in the next chamber, he turned round to the wall, and hid his curiosity under his pillow until it fell asleep. Of course he could not help remarking that the priest's journeys were constant, and understanding by a hundred signs that some active though secret business employed him: what this was may pretty well be guessed by what soon happened to my Lord.

No garrison or watch was put into Castlewood when my Lord came back, but a guard was in the village; and one or other of them was always on the Green keeping a look-out on our great gate, and those who went out and in. Lockwood said that at night especially every person who came in or went out was watched by the outlying sentries. 'Twas lucky that we had a gate which their Worships knew nothing about. My Lord and Father Holt must have made constant journeys at night: once or twice little Harry acted as their messenger and discreet aide-de-camp. He remembers he was bidden to go into the village with his fishing-rod, enter certain houses, ask for a drink of water, and tell the good man, "There would be a horse-market at Newbury next Thursday," and so carry the same message on to the next house on his list.

He did not know what the message meant at the time, nor what was happening: which may as well, however, for clearness' sake, be explained here. The Prince of Orange being gone to Ireland, where the King was ready to meet him with a great army, it was determined that a great rising of his Majesty's party should take place in this country; and my Lord was to head the force in our county. Of late he had taken a greater lead in affairs than before, having the indefatigable Mr. Holt at his elbow, and my Lady Viscountess strongly urging him on; and my Lord Sark being in the Tower a prisoner, and Sir Wilmot Crawley, of Queen's Crawley, having gone over to the Prince of Orange's side—my Lord became the most considerable person in our part of the county for the affairs of the King.

It was arranged that the regiment of Scots Greys and Dragoons, then quartered at Newbury, should declare for the King on a certain day, when likewise the gentry affected to his Majesty's cause were to come in with their tenants and adherents to Newbury, march upon the Dutch troops at Reading under Ginckel; and, these overthrown, and their indomitable little master away in Ireland, 'twas thought that our side might move on London itself, and a confident victory was predicted for the King.

As these great matters were in agitation, my Lord lost his listless manner and seemed to gain health; my Lady did not scold him, Mr Holt came to and fro, busy always; and little Harry longed to have been a few inches taller, that he might draw a sword in this good cause.

One day, it must have been about the month of June 1690, my Lord, in a great horseman's coat, under which Harry could see the shining of a steel breastplate he had on, called little Harry to him, put the hair off the child's forehead, and kissed him, and bade God bless him in such an affectionate way as he never had used before. Father Holt blessed him too, and then they took leave of my Lady Viscountess, who came from her apartment with a pocket-handkerchief to her eyes, and her gentlewoman and Mrs. Tusher supporting her. "You are going to—to ride," says she. "Oh, that I might come too!—but in my situation I am forbidden horse exercise."

"We kiss my Lady Marchioness's hand," says Mr. Holt.

"My Lord, God speed you!" she said, stepping up and embracing my Lord in a grand manner. "Mr. Holt, I ask your blessing:" and she knelt down for that, whilst Mrs. Tusher tossed her head up.

Mr. Holt gave the same benediction to the little page, who went down and held my Lord's stirrups for him to mount; there were two servants waiting there too—and they rode out of Castlewood gate.

As they crossed the bridge, Harry could see an officer in scarlet ride up touching his hat, and address my Lord.

The party stopped, and came to some parley or discussion, which presently ended, my Lord putting his horse into a canter after taking off his hat and making a bow to the officer, who rode alongside him step for step: the trooper accompanying him falling back, and riding with my Lord's two men. They cantered over the green, and behind the elms (my Lord waving his hand, Harry thought), and so they disappeared. That evening we had a great panic, the cowboy coming at milking-time riding one of our horses, which he had found grazing at the outer park-wall.

All night my Lady Viscountess was in a very quiet and subdued mood. She scarce found fault with anybody; she played at cards for six hours; little page Esmond went to sleep. He prayed for my Lord and the good cause before closing his eyes.

It was quite in the grey of the morning when the porter's bell rang, and old Lockwood, waking up, let in one of my Lord's servants, who had gone with him in the morning, and who returned with a melancholy story. The officer who rode up to my Lord had, it appeared, said to him, that it was his duty to inform his Lordship that he was not under arrest, but under surveillance, and to request him not to ride abroad that day.

My Lord replied that riding was good for his health, that if the Captain chose to accompany him he was welcome; and it was then that he made a bow, and they cantered away together.

When he came on to Wansey Down, my Lord all of a sudden pulled up, and the party came to a halt at the crossway.

"Sir," says he to the officer, "we are four to two: will you be so kind as to take that road, and leave me to go mine?"

"Your road is mine, my Lord," says the officer.

"Then—" says my Lord; but he had no time to say more, for the officer, drawing a pistol, snapped it at his Lordship; as at the same moment Father Holt, drawing a pistol, shot the officer through the head. It was done, and the man dead in an instant of time. The orderly, gazing at the officer, looked scared for a moment, and galloped away for his life.

"Fire! fire!" cries out Father Holt, sending another shot after the trooper, but the two servants were too much surprised to use their pieces, and my Lord calling to them to hold their hands, the fellow got away.

"Mr. Holt, *qui pensait à tout*," says Blaise, "gets off his horse, examines the pockets of the dead officer for papers, gives his money to us two, and says, 'The wine is drawn, M. le Marquis,'—why did he say Marquis to M. le Vicomte?—'we must drink it.'

"The poor gentleman's horse was a better one than that I rode," Blaise continues: "Mr. Holt bids me get on him, and so I gave a cut to Whitefoot, and she trotted home. We rode on towards Newbury; we heard firing towards mid-day: at two o'clock a horseman comes up to us as we were giving our cattle water at an inn—and says, 'All is done! The Ecossais declared an hour too soon—General Ginckel was down upon them.' The whole thing was at an end.

"'And we've shot an officer on duty, and let his orderly escape,' says my Lord.

"'Blaise,' says Mr. Holt, writing two lines on his table-book, one for my Lady, and one for you, Master Harry; 'you must go back to Castlewood, and deliver these,' and behold me."

And he gave Harry the two papers. He read that to himself, which only said, "Burn the papers in the cupboard, burn this. You know nothing about anything." Harry read this, ran upstairs to his mistress's apartment, where her gentlewoman slept near to the door, made her bring a light and wake my Lady, into whose hands he gave the paper. She was a wonderful object to look at in her night attire, nor had Harry ever seen the like.

As soon as she had the paper in her hand, Harry stepped back to the Chaplain's room, opened the secret cupboard over the fireplace, burned all the papers in it, and, as he had seen the priest do before, took down one of his reverence's manuscript sermons, and half burnt that in the brazier. By the time the papers were quite destroyed it was daylight. Harry ran back to his mistress again. Her gentlewoman ushered him again into her Ladyship's chamber; she told him (from behind her nuptial curtains) to bid the coach be got ready, and that she would ride away anon.

But the mysteries of her Ladyship's toilet were as awfully long on this day as on any other, and, long after the coach was ready, my Lady was still attiring herself. And just as the Viscountess stepped forth from her room, ready for departure, young John Lockwood comes running up from the village with news that a lawyer, three officers, and twenty or four-and-twenty soldiers, were marching thence upon the house. John had but two minutes the start of them, and, ere he had well told his story, the troop rode into our courtyard.

CHAPTER VI

THE ISSUE OF THE PLOTS—THE DEATH OF THOMAS, THIRD VISCOUNT OF CASTLEWOOD; AND THE IMPRISONMENT OF HIS VISCOUNTESS

AT first my Lady was for dying like Mary, Queen of Scots (to whom she fancied she bore a resemblance in beauty), and, stroking her scraggy neck, said, "They will find Isabel of Castlewood is equal to her fate." Her gentlewoman, Victoire, persuaded her that her prudent course was, as she could not fly, to receive the troops as though she suspected nothing, and that her chamber was the best place wherein to await them. So her black Japan casket, which Harry was to carry to the coach, was taken back to her Ladyship's chamber, whither the maid and mistress retired. Victoire came out presently, bidding the page to say her Ladyship was ill, confined to her bed with the rheumatism.

By this time the soldiers had reached Castlewood. Harry Esmond saw them from the window of the tapestry parlour; a couple of sentinels were posted at the gate—a half-dozen more walked towards the stable; and some others, preceded by their commander, and a man in black, a lawyer probably, were conducted by one of the servants to the stair leading up to the part of the house which my Lord and Lady inhabited.

So the Captain, a handsome kind man, and the lawyer, came through the ante-room to the tapestry parlour, and where now was nobody but young Harry Esmond, the page.

"Tell your mistress, little man," says the Captain kindly, "that we must speak to her."

"My mistress is ill a-bed," said the page.

"What complaint has she?" asked the Captain.

The boy said, "The rheumatism."

"Rheumatism! that's a sad complaint," continues the good-natured Captain; "and the coach is in the yard to fetch the Doctor, I suppose?"

"I don't know," says the boy.

"And how long has her Ladyship been ill?"

"I don't know," says the boy.

"When did my Lord go away?"

"Yesterday night."

"With Father Holt?"

"With Mr. Holt."

"And which way did they travel?" asks the lawyer.

"They travelled without me," says the page.

"We must see Lady Castlewood."

"I have orders that nobody goes in to her Ladyship—she is sick," says the page; but at this moment Victoire came out. "Hush!" says she; and, as if not knowing that any one was near, "What's this noise?" says she. "Is this gentleman the Doctor?"

"Stuff! we must see Lady Castlewood," says the lawyer, pushing by.

The curtains of her Ladyship's room were down, and the chamber dark, and she was in bed with a nightcap on her head, and propped up by her pillows, looking none the less ghastly because of the red which was still on her cheeks, and which she could not afford to forego.

"Is that the Doctor?" she said.

"There is no use with this deception, madam," Captain Westbury said (for so he was named). "My duty is to arrest the person of Thomas, Viscount Castlewood, a nonjuring peer—of Robert Tusher, Vicar of Castlewood—and Henry Holt, known under various other names and designations, a Jesuit priest, who officiated as chaplain here in the late king's time, and is now at the head of the conspiracy which was about to break out in this country against the authority of their Majesties King William and Queen Mary—and my orders are to search the house for such papers or traces of the conspiracy as may be found here. Your Ladyship will please to give me your keys, and it will be as well for yourself that you should help us, in every way, in our search."

"You see, sir, that I have the rheumatism, and cannot move," said the lady, looking uncommonly ghastly, as she sat up in her bed, where, however, she had had her cheeks painted, and a new cap put on, so that she might at least look her best when the officers came.

"I shall take leave to place a sentinel in the chamber, so that your Ladyship, in case you should wish to rise, may have an arm to lean on," Captain Westbury said. "Your woman will show me where I am to look;" and Madame Victoire, chattering in her half French and half English jargon, opened while the Captain examined one drawer after another; but, as Harry Esmond thought, rather carelessly, with a smile on his face, as if he was only conducting the examination for form's sake.

Before one of the cupboards Victoire flung herself down, stretching out her arms, and, with a piercing shriek, cried, "Non, jamais, monsieur l'officier! Jamais! I will rather die than let you see this wardrobe."

But Captain Westbury would open it, still with a smile on his face, which, when the box was opened, turned into a fair burst of laughter. It contained—not papers regarding the conspiracy—but my Lady's wigs, washes, and rouge-pots, and Victoire said men were monsters, as the Captain went on with his perquisition. He tapped the back to see whether or no it was hollow, and as he thrust his hands into the cupboard, my Lady from her bed called out, with a voice that did not sound like that of a very sick woman, "Is it your commission to insult ladies as well as to arrest gentlemen, Captain?"

"These articles are only dangerous when worn by your Ladyship," the Captain said, with a low bow, and a mock grin of politeness. "I have found nothing which concerns the Government as yet—only the weapons with which beauty is authorised to kill," says he, pointing to a wig with his sword-tip. "We must now proceed to search the rest of the house."

"You are not going to leave that wretch in the room with me?" cried my Lady, pointing to the soldier.

"What can I do, madam? Somebody you must have to smooth your pillow and bring your medicine—permit me——"

"Sir!" screamed out my Lady.

"Madam, if you are too ill to leave the bed," the Captain then said, rather sternly, "I must have in four of my men to lift you off in the sheet. I must examine this bed, in a word; papers may be hidden in a bed as elsewhere; we know that very well, and——"

Here it was her Ladyship's turn to shriek, for the Captain, with his fist shaking the pillows and bolsters, at last came to "burn" as they say in the play of forfeits, and wrenching away one of the pillows, said, "Look! did not I tell you so? Here is a pillow stuffed with paper."

"Some villain has betrayed us," cried out my Lady, sitting up in the bed, showing herself full dressed under her night-rail.

"And now your Ladyship can move, I am sure; permit me to give you my hand to rise. You will have to travel for some distance, as far as Hexton Castle, to-night. Will you have your coach? Your woman shall attend you if you like—and the Japan box?"

"Sir! you don't strike a *man* when he is down," said my Lady, with some dignity: "can you not spare a woman?"

"Your Ladyship must please to rise, and let me search the

bed," said the Captain; "there is no more time to lose in bandying talk."

And, without more ado, the gaunt old woman got up. Harry Esmond recollected to the end of his life that figure with the brocade dress and the white night-rail, and the gold-clocked red stockings, and white red-heeled shoes, sitting up in the bed, and stepping down from it. The trunks were ready packed for departure in her ante-room, and the horses ready harnessed in the stable: about all which the Captain seemed to know, by information got from some quarter or other; and whence Esmond could make a pretty shrewd guess in aftertimes, when Doctor Tusher complained that King William's government had basely treated him for services done in that cause.

And here he may relate, though he was then too young to know all that was happening, what the papers contained, of which Captain Westbury had made a seizure, and which papers had been transferred from the Japan box to the bed when the officers arrived.

There was a list of gentlemen of the county in Father Holt's handwriting — Mr. Freeman's (King James's) friends — a similar paper being found among those of Sir John Fenwick and Mr. Coplestone, who suffered death for this conspiracy.

There was a patent conferring the title of Marquis of Esmond on my Lord Castlewood and the heirs-male of his body; his appointment as Lord-Lieutenant of the County, and Major-General.*

There were various letters from the nobility and gentry, some ardent and some doubtful, in the King's service; and (very luckily for him) two letters concerning Colonel Francis Esmond: one from Father Holt, which said, "I have been to see this Colonel at his house at Walcote, near to Wells, where he resides since the King's departure, and pressed him very eagerly in Mr. Freeman's cause, showing him the great advantage he would have by trading with that merchant, offering him large premiums there as agreed between us. But he says no: he considers Mr. Freeman the head of the firm, will never trade against him or embark with any other trading company, but considers his duty was done when Mr. Freeman left England. This Colonel seems to care more for his wife and his

* To have this rank of Marquis restored in the family had always been my Lady Viscountess's ambition; and her old maiden aunt, Barbara Topham, the goldsmith's daughter, dying about this time, and leaving all her property to Lady Castlewood, I have heard that her Ladyship sent almost the whole of the money to King James, a proceeding which so irritated my Lord Castlewood that he actually went to the parish church, and was only appeased by the Marquis's title which his exiled Majesty sent to him in return for the £15,000 his faithful subject lent him.

beagles than for affairs. He asked me much about young H. E., 'that bastard,' as he called him; doubting my Lord's intentions respecting him. I reassured him on this head, stating what I knew of the lad, and our intentions respecting him, but with regard to Freeman he was inflexible."

And another letter was from Colonel Esmond to his kinsman, to say that one Captain Holton had been with him offering him large bribes to join, *you know who*, and saying that the head of the house of Castlewood was deeply engaged in that quarter. But for his part he had broke his sword when the K. left the country, and would never again fight in that quarrel. The P. of O. was a man, at least, of a noble courage, and his duty, and, as he thought, every Englishman's, was to keep the country quiet, and the French out of it; and, in fine, that he would have nothing to do with the scheme.

Of the existence of these two letters and the contents of the pillow, Colonel Frank Esmond, who became Viscount Castlewood, told Henry Esmond afterwards, when the letters were shown to his Lordship, who congratulated himself, as he had good reason, that he had not joined in the scheme which proved so fatal to many concerned in it. But, naturally, the lad knew little about these circumstances when they happened under his eyes: only being aware that his patron and his mistress were in some trouble, which had caused the flight of the one and the apprehension of the other by the officers of King William.

The seizure of the papers effected, the gentlemen did not pursue their further search through Castlewood House very rigorously. They examined Mr. Holt's room, being led thither by his pupil, who showed, as the Father had bidden him, the place where the key of his chamber lay, opened the door for the gentlemen, and conducted them into the room.

When the gentlemen came to the half-burned papers in the brazier, they examined them eagerly enough, and their young guide was a little amused at their perplexity.

"What are these?" says one.

"They're written in a foreign language," says the lawyer. "What are you laughing at, little whelp?" adds he, turning round as he saw the boy smile.

"Mr. Holt said they were sermons," Harry said, "and bade me to burn them;" which indeed was true of those papers.

"Sermons indeed—it's treason, I would lay a wager," cries the lawyer.

"Egad! it's Greek to me," says Captain Westbury. "Can you read it, little boy?"

"Yes, sir, a little," Harry said.

"Then read, and read in English, sir, on your peril," said the lawyer. And Harry began to translate:—

"'Hath not one of your own writers said, "The children of Adam are now labouring as much as he himself ever did, about the tree of the knowledge of good and evil, shaking the boughs thereof, and seeking the fruit, being for the most part unmindful of the tree of life." O blind generation! 'tis this tree of knowledge to which the serpent has led you'"—and here the boy was obliged to stop, the rest of the page being charred by the fire: and asked of the lawyer, "Shall I go on, sir?"

The lawyer said, "This boy is deeper than he seems: who knows that he is not laughing at us?"

"Let's have in Dick the Scholar," cried Captain Westbury, laughing: and he called to a trooper out of the window—"Ho, Dick! come in here and construe."

A thick-set soldier, with a square good-humoured face, came in at the summons, saluting his officer.

"Tell us what is this, Dick," says the lawyer.

"My name is Steele, sir," says the soldier. "I may be Dick for my friends, but I don't name gentlemen of your cloth amongst them."

"Well then, Steele."

"Mr. Steele, sir, if you please. When you address a gentleman of his Majesty's Horse Guards, be pleased not to be so familiar."

"I didn't know, sir," said the lawyer.

"How should you? I take it you are not accustomed to meet with gentlemen," says the trooper.

"Hold thy prate, and read that bit of paper," says Westbury.

"'Tis Latin," says Dick, glancing at it, and again saluting his officer, "and from a sermon of Mr. Cudworth's;" and he translated the words pretty much as Henry Esmond had rendered them.

"What a young scholar you are!" says the Captain to the boy.

"Depend on't, he knows more than he tells," says the lawyer. "I think we will pack him off in the coach with old Jezebel."

"For construing a bit of Latin?" said the Captain, very good-naturedly.

"I would as lief go there as anywhere," Harry Esmond said simply, "for there is nobody to care for me."

There must have been something touching in the child's voice, or in this description of his solitude—for the Captain looked at him very good-naturedly, and the trooper called Steele put his hand kindly on the lad's head, and said some words in the Latin tongue.

"What does he say?" says the lawyer.

"Faith, ask Dick yourself," cried Captain Westbury.

"I said I was not ignorant of misfortune myself, and had learned to succour the miserable, and that's not *your* trade, Mr. Sheepskin," said the trooper.

"You had better leave Dick the Scholar alone, Mr. Corbet," the Captain said. And Harry Esmond, always touched by a kind face and kind word, felt very grateful to this good-natured champion.

The horses were by this time harnessed to the coach; and the Countess and Victoire came down and were put into the vehicle. This woman, who quarrelled with Harry Esmond all day, was melted at parting with him, and called him "dear angel," and "poor infant," and a hundred other names.

The Viscountess, giving him her lean hand to kiss, bade him always be faithful to the house of Esmond. "If evil should happen to my Lord," says she, "his *successor*, I trust, will be found, and give you protection. Situated as I am, they will not dare wreak their vengeance on me *now*." And she kissed a medal she wore with great fervour, and Henry Esmond knew not in the least what her meaning was; but hath since learned that, old as she was, she was for ever expecting, by the good offices of saints and relics, to have an heir to the title of Esmond.

Harry Esmond was too young to have been introduced into the secrets of politics in which his patrons were implicated; for they put but few questions to the boy (who was little of stature, and looked much younger than his age), and such questions as they put he answered cautiously enough, and professing even more ignorance than he had, for which his examiners willingly enough gave him credit. He did not say a word about the window or the cupboard over the fireplace; and these secrets quite escaped the eyes of the searchers.

So then my Lady was consigned to her coach, and sent off to Hexton, with her woman and the man of law to bear her company, a couple of troopers riding on either side of the coach. And Harry was left behind at the Hall, belonging as it were to nobody, and quite alone in the world. The captain and a guard of men remained in possession there; and the soldiers, who were very good-natured and kind, ate my Lord's mutton and drank his wine, and made themselves comfortable, as they well might do in such pleasant quarters.

The captains had their dinner served in my Lord's tapestry parlour, and poor little Harry thought his duty was to wait upon Captain Westbury's chair, as his custom had been to serve his Lord when he sat there.

After the departure of the Countess, Dick the Scholar took Harry Esmond under his special protection, and would examine him in his humanities, and talk to him both of French and Latin, in which tongues the lad found, and his new friend was willing enough to acknowledge, that he was even more proficient than Scholar Dick. Hearing that he had learned them from a Jesuit, in the praise of whom and whose goodness Harry was never tired of speaking, Dick, rather to the boy's surprise, who began to have an early shrewdness, like many children bred up alone, showed a great deal of theological science, and knowledge of the points at issue between the two churches; so that he and Harry would have hours of controversy together, in which the boy was certainly worsted by the arguments of this singular trooper. "I am no common soldier," Dick would say, and indeed it was easy to see by his learning, breeding, and many accomplishments, that he was not. "I am of one of the most ancient families in the empire; I have had my education at a famous school, and a famous university; I learned my first rudiments of Latin near to Smithfield, in London, where the martyrs were roasted."

"You hanged as many of ours," interposed Harry; "and, for the matter of persecution, Father Holt told me that a young gentleman of Edinburgh, eighteen years of age, student at the college there, was hanged for heresy only last year, though he recanted, and solemnly asked pardon for his errors."

"Faith! there has been two much persecution on both sides: but 'twas you taught us."

"Nay, 'twas the Pagans began it," cried the lad, and began to instance a number of saints of the Church, from the Protomartyr downwards—"this one's fire went out under him: that one's oil cooled in the caldron: at a third holy head the executioner chopped three times and it would not come off. Show us martyrs in *your* Church for whom such miracles have been done."

"Nay," says the trooper gravely, "the miracles of the first three centuries belong to my Church as well as yours, Master Papist," and then added, with something of a smile upon his countenance, and a queer look at Harry—"And yet, my little catechiser, I have sometimes thought about those miracles, that there was not much good in them, since the victim's head always finished by coming off at the third or fourth chop, and the caldron, if it did not boil one day, boiled the next. Howbeit, in our times, the Church has lost that questionable advantage of respites. There never was a shower to put out Ridley's fire, nor an angel to turn the edge of Campion's axe. The rack tore the limbs of Southwell the Jesuit and Sympson the Protestant alike. For faith, everywhere multitudes die willingly enough. I have read in Monsieur Rycaut's 'History of the Turks,' of thousands of Mahomet's followers rushing upon death in battle as upon certain Paradise; and in the Great Mogul's dominions people fling themselves by hundreds under the cars of the idols annually, and the widows burn themselves on their husbands' bodies, as 'tis well known. 'Tis not the dying for a faith that's so hard, Master Harry—every man of every nation has done that—'tis the living up to it that is difficult, as I know to my cost," he added with a sigh. "And ah!" he added, "my poor lad, I am not strong enough to convince thee by my life—though to die for my religion would give me the greatest of joys—but I had a dear friend in Magdalen College in Oxford: I wish Joe Addison were here to convince thee, as he quickly could—for I think he's a match for the whole College of Jesuits; and what's more, in his life too. In that very sermon of Doctor Cudworth's which your priest was quoting from, and which suffered martyrdom in the brazier"—Dick added with a smile, "I had a thought of wearing the black coat (but was ashamed of my life, you see, and took to this sorry red one); I have often thought of Joe Addison—Doctor Cudworth says, 'A good conscience is the best looking-glass of heaven'—and there's a serenity in my friend's face which always reflects it—I wish you could see him, Harry."

"Did he do you a great deal of good?" asked the lad simply.

"He might have done," said the other—"at least he taught me to see and approve better things. 'Tis my own fault, *deteriora sequi*."

"You seem very good," the boy said.

"I'm not what I seem, alas!" answered the trooper—and indeed, as it turned out, poor Dick told the truth—for that very night, at supper in the hall, where the gentlemen of the troop took their repasts, and passed most part of their days dicing and smoking of tobacco, and singing and cursing, over the Castlewood ale—Harry Esmond found Dick the Scholar in a woeful state of drunkenness. He hiccupped out a sermon; and his laughing companions bade him sing a hymn, on which Dick, swearing he would run the scoundrel through the body who insulted his religion, made for his sword, which was hanging on the wall, and fell down flat on the floor under it, saying to Harry, who ran forward to help him, "Ah, little Papist, I wish Joseph Addison was here!"

Though the troopers of the King's Life Guards were all gentlemen, yet the rest of the gentlemen seemed ignorant and vulgar boors to Harry Esmond, with the exception of this good-natured Corporal Steele the Scholar, and Captain Westbury and Lieutenant Trant, who were always kind to the lad. They remained for some weeks or months encamped in Castlewood, and Harry learned from them, from time to time, how the lady at Hexton Castle was treated, and the particulars of her confinement there. 'Tis known that King William was disposed to deal very leniently with the gentry who remained faithful to the old King's cause; and no prince usurping a crown, as his enemies said he did (righteously taking it, as I think now), ever caused less blood to be shed. As for women conspirators, he kept spies on the least dangerous, and locked up the others. Lady Castlewood had the best rooms in Hexton Castle, and the gaoler's garden to walk in; and though she repeatedly desired to be led out to execution, like Mary, Queen of Scots, there never was any thought of taking her painted old head off, or any desire to do aught but keep her person in security.

And it appeared she found that some were friends in her misfortune, whom she had, in her prosperity, considered as her worst enemies. Colonel Francis Esmond, my Lord's cousin and her Ladyship's, who had married the Dean of Winchester's daughter, and, since King James's departure out of England, had lived not very far away from Hexton town, hearing of his kinswoman's strait, and being friends with Colonel Brice, commanding for King William in Hexton, and with the Church dignitaries there, came to visit her Ladyship in prison, offering to his uncle's daughter any friendly services which lay in his power. And he brought his lady and little daughter to see the prisoner, to the latter of whom, a child of great beauty and many winning ways, the old Viscountess took not a little liking, although between her Ladyship and the child's mother there was little more love than formerly. There are some injuries which women never forgive one another: and Madam Francis Esmond, in marrying her cousin, had done one of those irretrievable wrongs to Lady Castlewood. But as she was now humiliated, and in misfortune, Madam Francis could allow a truce to her enmity, and could be kind for a while, at least, to her husband's discarded mistress. So the little Beatrix, her daughter, was permitted often to go and visit the imprisoned Viscountess, who, in so far as the child and its father were concerned, got to abate in her anger towards that branch of the Castlewood family. And the letters of Colonel Esmond coming to light, as has been said, and his conduct being known to the King's Council, the Colonel was put in a better position with the existing government than he had ever before been; any suspicions regarding his loyalty were entirely done away; and so he was enabled to be of more service to his kinswoman than he could otherwise have been.

And now there befell an event by which this lady recovered her liberty, and the house of Castlewood got a new owner, and fatherless little Harry Esmond a new and most kind protector and friend. Whatever that secret was which Harry was to hear from my Lord, the boy never heard it; for that night when Father Holt arrived, and carried my Lord away with him, was the last on which Harry ever saw his patron. What happened to my Lord may be briefly told here. Having found the horses at the place where they were lying, my Lord and Father Holt rode together to Chatteris, where they had temporary refuge with one of the Father's penitents in that city; but the pursuit being hot for them, and the reward for the apprehension of one or the other considerable, it was deemed advisable that they should separate; and the priest betook himself to other places of retreat known to him, whilst my Lord passed over from Bristol into Ireland, in which kingdom King James had a court and an army. My Lord was but a small addition to this; bringing, indeed, only his sword and the few pieces in his pocket; but the King received him with some kindness and distinction in spite of his poor plight, confirmed him in his new title of Marquis, gave him a regiment, and promised him further promotion. But title or promotion were not to benefit him now. My Lord was wounded at the fatal battle of the Boyne, flying from which field (long after his master had set him an example) he lay for a while concealed in the marshy country near to the town of Trim, and more from catarrh and fever caught in the bogs than from the steel of the enemy in the battle, sank and died. May the earth lie light upon Thomas of Castlewood! He who writes this must speak in charity, though this lord did him and his two grievous wrongs: for one of these he would have made amends, perhaps, had life been spared him; but the other lay beyond his power to repair, though 'tis to be hoped that a greater Power than a priest has absolved him of it. He got the comfort of this absolution, too, such as it was: a priest of Trim writing a letter to my Lady to inform her of this calamity.

But in those days letters were slow of travelling, and our priest's took two months or more on its journey from Ireland to England: where, when it did arrive, it did not find my Lady at her own house; she was at the King's house of Hexton Castle when the letter came to Castlewood, but it was opened for all that by the officer in command there.

Harry Esmond well remembered the receipt of this letter, which Lockwood brought in as Captain Westbury and Lieutenant Trant were on the Green playing at bowls, young Esmond looking on at the sport, or reading his book in the arbour.

"Here's news for Frank Esmond," says Captain Westbury. "Harry, did you ever see Colonel Esmond?" And Captain Westbury looked very hard at the boy as he spoke.

Harry said he had seen him but once when he was at Hexton, at the ball there.

"And did he say anything?"

"He said what I don't care to repeat," Harry answered. For he was now twelve years of age; he knew what his birth was, and the disgrace of it; and he felt no love towards the man who had most likely stained his mother's honour and his own.

"Did you love my Lord Castlewood?"

"I wait until I know my mother, sir, to say," the boy answered, his eyes filling with tears.

"Something has happened to Lord Castlewood," Captain Westbury said in a very grave tone—"something which must happen to us all. He is dead of a wound received at the Boyne, fighting for King James."

"I am glad my Lord fought for the right cause," the boy said.

"It was better to meet death on the field like a man, than face it on Tower Hill, as some of them may," continued Mr. Westbury. "I hope he has made some testament, or provided for thee somehow. This letter says he recommends *unicum filium suum dilectissimum* to his Lady. I hope he has left you more than that."

Harry did not know, he said. He was in the hands of Heaven and Fate; but more lonely now, as it seemed to him, than he had been all the rest of his life; and that night, as he lay in his little room which he still occupied, the boy thought with many a pang of shame and grief of his strange and solitary condition:—how he had a father and no father; a nameless mother that had been brought to ruin, perhaps, by that very father whom Harry could only acknowledge in secret and with a blush, and whom he could neither love nor revere. And he sickened to think how Father Holt, a stranger, and two or three soldiers, his acquaintances of the last six weeks, were the only friends he had in the great wide world, where he was now quite alone. The soul of the boy was full of love, and he longed as he lay in the darkness there for some one upon whom he could bestow it. He remembers, and must to his dying day, the thoughts and tears of that long night, the hours tolling through it. Who was he, and what? Why here rather than elsewhere? I have a mind, he thought, to go to that priest at Trim, and find out what my father said to him on his death-bed confession. Is there any child in the whole world so unprotected as I am? Shall I get up and quit this place, and run to Ireland? With these thoughts and tears the lad passed that night away until he wept himself to sleep.

The next day, the gentlemen of the guard, who had heard what had befallen him, were more than usually kind to the child, especially his friend Scholar Dick, who told him about his own father's death, which had happened when Dick was a child at Dublin, not quite five years of age. "That was the first sensation of grief," Dick said, "I ever knew. I remember I went into the room where his body lay, and my mother sat weeping beside it. I had my battledore in my hand, and fell a-beating the coffin, and calling papa; on which my mother caught me in her arms, and told me in a flood of tears papa could not hear me, and would play with me no more, for they were going to put him under ground, whence he could never come to us again. And this," said Dick kindly, "has made me pity all children ever since; and caused me to love thee, my poor fatherless, motherless lad. And, if ever thou wantest a friend, thou shalt have one in Richard Steele."

Harry Esmond thanked him, and was grateful. But what could Corporal Steele do for him? take him to ride a spare horse, and be servant to the troop? Though there might be a bar in Harry Esmond's shield, it was a noble one. The counsel of the two friends was, that little Harry should stay where he was, and abide his fortune: so Esmond stayed on at Castlewood, awaiting with no small anxiety the fate, whatever it was, which was over him.

CHAPTER VII

I AM LEFT AT CASTLEWOOD AN ORPHAN, AND FIND MOST KIND PROTECTORS THERE

DURING the stay of the soldiers in Castlewood, honest Dick the Scholar was the constant companion of the lonely little orphan lad, Harry Esmond: and they read together, and they played bowls together, and when the other troopers or their officers, who were free-spoken over their cups (as was the way of that day, when neither men nor women were over-nice), talked unbecomingly of their amours and gallantries before the child, Dick, who very likely was setting the whole company laughing, would stop their jokes with a *maxima debetur pueris reverentia*, and once offered to lug out against another trooper called Hulking Tom, who wanted to ask Harry Esmond a ribald question.

Also Dick, seeing that the child had, as he said, a sensibility above his years, and a great and praiseworthy discretion, confided to Harry his love for a vintner's daughter, near to the Tollyard, Westminster, whom Dick addressed as Saccharissa in many verses of his composition, and without whom he said it would be impossible that he could continue to live. He vowed this a thousand times in a day, though Harry smiled to see the love-lorn swain had his health and appetite as well as the most heart-whole trooper in the regiment: and he swore Harry to secrecy too, which vow the lad religiously kept, until he found that officers and privates were all taken into Dick's confidence, and had the benefit of his verses. And it must be owned likewise that, while Dick was sighing after Saccharissa in London, he had consolations in the country; for there came a wench out of Castlewood village who had washed his linen, and who cried sadly when she heard he was gone: and without paying her bill too, which Harry Esmond took upon himself to discharge by giving the girl a silver pocket-piece, which Scholar Dick had presented to him, when, with many embraces and prayers for his prosperity, Dick parted from him, the garrison of Castlewood being ordered away. Dick the Scholar said he would never forget his young friend, nor indeed did he: and Harry was sorry when the kind soldiers vacated Castlewood, looking forward with no small anxiety (for care and solitude had made him thoughtful beyond his years) to his fate when the new lord and lady of the house came to live there. He had lived to be past twelve years old now; and had never had a friend, save this wild trooper perhaps, and Father Holt; and had a fond and affectionate heart, tender to weakness, that would fain attach itself to somebody, and did not seem at rest until it had found a friend who would take charge of it.

The instinct which led Henry Esmond to admire and love the gracious person, the fair apparition of whose beauty and kindness had so moved him when he first beheld her, became soon a devoted affection and passion of gratitude, which entirely filled his young heart, that as yet, except in the case of dear Father Holt, had had very little kindness for which to be thankful. *O Dea certè*, thought he, remembering the lines of the Æneis which Mr. Holt had taught him. There seemed, as the boy thought, in every look or gesture of this fair creature, an angelical softness and bright pity—in motion or repose she seemed gracious alike; the tone of her voice, though she uttered words ever so trivial, gave him a pleasure that amounted almost to anguish. It cannot be called love, that a lad of twelve years of age, little more than a menial, felt for an exalted lady, his mistress: but it was worship. To catch her glance, to divine her errand and run on it before she had spoken it; to watch, follow, adore her; became the business of his life. Meanwhile, as is the way often, his idol had idols of her own, and never thought of or suspected the admiration of her little pigmy adorer.

My Lady had on her side her three idols: first and foremost, Jove and supreme ruler, was her lord, Harry's patron, the good Viscount of Castlewood. All wishes of his were laws with her. If he had a headache, she was ill. If he frowned, she trembled. If he joked, she smiled and was charmed. If he went a-hunting, she was always at the window to see him ride away, her little son crowing on her arm, or on the watch till his return. She made dishes for his dinner: spiced his wine for him: made the toast for his tankard at breakfast: hushed the house when he slept in his chair, and watched for a look when he woke. If my Lord was not a little proud of his beauty, my Lady adored it. She clung to his arm as he paced the terrace, her two fair little hands clasped round his great one; her eyes were never tired of looking in his face and wondering at its perfection. Her little son was his son, and had his father's look and curly brown hair. Her daughter Beatrix was his daughter, and had his eyes—were there ever such beautiful eyes in the world? All the house was arranged so as to bring him ease and give him pleasure. She liked the small gentry round about to come and pay him court, never caring for admiration for herself;

those who wanted to be well with the lady must admire him. Not regarding her dress, she would wear a gown to rags, because he had once liked it: and, if he brought her a brooch or a ribbon, would prefer it to all the most costly articles of her wardrobe.

My Lord went to London every year for six weeks, and the family being too poor to appear at Court with any figure, he went alone. It was not until he was out of sight that her face showed any sorrow: and what a joy when he came back! What preparation before his return! The fond creature had his armchair at the chimney-side—delighting to put the children in it, and look at them there. Nobody took his place at the table; but his silver tankard stood there as when my Lord was present.

A pretty sight it was to see, during my Lord's absence, or on those many mornings when sleep or headache kept him a-bed, this fair young lady of Castlewood, her little daughter at her knee, and her domestics gathered round her, reading the Morning Prayer of the English Church. Esmond long remembered how she looked and spoke, kneeling reverently before the sacred book, the sun shining upon her golden hair until it made a halo round about her. A dozen of the servants of the house kneeled in a line opposite their mistress. For a while Harry Esmond kept apart from these mysteries, but Doctor Tusher showing him that the prayers read were those of the Church of all ages, and the boy's own inclination prompting him to be always as near as he might to his mistress, and to think all things she did right, from listening to the prayers in the ante-chamber, he came presently to kneel down with the rest of the household in the parlour; and before a couple of years my Lady had made a thorough convert. Indeed the boy loved his catechiser so much that he would have subscribed to anything she bade him, and was never tired of listening to her fond discourse and simple comments upon the book, which she read to him in a voice of which it was difficult to resist the sweet persuasion and tender appealing kindness. This friendly controversy, and the intimacy which it occasioned, bound the lad more fondly than ever to his mistress. The happiest period of all his life was this; and the young mother, with her daughter and son, and the orphan lad whom she protected, read and worked and played, and were children together. If the lady looked forward—as what fond woman does not?—towards the future, she had no plans from which Harry Esmond was left out; and a thousand and a thousand times, in his passionate and impetuous way, he vowed that no power should separate him from his mistress; and only asked for some chance to happen by which he might show his fidelity to her. Now, at the close of his life, as he sits and recalls in tranquillity the happy and busy scenes of it, he can think, not ungratefully, that he has been faithful to that early vow. Such a life is so simple that years may be chronicled in a few lines. But few men's life-voyages are destined to be all prosperous; and this calm of which we are speaking was soon to come to an end.

As Esmond grew, and observed for himself, he found of necessity much to read and think of outside that fond circle of kinsfolk who had admitted him to join hand with them. He read more books than they cared to study with him; was alone in the midst of them many a time, and passed nights over labours, futile perhaps, but in which they could not join him. His dear mistress divined his thoughts with her usual jealous watchfulness of affection: began to forebode a time when he would escape from his home-nest; and, at his eager protestations to the contrary, would only sigh and shake her head. Before those fatal decrees in life are executed, there are always secret previsions and warning omens. When everything yet seems calm, we are aware that the storm is coming. Ere the happy days were over, two at least of that home-party felt that they were drawing to a close; and were uneasy, and on the look-out for the cloud which was to obscure their calm.

'Twas easy for Harry to see, however much his lady persisted in obedience and admiration for her husband, that my Lord tired of his quiet life, and grew weary, and then testy, at those gentle bonds with which his wife would have held him. As they say the Grand Lama of Thibet is very much fatigued by his character of divinity, and yawns on his altar as his bonzes kneel and worship him, many a home-god grows heartily sick of the reverence with which his family-devotees pursue him, and sighs for freedom and for his old life, and to be off the pedestal on which his dependants would have him sit for ever, whilst they adore him, and ply him with flowers, and hymns, and incense, and flattery;—so, after a few years of his marriage my honest Lord Castlewood began to tire; all the high-flown raptures and devotional ceremonies with which his wife, his chief-priestess, treated him, first sent him to sleep, and then drove him out of doors; for the truth must be told, that my Lord was a jolly gentleman, with very little of the august or divine in his nature, though his fond wife persisted in revering it—and, besides, he had to pay a penalty for this love, which persons of his disposition seldom like to defray: and, in a word, if he had a loving wife, had a very jealous and exacting one. Then he wearied of this jealousy; then he broke away from it; then came, no doubt, complaints and recriminations; then, perhaps, promises of amendment not fulfilled; then upbraidings not the more pleasant because they were silent, and only sad looks and tearful eyes conveyed them. Then, perhaps, the pair reached that other stage which is not uncommon in married life, when the woman perceives that the god of the honeymoon is a god no more; only a mortal like the rest of us—and so she looks into her heart, and lo! *vacuæ sedes et inania arcana.* And now, supposing our lady to have a fine genius and a brilliant wit of her own, and the magic spell and infatuation removed from her which had led her to worship as a god a very ordinary mortal—and what follows? They live together, and they dine together, and they say "my dear" and "my love" as heretofore; but the man is himself, and the woman herself: that dream of love is over as everything else is over in life; as flowers and fury, and griefs and pleasures are over.

Very likely the Lady Castlewood had ceased to adore her husband herself long before she got off her knees, or would allow her household to discontinue worshipping him. To do him justice, my Lord never exacted this subservience: he laughed and joked and drank his bottle, and swore when he was angry, much too familiarly for any one pretending to sublimity; and did his best to destroy the ceremonial with which his wife chose to surround him. And it required no great conceit on young Esmond's part to see that his own brains were better than his patron's, who, indeed, never assumed any airs of superiority over the lad, or over any dependant of his, save when he was displeased, in which case he would express his mind in oaths very freely; and who, on the contrary, perhaps, spoiled "Parson Harry," as he called young Esmond, by constantly praising his parts and admiring his boyish stock of learning.

It may seem ungracious in one who has received a hundred favours from his patron to speak in any but a reverential manner of his elders; but the present writer has had descendants of his own, whom he has brought up with as little as possible of the servility at present exacted by parents from children (under which mask of duty there often lurks indifference, contempt, or rebellion): and as he would have his grandsons believe or represent him to be not an inch taller than Nature has made him: so, with regard to his past acquaintances, he would speak without anger, but with truth, as far as he knows it, neither extenuating nor setting down aught in malice.

So long, then, as the world moved according to Lord Castlewood's wishes, he was good-humoured enough; of a temper naturally sprightly and easy, liking to joke, especially with his inferiors, and charmed to receive the tribute of their laughter. All exercises of the body he could perform to perfection—shooting at a mark and flying, breaking horses, riding at the ring, pitching the quoit, playing at all games with great skill. And not only did he do these things well, but he thought he did them to perfection; hence he was often tricked about horses, which he pretended to know better than any jockey; was made to play at ball and billiards by sharpers who took his money, and came back from London woefully poorer each time than he went, as the state of his affairs testified when the sudden accident came by which his career was brought to an end.

He was fond of the parade of dress, and passed as many hours daily at his toilette as an elderly coquette. A tenth part of his day was spent in the brushing of his teeth, and the oiling of his hair, which was curling and brown, and which he did not like to conceal under a periwig, such as almost everybody of that time wore. (We have the liberty of our hair back now, but powder and pomatum along with it. When, I wonder, will these monstrous poll-taxes of our age be withdrawn, and men allowed to carry their colours, black, red, or grey, as Nature made them?) And as he liked her to be well dressed, his lady spared no pains in that matter to please him; indeed, she would dress her head or cut it off if he had bidden her.

It was a wonder to young Esmond, serving as page to my Lord and Lady, to hear, day after day, to such company as came, the same boisterous stories told by my Lord, at which his lady never failed to smile or hold down her head, and Doctor Tusher to burst out laughing at the proper point, or cry, "Fie, my Lord, remember my cloth!" but with such a faint show of resistance, that it only provoked my Lord further. Lord Castlewood's stories rose by degrees, and became stronger after the ale at dinner and the bottle afterwards; my Lady always taking flight after the very first glass to Church and King, and leaving the gentlemen to drink the rest of the toasts by themselves.

And, as Harry Esmond was her page, he also was called from duty at this time. "My Lord has lived in the army and with soldiers," she would say to the lad, "amongst whom great licence is allowed. You have had a different nurture, and I trust these things will change as you grow older; not that any fault attaches to my Lord, who is one of the best and most religious men in this kingdom." And very likely she believed so. 'Tis strange what a man may do, and a woman yet think him an angel.

And as Esmond has taken truth for his motto, it must be owned, even with regard to that other angel, his mistress, that she had a fault of character which flawed her perfections. With the other sex perfectly tolerant and kindly, of her own she was invariably jealous; and a proof that she had this vice is, that though she would acknowledge a thousand faults that she had not, to this which she had she could never be got to own. But if there came a woman with even a semblance of beauty to Castlewood, she was so sure to find out some wrong in her, that my Lord, laughing in his jolly way, would often joke with her concerning her foible. Comely servant-maids might come for hire, but none were taken at Castlewood. The housekeeper was old; my Lady's own waiting-woman squinted, and was marked with the smallpox; the housemaids and scullion were ordinary country wenches, to whom Lady Castlewood was kind, as her nature made her to everybody almost; but as soon as ever she had to do with a pretty woman, she was cold, retiring, and haughty. The country ladies found this fault in her; and though the men all admired her, their wives and daughters complained of her coldness and airs, and said that Castlewood was pleasanter in Lady Jezebel's time (as the dowager was called) than at present. Some few were of my mistress's side. Old Lady Blenkinsop Jointure, who had been at Court in King James the First's time, always took her side; and so did old Mistress Crookshank, Bishop Crookshank's daughter, of Hexton, who, with some more of their like, pronounced my Lady an angel: but the pretty women were not of this mind; and the opinion of the country was that my Lord was tied to his wife's apron-strings, and that she ruled over him.

The second fight which Harry Esmond had, was at fourteen years of age, with Bryan Hawkshaw, Sir John Hawkshaw's son, of Bramblebrook, who, advancing his opinion, that my Lady was jealous and henpecked my Lord, put Harry in such a fury, that Harry fell on him and with such rage, that the other boy, who was two years older and by far bigger than he, had by far the worst of the assault, until it was interrupted by Doctor Tusher walking out of the dinner-room.

Bryan Hawkshaw got up bleeding at the nose, having, indeed, been surprised, as many a stronger man might have been, by the fury of the assault upon him.

"You little bastard beggar!" he said, "I'll murder you for this!"

And indeed he was big enough.

"Bastard or not," said the other, grinding his teeth, "I have a couple of swords, and if you like to meet me, as a man, on the terrace to-night——"

And here the Doctor coming up, the colloquy of the young champions ended. Very likely, big as he was, Hawkshaw did not care to continue a fight with such a ferocious opponent as this had been.

CHAPTER VIII

AFTER GOOD FORTUNE COMES EVIL

SINCE my Lady Mary Wortley Montagu brought home the custom of inoculation from Turkey (a perilous practice many deem it, and only a useless rushing into the jaws of danger), I think the severity of the smallpox, that dreadful scourge of the world, has somewhat been abated in our part of it; and remember in my time hundreds of the young and beautiful who have been carried to the grave, or have only risen from their pillows frightfully scarred and disfigured by this malady. Many a sweet face hath left its roses on the bed on which this dreadful and withering blight has laid them. In my early days, this pestilence would enter a village and destroy half its inhabitants: at its approach, it may well be imagined not only the beautiful but the strongest were alarmed, and those fled who could. One day in the year 1694 (I have good reason to remember it), Dr. Tusher ran into Castlewood house, with a face of consternation, saying that the malady had made its appearance at the blacksmith's house in the village, and that one of the maids there was down in the smallpox.

The blacksmith, besides his forge and irons for horses, had an alehouse for men, which his wife kept, and his company sat on benches before the inn door, looking at the smithy while they drank their beer. Now, there was a pretty girl at this inn, the landlord's men called Nancy Sievewright, a bouncing, fresh-looking lass, whose face was as red as the hollyhocks over the pales of the garden behind the inn. At this time Harry Esmond was a lad of sixteen, and somehow in his walks and rambles it often happened that he fell in with Nancy Sievewright's bonny face; if he did not want something done at the blacksmith's he would go and drink ale at the "Three Castles," or find some pretext for seeing this poor Nancy. Poor thing, Harry meant or imagined no harm; and she, no doubt, as little; but the truth is they were always meeting—in the lanes, or by the brook, or at the garden palings, or about Castlewood: it was, "Lord, Mr. Henry!" and "How do you do, Nancy?" many and many a time in the week. 'Tis surprising the magnetic attraction which draws people together from ever so far.

I blush as I think of poor Nancy now, in a red bodice and buxom purple cheeks and a canvas petticoat; and that I devised schemes, and set traps, and made speeches in my heart, which I seldom had courage to say when in presence of that humble enchantress, who knew nothing beyond milking a cow, and opened her black eyes with wonder, when I made one of my fine speeches out of Waller or Ovid. Poor Nancy! from the midst of far-off years thine honest country face beams out; and I remember thy kind voice as if I had heard it yesterday.

When Dr. Tusher brought the news that the smallpox was at the "Three Castles," whither a tramper, it was said, had brought the malady, Henry Esmond's first thought was of alarm for poor Nancy, and then of shame and disquiet for the Castlewood family, lest he might have brought this infection; for the truth is that Mr. Harry had been sitting in a back room for an hour that day, where Nancy Sievewright was with a little brother who complained of headache, and was lying stupefied and crying, either in a chair by the corner of the fire, or in Nancy's lap, or on mine.

Little Lady Beatrix screamed out at Dr. Tusher's news; and my Lord cried out, "God bless me!" He was a brave man, and not afraid of death in any shape but this. He was very proud of his pink complexion and fair hair—but the idea of death by smallpox scared him beyond all other ends. "We will take the children and ride away to-morrow to Walcote:" this was my Lord's small house, inherited from his mother, near to Winchester.

"That is the best refuge in case the disease spreads," said Doctor Tusher. "'Tis awful to think of it beginning at the alehouse; half the people of the village have visited that to-day, or the blacksmith's, which is the same thing. My clerk Nahum lodges with them—I can never go into my reading-desk and have that fellow so near me. I *won't* have that man near me."

"If a parishioner dying in the smallpox sent to you, would you not go?" asked my Lady, looking up from her frame of work, with her calm blue eyes.

"By the Lord, *I* wouldn't," said my Lord.

"We are not in a Popish country; and a sick man doth not absolutely need absolution and confession," said the Doctor. "'Tis true they are a comfort and a help to him when attainable, and to be administered with hope of good. But in a case where the life of a parish priest in the midst of his flock is highly valuable to them, he is not called upon to risk it (and therewith the lives, future prospects, and temporal, even spiritual welfare of his own family) for the sake of a single person, who is not very likely in a condition even to understand the religious message whereof the priest is the bringer—being uneducated, and likewise stupefied or delirious by disease. If your Ladyship or his Lordship, my excellent good friend and patron, were to take it——"

"God forbid!" cried my Lord.

"Amen," continued Dr. Tusher. "Amen to that prayer, my very good Lord! for your sake I would lay my life down"—and, to judge from the alarmed look of the Doctor's purple face, you would have thought that that sacrifice was about to be called for instantly.

To love children, and be gentle with them, was an instinct, rather than a merit, in Henry Esmond; so much so, that he thought almost with a sort of shame of his liking for them, and of the softness into which it betrayed him; and on this day the poor fellow had not only had his young friend, the milkmaid's brother, on his knee, but had been drawing pictures and telling stories to the little Frank Castlewood, who had occupied the same place for an hour after dinner, and was never tired of Henry's tales, and his pictures of soldiers and horses. As luck would have it, Beatrix had not on that evening taken her usual place, which generally she was glad enough to have, upon her tutor's lap. For Beatrix, from the earliest time, was jealous of every caress which was given to her little brother Frank. She would fling away even from the maternal arms, if she saw Frank had been there before her; insomuch that Lady Esmond was obliged not to show her love for her son in the presence of the little girl, and embrace one or the other alone. She would turn pale and red with rage if she caught signs of intelligence or affection between Frank and his mother; would sit apart, and not speak for a whole night, if she thought the boy had a better fruit or a larger cake than hers; would fling away a riband if he had one; and from the earliest age, sitting up in her little chair by the great fireplace opposite to the corner where Lady Castlewood commonly sat at her embroidery, would utter infantine sarcasms about the favour shown to her brother. These, if spoken in the presence of Lord Castlewood, tickled and amused his humour; he would pretend to love Frank best, and dandle and kiss him, and roar with laughter at Beatrix's jealousy. But the truth is, my Lord did not often witness these scenes, nor very much trouble the quiet fireside at which his lady passed many long evenings. My Lord was hunting all day when the season admitted; he frequented all the cock-fights and fairs in the country, and would ride twenty miles to see a main fought, or two clowns break their heads at a cudgelling match; and he liked better to sit in his parlour drinking ale and punch with Jack and Tom, than in his wife's drawing-room: whither, if he came, he brought only too often bloodshot eyes, a hiccupping voice, and a reeling gait. The management of the house, and the property, the care of the few tenants and the village poor, and the accounts of the estate, were in the hands of his lady and her young secretary, Harry Esmond. My Lord took charge of the stables, the kennel, and the cellar—and he filled this, and emptied it too.

So it chanced that upon this very day, when poor Harry Esmond had had the blacksmith's son, and the peer's son, alike upon his knee, little Beatrix, who would come to her tutor willingly enough with her book and her writing, had refused him, seeing the place occupied by her brother, and, luckily for her, had sat at the farther end of the room, away from him, playing with a spaniel dog which she had (and for which, by fits and starts, she would take a great affection), and talking at Harry Esmond over her shoulder, as she pretended to caress the dog, saying that Fido would love her, and she would love Fido, and nothing but Fido, all her life.

When, then, the news was brought that the little boy at the "Three Castles" was ill with the smallpox, poor Harry Esmond felt a shock of alarm, not so much for himself as for his mistress's son, whom he might have brought into peril. Beatrix, who had pouted sufficiently (and who, whenever a stranger appeared, began, from infancy almost, to play off little graces to catch his attention), her brother being now gone to bed, was for taking her place upon Esmond's knee: for, though the Doctor was very obsequious to her, she did not like him, because he had thick boots and dirty hands (the pert young miss said), and because she hated learning the Catechism.

But as she advanced towards Esmond from the corner where she had been sulking, he started back and placed the great chair on which he was sitting between him and her—saying in the French language to Lady Castlewood, with whom the young lad had read much, and whom he had perfected in this tongue—"Madam, the child must not approach me; I must tell you that I was at the blacksmith's to-day, and had his little boy upon my lap."

"Where you took my son afterwards," Lady Castlewood said, very angry, and turning red. "I thank you, sir, for giving him such company. Beatrix," she said in English, "I forbid you to touch Mr. Esmond. Come away, child—come to your room. Come to your room—I wish your Reverence good-night—and you, sir, had you not better go back to your friends at the alehouse?" Her eyes, ordinarily so kind, darted flashes of anger as she spoke; and she tossed up her head (which hung down commonly) with the mien of a princess.

"Heyday!" says my Lord, who was standing by the fireplace—

indeed he was in the position to which he generally came by that hour of the evening—"Heyday! Rachel, what are you in a passion about? Ladies ought never to be in a passion—ought they, Doctor Tusher?—though it does good to see Rachel in a passion. Damme, Lady Castlewood, you look dev'lish handsome in a passion."

"It is, my Lord, because Mr. Henry Esmond, having nothing to do with his time here, and not having a taste for our company, has been to the alehouse, where he has *some friends.*"

My Lord burst out, with a laugh and an oath: "You young slyboots, you've been at Nancy Sievewright. D—— the young hypocrite, who'd have thought it in him? I say, Tusher, he's been after——"

"Enough, my Lord," said my Lady; "don't insult me with this talk."

"Upon my word," said poor Harry, ready to cry with shame and mortification, "the honour of that young person is perfectly unstained for me."

"Oh, of course, of course," says my Lord, more and more laughing and tipsy. "Upon his *honour*, Doctor—Nancy Sieve——"

"Take Mistress Beatrix to bed," my Lady cried at this moment to Mrs. Tucker her woman, who came in with her Ladyship's tea. "Put her into my room—no, into yours," she added quickly. "Go, my child: go, I say: not a word!" And Beatrix, quite surprised at so sudden a tone of authority from one who was seldom accustomed to raise her voice, went out of the room with a scared countenance, and waited even to burst out a-crying until she got to the door with Mrs. Tucker.

For once her mother took little heed of her sobbing, and continued to speak eagerly—"My Lord," she said, "this young man—your dependant—told me just now in French—he was ashamed to to speak in his own language—that he had been at the alehouse all day, where he has had that little wretch who is now ill of the smallpox on his knee. And he comes home reeking from that place—yes, reeking from it—and takes my boy into his lap without shame, and sits down by me, yes, by *me.* He may have killed Frank for what I know—killed our child. Why was he brought in to disgrace our house? Why is he here? Let him go—let him go, I say, to-night, and pollute the place no more."

She had never once uttered a syllable of unkindness to Harry Esmond; and her cruel words smote the poor boy, so that he stood for some moments bewildered with grief and rage at the injustice of such a stab from such a hand. He turned quite white from red, which he had been.

"I cannot help my birth, madam," he said, "nor my other misfortune. And as for your boy, if—if my coming nigh to him pollutes him now, it was not so always. Good-night, my Lord. Heaven bless you and yours for your goodness to me. I have tired her Ladyship's kindness out, and I will go;" and, sinking down on his knee, Harry Esmond took the rough hand of his benefactor and kissed it.

"He wants to go to the alehouse—let him go," cried my Lady.

"I'm d——d if he shall," said my Lord. "I didn't think you could be so d——d ungrateful, Rachel."

Her reply was to burst into a flood of tears, and to quit the room with a rapid glance at Harry Esmond,—as my Lord, not heeding them, and still in great good-humour, raised up his young client from his kneeling posture (for a thousand kindnesses had caused the lad to revere my Lord as a father), and put his broad hand on Harry Esmond's shoulder.

"She was always so," my Lord said; "the very notion of a woman drives her mad. I took to liquor on that very account, by Jove, for no other reason than that; for she can't be jealous of a beer-barrel or a bottle of rum, can she, Doctor? D—— it, look at the maids—just look at the maids in the house" (my Lord pronounced all the words together—just-look-at-the-maze-in-the-house: jever-see-such-maze?). "You wouldn't take a wife out of Castlewood now, would you, Doctor?" and my Lord burst out laughing.

The Doctor, who had been looking at my Lord Castlewood from under his eyelids, said, "But joking apart, and, my Lord, as a divine, I cannot treat the subject in a jocular light, nor, as a pastor of this congregation, look with anything but sorrow at the idea of so very young a sheep going astray."

"Sir," said young Esmond, bursting out indignantly, "she told me that you yourself were a horrid old man, and had offered to kiss her in the dairy."

"For shame, Henry," cried Doctor Tusher, turning as red as a turkey-cock, while my Lord continued to roar with laughter. "If you listen to the falsehoods of an abandoned girl——"

"She is as honest as any woman in England, and as pure for me," cried out Henry, "and as kind, and as good. For shame on you to malign her!"

"Far be it from me do so," cried the Doctor. "Heaven grant I may be mistaken in the girl, and in you, sir, who have a truly *precocious* genius; but that is not the point at issue at present. It appears that the smallpox broke out in the little boy at the 'Three Castles'; that it was on him when you visited the alehouse, for your *own* reasons; and that you sat with the child for some time, and immediately afterwards with my young Lord." The Doctor raised his voice as he spoke, and looked towards my Lady, who had now come back, looking very pale, with a handkerchief in her hand.

"This is all very true, sir," said Lady Esmond, looking at the young man.

"'Tis to be feared that he may have brought the infection with him."

"From the alehouse—yes," said my Lady.

"D—— it, I forgot when I collared you, boy," cried my Lord, stepping back. "Keep off, Harry my boy; there's no good in running into the wolf's jaws, you know."

My Lady looked at him with some surprise, and instantly advancing to Henry Esmond, took his hand. "I beg your pardon, Henry," she said; "I spoke very unkindly. I have no right to interfere with you—with your——"

My Lord broke out into an oath. "Can't you leave the boy alone, my Lady?" She looked a little red, and faintly pressed the lad's hand as she dropped it.

"There is no use, my Lord," she said; "Frank was on his knee as he was making pictures, and was running constantly from Henry to me. The evil is done, if any."

"Not with me, damme," cried my Lord. "I've been smoking," —and he lighted his pipe again with a coal—"and it keeps off infection; and as the disease is in the village—plague take it!— I would have you leave it. We'll go to-morrow to Walcote, my Lady."

"I have no fear," said my Lady; "I may have had it as an infant: it broke out in our house then; and when four of my sisters had it at home, two years before our marriage, I escaped it, and two of my dear sisters died."

"I won't run the risk," said my Lord; "I'm as bold as any man, but I'll not bear that."

"Take Beatrix with you and go," said my Lady. "For us the mischief is done; and Tucker can wait upon us, who has had the disease."

"You take care to choose 'em ugly enough," said my Lord, at which her Ladyship hung down her head and looked foolish: and my Lord, calling away Tusher, bade him come to the oak parlour and have a pipe. The Doctor made a low bow to her Ladyship (of which salaams he was profuse), and walked off on his creaking square-toes after his patron.

When the lady and the young man were alone, there was a

silence of some moments, during which he stood at the fire, looking rather vacantly at the dying embers, whilst her Ladyship busied herself with the tambour-frame and needles.

"I am sorry," she said, after a pause, in a hard, dry voice,—"I *repeat* I am sorry that I showed myself so ungrateful for the safety of my son. It was not at all my wish that you should leave us, I am sure, unless you found pleasure elsewhere. But you must perceive, Mr. Esmond, that at your age, and with your tastes, it is impossible that you can continue to stay upon the intimate footing in which you have been in this family. You have wished to go to the University, and I think 'tis quite as well that you should be sent thither. I did not press this matter, thinking you a child, as you are, indeed, in years—quite a child; and I should never have thought of treating you otherwise until—until these *circumstances* came to light. And I shall beg my Lord to despatch you as quick as possible: and will go on with Frank's learning as well as I can (I owe my father thanks for a little grounding, and you, I'm sure, for much that you have taught me),—and—and I wish you a good-night, Mr. Esmond."

And with this she dropped a stately curtsey, and, taking her candle, went away through the tapestry door, which led to her apartments. Esmond stood by the fireplace, blankly staring after her. Indeed, he scarce seemed to see until she was gone; and then her image was impressed upon him, and remained for ever fixed upon his memory. He saw her retreating, the taper lighting up her marble face, her scarlet lip quivering, and her shining golden hair. He went to his own room, and to bed, where he tried to read, as his custom was; but he never knew what he was reading until afterwards he remembered the appearance of the letters of the book (it was in Montaigne's Essays), and the events of the day passed before him—that is, of the last hour of the day; for as for the morning, and the poor milkmaid yonder, he never so much as once thought. And he could not get to sleep until daylight, and woke with a violent headache, and quite unrefreshed.

He had brought the contagion with him from the "Three Castles" sure enough, and was presently laid up with the smallpox, which spared the hall no more than it did the cottage.

CHAPTER IX

I HAVE THE SMALLPOX, AND PREPARE TO LEAVE CASTLEWOOD

WHEN Harry Esmond passed through the crisis of that malady, and returned to health again, he found that little Frank Esmond had also suffered and rallied after the disease, and the lady his mother was down with it, with a couple more of the household. "It was a Providence, for which we all ought to be thankful," Doctor Tusher said, "that my Lady and her son were spared, while Death carried off the poor domestics of the house;" and rebuked Harry for asking, in his simple way, For which we ought to be thankful—that the servants were killed, or the gentlefolks were saved? Nor could young Esmond agree in the Doctor's vehement protestations to my Lady, when he visited her during her convalescence, that the malady had not in the least impaired her charms, and had not been churl enough to injure the fair features of the Viscountess of Castlewood; whereas, in spite of these fine speeches, Harry thought that her Ladyship's beauty was very much injured by the smallpox. When the marks of the disease cleared away, they did not, it is true, leave furrows or scars on her face (except one, perhaps, on her forehead over her left eyebrow); but the delicacy of her rosy colour and complexion was gone: her eyes had lost their brilliancy, her hair fell, and her face looked older. It was as if a coarse hand had rubbed off the delicate tints of that sweet picture, and brought it, as one has seen unskilful painting-cleaners do, to the dead colour. Also, it must be owned, that for a year or two after the malady, her Ladyship's nose was swollen and redder.

There would be no need to mention these trivialities, but that they actually influenced many lives, as trifles will in the world, where a gnat often plays a greater part than an elephant, and a molehill, as we know in King William's case, can upset an empire. When Tusher in his courtly way (at which Harry Esmond always chafed and spoke scornfully) vowed and protested that my Lady's face was none the worse—the lad broke out and said, "It *is* worse: and my mistress is not near so handsome as she was;" on which poor Lady Castlewood gave a rueful smile, and a look into a little Venice glass she had, which showed her, I suppose, that what the stupid boy said was only too true, for she turned away from the glass, and her eyes filled with tears.

The sight of these in Esmond's heart always created a sort of rage of pity, and seeing them on the face of the lady whom he loved best, the young blunderer sank down on his knees, and besought her to pardon him, saying that he was a fool and an idiot, that he was a brute to make such a speech, he who had caused her malady; and Doctor Tusher told him that a bear he was indeed, and a bear he would remain, at which speech poor young Esmond was so dumb-stricken that he did not even growl.

"He is *my* bear, and I will not have him baited, Doctor," my Lady said, patting her hand kindly on the boy's head, as he was still kneeling at her feet. "How your hair has come off! And mine, too," she added with another sigh.

"It is not for myself that I cared," my Lady said to Harry, when the parson had taken his leave; "but *am* I very much changed? Alas! I fear 'tis too true."

"Madam, you have the dearest, and kindest, and sweetest face in the world, I think," the lad said; and indeed he thought and thinks so.

"Will my Lord think so when he comes back?" the lady asked with a sigh, and another look at her Venice glass. "Suppose he should think as you do, sir, that I am hideous—yes, you said hideous—he will cease to care for me. 'Tis all men care for in women, our little beauty. Why did he select me from among my sisters? 'Twas only for that. We reign but for a day or two: and be sure that Vashti knew Esther was coming."

"Madam," said Mr. Esmond, "Ahasuerus was the Grand Turk, and to change was the manner of his country, and according to his law."

"You are all Grand Turks for that matter," said my Lady, "or would be if you could. Come, Frank, come, my child. You are well, praised be Heaven. *Your* locks are not thinned by this dreadful smallpox: nor your poor face scarred—is it, my angel?"

Frank began to shout and whimper at the idea of such a misfortune. From the very earliest time the young Lord had been taught to admire his beauty by his mother: and esteemed it as highly as any reigning toast valued hers.

One day, as he himself was recovering from his fever and illness, a pang of something like shame shot across young Esmond's breast, as he remembered that he had never once during his illness given a thought to the poor girl at the smithy, whose red cheeks but a month ago he had been so eager to see. Poor Nancy! her cheeks had shared the fate of roses, and were withered now. She had taken the illness on the same day with Esmond—she and her brother were both dead of the smallpox, and buried under the Castlewood yew-trees. There was no bright face looking now from the garden, or to cheer the old smith at his lonely fireside. Esmond would have liked to have kissed her in her shroud (like the lass in Mr. Prior's pretty poem); but she rested many a foot below the ground, when Esmond after his malady first trod on it.

Doctor Tusher brought the news of this calamity, about which Harry Esmond longed to ask, but did not like. He said almost the whole village had been stricken with the pestilence; seventeen persons were dead of it, among them mentioning the names of poor Nancy and her little brother. He did not fail to say how thankful we survivors ought to be. It being this man's business to flatter and make sermons, it must be owned he was most industrious in it, and was doing the one or the other all day.

And so Nancy was gone; and Harry Esmond blushed that he had not a single tear for her, and fell to composing an elegy in Latin verses over the rustic little beauty. He bade the dryads mourn and the river-nymphs deplore her. As her father followed the calling of Vulcan, he said that surely she was like a daughter of Venus, though Sievewright's wife was an ugly shrew, as he remembered to have heard afterwards. He made a long face, but, in truth, felt scarcely more sorrowful than a mute at a funeral. These first passions of men and women are mostly abortive; and are dead almost before they are born. Esmond could repeat, to his last day, some of the doggerel lines in which his muse bewailed his pretty lass; not without shame to remember how bad the verses were, and how good he thought them; how false the grief, and yet how he was rather proud of it. 'Tis an error, surely, to talk of the simplicity of youth. I think no persons are more hypocritical, and have a more affected behaviour to one another, than the young. They deceive themselves and each other with artifices that do not impose upon men of the world; and so we get to understand truth better, and grow simpler as we grow older.

When my Lady heard of the fate which had befallen poor Nancy, she said nothing so long as Tusher was by, but when he was gone, she took Harry Esmond's hand and said—

"Harry, I beg your pardon for those cruel words I used on the night you were taken ill. I am shocked at the fate of the poor creature, and am sure that nothing had happened of that with which, in my anger, I charged you. And the very first day we go out, you must take me to the blacksmith, and we must see if there is anything I can do to console the poor old man. Poor man! to lose both his children! What should I do without mine?"

And this was, indeed, the very first walk which my Lady took, leaning on Esmond's arm, after her illness. But her visit brought no consolation to the old father; and he showed no softness, or desire to speak. "The Lord gave and took away," he said; and he knew what His servant's duty was. He wanted for nothing—less now than ever before, as there were fewer mouths to feed. He wished her Ladyship and Master Esmond good-morning—he had grown tall in his illness, and was but very little marked; and with this, and a surly bow, he went in from the smithy to the house, leaving my Lady, somewhat silenced and shamefaced, at the door. He had a handsome stone put up for his two children, which may be seen in Castlewood churchyard to this very day; and before a year was out his own name was upon the stone. In the presence of Death, that sovereign ruler, a woman's coquetry is scared; and her jealousy will hardly pass the boundaries of that grim kingdom. 'Tis entirely of the earth that passion, and expires in the cold blue air beyond our sphere.

At length, when the danger was quite over, it was announced that my Lord and his daughter would return. Esmond well remembered the day. The lady his mistress was in a flurry of fear: before my Lord came, she went into her room, and returned from it with reddened cheeks. Her fate was about to be decided. Her beauty was gone—was her reign, too, over? A minute would say. My Lord came riding over the bridge—he could be seen from the great window, clad in scarlet, and mounted on his grey hackney—his little daughter ambled by him in a bright riding-dress of blue, on a shining chestnut horse. My Lady leaned against the great mantelpiece, looking on, with one hand on her heart—she seemed only the more pale for those red marks on either cheek. She put her handkerchief to her eyes, and withdrew it, laughing hysterically—the cloth was quite red with the rouge when she took it away. She ran to her room again, and came back with pale cheeks and red eyes—her son in her hand—just as my Lord entered, accompanied by young Esmond, who had gone out to meet his protector, and to hold his stirrup as he descended from horseback.

"What, Harry, boy!" my Lord said good-naturedly, "you look as gaunt as a greyhound. The smallpox hasn't improved your beauty, and your side of the house hadn't never too much of it—ho, ho!"

And he laughed, and sprang to the ground with no small agility, looking handsome and red, with a jolly face and brown hair, like a

Beefeater; Esmond kneeling again, as soon as his patron had descended, performed his homage, and then went to greet the little Beatrix, and help her from her horse.

"Fie! how yellow you look!" she said; "and there are one, two, red holes in your face;" which, indeed, was very true; Harry Esmond's harsh countenance bearing, as long as it continued to be a human face, the marks of the disease.

My Lord laughed again, in high good-humour.

"D—— it!" said he, with one of his usual oaths, "the little slut sees everything. She saw the Dowager's paint t'other day, and asked her why she wore that red stuff—didn't you, Trix? and the Tower; and St. James's; and the play; and the Prince George, and the Princess Anne—didn't you, Trix?"

"They are both very fat, and smelt of brandy," the child said.

Papa roared with laughing.

"Brandy!" he said. "And how do you know, Miss Pert?"

"Because your Lordship smells of it after supper, when I embrace you before I go to bed," said the young lady, who, indeed, was as pert as her father said, and looked as beautiful a little gipsy as eyes ever gazed on.

"And now for my Lady," said my Lord, going up the stairs, and passing under the tapestry curtain that hung before the drawing-room door. Esmond remembered that noble figure, handsomely arrayed in scarlet. Within the last few months he himself had grown from a boy to be a man, and with his figure his thoughts had shot up and grown manly.

My Lady's countenance, of which Harry Esmond was accustomed to watch the changes, and with a solicitous affection to note and interpret the signs of gladness or care, wore a sad and depressed look for many weeks after her Lord's return: during which it seemed as if, by caresses and entreaties, she strove to win him back from some ill-humour he had, and which he did not choose to throw off. In her eagerness to please him she practised a hundred of those arts which had formerly charmed him, but which seemed now to have lost their potency. Her songs did not amuse him; and she hushed them and the children when in his presence. My Lord sat silent at his dinner, drinking greatly, his lady opposite to him, looking furtively at his face, though also speechless. Her silence annoyed him as much as her speech; and he would peevishly, and with an oath, ask her why she held her tongue and looked so glum; or he would roughly check her when speaking, and bid her not talk nonsense. It seemed as if, since his return, nothing she could do or say could please him.

When a master and mistress are at strife in a house, the subordinates in the family take the one side or the other. Harry Esmond stood in so great fear of my Lord, that he would run a league barefoot to do a message for him; but his attachment for Lady Esmond was such a passion of grateful regard, that to spare her a grief, or to do her a service, he would have given his life daily: and it was by the very depth and intensity of this regard that he began to divine how unhappy his adored lady's life was, and that a secret care (for she never spoke of her anxieties) was weighing upon her.

Can any one, who has passed through the world and watched the nature of men and women there, doubt what had befallen her? I have seen, to be sure, some people carry down with them into old age the actual bloom of their youthful love, and I know that Mr. Thomas Parr lived to be a hundred and sixty years old. But, for all that, threescore and ten is the age of men, and few get beyond it; and 'tis certain that a man who marries for mere *beaux yeux*, as my Lord did, considers this part of the contract at an end when the woman ceases to fulfil hers, and his love does not survive her beauty. I know 'tis often otherwise, I say; and can think (as most men in their own experience may) of many a house, where, lighted in early years, the sainted lamp of love hath never been extinguished; but so there is Mr. Parr, and so there is the great giant at the fair that is eight feet high—exceptions to men—and that poor lamp whereof I speak, that lights at first the nuptial chamber, is extinguished by a hundred winds and draughts down the chimney, or sputters out for want of feeding. And then—and then it is Chloe, in the dark, stark awake, and Strephon snoring unheeding; or *vice versâ*, 'tis poor Strephon that has married a heartless jilt, and awoke out of that absurd vision of conjugal felicity, which was to last for ever, and is over like any other dream. One and other has made his bed, and so must lie in it, until that final day when life ends, and they sleep separate.

About this time young Esmond, who had a knack of stringing verses, turned some of Ovid's Epistles into rhymes, and brought them to his lady for her delectation. Those which treated of forsaken women touched her immensely, Harry remarked; and when Œnone called after Paris, and Medea bade Jason come back again, the Lady of Castlewood sighed, and said she thought that part of the verses was the most pleasing. Indeed, she would have chopped up the Dean, her old father, in order to bring her husband back again. But her beautiful Jason was gone, as beautiful Jasons will go, and the poor enchantress had never a spell to keep him.

My Lord was only sulky as long as his wife's anxious face or behaviour seemed to upbraid him. When she had got to master these, and to show an outwardly cheerful countenance and behaviour, her husband's good-humour returned partially, and he swore and stormed no longer at dinner, but laughed sometimes, and yawned unrestrainedly; absenting himself often from home, inviting more company thither, passing the greater part of his days in the hunting-field, or over the bottle as before; but with this difference, that the poor wife could no longer see now, as she had done formerly, the light of love kindled in his eyes. He was with her, but that flame was out: and that once welcome beacon no more shone there.

What were this lady's feelings when forced to admit the truth whereof her foreboding glass had given her only too true warning, that with her beauty her reign had ended, and the days of her love were over? What does a seaman do in a storm if mast and rudder are carried away? He ships a jurymast, and steers as he best can with an oar. What happens if your roof falls in a tempest? After the first stun of the calamity the sufferer starts up, gropes around to see that the children are safe, and puts them under a shed out of the rain. If the palace burns down, you take shelter in the barn. What man's life is not overtaken by one or more of these tornadoes that send us out of the course, and fling us on rocks to shelter as best we may?

When Lady Castlewood found that her great ship had gone down, she began as best she might, after she had rallied from the effects of the loss, to put out small ventures of happiness; and hope for little gains and returns, as a merchant on 'Change, *indocilis pauperiem pati*, having lost his thousands, embarks a few guineas upon the next ship. She laid out her all upon her children, indulging them beyond all measure, as was inevitable with one of her kindness of disposition; giving all her thoughts to their welfare—learning, that she might teach them; and improving her own many natural gifts and feminine accomplishments, that she might impart them to her young ones. To be doing good for some one else, is the life of most good women. They are exuberant of kindness, as it were, and must impart it to some one. She made herself a good scholar of French, Italian, and Latin, having been grounded in these by her father in her youth; hiding these gifts from her husband out of fear, perhaps, that they should offend him, for my Lord was no bookman—pish'd and psha'd at the notion of learned ladies, and would have been angry that his wife could construe out of a Latin book of which he could scarce understand two words. Young Esmond was usher, or house tutor, under her or over her, as it might happen. During my Lord's many absences, these school-days would go on uninterruptedly: the mother and daughter learning with surprising quickness; the latter by fits and starts only, and as suited her wayward humour. As for the little lord, it must be owned that he took after his father in the matter of learning—liked marbles and play, and the great horse and the little one which his father brought him, and on which he took him out a-hunting, a great deal better than Corderius and Lily; marshalled the village boys, and had a little court of them, already flogging them, and domineering over them with a fine imperious spirit, that made his father laugh when he beheld it, and his mother fondly warn him. The cook had a son, the woodman had two, the big lad at the porter's lodge took his cuffs and his orders. Doctor Tusher said he was a young nobleman of gallant spirit; and Harry Esmond, who was his tutor, and ten years his little Lordship's senior, had hard work sometimes to keep his own temper, and hold his authority over his rebellious little chief and kinsman.

In a couple of years after that calamity had befallen which had robbed Lady Castlewood of a little—a very little—of her beauty, and of her careless husband's heart (if the truth must be told, my Lady had found not only that her reign was over, but that her successor was appointed, a Princess of a noble house in Drury Lane somewhere, who was installed and visited by my Lord at the town eight miles off—*pudet hæc approbria dicere nobis*)—a great change had taken place in her mind, which, by struggles only known to herself, at least never mentioned to any one; and unsuspected by the person who caused the pain she endured—had been schooled into such a condition as she could not very likely have imagined possible a score of months since, before her misfortunes had begun.

She had oldened in that time as people do who suffer silently great mental pain; and learned much that she had never suspected before. She was taught by that bitter teacher Misfortune. A child the mother of other children, but two years back her lord was a god to her; his words her law; his smile her sunshine; his lazy commonplaces listened to eagerly, as if they were words of wisdom —all his wishes and freaks obeyed with a servile devotion. She had been my Lord's chief slave and blind worshipper. Some women bear further than this, and submit not only to neglect but to unfaithfulness too—but here this lady's allegiance had failed her. Her spirit rebelled, and disowned any more obedience. First she had to bear in secret the passion of losing the adored object; then to get a further initiation, and to find this worshipped being was but a clumsy idol: then to admit the silent truth, that it was she was superior, and not the monarch her master: that she had thoughts which his brains could never master, and was the better of the two; quite separate from my Lord although tied to him, and bound, as almost all people (save a very happy few), to work all her life alone. My Lord sat in his chair, laughing his laugh, cracking his joke, his face flushing with wine—my Lady in her place over against him—he never suspecting that his superior was there, in the calm resigned lady, cold of manner, with downcast eyes. When he was merry in his cups, he would make jokes about her coldness, and "D—— it, now my Lady is gone, we will have t'other bottle," he would say. He was frank enough in telling his thoughts, such as they were. There was little mystery about my Lord's words or actions. His Fair Rosamond did not live in a Labyrinth, like the lady of Mr. Addison's opera, but paraded with painted cheeks and a tipsy retinue in the country town. Had she a mind to be revenged, Lady Castlewood could have found the way to her rival's house easily enough; and, if she had come with bowl and dagger, would have been routed off the ground by the enemy with a volley of Billingsgate, which the fair person always kept by her.

Meanwhile, it has been said, that for Harry Esmond his benefactress' sweet face had lost none of its charms. It had always the kindest of looks and smiles for him—smiles, not so gay and artless perhaps as those which Lady Castlewood had formerly worn, when, a child herself, playing with her children, her husband's pleasure and authority were all she thought of; but out of her griefs and cares, as will happen I think when these trials fall upon a kindly heart, and are not too unbearable, grew up a number of thoughts and excellences which had never come into existence, had not her sorrow and misfortunes engendered them. Sure, occasion is the father of most that is good in us. As you have seen the awkward fingers and clumsy tools of a prisoner cut and fashion the most delicate little pieces of carved work; or achieve the most prodigious underground labours, and cut through walls of masonry, and saw iron bars and fetters; 'tis misfortune that awakens ingenuity, or fortitude, or endurance, in hearts where these qualities had never come to life but for the circumstance which gave them a being.

"'Twas after Jason left her, no doubt," Lady Castlewood once said with one of her smiles to young Esmond (who was reading to her a version of certain lines out of Euripides), "that Medea became a learned woman and a great enchantress."

"And she could conjure the stars out of heaven," the young tutor added, "but she could not bring Jason back again."

"What do you mean?" asked my Lady, very angry.

"Indeed I mean nothing," said the other, "save what I've read in books. What should I know about such matters? I have seen no woman save you and little Beatrix, and the parson's wife and my late mistress, and your Ladyship's woman here."

"The men who wrote your books," says my Lady, "your Horaces, and Ovids, and Virgils, as far as I know of them, all thought ill of us, as all the heroes they wrote about used us basely. We were bred to be slaves always; and even of our own times, as you are still the only lawgivers, I think our sermons seem to say that the best woman is she who bears her master's chains most gracefully. 'Tis a pity there are no nunneries permitted by our Church: Beatrix and I would fly to one, and end our days in peace there away from you."

"And is there no slavery in a convent?" says Esmond.

"At least if women are slaves there, no one sees them," answered the lady. "They don't work in street gangs with the public to jeer them: and if they suffer, suffer in private. Here comes my Lord home from hunting. Take away the books. My Lord does not love to see them. Lessons are over for to-day, Mr. Tutor." And with a curtsey and a smile she would end this sort of colloquy.

Indeed "Mr. Tutor," as my Lady called Esmond, had now business enough on his hands in Castlewood House. He had three pupils, his lady and her two children, at whose lessons she would always be present; besides writing my Lord's letters, and arranging his accompts for him—when these could be got from Esmond's indolent patron.

Of the pupils the two young people were but lazy scholars, and as my Lady would admit no discipline such as was then in use, my Lord's son only learned what he liked, which was but little, and never to his life's end could be got to construe more than six lines of Virgil. Mistress Beatrix chattered French prettily, from a very early age; and sang sweetly, but this was from her mother's teaching—not Harry Esmond's, who could scarce distinguish between "Green Sleeves" and "Lillibullero"; although he had no greater delight in life than to hear the ladies sing. He sees them now (will he ever forget them?) as they used to sit together of the summer evenings — the two golden heads over the page — the child's little hand and the mother's beating the time, with their voices rising and falling in unison.

But if the children were careless, 'twas a wonder how eagerly the mother learnt from her young tutor—and taught him too. The happiest instinctive faculty was this lady's—a faculty for discerning latent beauties and hidden graces of books, especially books of poetry, as in a walk she would spy out field-flowers and make posies of them, such as no other hand could. She was a critic, not by reason but by feeling; the sweetest commentator of those books they read together; and the happiest hours of young Esmond's life, perhaps, were those passed in the company of this kind mistress and her children.

These happy days were to end soon, however; and it was by the Lady Castlewood's own decree that they were brought to a conclusion. It happened about Christmas-time, Harry Esmond being now past sixteen years of age, that his old comrade, adversary, and friend, Tom Tusher, returned from his school in London, a fair, well-grown, and sturdy lad, who was about to enter college, with an exhibition from his school, and a prospect of after promotion in the Church. Tom Tusher's talk was of nothing but Cambridge now; and the boys, who were good friends, examined each other eagerly about their progress in books. Tom had learned some Greek and Hebrew, besides Latin, in which he was pretty well skilled, and also had given himself to mathematical studies under his father's guidance, who was a proficient in those sciences, of which Esmond knew nothing; nor could he write Latin so well as Tom, though he could talk it better, having been taught by his dear friend the Jesuit Father, for whose memory the lad ever retained the warmest affection, reading his books, keeping his swords clean in the little crypt where the Father had shown them to Esmond on the night of his visit; and often of a night sitting in the chaplain's room, which he inhabited, over his books, his verses, and rubbish, with which the lad occupied himself, he would look up at the window, thinking he wished it might open and let in the good Father. He had come and passed away like a dream; but for the swords and books Harry might almost think the Father was an imagination of his mind—and for two letters which had come to him, one from abroad full of advice and affection, another soon after he had been confirmed by the Bishop of Hexton, in which Father Holt deplored his falling away. But Harry Esmond felt so confident now of his being in the right, and of his own powers as a casuist, that he thought he was able to face the Father himself in argument, and possibly convert him.

To work upon the faith of her young pupil, Esmond's kind mistress sent to the library of her father the Dean, who had been distinguished in the disputes of the late King's reign; and, an old soldier now, had hung up his weapons of controversy. These he took down from his shelves willingly for young Esmond, whom he benefited by his own personal advice and instruction. It did not require much persuasion to induce the boy to worship with his beloved mistress. And the good old nonjuring Dean flattered himself with a conversion which, in truth, was owing to a much gentler and fairer persuader.

Under her Ladyship's kind eyes (my Lord's being sealed in sleep pretty generally) Esmond read many volumes of the works of the famous British divines of the last age, and was familiar with Wake and Sherlock, with Stillingfleet and Patrick. His mistress never tired to listen or to read, to pursue the texts with fond comments, to urge those points which her fancy dwelt on most, or her reason deemed most important. Since the death of her father the Dean, this lady had admitted a certain latitude of theological reading which her orthodox father would never have allowed; his favourite writers appealing more to reason and antiquity than to the passions or imaginations of their readers, so that the works of Bishop Taylor, nay, those of Mr. Baxter and Mr. Law, have in reality found more favour with my Lady Castlewood than the severer volumes of our great English schoolmen.

In later life, at the University, Esmond reopened the controversy, and pursued it in a very different manner, when his patrons had determined for him that he was to embrace the ecclesiastical life. But though his mistress' heart was in this calling, his own never was much. After that first fervour of simple devotion, which his beloved Jesuit priest had inspired in him, speculative theology took but little hold upon the young man's mind. When his early credulity was disturbed, and his saints and virgins taken out of his worship, to rank little higher than the divinities of Olympus, his belief became acquiescence rather than ardour; and he made his mind up to assume the cassock and bands, as another man does to wear a breastplate and jackboots, or to mount a merchant's desk, for a livelihood, and from obedience and necessity, rather than from choice. There were scores of such men in Mr. Esmond's time at the universities, who were going to the Church with no better calling than his.

When Thomas Tusher was gone, a feeling of no small depression and disquiet fell upon young Esmond, of which, though he did not complain, his kind mistress must have divined the cause: for soon after she showed not only that she understood the reason of Harry's melancholy, but could provide a remedy for it. Her habit was thus to watch, unobservedly, those to whom duty or affection bound her, and to prevent their designs, or to fulfil them, when she had the power. It was this lady's disposition to think kindnesses, and devise silent bounties and to scheme benevolence, for those about her. We take such goodness, for the most part, as if it was our due; the Marys who bring ointment for our feet get but little thanks. Some of us never feel this devotion at all, or are moved by it to gratitude or acknowledgment; others only recall it years after, when the days are past in which those sweet kindnesses were spent on us, and we offer back our return for the debt by a poor tardy payment of tears. Then forgotten tones of love recur to us, and kind glances shine out of the past—oh, so bright and clear!—oh, so longed after!—because they are out of reach; as holiday music from withinside a prison wall—or sunshine seen through the bars; more prized because unattainable—more bright because of the contrast of present darkness and solitude, whence there is no escape.

All the notice, then, which Lady Castlewood seemed to take of Harry Esmond's melancholy, upon Tom Tusher's departure, was, by a gaiety unusual to her, to attempt to dispel his gloom. She made his three scholars (herself being the chief one) more cheerful than ever they had been before, and more docile, too, all of them learning and reading much more than they had been accustomed to do. "For who knows," said the lady, "what may happen, and whether we may be able to keep such a learned tutor long?"

Frank Esmond said he for his part did not want to learn any more, and cousin Harry might shut up his book whenever he liked, if he would come out a-fishing; and little Beatrix declared she would send for Tom Tusher, and *he* would be glad enough to come to Castlewood, if Harry chose to go away.

At last comes a messenger from Winchester one day, bearer of a letter, with a great black seal, from the Dean there, to say that his sister was dead, and had left her fortune of £2000 among her six nieces, the Dean's daughters; and many a time since has Harry Esmond recalled the flushed face and eager look wherewith, after this intelligence, his kind lady regarded him. She did not pretend to any grief about the deceased relative, from whom she and her family had been many years parted.

When my Lord heard of the news, he also did not make any very long face. "The money will come very handy to furnish the music-room and the cellar, which is getting low, and buy your Ladyship a coach and a couple of horses, that will do indifferent to ride or for the coach. And, Beatrix, you shall have a spinnet; and, Frank, you shall have a little horse from Hexton Fair; and, Harry, you shall have five pounds to buy some books," said my Lord, who was generous with his own, and indeed with other folks' money. "I wish your aunt would die once a year, Rachel; we could spend your money, and all your sisters', too."

"I have but one aunt—and—and I have another use for the money, my Lord," says my Lady, turning very red.

"Another use, my dear; and what do you know about money?" cries my Lord. "And what the devil is there that I don't give you which you want?"

"I intend to give this money—can't you fancy how, my Lord?"

My Lord swore one of his large oaths that he did not know in the least what she meant.

"I intend it for Harry Esmond to go to college. Cousin Harry," says my Lady, "you mustn't stay longer in this dull place, but make a name to yourself, and for us, too, Harry."

"D—— it, Harry's well enough here," says my Lord, for a moment looking rather sulky.

"Is Harry going away? You don't mean to say you will go away?" cry out Frank and Beatrix at one breath.

"But he will come back: and this will always be his home," cries my Lady, with blue eyes looking a celestial kindness: "and his scholars will always love him; won't they?"

"By G—, Rachel, you're a good woman!" says my Lord, seizing my Lady's hand, at which she blushed very much, and shrank back, putting her children before her. "I wish you joy, my kinsman," he continued, giving Harry Esmond a hearty slap on the shoulder. "I won't balk your luck. Go to Cambridge, boy; and when Tusher dies you shall have the living here, if you are not better provided by that time. We'll furnish the dining-room and buy the horses another year. I'll give thee a nag out of the stable: take any one except my hack and the bay gelding and the coach horses; and God speed thee, my boy!"

"Have the sorrel, Harry; 'tis a good one. Father says 'tis the best in the stable," says little Frank, clapping his hands, and jumping up. "Let's come and see him in the stable." And the other, in his delight and eagerness, was for leaving the room that instant to arrange about his journey.

The Lady Castlewood looked after him with sad penetrating glances. "He wishes to be gone already, my Lord," said she to her husband.

The young man hung back abashed. "Indeed, I would stay for ever, if your Ladyship bade me," he said.

"And thou wouldst be a fool for thy pains, kinsman," said my Lord. "Tut, tut, man. Go and see the world. Sow thy wild oats; and take the best luck that Fate sends thee. I wish I were a boy again that I might go to college, and taste the Trumpington ale."

"Ours, indeed, is but a dull home," cries my Lady, with a little of sadness and, maybe, of satire, in her voice: "an old glum house, half ruined, and the rest only half furnished; a woman and two children are but poor company for men that are accustomed to better. We are only fit to be your worships' handmaids, and your pleasures must of necessity lie elsewhere than at home."

"Curse me, Rachel, if I know now whether thou art in earnest or not," said my Lord.

"In earnest, my Lord!" says she, still clinging by one of her children. "Is there much subject here for joke?" And she made him a grand curtsey, and, giving a stately look to Harry Esmond, which seemed to say, "Remember; you understand me, though he does not," she left the room with her children.

"Since she found out that confounded Hexton business," my Lord said—"and be hanged to them that told her!—she has not been the same woman. She, who used to be as humble as a milk-maid, is as proud as a princess," says my Lord. "Take my counsel, Harry Esmond, and keep clear of women. Since I have had any-thing to do with the jades, they have given me nothing but disgust. I had a wife at Tangier, with whom, as she couldn't speak a word of my language, you'd have thought I might lead a quiet life. But she tried to poison me, because she was jealous of a Jew girl. There was your aunt, for aunt she is—Aunt Jezebel, a pretty life your father led with *her!* And here's my Lady. When I saw her on a pillion riding behind the Dean her father, she looked and was such a baby, that a sixpenny doll might have pleased her. And now you see what she is—hands off, highty-tighty, high and mighty, an empress couldn't be grander. Pass us the tankard, Harry my boy. A mug of beer and a toast at morn, says my host. A toast and a mug of beer at noon, says my dear. D—— it, Polly loves a mug of ale, too, and laced with brandy, by Jove!" Indeed, I suppose they drank it together; for my Lord was often thick in his speech at mid-day dinner; and at night, at supper, speechless altogether.

Harry Esmond's departure resolved upon, it seemed as if the Lady Castlewood, too, rejoiced to lose him; for more than once, when the lad, ashamed perhaps at his own secret eagerness to go away (at any rate stricken with sadness at the idea of leaving those from whom he had received so many proofs of love and kindness inestimable), tried to express to his mistress his sense of gratitude to her, and his sorrow at quitting those who had so sheltered and tended a nameless and houseless orphan, Lady Castlewood cut short his protests of love and his lamentations, and would hear of no grief, but only look forward to Harry's fame and prospects in life. "Our little legacy will keep you for four years like a gentleman. Heaven's Providence, your own genius, industry, honour, must do the rest for you. Castlewood will always be a home for you; and these children, whom you have taught and loved, will not forget to love you. And, Harry," said she (and this was the only time when she spoke with a tear in her eye, or a tremor in her voice), "it may happen in the course of nature that I shall be called away from them: and their father—and—and they will need true friends and protectors. Promise me that you will be true to them—as—as I think I have been to you—and a mother's fond prayer and blessing go with you."

"So help me God, madam, I will," said Harry Esmond, falling on his knees, and kissing the hand of his dearest mistress. "If you will have me stay now, I will. What matters whether or no I make my way in life, or whether a poor bastard dies as unknown as he is now? 'Tis enough that I have your love and kindness surely; and to make you happy is duty enough for me."

"Happy!" says she; "but indeed I ought to be, with my children, and——"

"Not happy!" cried Esmond (for he knew what her life was, though he and his mistress never spoke a word concerning it). "If not happiness, it may be ease. Let me stay and work for you—let me stay and be your servant."

"Indeed, you are best away," said my Lady, laughing, as she put her hand on the boy's head for a moment. "You shall stay in no such dull place. You shall go to college and distinguish yourself as becomes your name. That is how you shall please me best; and—and if my children want you, or I want you, you shall come to us; and I know we may count on you."

"May Heaven forsake me if you may not!" Harry said, getting up from his knee.

"And my knight longs for a dragon this instant that he may fight," said my lady, laughing; which speech made Harry Esmond start, and turn red; for indeed the very thought was in his mind, that he would like that some chance should immediately happen whereby he might show his devotion. And it pleased him to think that his lady had called him "her knight," and often and often he recalled this to his mind, and prayed that he might be her true knight, too.

My Lady's bedchamber window looked out over the country, and you could see from it the purple hills beyond Castlewood village, the green common betwixt that and the Hall, and the old bridge which crossed over the river. When Harry Esmond went away for Cambridge, little Frank ran alongside his horse as far as the bridge, and there Harry stopped for a moment, and looked back at the house where the best part of his life had been passed. It lay before him with its grey familiar towers, a pinnacle or two shining in the sun, the buttresses and terrace walls casting great blue shades on the grass. And Harry remembered, all his life after, how he saw his mistress at the window looking out on him in a white robe, the little Beatrix's chestnut curls resting at her mother's side. Both waved a farewell to him, and little Frank sobbed to leave him. Yes, he *would* be his Lady's true knight, he vowed in his heart; he waved her an adieu with his hat. The village people had Good-bye to say to him too. All knew that Master Harry was going to college, and most of them had a kind word and a look of farewell. I do not stop to say what adventures he began to imagine, or what career to devise for himself before he had ridden three miles from home. He had not read Monsieur Galland's ingenious Arabian tales as yet; but be sure that there are other folks who build castles in the air, and have fine hopes, and kick them down too, besides honest Alnaschar.

CHAPTER X

I GO TO CAMBRIDGE, AND DO BUT LITTLE GOOD THERE

MY LORD, who said he should like to revisit the old haunts of his youth, kindly accompanied Harry Esmond in his first journey to Cambridge. Their road lay through London, where my Lord Viscount would also have Harry stay a few days to show him the pleasures of the town before he entered upon his university studies, and whilst here Harry's patron conducted the young man to my Lady Dowager's house at Chelsey near London: the kind lady at Castlewood having specially ordered that the young gentleman and the old should pay a respectful visit in that quarter.

Her Ladyship the Viscountess Dowager occupied a handsome new house in Chelsey, with a garden behind it, and facing the river, always a bright and animated sight with its swarms of sailors, barges, and wherries. Harry laughed at recognising in the parlour the well-remembered old piece of Sir Peter Lely, wherein his father's widow was represented as a virgin huntress, armed with a gilt bow-and-arrow, and encumbered only with that small quantity of drapery which it would seem the virgins in King Charles's day were accustomed to wear.

My Lady Dowager had left off this peculiar habit of huntress when she married. But though she was now considerably past sixty years of age, I believe she thought that airy nymph of the picture could still be easily recognised in the venerable personage who gave an audience to Harry and his patron.

She received the young man with even more favour than she showed to the elder, for she chose to carry on the conversation in French, in which my Lord Castlewood was no great proficient, and expressed her satisfaction at finding that Mr. Esmond could speak fluently in that language. "'Twas the only one fit for polite conversation," she condescended to say, "and suitable to persons of high breeding."

My Lord laughed afterwards, as the gentlemen went away, at his kinswoman's behaviour. He said he remembered the time when she could speak English fast enough, and joked in his jolly way at the loss he had had of such a lovely wife as that.

My Lady Viscountess deigned to ask his Lordship news of his wife and children: she had heard that Lady Castlewood had had the smallpox; she hoped she was not so *very* much disfigured as people said.

At this remark about his wife's malady, my Lord Viscount winced and turned red; but the Dowager, in speaking of the disfigurement of the young lady, turned to her looking-glass and examined her old wrinkled countenance in it with such a grin of satisfaction, that it was all her guests could do to refrain from laughing in her ancient face.

She asked Harry what his profession was to be; and my Lord, saying that the lad was to take orders, and have the living of Castlewood when old Doctor Tusher vacated it, she did not seem to show any particular anger at the notion of Harry's becoming a Church of England clergyman, nay, was rather glad than otherwise that the youth should be so provided for. She bade Mr. Esmond not to forget to pay her a visit whenever he passed through London, and carried her graciousness so far as to send a purse with twenty guineas for him, to the tavern at which my Lord put up (the "Greyhound," in Charing Cross); and, along with this welcome gift for her kinsman, she sent a little doll for a present to my Lord's little daughter Beatrix, who was growing beyond the age of dolls by this time, and was as tall almost as her venerable relative.

After seeing the town, and going to the plays, my Lord Castlewood and Esmond rode together to Cambridge, spending two pleasant days upon the journey. Those rapid new coaches were not established, as yet, that performed the whole journey between London and the University in a single day; however, the road was pleasant and short enough to Harry Esmond, and he always gratefully remembered that happy holiday which his kind patron gave him.

Mr. Esmond was entered a pensioner of Trinity College in Cambridge, to which famous college my Lord had also in his youth belonged. Doctor Montague was master at this time, and received my Lord Viscount with great politeness: so did Mr. Bridge, who was appointed to be Harry's tutor. Tom Tusher, who was of Emanuel College, and was by this time a junior soph, came to wait upon my Lord, and to take Harry under his protection; and comfortable rooms being provided for him in the great court close by the gate, and near to the famous Mr. Newton's lodgings, Harry's patron took leave of him with many kind words and blessings, and an admonition to him to behave better at the University than my Lord himself had ever done.

'Tis needless in these memoirs to go at any length into the particulars of Harry Esmond's college career. It was like that of a hundred young gentlemen of that day. But he had the ill-fortune to be older by a couple of years than most of his fellow-students; and by his previous solitary mode of bringing up, the circumstances of his life, and the peculiar thoughtfulness and melancholy that had naturally engendered, he was, in a great measure, cut off from the society of comrades who were much younger and higher-spirited than he. His tutor, who had bowed down to the ground, as he walked my Lord over the college grass-plats, changed his behaviour as soon as the nobleman's back was turned, and was—at least Harry thought so—harsh and overbearing. When the lads used to assemble in their *greges* in hall, Harry found himself alone in the midst of that little flock of boys; they raised a great laugh at him when he was set on to read Latin, which he did with the foreign pronunciation taught to him by his old master, the Jesuit, than which he knew no other. Mr. Bridge, the tutor, made him the object of clumsy jokes, in which he was fond of indulging. The young man's spirit was chafed, and his vanity mortified; and he found himself, for some time, as lonely in this place as ever he had been at Castlewood, whither he longed to return. His birth was a source of shame to him, and he fancied a hundred slights and sneers from young and old, who, no doubt, had treated him better had he met them himself more frankly. And as he looks back, in calmer days, upon this period of his life, which he thought so unhappy, he can see that his own pride and vanity caused no small part of the mortifications which he attributed to others' ill-will. The world deals good-naturedly with good-natured people, and I never knew a sulky misanthropist who quarrelled with it, but it was he, and not it, that was in the wrong. Tom Tusher gave Harry plenty of good advice on this subject, for Tom had both good sense and good-humour; but Mr. Harry chose to treat his senior with a great deal of superfluous disdain and absurd scorn, and would by no means part from his darling injuries, in which, very likely, no man believed but himself. As for honest Doctor Bridge, the tutor found, after a few trials of wit with the pupil, that the young man was an ugly subject for wit, and that the laugh was often turned against him. This did not make tutor and pupil any better friends; but had, so far, an advantage for Esmond, that Mr. Bridge was induced to leave him alone; and so long as he kept his chapels, and did the college exercises required of him, Bridge was content not to see Harry's glum face in his class, and to leave him to read and sulk for himself in his own chamber.

A poem or two in Latin and English, which were pronounced to have some merit, and a Latin oration (for Mr. Esmond could write that language better than pronounce it), got him a little reputation both with the authorities of the University and amongst the young men, with whom he began to pass for more than he was worth. A few victories over their common enemy, Mr. Bridge, made them incline towards him, and look upon him as the champion of their order against the seniors. Such of the lads as he took into his confidence found him not so gloomy and haughty as his appearance led them to believe; and Don Dismallo, as he was called, became presently a person of some little importance in his college, and was, as he believes, set down by the seniors there as rather a dangerous character.

Don Dismallo was a staunch young Jacobite, like the rest of his family; gave himself many absurd airs of loyalty; used to invite young friends to burgundy, and give the King's health on King James's birthday; wore black on the day of his abdication; fasted on the anniversary of King William's coronation; and performed a thousand absurd antics, of which he smiles now to think.

These follies caused many remonstrances on Tom Tusher's part, who was always a friend to the powers that be, as Esmond was always in opposition to them. Tom was a Whig, while Esmond was a Tory. Tom never missed a lecture, and capped the proctor with the profoundest of bows. No wonder he sighed over Harry's insubordinate courses, and was angry when the others laughed at him. But that Harry was known to have my Lord Viscount's protection, Tom no doubt would have broken with him altogether. But honest Tom never gave up a comrade as long as he was the friend of a great man. This was not out of scheming on Tom's part, but a natural inclination towards the great. 'Twas no hypocrisy in him to flatter, but the bent of his mind, which was always perfectly good-humoured, obliging, and servile.

Harry had very liberal allowances, for his dear mistress of Castlewood not only regularly supplied him, but the Dowager of Chelsey made her donation annual, and received Esmond at her house near London every Christmas; but, in spite of these benefactions, Esmond was constantly poor; whilst 'twas a wonder with how small a stipend from his father Tom Tusher contrived to make a good figure. 'Tis true that Harry both spent, gave, and lent his money very freely, which Thomas never did. I think he was like the famous Duke of Marlborough in this instance, who, getting a present of fifty pieces, when a young man, from some foolish woman who fell in love with his good looks, showed the money to Cadogan in a drawer scores of years after, where it had lain ever since he had sold his beardless honour to procure it. I do not mean to say that Tom ever let out his good looks so profitably, for nature had not endowed him with any particular charms of person, and he ever was a pattern of moral behaviour, losing no opportunity of giving the very best advice to his younger comrade; with which article, to do him justice, he parted very freely. Not but that he was a merry fellow, too, in his way; he loved a joke, if by good fortune he understood it, and took his share generously of a bottle if another paid for it, and especially if there was a young lord in company to drink it. In these cases there was not a harder drinker in the University than Mr. Tusher could be; and it was edifying to behold him, fresh shaved and with smug face, singing out "Amen!" at early chapel in the morning. In his reading, poor Harry permitted himself to go a-gadding after all the Nine Muses, and so very likely had but little favour from any one of them; whereas Tom Tusher, who had no more turn for poetry than a ploughboy, nevertheless, by a dogged perseverance and obsequiousness in courting the divine Calliope, got himself a prize, and some credit in the University, and a fellowship at his college, as a reward for his scholarship. In this time of Mr. Esmond's life, he got the little reading which he ever could boast of, and passed a good part of his days greedily devouring all the books on which he could lay hand. In this desultory way the works of most of the English, French, and Italian poets came under his eyes, and he had a smattering of the Spanish tongue likewise, besides the ancient languages, of which, at least of Latin, he was a tolerable master.

Then, about midway in his University career, he fell to reading for the profession to which worldly prudence rather than inclination called him, and was perfectly bewildered in theological controversy. In the course of his reading (which was neither pursued with that seriousness nor that devout mind which such a study requires) the youth found himself at the end of one month a Papist, and was about to proclaim his faith; the next month a Protestant, with Chillingworth; and the third a sceptic, with Hobbes and Bayle. Whereas honest Tom Tusher never permitted his mind to stray out of the prescribed University path, accepted the Thirty-Nine Articles with all his heart, and would have signed and sworn to other nine-and-thirty with entire obedience. Harry's wilfulness in this matter, and disorderly thoughts and conversation, so shocked and afflicted his senior, that there grew up a coldness and estrangement between them, so that they became scarce more than mere acquaintances, from having been intimate friends when they came to college first. Politics ran high, too, at the University; and here, also, the young men were at variance. Tom professed himself, albeit a High Churchman, a strong King William's man; whereas Harry brought his family Tory politics to college with him, to which he must add a dangerous admiration for Oliver Cromwell, whose side, or King James's by turns, he often chose to take in the disputes which the young gentlemen used to hold in each other's rooms, where they debated on the state of the nation, crowned and deposed kings, and toasted past and present heroes and beauties in flagons of college ale.

Thus, either from the circumstances of his birth, or the natural melancholy of his disposition, Esmond came to live very much by himself during his stay at the University, having neither ambition enough to distinguish himself in the college career, nor caring to mingle with the mere pleasures and boyish frolics of the students, who were, for the most part, two or three years younger than he. He fancied that the gentlemen of the common-room of his college slighted him on account of his birth, and hence kept aloof from their society. It may be that he made the ill-will, which he imagined came from them, by his own behaviour, which, as he looks back on it in after-life, he now sees was morose and haughty. At any rate, he was as tenderly grateful for kindness as he was susceptible of slight and wrong; and, lonely as he was generally, yet had one or two very warm friendships for his companions of those days.

One of these was a queer gentleman that resided in the University, though he was no member of it, and was the professor of a science scarce recognised in the common course of college education. This was a French refugee officer, who had been driven out of his native country at the time of the Protestant persecutions there, and who came to Cambridge, where he taught the science of the small-sword, and set up a saloon-of-arms. Though he declared himself a Protestant, 'twas said Mr. Moreau was a Jesuit in disguise; indeed, he brought very strong recommendations to the Tory party, which was pretty strong in that University, and very likely was one of the many agents whom King James had in this country. Esmond found this gentleman's conversation very much more agreeable and to his taste than the talk of the college divines in the common-room; he never wearied of Moreau's stories of the wars of Turenne and Condé, in which he had borne a part; and being familiar with the French tongue from his youth, and in a place where but few spoke it, his company became very agreeable to the brave old professor of arms, whose favourite pupil he was, and who made Mr. Esmond a very tolerable proficient in the noble science of *escrime*.

At the next term Esmond was to take his degree of Bachelor of Arts, and afterwards, in proper season, to assume the cassock and bands which his fond mistress would have him wear. Tom Tusher himself was a parson and a fellow of his college by this time; and Harry felt that he would very gladly cede his right to the living of Castlewood to Tom, and that his own calling was in no way the pulpit. But as he was bound, before all things in the world, to his dear mistress at home, and knew that a refusal on his part would grieve her, he determined to give her no hint of his unwillingness to the clerical office: and it was in this unsatisfactory mood of mind that he went to spend the last vacation he should have at Castlewood before he took orders.

CHAPTER XI

I COME HOME FOR A HOLIDAY TO CASTLEWOOD, AND FIND A SKELETON IN THE HOUSE

AT his third long vacation, Esmond came as usual to Castlewood, always feeling an eager thrill of pleasure when he found himself once more in the house where he had passed so many years, and beheld the kind familiar eyes of his mistress looking upon him. She and her children (out of whose company she scarce ever saw him) came to greet him. Miss Beatrix was grown so tall that Harry did not quite know whether he might kiss her or no; and she blushed and held back when he offered that salutation, though she took it, and even courted it, when they were alone. The young lord was shooting up to be like his gallant father in look, though with his mother's kind eyes: the lady of Castlewood herself seemed grown, too, since Harry saw her—in her look more stately, in her person fuller, in her face still as ever most tender and friendly, a greater air of command and decision than had appeared in that guileless sweet countenance which Harry remembered so gratefully. The tone of her voice was so much deeper and sadder when she spoke and welcomed him, that it quite startled Esmond, who looked up at her surprised as she spoke, when she withdrew her eyes from him; nor did she ever look at him afterwards when his own eyes were gazing upon her. A something hinting at grief and secret, and filling his mind with alarm undefinable, seemed to speak with that low thrilling voice of hers, and look out of those clear sad eyes. Her greeting to Esmond was so cold that it almost pained the lad (who would have liked to fall on his knees, and kiss the skirt of her robe, so fond and ardent was his respect and regard for her), and he faltered in answering the questions which she, hesitating on her side, began to put to him. Was he happy at Cambridge? Did he study too hard? She hoped not. He had grown very tall, and looked very well.

"He has got a moustache!" cries out Master Esmond.

"Why does he not wear a peruke like my Lord Mohun?" asked Miss Beatrix. "My Lord says that nobody wears their own hair."

"I believe you will have to occupy your old chamber," says my Lady. "I hope the housekeeper has got it ready."

"Why, Mamma, you have been there ten times these three days yourself!" exclaims Frank.

"And she cut some flowers which you planted in my garden—do you remember, ever so many years ago?—when I was quite a little girl," cries out Miss Beatrix, on tiptoe. "And Mamma put them in your window."

"I remember when you grew well after you were ill that you used to like roses," said the lady, blushing like one of them. They all conducted Harry Esmond to his chamber; the children running before, Harry walking by his mistress hand-in-hand.

The old room had been ornamented and beautified not a little to receive him. The flowers were in the window in a china vase; and there was a fine new counterpane on the bed, which chatterbox Beatrix said Mamma had made too. A fire was crackling on the hearth, although it was June. My Lady thought the room wanted warming; everything was done to make him happy and welcome: "And you are not to be a page any longer, but a gentleman and kinsman, and to walk with papa and mamma," said the children. And as soon as his dear mistress and children had left him to himself, it was with a heart overflowing with love and gratefulness that he flung himself down on his knees by the side of the little bed, and asked a blessing upon those who were so kind to him.

The children, who are always house telltales, soon made him acquainted with the little history of the house and family. Papa had been to London twice. Papa often went away now. Papa had taken Beatrix to Westlands, where she was taller than Sir George Harper's second daughter, though she was two years younger. Papa had taken Beatrix and Frank both to Bellminster, where Frank had got the better of Lord Bellminster's son in a boxing-match—my Lord, laughing, told Harry afterwards. Many gentlemen came to stop with papa, and papa had gotten a new game from London, a French game, called a billiard—that the French king played it very well: and the Dowager Lady Castlewood had sent Miss Beatrix a present; and papa had gotten a new chaise, with two little horses, which he drove himself, beside the coach, which mamma went in; and Doctor Tusher was a cross old plague, and they did not like to learn from him at all; and papa did not care about them learning, and laughed when they were at their books, but mamma liked them to learn, and taught them; and "I don't think papa is fond of mamma," said Miss Beatrix, with her great eyes. She had come quite close up to Harry Esmond by the time this prattle took place, and was on his knee, and had examined

L

all the points of his dress, and all the good or bad features of his homely face.

"You shouldn't say that papa is not fond of mamma," said the boy, at this confession. "Mamma never said so; and mamma forbade you to say it, Miss Beatrix."

'Twas this, no doubt, that accounted for the sadness in Lady Castlewood's eyes, and the plaintive vibrations of her voice. Who does not know of eyes, lighted by love once, where the flame shines no more?—of lamps extinguished, once properly trimmed and tended? Every man has such in his house. Such mementoes make our splendidest chambers look blank and sad; such faces seen in a day cast a gloom upon our sunshine. So oaths mutually sworn, and invocations of Heaven, and priestly ceremonies, and fond belief, and love, so fond and faithful that it never doubted but that it should live for ever, are all of no avail towards making love eternal: it dies, in spite of the banns and the priest; and I have often thought there should be a visitation of the sick for it, and a funeral service, and an extreme unction, and an *abi in pace.* It has its course, like all mortal things—its beginning, progress, and decay. It buds and it blooms out into sunshine, and it withers and ends. Strephon and Chloe languish apart; join in a rapture: and presently you hear that Chloe is crying, and Strephon has broken his crook across her back. Can you mend it so as to show no marks of rupture? Not all the priests of Hymen, not all the incantations to the gods, can make it whole!

Waking up from dreams, books, and visions of college honours, in which for two years Harry Esmond had been immersed, he found himself, instantly, on his return home, in the midst of this actual tragedy of life, which absorbed and interested him more than all his tutor had taught him. The persons whom he loved best in the world, and to whom he owed most, were living unhappily together. The gentlest and kindest of women was suffering ill-usage and shedding tears in secret: the man who made her wretched by neglect, if not by violence, was Harry's benefactor and patron. In houses where, in place of that sacred, inmost flame of love, there is discord at the centre, the whole household becomes hypocritical, and each lies to his neighbour. The husband (or it may be the wife) lies when the visitor comes in, and wears a grin of reconciliation or politeness before him. The wife lies (indeed, her business is to do that, and to smile, however much she is beaten), swallows her tears, and lies to her lord and master; lies in bidding little Jacky respect dear papa: lies in assuring Grandpapa that she is perfectly happy. The servants lie, wearing grave faces behind their master's chair, and pretending to be unconscious of the fighting;

and so, from morning till bedtime, life is passed in falsehood. And wiseacres call this a proper regard of morals, and point out Baucis and Philemon as examples of a good life.

If my Lady did not speak of her griefs to Harry Esmond, my Lord was by no means reserved when in his cups, and spoke his mind very freely, bidding Harry in his coarse way, and with his blunt language, beware of all women as cheats, jades, jilts, and using other unmistakable monosyllables in speaking of them. Indeed, 'twas the fashion of the day, as I must own; and there's not a writer of my time of any note, with the exception of poor Dick Steele, that does not speak of a woman as of a slave, and scorn and use her as such. Mr. Pope, Mr. Congreve, Mr. Addison, Mr. Gay, every one of 'em, sing in this key, each according to his nature and politeness, and louder and fouler than all in abuse is Doctor Swift, who spoke of them, as he treated them, worst of all.

Much of the quarrels and hatred which arise between married people come in my mind from the husband's rage and revolt at discovering that his slave and bedfellow, who is to minister to all his wishes, and is church-sworn to honour and obey him—is his superior; and that *he*, and not she, ought to be the subordinate of the twain; and in these controversies, I think, lay the cause of my Lord's anger against his lady. When he left her, she began to think for herself, and her thoughts were not in his favour. After the illumination, when the love-lamp is put out that anon we spoke of, and by the common daylight we look at the picture, what a daub it looks! what a clumsy effigy! How many men and wives come to this knowledge, think you? And if it be painful to a woman to find herself mated for life to a boor, and ordered to love and honour a dullard, it is worse still for the man himself perhaps, whenever in his dim comprehension the idea dawns that his slave and drudge yonder is, in truth, his superior; that the woman who does his bidding, and submits to his humour, should be his lord; that she can think a thousand things beyond the power of his muddled brains; and that in yonder head, on the pillow opposite to him, lie a thousand feelings, mysteries of thought, latent scorns and rebellions, whereof he only dimly perceives the existence as they look out furtively from her eyes: treasures of love doomed to perish without a hand to gather them; sweet fancies and images of beauty that would grow and unfold themselves into flower; bright wit that would shine like diamonds could it be brought into the sun: and the tyrant in possession crushes the outbreak of all these, drives them back like slaves into the dungeon and darkness, and chafes without that his prisoner is rebellious, and his sworn subject undutiful and refractory. So the lamp was out in Castlewood Hall, and the lord and lady there saw each other as they were. With her illness and altered beauty my Lord's fire for his wife disappeared; with his selfishness and faithlessness her foolish fiction of love and reverence was rent away. Love!—who is to love what is base and unlovely? Respect!—who is to respect what is gross and sensual? Not all the marriage oaths sworn before all the parsons, cardinals, ministers, muftis, and rabbins in the world, can bind to that monstrous allegiance. This couple was living apart then; the woman happy to be allowed to love and tend her children (who were never of her own good-will away from her), and thankful to have saved such treasures as these out of the wreck in which the better part of her heart went down.

These young ones had had no instructors save their mother, and Doctor Tusher for their theology occasionally, and had made more progress than might have been expected under a tutor so indulgent and fond as Lady Castlewood. Beatrix could sing and dance like a nymph. Her voice was her father's delight after dinner. She ruled over the house with little imperial ways, which her parents coaxed and laughed at. She had long learned the value of her bright eyes, and tried experiments in coquetry, *in corpore vili*, upon rustics and country squires, until she should prepare to conquer the world and the fashion. She put on a new riband to welcome Harry Esmond, made eyes at him, and directed her young smiles at him, not a little to the amusement of the young man, and the joy of her father, who laughed his great laugh, and encouraged her in her thousand antics. Lady Castlewood watched the child gravely and sadly: the little one was pert in her replies to her mother, yet eager in her protestations of love and promises of amendment; and as ready to cry (after a little quarrel brought on by her own giddiness) until she had won back her mamma's favour, as she was to risk the kind lady's displeasure by fresh outbreaks of restless vanity. From her mother's sad looks she fled to her father's chair and boozy laughter. She already set the one against the other: and the little rogue delighted in the mischief which she knew how to make so early.

The young heir of Castlewood was spoiled by father and mother both. He took their caresses as men do, and as if they were his right. He had his hawks and his spaniel dog, his little horse and his beagles. He had learned to ride, and to drink, and to shoot flying: and he had a small court, the sons of the huntsman and woodman, as became the heir-apparent, taking after the example of my Lord his father. If he had a headache, his mother was as much frightened as if the plague were in the house: my Lord laughed and jeered in his abrupt way—(indeed, 'twas on the day after New

Year's Day, and an excess of mince-pie)—and said with some of his usual oaths, "D—— it, Harry Esmond—you see how my Lady takes on about Frank's megrim. She used to be sorry about me, my boy (pass the tankard, Harry), and to be frightened if I had a headache once. She don't care about my head now. They're like that—women are—all the same, Harry, all jilts in their hearts. Stick to college —stick to punch and buttery ale: and never see a woman that's handsomer than an old cinder-faced bedmaker. That's my counsel."

It was my Lord's custom to fling out many jokes of this nature, in presence of his wife and children, at meals—clumsy sarcasms which my Lady turned many a time, or which, sometimes, she affected not to hear, or which now and again would hit their mark and make the poor victim wince (as you could see by her flushing face and eyes filling with tears), or which again worked her up to anger and retort, when, in answer to one of these heavy bolts, she would flash back with a quivering reply. The pair were not happy; nor indeed was it happy to be with them. Alas that youthful love and truth should end in bitterness and bankruptcy! To see a young couple loving each other is no wonder; but to see an old couple loving each other is the best sight of all. Harry Esmond became the confidant of one and the other—that is, my Lord told the lad all his griefs and wrongs (which were indeed of Lord Castlewood's own making), and Harry divined my Lady's; his affection leading him easily to penetrate the hypocrisy under which Lady Castlewood generally chose to go disguised, and see her heart aching whilst her face wore a smile. 'Tis a hard task for women in life, that mask which the world bids them wear. But there is no greater crime than for a woman who is ill-used and unhappy to show that she is so. The world is quite relentless about bidding her to keep a cheerful face; and our women, like the Malabar wives, are forced to go smiling and painted to sacrifice themselves with their husbands; their relations being the most eager to push them on to their duty, and, under their shouts and applauses, to smother and hush their cries of pain.

So, into the sad secret of his patron's household, Harry Esmond became initiated, he scarce knew how. It had passed under his eyes two years before, when he could not understand it; but reading, and thought, and experience of men, had oldened him; and one of the deepest sorrows of a life which had never, in truth, been very happy, came upon him now, when he was compelled to understand and pity a grief which he stood quite powerless to relieve.

It hath been said my Lord would never take the oath of allegiance, nor his seat as a peer of the kingdom of Ireland, where, indeed, he had but a nominal estate; and refused an English peerage which King William's government offered him as a bribe to secure his loyalty.

He might have accepted this, and would, doubtless, but for the earnest remonstrances of his wife, who ruled her husband's opinions better than she could govern his conduct, and who, being a simple-hearted woman, with but one rule of faith and right, never thought of swerving from her fidelity to the exiled family, or of recognising any other sovereign but King James; and though she acquiesced in the doctrine of obedience to the reigning power, no temptation, she thought, could induce her to acknowledge the Prince of Orange as rightful monarch, nor to let her lord so acknowledge him. So my Lord Castlewood remained a nonjuror all his life nearly, though his self-denial caused him many a pang, and left him sulky and out of humour.

The year after the Revolution, and all through King William's life, 'tis known there were constant intrigues for the restoration of the exiled family; but if my Lord Castlewood took any share of these, as is probable, 'twas only for a short time, and when Harry Esmond was too young to be introduced into such important secrets.

But in the year 1695, when that conspiracy of Sir John Fenwick, Colonel Lowick, and others, was set on foot, for waylaying King William as he came from Hampton Court to London, and a secret plot was formed, in which a vast number of the nobility and people of honour were engaged, Father Holt appeared at Castlewood, and brought a young friend with him, a gentleman whom 'twas easy to see that both my Lord and the Father treated with uncommon deference. Harry Esmond saw this gentleman, and knew and recognised him in after life, as shall be shown in its place; and he has little doubt now that my Lord Viscount was implicated somewhat in the transactions which always kept Father Holt employed and travelling hither and thither under a dozen of different names and disguises. The Father's companion went by the name of Captain James; and it was under a very different name and appearance that Harry Esmond afterwards saw him.

It was the next year that the Fenwick conspiracy blew up, which is a matter of public history now, and which ended in the execution of Sir John and many more, who suffered manfully for their treason, and who were attended to Tyburn by my Lady's father Dean Armstrong, Mr. Collier, and other stout nonjuring clergymen, who absolved them at the gallows-foot.

'Tis known that when Sir John was apprehended, discovery was made of a great number of names of gentlemen engaged in the conspiracy; when, with a noble wisdom and clemency, the Prince burned the list of conspirators furnished to him, and said he would know no more. Now it was after this that Lord Castlewood swore his great oath, that he would never, so help him Heaven, be engaged in any transaction against that brave and merciful man; and so he told Holt when the indefatigable priest visited him, and would have had him engaged in a further conspiracy. After this my Lord ever spoke of King William as he was—as one of the wisest, the bravest, and the greatest of men. My Lady Esmond (for her part) said she could never pardon the King, first, for ousting his father-in-law from his throne, and, secondly, for not being constant to his wife, the Princess Mary. Indeed, I think if Nero were to rise again, and be King of England, and a good family man, the ladies would pardon him. My Lord laughed at his wife's objections—the standard of virtue did not fit him much.

The last conference which Mr. Holt had with his Lordship took place when Harry was come home for his first vacation from college (Harry saw his old tutor but for a half-hour, and exchanged no private words with him), and their talk, whatever it might be, left my Lord Viscount very much disturbed in mind—so much so that his wife, and his young kinsman, Henry Esmond, could not but observe his disquiet. After Holt was gone, my Lord rebuffed Esmond, and again treated him with the greatest deference; he shunned his wife's questions and company, and looked at his children with such a face of gloom and anxiety, muttering, "Poor children—poor children!" in a way that could not but fill those whose life it was to watch him and obey him with great alarm. For which gloom, each person interested in the Lord Castlewood framed in his or her own mind an interpretation.

My Lady, with a laugh of cruel bitterness, said, "I suppose the person at Hexton has been ill, or has scolded him" (for my Lord's infatuation about Mrs. Marwood was known only too well). Young Esmond feared for his money affairs, into the condition of which he had been initiated; and that the expenses, always greater than his revenue, had caused Lord Castlewood disquiet.

One of the causes why my Lord Viscount had taken young Esmond into his special favour was a trivial one, that hath not before been mentioned, though it was a very lucky accident in Henry Esmond's life. A very few months after my Lord's coming to Castlewood, in the winter time—the little boy being a child in a petticoat, trotting about—it happened that little Frank was with his father after dinner, who fell asleep over his wine, heedless of the child, who crawled to the fire; and, as good fortune would have it, Esmond was sent by his mistress for the boy just as the poor little screaming urchin's coat was set on fire by a log; when Esmond, rushing forward, tore the dress off the infant, so that his own hands were burned more than the child's, who was frightened rather than hurt by this accident. But certainly 'twas providential that a resolute person should have come in at that instant, or the child had been burned to death probably, my Lord sleeping very heavily after drinking, and not waking so cool as a man should who had a danger to face.

Ever after this the father, loud in his expressions of remorse and humility for being a tipsy good-for-nothing, and of admiration for Harry Esmond, whom his Lordship would style a hero for doing a very trifling service, had the tenderest regard for his son's preserver, and Harry became quite as one of the family. His burns were tended with the greatest care by his kind mistress, who said that Heaven had sent him to be the guardian of her children, and that she would love him all her life.

And it was after this, and from the very great love and tenderness which had grown up in this little household, rather than from the exhortations of Dean Armstrong (though these had no small weight with him), that Harry came to be quite of the religion of his house and his dear mistress, of which he has ever since been a professing member. As for Doctor Tusher's boasts that he was the cause of this conversion—even in these young days Mr. Esmond had such a contempt for the Doctor, that had Tusher bade him believe anything (which he did not—never meddling at all), Harry would that instant have questioned the truth on't.

My Lady seldom drank wine; but on certain days of the year, such as birthdays (poor Harry had never a one) and anniversaries, she took a little; and this day, the 29th December, was one. At the end, then, of this year, '96, it might have been a fortnight after Mr. Holt's last visit, Lord Castlewood being still very gloomy in mind, and sitting at table—my Lady bidding a servant bring her a glass of wine, and looking at her husband with one of her sweet smiles, said—

"My Lord, will you not fill a bumper too, and let me call a toast?"

"What is it, Rachel?" says he, holding out his empty glass to be filled.

"'Tis the 29th of December," says my Lady, with her fond look of gratitude: "and my toast is, 'Harry—and God bless him, who saved my boy's life!'"

My Lord looked at Harry hard, and drank the glass, but clapped it down on the table in a moment, and, with a sort of groan, rose up, and went out of the room. What was the matter? We all knew that some great grief was over him.

Whether my Lord's prudence had made him richer, or legacies had fallen to him, which enabled him to support a greater establishment than that frugal one which had been too much for his small means, Harry Esmond knew not; but the house of Castlewood was now on a scale much more costly than it had been during the first years of his Lordship's coming to the title. There were more horses in the stable and more servants in the hall, and many more guests coming and going now than formerly, when it was found difficult enough by the strictest economy to keep the house as befitted one of his Lordship's rank, and the estate out of debt. And it did not require very much penetration to find that many of the new acquaintances at Castlewood were not agreeable to the lady there: not that she ever treated them or any mortal with anything but courtesy; but they were persons who could not be welcome to her; and whose society a lady so refined and reserved could scarce desire for her children. There came fuddling squires from the country round, who bawled their songs under her windows and drank themselves tipsy with my Lord's punch and ale: there came officers from Hexton, in whose company our little lord was made to hear talk and to drink, and swear too, in a way that made the delicate lady tremble for her son. Esmond tried to console her by saying, what he knew of his College experience, that with this sort of company and conversation a man must fall in sooner or late in his course through the world; and it mattered very little whether he heard it at twelve years old or twenty—the youths who quitted mothers' apron strings the latest being not uncommonly the wildest rakes. But it was about her daughter that Lady Castlewood was the most anxious, and the danger which she thought menaced the little Beatrix from the indulgences which her father gave her (it must be owned that my Lord, since these unhappy domestic differences especially, was at once violent in his language to the children when angry, as he was too familiar, not to say coarse, when he was in a good humour), and from the company into which the careless lord brought the child.

Not very far off from Castlewood is Sark Castle, where the Marchioness of Sark lived, who was known to have been a mistress of the late King Charles—and to this house, whither indeed a great part of the country gentry went, my Lord insisted upon going, not only himself, but on taking his little daughter and son, to play with the children there. The children were nothing loth, for the house was splendid, and the welcome kind enough. But my Lady, justly no doubt, thought that the children of such a mother as that noted

Lady Sark had been, could be no good company for her two; and spoke her mind to her lord. His own language when he was thwarted was not indeed of the gentlest: to be brief, there was a family dispute on this, as there had been on many other points—and the lady was not only forced to give in, for the other's will was law—nor could she, on account of their tender age, tell her children what was the nature of her objection to their visit of pleasure, or indeed mention to them any objection at all—but she had the additional secret mortification to find them returning delighted with their new friends, loaded with presents from them, and eager to be allowed to go back to a place of such delights as Sark Castle. Every year she thought the company there would be more dangerous to her daughter, as from a child Beatrix grew to a woman, and her daily increasing beauty, and many faults of character too, expanded.

It was Harry Esmond's lot to see one of the visits which the old Lady of Sark paid to the lady of Castlewood Hall: whither she came in state with six chestnut horses and blue ribands, a page on each carriage step, a gentleman of the horse, and armed servants riding before and behind her. And, but that it was unpleasant to see Lady Castlewood's face, it was amusing to watch the behaviour of the two enemies: the frigid patience of the younger lady, and the unconquerable good-humour of the elder—who would see no offence whatever her rival intended, and who never ceased to smile and to laugh, and to coax the children, and to pay compliments to every man, woman, child, nay dog, or chair and table, in Castlewood, so bent was she upon admiring everything there. She lauded the children, and wished—as indeed she well might—that her own family had been brought up as well as those cherubs. She had never seen such a complexion as dear Beatrix's—though to be sure she had a right to it from father and mother—Lady Castlewood's was indeed a wonder of freshness, and Lady Sark sighed to think she had not been born a fair woman; and remarking Harry Esmond, with a fascinating superannuated smile, she complimented him on his wit, which she said she could see from his eyes and forehead; and vowed that she would never have *him* at Sark until her daughter were out of the way.

CHAPTER XII

MY LORD MOHUN COMES AMONG US FOR NO GOOD

THERE had ridden along with this old Princess's cavalcade two gentlemen: her son my Lord Firebrace and his friend my Lord Mohun, who both were greeted with a great deal of cordiality by the hospitable Lord of Castlewood. My Lord Firebrace was but a feeble-minded and weak-limbed young nobleman, small in stature and limited in understanding—to judge from the talk young Esmond had with him; but the other was a person of a handsome presence, with the *bel air*, and a bright daring warlike aspect, which, according to the chronicle of those days, had already achieved for him the conquest of several beauties and toasts. He had fought and conquered in France, as well as in Flanders; he had served a couple of campaigns with the Prince of Baden on the Danube, and witnessed the rescue of Vienna from the Turk. And he spoke of his military exploits pleasantly, and with the manly freedom of a soldier, so as to delight all his hearers at Castlewood, who were little accustomed to meet a companion so agreeable.

On the first day this noble company came, my Lord would not hear of their departure before dinner, and carried away the gentlemen to amuse them, whilst his wife was left to do the honours of her house to the old Marchioness and her daughter within. They looked at the stables, where my Lord Mohun praised the horses, though there was but a poor show there: they walked over the old house and gardens, and fought the siege of Oliver's time over again: they played a game of rackets in the old court, where my Lord Castlewood beat my Lord Mohun, who said he loved ball of all things, and would quickly come back to Castlewood for his revenge. After dinner they played bowls, and drank punch in the green alley; and when they parted they were sworn friends, my Lord Castlewood kissing the other lord before he mounted on horseback, and pronouncing him the best companion he had met for many a long day. All night long, over his tobacco-pipe, Castlewood did not cease to talk to Harry Esmond in praise of his new friend, and in fact did not leave off speaking of him until his Lordship was so tipsy that he could not speak plainly any more.

At breakfast next day it was the same talk renewed; and when my Lady said there was something free in the Lord Mohun's looks and manner of speech which caused her to mistrust him, her lord burst out with one of his laughs and oaths; said that he never liked man, woman, or beast, but what she was sure to be jealous of it; that Mohun was the prettiest fellow in England; that he hoped to see more of him whilst in the country; and that he would let Mohun know what my Lady Prude said of him.

"Indeed," Lady Castlewood said, "I liked his conversation well enough. 'Tis more amusing than that of most people I know. I thought it, I own, too free; not from what he said, as rather from what he implied."

"Psha! your Ladyship does not know the world," said her husband; "and you have always been as squeamish as when you were a miss of fifteen."

"You found no fault when I was a miss at fifteen."

"Begad, madam, you are grown too old for a pinafore now; and I hold that 'tis for me to judge what company my wife shall see," said my Lord, slapping the table.

"Indeed, Francis, I never thought otherwise," answered my Lady, rising and dropping him a curtsey, in which stately action, if there was obedience, there was defiance too; and in which a bystander deeply interested in the happiness of that pair as Harry Esmond was, might see how hopelessly separated they were; what a great gulf of difference and discord had run between them.

"By G—d! Mohun is the best fellow in England; and I'll invite him here, just to plague that woman. Did you ever see such a frigid insolence as it is, Harry? That's the way she treats me," he broke out, storming, and his face growing red as he clenched his fists and went on. "I'm nobody in my own house. I'm to be the humble servant of that parson's daughter. By Jove! I'd rather she should fling the dish at my head than sneer at me as she does. She puts me to shame before the children with her d—d airs; and, I'll swear, tells Frank and Beaty that papa's a reprobate, and that they ought to despise me."

"Indeed and indeed, sir, I never heard her say a word but of respect regarding you," Harry Esmond interposed.

"No, curse it! I wish she would speak. But she never does. She scorns me, and holds her tongue. She keeps off from me, as if I was a pestilence. By George! she was fond enough of her pestilence once. And when I came a-courting, you would see miss blush—blush red, by George! for joy. Why, what do you think she said to me, Harry? She said herself, when I joked with her about her d—d smiling red cheeks: ''Tis as they do at Saint James's; I put up my red flag when my king comes.' I was the king, you see, she meant. But now, sir, look at her! I believe she would be glad if I was dead; and dead I've been to her these five years—ever since you all of you had the smallpox: and she never forgave me for going away."

"Indeed, my Lord, though 'twas hard to forgive, I think my mistress forgave it," Harry Esmond said; "and remember how eagerly she watched your Lordship's return, and how sadly she turned away when she saw your cold looks."

"Damme!" cries out my Lord; "would you have had me wait and catch the smallpox? Where the deuce had been the good of that? I'll bear danger with any man—but not useless danger—no, no. Thank you for nothing. And—you nod your head, and I know very well, Parson Harry, what you mean. There was the—the other affair to make her angry. But is a woman never to forgive a husband who goes a-tripping? Do you take me for a saint?"

"Indeed, sir, I do not," says Harry, with a smile.

"Since that time my wife's as cold as the statue at Charing Cross. I tell thee she has no forgiveness in her, Henry. Her coldness blights my whole life, and sends me to the punch-bowl, or driving about the country. My children are not mine, but hers, when we are together. 'Tis only when she is out of sight with her abominable cold glances, that run through me, that they'll come to me, and that I dare to give them so much as a kiss; and that's why I take 'em and love 'em in other people's houses, Harry. I'm killed by the very virtue of that proud woman. Virtue! give me the virtue that can forgive; give me the virtue that thinks not of preserving itself, but of making other folks happy. Damme, what matters a scar or two if 'tis got in helping a friend in ill fortune?"

And my Lord again slapped the table, and took a great draught from the tankard. Harry Esmond admired as he listened to him, and thought how the poor preacher of this self-sacrifice had fled from the smallpox, which the lady had borne so cheerfully, and which had been the cause of so much disunion in the lives of all in this house. "How well men preach," thought the young man, "and each is the example in his own sermon! How each has a story in a dispute, and a true one, too, and both are right or wrong as you will." Harry's heart was pained within him, to watch the struggles and pangs that tore the breast of this kind, manly friend and protector.

"Indeed, sir," said he, "I wish to God that my mistress could hear you speak as I have heard you; she would know much that would make her life the happier, could she hear it." But my Lord flung away with one of his oaths, and a jeer; he said that Parson Harry was a good fellow; but that as for women, all women were alike—all jades and heartless. So a man dashes a fine vase down, and despises it for being broken. It may be worthless—true: but who had the keeping of it, and who shattered it?

Harry, who would have given his life to make his benefactress and her husband happy, bethought him, now that he saw what my Lord's state of mind was, and that he really had a great deal of that love left in his heart, and ready for his wife's acceptance if she would take it, whether he could not be a means of reconciliation between these two persons, whom he revered the most in the world. And he cast about how he should break a part of his mind to his mistress, and warn her that in his, Harry's opinion, at least, her husband was still her admirer, and even her lover.

But he found the subject a very difficult one to handle, when he ventured to remonstrate, which he did in the very gravest tone (for long confidence and reiterated proofs of devotion and loyalty had given him a sort of authority in the house, which he resumed as soon as ever he returned to it), and with a speech that should have some effect, as, indeed, it was uttered with the speaker's own heart, he ventured most gently to hint to his adored mistress that she was doing her husband harm by her ill opinion of him, and that the happiness of all the family depended upon setting her right.

She, who was ordinarily calm and most gentle, and full of smiles and soft attentions, flushed up when young Esmond so spoke to her, and rose from her chair, looking at him with a haughtiness and indignation that he had never before known her to display. She was quite an altered being for that moment; and looked an angry princess insulted by a vassal.

"Have you ever heard me utter a word in my Lord's disparagement?" she asked hastily, hissing out her words, and stamping her foot.

"Indeed, no," Esmond said, looking down.

"Are you come to me as his ambassador—*you?*" she continued.

"I would sooner see peace between you than anything else in the world," Harry answered, "and would go of any embassy that had that end."

"So *you* are my Lord's go-between?" she went on, not regarding this speech. "You are sent to bid me back into slavery again, and inform me that my Lord's favour is graciously restored to his handmaid? He is weary of Covent Garden, is he, that he comes home and would have the fatted calf killed?"

"There's good authority for it surely," said Esmond.

"For a son, yes; but my Lord is not my son. It was he who cast me away from him. It was he who broke our happiness down, and he bids me to repair it. It was he who showed himself to me at last, as he was, not as I had thought him. It is he who comes before my children stupid and senseless with wine—who leaves our company for that of frequenters of taverns and bagnios—who goes from his home to the city yonder and his friends there, and when he is tired of them returns hither, and expects that I shall kneel and welcome him. And he sends *you* as his chamberlain! What a proud embassy! Monsieur, I make you my compliment of the new place."

"It would be a proud embassy, and a happy embassy too, could I bring you and my Lord together," Esmond replied.

"I presume you have fulfilled your mission now, sir. 'Twas a pretty one for you to undertake. I don't know whether 'tis your Cambridge philosophy, or time, that has altered your ways of thinking," Lady Castlewood continued, still in a sarcastic tone. "Perhaps you too have learned to love drink, and to hiccup over your wine or punch;—which is your worship's favourite liquor? Perhaps you too put up at the 'Rose' on your way to London, and have your acquaintances in Covent Garden. My services to you, sir, to principal and ambassador, to master and—and lacquey."

"Great heavens! madam," cried Harry, "what have I done that thus, for a second time, you insult me? Do you wish me to blush for what I used to be proud of, that I lived on your bounty? Next to doing you a service (which my life would pay for), you know that to receive one from you is my highest pleasure. What wrong have I done you that you should wound me so, cruel woman?"

"What wrong!" she said, looking at Esmond with wild eyes. "Well, none—none that you know of, Harry, or could help. Why did you bring back the smallpox," she added, after a pause, "from Castlewood village? You could not help it, could you? Which of us knows whither fate leads us? But we were all happy, Henry, till then." And Harry went away from this colloquy, thinking still that the estrangement between his patron and his beloved mistress was remediable, and that each had at heart a strong attachment to the other.

The intimacy between the Lords Mohun and Castlewood appeared to increase as long as the former remained in the country;

and my Lord of Castlewood especially seemed never to be happy out of his new comrade's sight. They sported together, they drank, they played bowls and tennis: my Lord Castlewood would go for three days to Sark, and bring back my Lord Mohun to Castlewood —where indeed his Lordship made himself very welcome to all persons, having a joke or a new game at romps for the children, all the talk of the town for my Lord, and music and gallantry and plenty of the *beau langage* for my Lady, and for Harry Esmond, who was never tired of hearing his stories of his campaigns and his life at Vienna, Venice, Paris, and the famous cities of Europe which he had visited both in peace and war. And he sang at my Lady's harpsichord, and played cards or backgammon, or his new game of billiards with my Lord (of whom he invariably got the better); always having a consummate good-humour, and bearing himself with a certain manly grace, that might exhibit somewhat of the camp and Alsatia perhaps, but that had its charm, and stamped him a gentleman: and his manner to Lady Castlewood was so devoted and respectful, that she soon recovered from the first feelings of dislike which she had conceived against him—nay, before long, began to be interested in his spiritual welfare, and hopeful of his conversion, lending him books of piety, which he promised dutifully to study. With her my Lord talked of reform, of settling into quiet life, quitting the court and town, and buying some land in the neighbourhood—though it must be owned that, when the two Lords were together over their burgundy after dinner, their talk was very different, and there was very little question of conversion on my Lord Mohun's part. When they got to their second bottle, Harry Esmond used commonly to leave these two noble topers, who, though they talked freely enough, Heaven knows, in his presence (Good Lord, what a set of stories, of Alsatia and Spring Garden, of the taverns and gaming-houses, of the ladies of the Court, and mesdames of the theatres, he can recall out of their godly conversation!)—although, I say, they talked before Esmond freely, yet they seemed pleased when he went away, and then they had another bottle, and then they fell to cards, and then my Lord Mohun came to her Ladyship's drawing-room; leaving his boon companion to sleep off his wine.

'Twas a point of honour with the fine gentlemen of those days to lose or win magnificently at their horse-matches, or games of cards and dice—and you could never tell, from the demeanour of these two lords afterwards, which had been successful and which the loser at their games. And when my Lady hinted to my Lord that he played more than she liked, he dismissed her with a "pish," and swore that nothing was more equal than play betwixt gentlemen, if they did but keep it up long enough. And these kept it up long enough, you may be sure. A man of fashion of that time often passed a quarter of his day at cards, and another quarter at drink: I have known many a pretty fellow, who was a wit, too, ready of repartee, and possessed of a thousand graces, who would be puzzled if he had to write more than his name.

There is scarce any thoughtful man or woman, I suppose, but can look back upon his course of past life, and remember some point, trifling as it may have seemed at the time of occurrence, which has nevertheless turned and altered his whole career. 'Tis with almost all of us, as in M. Massillon's magnificent image regarding King William, a *grain de sable* that perverts or perhaps overthrows us; and so it was but a light word flung in the air, a mere freak of perverse child's temper, that brought down a whole heap of crushing woes upon that family whereof Harry Esmond formed a part.

Coming home to his dear Castlewood in the third year of his academical course (wherein he had now obtained some distinction, his Latin poem on the death of the Duke of Gloucester, Princess Anne of Denmark's son, having gained him a medal, and introduced him to the society of the University wits), Esmond found his little friend and pupil Beatrix grown to be taller than her mother, a slim and lovely young girl, with cheeks mantling with health and roses: with eyes like stars shining out of azure, with waving bronze hair clustered about the fairest young forehead ever seen: and a mien and shape haughty and beautiful, such as that of the famous antique statue of the huntress Diana—at one time haughty, rapid, imperious, with eyes and arrows that dart and kill. Harry watched and wondered at this young creature, and likened her in his mind to Artemis with the ringing bow and shafts flashing death upon the children of Niobe; at another time she was coy and melting as Luna shining tenderly upon Endymion. This fair creature, this lustrous Phœbe, was only young as yet, nor had nearly reached her full splendour: but crescent and brilliant, our young gentleman of the University, his head full of poetical fancies, his heart perhaps throbbing with desires undefined, admired this rising young divinity; and gazed at her (though only as at some "bright particular star," far above his earth) with endless delight and wonder. She had been a coquette from the earliest times almost, trying her freaks and jealousies, her wayward frolics and winning caresses, upon all that came within her reach; she set her women quarrelling in the nursery, and practised her eyes on the groom as she rode behind him on the pillion.

She was the darling and torment of father and mother. She intrigued with each secretly; and bestowed her fondness and withdrew it, plied them with tears, smiles, kisses, cajolements;—when the mother was angry, as happened often, flew to the father, and sheltering behind him, pursued her victim; when both were displeased, transferred her caresses to the domestics, or watched until she could win back her parents' good graces, either by surprising them into laughter and good-humour, or appeasing them by submission and artful humility. She was *sævo læta negotio*, like that fickle goddess Horace describes, and of whose "malicious joy" a great poet of our own has written so nobly—who, famous and heroic as he was, was not strong enough to resist the torture of women.

It was but three years before that the child, then but ten years old, had nearly managed to make a quarrel between Harry Esmond and his comrade, good-natured, phlegmatic Thomas Tusher, who never of his own seeking quarrelled with anybody: by quoting to the latter some silly joke which Harry had made regarding him—(it was the merest idlest jest, though it near drove two old friends to blows, and I think such a battle would have pleased her)—and from that day Tom kept at a distance from her; and she respected him, and coaxed him sedulously whenever they met. But Harry was much more easily appeased, because he was fonder of the child: and when she made mischief, used cutting speeches, or caused her friends pain, she excused herself for her fault not by admitting and deploring it, but by pleading not guilty, and asserting innocence so constantly and with such seeming artlessness, that it was impossible to question her plea. In her childhood, they were but mischiefs then which she did; but her power became more fatal as she grew older—as a kitten first plays with a ball, and then pounces on a bird and kills it. 'Tis not to be imagined that Harry Esmond had all this experience at this early stage of his life, whereof he is now writing the history—many things here noted were but known to him in later days. Almost everything Beatrix did or undid seemed good, or at least pardonable, to him then, and years afterwards.

It happened, then, that Harry Esmond came home to Castlewood for his last vacation, with good hopes of a fellowship at his College, and a contented resolve to advance his fortune that way. 'Twas in the first year of the present century, Mr. Esmond (as far as he knew the period of his birth) being then twenty-two years old. He found his quondam pupil shot up into this beauty of which we have spoken, and promising yet more: her brother, my Lord's son, a handsome, high-spirited, brave lad, generous and frank, and kind to everybody, save perhaps his sister, with whom Frank was at war (and not from his but her fault)—adoring his mother, whose joy he was: and taking her side in the unhappy matrimonial differences which were now permanent, while of course Mistress Beatrix ranged with her father. When heads of families fall out, it must naturally be that their dependants wear the one or the other party's colour; and even in the parliaments in the servants' hall or the stables, Harry, who had an early observant turn, could see which were my Lord's adherents and which my Lady's, and conjecture pretty shrewdly how their unlucky quarrel was debated. Our lacqueys sit in judgment on us. My Lord's intrigues may be ever so stealthily conducted, but his valet knows them; and my Lady's woman carries her mistress's private history to the servants' scandal-market, and exchanges it against the secrets of other abigails.

CHAPTER XIII

MY LORD LEAVES US AND HIS EVIL BEHIND HIM

MY Lord Mohun (of whose exploits and fame some of the gentlemen of the University had brought down but ugly reports) was once more a guest at Castlewood, and seemingly more intimately allied with my Lord even than before. Once in the spring those two noblemen had ridden to Cambridge from Newmarket, whither they had gone for the horse-racing, and had honoured Harry Esmond with a visit at his rooms; after which Doctor Montague, the Master of the College, who had treated Harry somewhat haughtily, seeing his familiarity with these great folks, and that my Lord Castlewood laughed and walked with his hand on Harry's shoulder, relented to Mr. Esmond, and condescended to be very civil to him; and some days after his arrival, Harry, laughing, told this story to Lady Esmond, remarking how strange it was that men famous for learning and renowned over Europe, should, nevertheless, so bow down to a title, and cringe to a nobleman ever so poor. At this Mistress Beatrix flung up her head, and said it became those of low origin to respect their betters; that the parsons made themselves a great deal too proud, she thought; and that she liked the way at Lady Sark's best, where the chaplain, though he loved pudding, as all parsons do, always went away before the custard.

"And when I am a parson," says Mr. Esmond, "will you give me no custard, Beatrix?"

"You—you are different," Beatrix answered. "You are of our blood."

"My father was a parson, as you call him," said my Lady.

"But mine is a peer of Ireland," says Mistress Beatrix, tossing her head. "Let people know their places. I suppose you will have me go down on my knees and ask a blessing of Mr. Thomas Tusher, that has just been made a curate, and whose mother was a waiting-maid."

And she tossed out of the room, being in one of her flighty humours then.

When she was gone, my Lady looked so sad and grave, that

Harry asked the cause of her disquietude. She said it was not merely what he said of Newmarket, but what she had remarked, with great anxiety and terror, that my Lord, ever since his acquaintance with the Lord Mohun especially, had recurred to his fondness for play, which he had renounced since his marriage.

"But men promise more than they are able to perform in marriage," said my Lady with a sigh. "I fear he has lost large sums; and our property, always small, is dwindling away under this reckless dissipation. I heard of him in London with very wild company. Since his return letters and lawyers are constantly coming and going: he seems to me to have a constant anxiety, though he hides it under boisterousness and laughter. I looked through—through the door last night, and—and before," said my Lady, "and saw them at cards after midnight; no estate will bear that extravagance, much less ours, which will be so diminished that my son will have nothing at all, and my poor Beatrix no portion!"

"I wish I could help you, madam," said Harry Esmond, sighing, and wishing that unavailingly, and for the thousandth time in his life.

"Who can? Only God," said Lady Esmond—"only God, in whose hands we are." And so it is, and for his rule over his family, and for his conduct to wife and children—subjects over whom his power is monarchical—any one who watches the world must think with trembling sometimes of the account which many a man will have to render. For in our society there's no law to control the King of the Fireside. He is master of property, happiness—life almost. He is free to punish, to make happy or unhappy—to ruin or to torture. He may kill a wife gradually, and be no more questioned than the Grand Seignior who drowns a slave at midnight. He may make slaves and hypocrites of his children; or friends and freemen; or drive them into revolt and enmity against the natural law of love. I have heard politicians and coffee-house wiseacres talking over the newspaper, and railing at the tyranny of the French King, and the Emperor, and wondered how these (who are monarchs, too, in their way) govern their own dominions at home, where each man rules absolute. When the annals of each little reign are shown to the Supreme Master, under whom we hold sovereignty, histories will be laid bare of household tyrants as cruel as Amurath, and as savage as Nero, and as reckless and dissolute as Charles.

If Harry Esmond's patron erred, 'twas in the latter way, from a disposition rather self-indulgent than cruel; and he might have been brought back to much better feelings, had time been given to him to bring his repentance to a lasting reform.

As my Lord and his friend Lord Mohun were such close companions, Mistress Beatrix chose to be jealous of the latter; and the two gentlemen often entertained each other by laughing, in their rude boisterous way, at the child's freaks of anger and show of dislike. "When thou art old enough, thou shalt marry Lord Mohun," Beatrix's father would say: on which the girl would pout and say, "I would rather marry Tom Tusher." And because the Lord Mohun always showed an extreme gallantry to my Lady Castlewood, whom he professed to admire devotedly, one day, in answer to this old joke of her father's, Beatrix said, "I think my Lord would rather marry mamma than marry me; and is waiting till you die to ask her."

The words were said lightly and pertly by the girl one night before supper, as the family party were assembled near the great fire. The two lords, who were at cards, both gave a start; my Lady turned as red as scarlet, and bade Mistress Beatrix go to her own chamber; whereupon the girl, putting on, as her wont was, the most innocent air, said, "I am sure I meant no wrong; I am sure mamma talks a great deal more to Harry Esmond than she does to papa—and she cried when Harry went away, and she never does when papa goes away! And last night she talked to Lord Mohun for ever so long, and sent us out of the room, and cried when we came back, and——"

"D——n!" cried out my Lord Castlewood, out of all patience. "Go out of the room, you little viper!" and he started up and flung down his cards.

"Ask Lord Mohun what I said to him, Francis," her Ladyship said, rising up with a scared face, but yet with a great and touching dignity and candour in her look and voice. "Come away with me, Beatrix." Beatrix sprang up too; she was in tears now.

"Dearest mamma, what have I done?" she asked. "Sure I meant no harm." And she clung to her mother, and the pair went out sobbing together.

"I will tell you what your wife said to me, Frank," my Lord Mohun cried. "Parson Harry may hear it; and, as I hope for heaven, every word I say is true. Last night, with tears in her eyes, your wife implored me to play no more with you at dice or at cards, and you know best whether what she asked was not for your good."

"Of course it was, Mohun," says my Lord in a dry hard voice. "Of course you are a model of a man: and the world knows what a saint you are."

My Lord Mohun was separated from his wife, and had had many affairs of honour: of which women as usual had been the cause.

"I am no saint, though your wife is—and I can answer foi my actions as other people must for their words," said my Lord Mohun.

"By G—, my Lord, you shall," cried the other, starting up.

"We have another little account to settle first, my Lord," says Lord Mohun. Whereupon Harry Esmond, filled with alarm for the consequences to which this disastrous dispute might lead, broke out into the most vehement expostulations with his patron and his adversary. "Gracious heavens!" he said, "my Lord, are you going to draw a sword upon your friend in your own house? Can you doubt the honour of a lady who is as pure as heaven, and would die a thousand times rather than do you a wrong? Are the idle words of a jealous child to set friends at variance? Has not my mistress, as much as she dared do, besought your Lordship, as the truth must be told, to break your intimacy with my Lord Mohun; and to give up the habit which may bring ruin on your family? But for my Lord Mohun's illness, had he not left you?"

"'Faith, Frank, a man with a gouty toe can't run after other men's wives," broke out my Lord Mohun, who indeed was in that way, and with a laugh and a look at his swathed limb so frank and comical, that the other, dashing his fist across his forehead, was caught by that infectious good-humour, and said with his oath, "D—— it, Harry, I believe thee," and so this quarrel was over, and the two gentlemen, at swords drawn but just now, dropped their points, and shook hands.

Beati pacifici. "Go bring my Lady back," said Harry's patron. Esmond went away only too glad to be the bearer of such good news. He found her at the door; she had been listening there, but went back as he came. She took both his hands; hers were marble cold. She seemed as if she would fall on his shoulder. "Thank you, and God bless you, my dear brother Harry," she said. She kissed his hand, Esmond felt her tears upon it: and leading her into the room, and up to my Lord, the Lord Castlewood, with an outbreak of feeling and affection such as he had not exhibited for many a long day, took his wife to his heart, and bent over and kissed her and asked her pardon.

"'Tis time for me to go to roost. I will have my gruel a-bed," said my Lord Mohun: and limped off comically on Harry Esmond's arm. "By George, that woman is a pearl!" he said; "and 'tis only a pig that wouldn't value her. Have you seen the vulgar. trapesing orange-girl whom Esmond"—but here Mr. Esmond interrupted him, saying, that these were not affairs for him to know.

My Lord's gentleman came in to wait upon his master, who was no sooner in his nightcap and dressing-gown than he had another visitor whom his host insisted on sending to him: and this was no other than the Lady Castlewood herself with the toast and gruel, which her husband bade her make and carry with her own hands in to her guest.

Lord Castlewood stood looking after his wife as she went on this errand, and as he looked, Harry Esmond could not but gaze on him, and remarked in his patron's face an expression of love, and grief, and care, which very much moved and touched the young man. Lord Castlewood's hands fell down at his sides, and his head on his breast, and presently he said—

"You heard what Mohun said, Parson?"

"That my Lady was a saint?"

"That there are two accounts to settle. I have been going wrong these five years, Harry Esmond. Ever since you brought that damned smallpox into the house, there has been a fate pursuing me, and I had best have died of it, and not run away from it like a coward. I left Beatrix with her relations, and went to London; and I fell among thieves, Harry, and I got back to confounded cards and dice, which I hadn't touched since my marriage—no, not since I was in the Duke's Guard, with those wild Mohocks. And I have been playing worse and worse, and going deeper and deeper into it; and I owe Mohun two thousand pounds now; and when it's paid I am little better than a beggar. I don't like to look my boy in the face: he hates me, I know he does. And I have spent Beaty's little portion: and the Lord knows what will come if I live. The best thing I can do is to die, and release what portion of the estate is redeemable for the boy."

Mohun was as much master at Castlewood as the owner of the Hall itself; and his equipages filled the stables, where, indeed, there was room in plenty for many more horses than Harry Esmond's impoverished patron could afford to keep. He had arrived on horseback with his people; but when his gout broke out my Lord Mohun sent to London for a light chaise he had, drawn by a pair of small horses, and running as swift, wherever roads were good, as a Laplander's sledge. When this carriage came, his Lordship was eager to drive the Lady Castlewood abroad in it, and did so many times, and at a rapid pace, greatly to his companion's enjoyment, who loved the swift motion and the healthy breezes over the downs which lie hard upon Castlewood, and stretch thence towards the sea. As this amusement was very pleasant to her, and her lord, far from showing any mistrust of her intimacy with Lord Mohun, encouraged her to be his companion—as if willing by his present extreme confidence to make up for any past mistrust which his jealousy had shown—the Lady Castlewood enjoyed herself freely in this harmless diversion, which, it must be owned, her guest was very eager to give her; and it seemed that she grew the more free with Lord Mohun, and pleased with his company, because of some sacrifice which his gallantry was pleased to make in her favour.

Seeing the two gentlemen constantly at cards still of evenings, Harry Esmond one day deplored to his mistress that this fatal infatuation of her lord should continue; and now they seemed reconciled together, begged his lady to hint to her husband that he should play no more.

But Lady Castlewood, smiling archly and gaily, said she would speak to him presently, and that, for a few nights more at least, he might be let to have his amusement.

"Indeed, madam," said Harry, "you know not what it costs you; and 'tis easy for any observer who knows the game, to see that Lord Mohun is by far the stronger of the two."

"I know he is," says my Lady, still with exceeding good-humour; "he is not only the best player, but the kindest player in the world."

"Madam, madam!" Esmond cried, transported and provoked. "Debts of honour must be paid some time or other; and my master will be ruined if he goes on."

"Harry, shall I tell you a secret?" my Lady replied, with kindness and pleasure still in her eyes. "Francis will not be ruined if he goes on; he will be rescued if he goes on. I repent of having spoken or thought unkindly of the Lord Mohun when he was here in the past year. He is full of much kindness and good; and 'tis my belief that we shall bring him to better things. I have lent him Tillotson and your favourite Bishop Taylor, and he is much touched, he says; and as a proof of his repentance—(and herein lies my secret)—what do you think he is doing with Francis? He is letting poor Frank win his money back again. He hath won already at the last four nights; and my Lord Mohun says that he will not be the means of injuring poor Frank and my dear children."

"And in God's name, what do you return him for the sacrifice?" asked Esmond, aghast; who knew enough of men, and of this one in particular, to be aware that such a finished rake gave nothing for nothing. "How, in Heaven's name, are you to pay him?"

"Pay him! With a mother's blessing and a wife's prayers!" cries my Lady, clasping her hands together. Harry Esmond did not know whether to laugh, to be angry, or to love his dear mistress more than ever for the obstinate innocency with which she chose to regard the conduct of a man of the world, whose designs he knew better how to interpret. He told the lady, guardedly, but so as to make his meaning quite clear to her, what he knew in respect of the former life and conduct of this nobleman; of other women against whom he had plotted, and whom he had overcome; of the conversation which he, Harry himself, had had with Lord Mohun, wherein the lord made a boast of his libertinism, and frequently avowed that he held all women to be fair game (as his Lordship styled this pretty sport), and that they were all, without exception, to be won. And the return Harry had for his entreaties and remonstrances was a fit of anger on Lady Castlewood's part, who would not listen to his accusations; she said and retorted that he himself must be very wicked and perverted to suppose evil designs where she was sure none were meant. "And this is the good meddlers get of interfering," Harry thought to himself with much bitterness; and his perplexity and annoyance were only the greater, because he could not speak to my Lord Castlewood himself upon a subject of this nature, or venture to advise or warn him regarding a matter so very sacred as his own honour, of which my Lord was naturally the best guardian.

But though Lady Castlewood would listen to no advice from her young dependant, and appeared indignantly to refuse it when offered, Harry had the satisfaction to find that she adopted the counsel which she professed to reject; for the next day she pleaded a headache, when my Lord Mohun would have had her drive out, and the next day the headache continued; and next day, in a laughing gay way, she proposed that the children should take her place in his Lordship's car, for they would be charmed with a ride of all things; and she must not have all the pleasure for herself. My Lord gave them a drive with a very good grace, though, I dare say, with rage and disappointment inwardly—not that his heart was very seriously engaged in his designs upon this simple lady: but the life of such men is often one of intrigue, and they can no more go through the day without a woman to pursue, than a fox-hunter without his sport after breakfast.

Under an affected carelessness of demeanour, and though there was no outward demonstration of doubt upon his patron's part since the quarrel between the two lords, Harry yet saw that Lord Castlewood was watching his guest very narrowly; and caught sight of distrust and smothered rage (as Harry thought) which foreboded no good. On the point of honour Esmond knew how touchy his patron was; and watched him almost as a physician watches a patient, and it seemed to him that this one was slow to take the disease, though he could not throw off the poison when once it had mingled with his blood. We read in Shakspeare (whom the writer for his part considers to be far beyond Mr. Congreve, Mr. Dryden, or any of the wits of the present period), that when jealousy is once declared, nor poppy, nor mandragora, nor all the drowsy syrups of the East, will ever soothe it or medicine it away.

In fine, the symptoms seemed to be so alarming to this young physician (who, indeed, young as he was, had felt the kind pulses of all those dear kinsmen), that Harry thought it would be his duty to warn my Lord Mohun, and let him know that his designs were suspected and watched. So one day, when in rather a pettish humour his Lordship had sent to Lady Castlewood, who had promised to drive with him, and now refused to come, Harry said, "My Lord, if you will kindly give me a place by your side I will thank you; I have much to say to you, and would like to speak to you alone."

"You honour me by giving me your confidence, Mr. Henry Esmond," says the other, with a very grand bow. My Lord was always a fine gentleman, and young as he was there was that in Esmond's manner which showed that he was a gentleman too, and that none might take a liberty with him—so the pair went out, and mounted the little carriage, which was in waiting for them in the court, with its two little cream-coloured Hanoverian horses covered with splendid furniture and champing at the bit.

"My Lord," says Harry Esmond, after they were got into the country, and pointing to my Lord Mohun's foot, which was swathed in flannel, and put up rather ostentatiously on a cushion—"my Lord, I studied medicine at Cambridge."

"Indeed, Parson Harry," says he; "and are you going to take out a diploma: and cure your fellow-students of the——"

"Of the gout," says Harry, interrupting him, and looking him hard in the face: "I know a good deal about the gout."

"I hope you may never have it. 'Tis an infernal disease," says my Lord, "and its twinges are diabolical. Ah!" and he made a dreadful wry face, as if he just felt a twinge.

"Your Lordship would be much better if you took off all that flannel—it only serves to inflame the toe," Harry continued, looking his man full in the face.

"Oh! it only serves to inflame the toe, does it?" says the other, with an innocent air.

"If you took off that flannel, and flung that absurd slipper away, and wore a boot," continues Harry.

"You recommend me boots, Mr. Esmond?" asks my Lord.

"Yes, boots and spurs. I saw your Lordship three days ago run down the gallery fast enough," Harry goes on. "I am sure that taking gruel at night is not so pleasant as claret to your Lordship; and besides it keeps your Lordship's head cool for play, whilst my patron's is hot and flustered with drink."

"'Sdeath, sir, you dare not say that I don't play fair?" cries my Lord, whipping his horses, which went away at a gallop.

"You are cool when my Lord is drunk," Harry continued; "your Lordship gets the better of my patron. I have watched you as I looked up from my books."

"You young Argus!" says Lord Mohun, who liked Harry Esmond—and for whose company and wit, and a certain daring manner, Harry had a great liking too—"You young Argus! you may look with all your hundred eyes and see we play fair. I've played away an estate of a night, and I've played my shirt off my back; and I've played away my periwig and gone home in a night-cap. But no man can say I ever took an advantage of him beyond the advantage of the game. I played a dice-cogging scoundrel in Alsatia for his ears and won 'em, and have one of 'em in my lodging in Bow Street in a bottle of spirits. Harry Mohun will play any man for anything—always would."

"You are playing awful stakes, my Lord, in my patron's house," Harry said, "and more games than are on the cards."

"What do you mean, sir?" cries my Lord, turning round, with a flush on his face.

"I mean," answers Harry, in a sarcastic tone, "that your gout is well—if ever you had it."

"Sir!" cried my Lord, getting hot.

"And to tell the truth, I believe your Lordship has no more gout than I have. At any rate, change of air will do you good, my Lord Mohun. And I mean fairly that you had better go from Castlewood."

"And were you appointed to give me this message?" cries the Lord Mohun. "Did Frank Esmond commission you?"

"No one did. 'Twas the honour of my family that commissioned me."

"And you are prepared to answer this?" cries the other, furiously lashing his horses.

"Quite, my Lord: your Lordship will upset the carriage if you whip so hotly."

"By George, you have a brave spirit!" my Lord cried out, bursting into a laugh. "I suppose 'tis that infernal *botte de Jesuite* that makes you so bold," he added.

"'Tis the peace of the family I love best in the world," Harry Esmond said warmly—"'tis the honour of a noble benefactor—the happiness of my dear mistress and her children. I owe them everything in life, my Lord; and would lay it down for any one of them. What brings you here to disturb this quiet household? What keeps you lingering month after month in the country? What makes you feign illness and invent pretexts for delay? Is it to win my poor patron's money? Be generous, my Lord, and spare his weakness for the sake of his wife and children. Is it to practise upon the simple heart of a virtuous lady? You might as well storm the Tower single-handed. But you may blemish her name by light comments on it, or by lawless pursuits—and I don't deny that 'tis in your power to make her unhappy. Spare these innocent people, and leave them."

"By the Lord, I believe thou hast an eye to the pretty Puritan thyself, Master Harry," says my Lord, with his reckless, good-humoured laugh, and as if he had been listening with interest to the passionate appeal of the young man. "Whisper, Harry. Art thou in love with her thyself? Hath tipsy Frank Esmond come by the way of all flesh?"

"My Lord, my Lord," cried Harry, his face flushing and his eyes filling as he spoke, "I never had a mother, but I love this lady as one. I worship her as a devotee worships a saint. To hear her name spoken lightly seems blasphemy to me. Would you dare think of your own mother so, or suffer any one so to speak of her? It is a horror to me to fancy that any man should think of her impurely. I implore you, I beseech you, to leave her. Danger will come out of it."

"Danger, psha!" says my Lord, giving a cut to the horses, which at this minute—for we were got on to the Downs—fairly ran off into a gallop that no pulling could stop. The rein broke in Lord Mohun's hands, and the furious beasts scampered madly forwards, the carriage swaying to and fro, and the persons within it holding on to the sides as best they might until, seeing a great ravine before them, where an upset was inevitable, the two gentlemen leapt for their lives, each out of his side of the chaise. Harry Esmond was quit for a fall on the grass, which was so severe that it stunned him for a minute; but he got up presently very sick, and bleeding at the nose, but with no other hurt. The Lord Mohun was not so fortunate; he fell on his head against a stone, and lay on the ground, dead to all appearance.

This misadventure happened as the gentlemen were on their return homewards; and my Lord Castlewood, with his son and daughter, who were going out for a ride, met the ponies as they were galloping with the car behind, the broken traces entangling their heels, and my Lord's people turned and stopped them. It was young Frank who spied out Lord Mohun's scarlet coat as he lay on the ground, and the party made up to that unfortunate gentleman and Esmond, who was now standing over him. His large periwig and feathered hat had fallen off, and he was bleeding profusely from a wound on the forehead, and looking, and being indeed, a corpse.

"Great God! he's dead!" says my Lord. "Ride, some one: fetch a doctor—stay. I'll go home and bring back Tusher; he knows surgery," and my Lord, with his son after him, galloped away.

They were scarce gone when Harry Esmond, who was indeed but just come to himself, bethought him of a similar accident which he had seen on a ride from Newmarket to Cambridge, and taking off a sleeve of my Lord's coat, Harry, with a penknife, opened a vein in his arm, and was greatly relieved, after a moment, to see the blood flow. He was near half-an-hour before he came to himself, by which time Doctor Tusher and little Frank arrived, and found my Lord not a corpse indeed, but as pale as one.

After a time, when he was able to bear motion, they put my Lord upon a groom's horse, and gave the other to Esmond, the men walking on each side of my Lord, to support him, if need were, and worthy Doctor Tusher with them. Little Frank and Harry rode together at a foot pace.

When we rode together home, the boy said: "We met mamma, who was walking on the terrace with the Doctor, and papa frightened her, and told her you were dead——"

"That I was dead?" asks Harry.

"Yes. Papa says: 'Here's poor Harry killed, my dear;' on which mamma gives a great scream; and oh, Harry! she drops down; and I thought she was dead too. And you never saw such a way as papa was in: he swore one of his great oaths: and he turned quite pale; and then he began to laugh somehow, and he told the Doctor to take his horse, and me to follow him; and we left him. And I looked back, and saw him dashing water out of the fountain on to mamma. Oh, she was so frightened!

Musing upon this curious history—for my Lord Mohun's name was Henry too, and they called each other Frank and Harry often—and not a little disturbed and anxious, Esmond rode home. His dear lady was on the terrace still, one of her women with her, and my Lord no longer there. There are steps and a little door thence down into the road. My Lord passed, looking very ghastly, with a handkerchief over his head, and without his hat and periwig, which a groom carried; but his politeness did not desert him, and he made a bow to the lady above.

"Thank Heaven, you are safe!" she said.

"And so is Harry too, mamma," says little Frank,—"huzzay!"

Harry Esmond got off the horse to run to his mistress, as did little Frank, and one of the grooms took charge of the two beasts, while the other, hat and periwig in hand, walked by my Lord's bridle to the front gate, which lay half-a-mile away.

"Oh my boy! what a fright you have given me!" Lady Castlewood said, when Harry Esmond came up, greeting him with one of her shining looks, and a voice of tender welcome; and she was so kind as to kiss the young man ('twas the second time she had so honoured him), and she walked into the house between him and her son, holding a hand of each.

CHAPTER XIV

WE RIDE AFTER HIM TO LONDON

AFTER a repose of a couple of days, the Lord Mohun was so far recovered of his hurt as to be able to announce his departure for the next morning; when, accordingly, he took leave of Castlewood, proposing to ride to London by easy stages, and lie two nights upon the road. His host treated him with a studied and ceremonious courtesy, certainly different from my Lord's usual frank and careless demeanour; but there was no reason to suppose that the two lords parted otherwise than good friends, though Harry Esmond remarked that my Lord Viscount only saw his guest in company with other persons, and seemed to avoid being alone with him. Nor did he ride any distance with Lord Mohun, as his custom was with most of his friends, whom he was always eager to welcome and unwilling to lose; but contented himself, when his Lordship's horses were announced, and their owner appeared, booted for his journey, to take a courteous leave of the ladies of Castlewood, by following the Lord Mohun downstairs to his horses, and by bowing and wishing him a good-day in the courtyard. "I shall see you in London before very long, Mohun," my Lord said, with a smile; "when we will settle our accounts together."

"Do not let them trouble you, Frank," said the other good-naturedly, and holding out his hand, looked rather surprised at the grim and stately manner in which his host received his parting salutation; and so, followed by his people, he rode away.

Harry Esmond was witness of the departure. It was very different to my Lord's coming, for which great preparation had been made (the old house putting on its best appearance to welcome its guest), and there was a sadness and constraint about all persons that day, which filled Mr. Esmond with gloomy forebodings, and sad indefinite apprehensions. Lord Castlewood stood at the door watching his guest and his people as they went out under the arch of the outer gate. When he was there, Lord Mohun turned once more; my Lord Viscount slowly raised his beaver and bowed. His face wore a peculiar livid look, Harry thought. He cursed and kicked away his dogs, which came jumping about him—then he walked up to the fountain in the centre of the court, and leaned against a pillar and looked into the basin. As Esmond crossed over to his own room, late the chaplain's, on the other side of the court, and turned to enter in at the low door, he saw Lady Castlewood looking through the curtains of the great window of the drawing-room overhead, at my Lord as he stood regarding the fountain. There was in the court a peculiar silence somehow; and the scene remained long in Esmond's memory:—the sky bright overhead; the buttresses of the building and the sundial casting shadow over the gilt *memento mori* inscribed underneath; the two dogs, a black greyhound and a spaniel nearly white, the one with his face up to the sun, and the other snuffing amongst the grass and stones, and my Lord leaning over the fountain, which was bubbling audibly. 'Tis strange how that scene, and the sound of that fountain, remain fixed on the memory of a man who has beheld a hundred sights of splendour, and danger too, of which he has kept no account.

It was Lady Castlewood—she had been laughing all the morning, and especially gay and lively before her husband and his guest—who as soon as the two gentlemen went together from her room, ran to Harry, the expression of her countenance quite changed now, and with a face and eyes full of care, and said, "Follow them, Harry, I am sure something has gone wrong." And so it was that Esmond was made an eavesdropper at this lady's orders: and retired to his own chamber, to give himself time in truth to try and compose a story which would soothe his mistress, for he could not but have his own apprehension that some serious quarrel was pending between the two gentlemen.

And now for several days the little company at Castlewood sat at table as of evenings: this care, though unnamed and invisible, being nevertheless present alway, in the minds of at least three persons there. My Lord was exceeding gentle and kind. Whenever he quitted the room, his wife's eyes followed him. He behaved to her with a kind of mournful courtesy and kindness remarkable in one of his blunt ways and ordinary rough manner. He called her by her Christian name often and fondly, was very soft and gentle with the children, especially with the boy, whom he did not love, and being lax about church generally, he went thither and performed all the offices (down even to listening to Doctor Tusher's sermon) with great devotion.

"He paces his room all night: what is it? Henry, find out what it is," Lady Castlewood said constantly to her young dependant. "He has sent three letters to London," she said, another day.

"Indeed, madam, they were to a lawyer," Harry answered,

who knew of these letters, and had seen a part of the correspondence, which related to a new loan my Lord was raising; and when the young man remonstrated with his patron, my Lord said he "was only raising money to pay off an old debt on the property, which must be discharged."

Regarding the money, Lady Castlewood was not in the least anxious. Few fond women feel money-distressed; indeed you can hardly give a woman a greater pleasure than to bid her pawn her diamonds for the man she loves; and I remember hearing Mr. Congreve say of my Lord Marlborough, that the reason why my Lord was so successful with women as a young man, was because he took money of them. "There are few men who will make such a sacrifice for them," says Mr. Congreve, who knew a part of the sex pretty well.

Harry Esmond's vacation was just over, and, as hath been said, he was preparing to return to the University for his last term before taking his degree and entering into the Church. He had made up his mind for this office, not indeed with that reverence which becomes a man about to enter upon a duty so holy, but with a worldly spirit of acquiescence in the prudence of adopting that profession for his calling. But his reasoning was that he owed all to the family of Castlewood, and loved better to be near them than anywhere else in the world; that he might be useful to his benefactors, who had the utmost confidence in him and affection for him in return; that he might aid in bringing up the young heir of the house and acting as his governor; that he might continue to be his dear patron's and mistress's friend and adviser, who both were pleased to say that they should ever look upon him as such; and so, by making himself useful to those he loved best, he proposed to console himself for giving up any schemes of ambition which he might have had in his own bosom. Indeed, his mistress had told him that she would not have him leave her; and whatever she commanded was will to him.

The Lady Castlewood's mind was greatly relieved in the last few days of this well-remembered holiday time, by my Lord's announcing one morning, after the post had brought him letters from London, in a careless tone, that the Lord Mohun was gone to Paris, and was about to make a great journey in Europe; and though Lord Castlewood's own gloom did not wear off, or his behaviour alter, yet this cause of anxiety being removed from his lady's mind, she began to be more hopeful and easy in her spirits, striving too, with all her heart, and by all the means of soothing in her power, to call back my Lord's cheerfulness and dissipate his moody humour.

He accounted for it himself, by saying that he was out of health; that he wanted to see his physician; that he would go to London, and consult Dr. Cheyne. It was agreed that his Lordship and Harry Esmond should make the journey as far as London together; and of a Monday morning, the 11th of October, in the year 1700, they set forwards towards London on horseback. The day before being Sunday, and the rain pouring down, the family did not visit church; and at night my Lord read the service to his family very finely, and with a peculiar sweetness and gravity—speaking the parting benediction, Harry thought, as solemn as ever he heard it. And he kissed and embraced his wife and children before they went to their own chambers with more fondness than he was ordinarily wont to show, and with a solemnity and feeling of which they thought in after days with no small comfort.

They took horse the next morning (after adieux from the family as tender as on the night previous), lay that night on the road, and entered London at nightfall; my Lord going to the "Trumpet," in the Cockpit, Whitehall, a house used by the military in his time as a young man, and accustomed by his Lordship ever since.

An hour after my Lord's arrival (which showed that his visit had been arranged beforehand), my Lord's man of business arrived from Gray's Inn; and thinking that his patron might wish to be private with the lawyer, Esmond was for leaving them: but my Lord said his business was short; introduced Mr. Esmond particularly to the lawyer, who had been engaged for the family in the old lord's time; who said that he had paid the money, as desired that day, to my Lord Mohun himself, at his lodgings in Bow Street; that his Lordship had expressed some surprise, as it was not customary to employ lawyers, he said, in such transactions between men of honour; but, nevertheless, he had returned my Lord Viscount's note of hand, which he held at his client's disposition.

"I thought the Lord Mohun had been in Paris?" cried Mr. Esmond, in great alarm and astonishment.

"He is come back at my invitation," said my Lord Viscount. "We have accounts to settle together."

"I pray Heaven they are over, sir," says Esmond.

"Oh, quite," replied the other, looking hard at the young man. "He was rather troublesome about that money which I told you I had lost to him at play. And now 'tis paid, and we are quits on that score, and we shall meet good friends again."

"My Lord," cried out Esmond, "I am sure you are deceiving me, and that there is a quarrel between the Lord Mohun and you."

"Quarrel—pish! We shall sup together this very night, and

drink a bottle. Every man is ill-humoured who loses such a sum as I have lost. But now 'tis paid, and my anger is gone with it."

"Where shall we sup, sir?" says Harry.

"*We!* Let some gentlemen wait till they are asked," says my Lord Viscount, with a laugh. "You go to Duke Street, and see Mr. Betterton. You love the play, I know. Leave me to follow my own devices: and in the morning we'll breakfast together, with what appetite we may, as the play says."

"By G—! my Lord, I will not leave you this night," says Harry Esmond. "I think I know the cause of your dispute. I swear to you 'tis nothing. On the very day the accident befell Lord Mohun, I was speaking to him about it. I know that nothing has passed but idle gallantry on his part."

"You know that nothing has passed but idle gallantry between Lord Mohun and my wife," says my Lord, in a thundering voice—"you knew of this and did not tell me?"

"I knew more of it than my dear mistress did herself, sir—a thousand times more. How was she, who was as innocent as a child, to know what was the meaning of the covert addresses of a villain?"

"A villain he is, you allow, and would have taken my wife away from me."

"Sir, she is as pure as an angel," cried young Esmond

"Have I said a word against her?" shrieks out my Lord. "Did I ever doubt that she was pure? It would have been the last day of her life when I did. Do you fancy I think that *she* would go astray? No, she hasn't passion enough for that. She neither sins nor forgives. I know her temper—and now I've lost her, by Heaven I love her ten thousand times more than ever I did—yes, when she was young and as beautiful as an angel—when she smiled at me in her old father's house, and used to lie in wait for me there as I came from hunting—when I used to fling my head down on her little knees and cry like a child on her lap—and swear I would reform, and drink no more, and play no more, and follow women no more; when all the men of the Court used to be following her—when she used to look with her child more beautiful, by George, than the Madonna in the Queen's Chapel. I am not good like her, I know it. Who is—by Heaven, who is? I tired and wearied her, I know that very well. I could not talk to her. You men of wit and books could do that, and I couldn't—I felt I couldn't. Why, when you was but a boy of fifteen I could hear you two together talking your poetry and your books till I was in such a rage that I was fit to strangle you. But you were always a good lad, Harry, and I loved you, you know I did. And

I felt she didn't belong to me: and the children don't. And I besotted myself, and gambled, and drank, and took to all sorts of devilries out of despair and fury. And now comes this Mohun, and she likes him, I know she likes him."

"Indeed, and on my soul, you are wrong, sir," Esmond cried.

"She takes letters from him," cries my Lord—"look here, Harry," and he pulled out a paper with a brown stain of blood upon it. "It fell from him that day he wasn't killed. One of the grooms picked it up from the ground and gave it to me. Here it is in their d——d comedy jargon. 'Divine Gloriana—Why look so coldly on your slave who adores you? Have you no compassion on the tortures you have seen me suffering? Do you vouchsafe no reply to billets that are written with the blood of my heart?' She had more letters from him."

"But she answered none," cries Esmond.

"That's not Mohun's fault," says my Lord, "and I will be revenged on him, as God's in heaven, I will."

"For a light word or two, will you risk your lady's honour and your family's happiness, my Lord?" Esmond interposed beseechingly.

"Psha! there shall be no question of my wife's honour," said my Lord; "we can quarrel on plenty of grounds beside. If I live, that villain will be punished; if I fall, my family will be only the better: there will only be a spendthrift the less to keep in the world: and Frank has better teaching than his father. My mind is made up, Harry Esmond, and whatever the event is, I am easy about it. I leave my wife and you as guardians to the children."

Seeing that my Lord was bent upon pursuing this quarrel, and that no entreaties would draw him from it, Harry Esmond (then of a hotter and more impetuous nature than now, when care, and reflection, and grey hairs have calmed him) thought it was his duty to stand by his kind, generous patron, and said, "My Lord, if you are determined upon war, you must not go into it alone. 'Tis the duty of our house to stand by its chief; and I should neither forgive myself nor you if you did not call me, or I should be absent from you at a moment of danger."

"Why, Harry, my poor boy, you are bred for a parson," says my Lord, taking Esmond by the hand very kindly; "and it were a great pity that you should meddle in the matter."

"Your Lordship thought of being a churchman once," Harry answered, "and your father's orders did not prevent him fighting at Castlewood against the Roundheads. Your enemies are mine, sir; I can use the foils, as you have seen, indifferently well, and don't think I shall be afraid when the buttons are taken off 'em."

And then Harry explained, with some blushes and hesitation (for the matter was delicate, and he feared lest, by having put himself forward in the quarrel, he might have offended his patron), how he had himself expostulated with the Lord Mohun, and proposed to measure swords with him if need were, and he could not be got to withdraw peaceably in this dispute. "And I should have beat him, sir," says Harry, laughing. "He never could parry that *botte* I brought from Cambridge. Let us have half-an-hour of it, and rehearse—I can teach it your Lordship: 'tis the most delicate point in the world, and if you miss it, your adversary's sword is through you."

"By George, Harry, you ought to be the head of the house," says my Lord gloomily. "You had been a better Lord Castlewood than a lazy sot like me," he added, drawing his hand across his eyes, and surveying his kinsman with very kind and affectionate glances.

"Let us take our coats off and have half-an-hour's practice before nightfall," says Harry, after thankfully grasping his patron's manly hand.

"You are but a little bit of a lad," says my Lord good-humouredly; "but, in faith, I believe you could do for that fellow. No, my boy," he continued, "I'll have none of your feints and tricks of stabbing: I can use my sword pretty well too, and will fight my own quarrel my own way."

"But I shall be by to see fair play?" cries Harry.

"Yes, God bless you—you shall be by."

"When is it, sir?" says Harry, for he saw that the matter had been arranged privately and beforehand by my Lord.

"'Tis arranged thus: I sent off a courier to Jack Westbury to say that I wanted him specially. He knows for what, and will be here presently, and drink part of that bottle of sack. Then we shall go to the theatre in Duke Street, where we shall meet Mohun; and then we shall all go sup at the 'Rose' or the 'Greyhound.' Then we shall call for cards, and there will be probably a difference over the cards—and then, God help us!—either a wicked villain and traitor shall go out of the world, or a poor worthless devil, that doesn't care to remain in it. I am better away, Hal—my wife will be all the happier when I am gone," says my Lord, with a groan, that tore the heart of Harry Esmond, so that he fairly broke into a sob over his patron's kind hand.

"The business was talked over with Mohun before he left home—Castlewood I mean"—my Lord went on. "I took the letter in to him, which I had read, and I charged him with his villainy, and he could make no denial of it, only he said that my wife was innocent."

"And so she is; before Heaven, my Lord, she is!" cries Harry.

"No doubt, no doubt. They always are," says my Lord. "No doubt, when she heard he was killed, she fainted from accident."

"But, my Lord, *my* name is Harry," cried out Esmond, burning red. "You told my Lady, 'Harry was killed!'"

"Damnation! shall I fight you too?" shouts my Lord in a fury. "Are you, you little serpent, warmed by my fire, going to sting—*you?*"—No, my boy, you're an honest boy; you are a good boy." (And here he broke from rage into tears even more cruel to see.) "You are an honest boy, and I love you; and, by heavens, I am so wretched that I don't care what sword it is that ends me. Stop, here's Jack Westbury. Well, Jack! Welcome, old boy! This is my kinsman, Harry Esmond."

"Who brought your bowls for you at Castlewood, sir," says Harry, bowing; and the three gentlemen sat down and drank of that bottle of sack which was prepared for them.

"Harry is number three," says my Lord. "You needn't be afraid of him, Jack." And the Colonel gave a look, as much as to say, "Indeed, he don't look as if I need." And then my Lord explained what he had only told by hints before. When he quarrelled with Lord Mohun he was indebted to his Lordship in a sum of sixteen hundred pounds, for which Lord Mohun said he proposed to wait until my Lord Viscount should pay him. My Lord had raised the sixteen hundred pounds and sent them to Lord Mohun that morning, and before quitting home had put his affairs into order, and was now quite ready to abide the issue of the quarrel.

When we had drunk a couple of bottles of sack, a coach was called, and the three gentlemen went to the Duke's Play-house, as agreed. The play was one of Mr. Wycherley's—"Love in a Wood."

Harry Esmond has thought of that play ever since with a kind of terror, and of Mrs. Bracegirdle, the actress who performed the girl's part in the comedy. She was disguised as a page, and came and stood before the gentlemen as they sat on the stage, and looked over her shoulder with a pair of arch black eyes, and laughed at my Lord, and asked what ailed the gentleman from the country, and had he had bad news from Bullock fair?

Between the acts of the play the gentlemen crossed over and conversed freely. There were two of Lord Mohun's party, Captain Macartney, in a military habit, and a gentleman in a suit of blue velvet and silver in a fair periwig, with a rich fall of point of Venice lace—my Lord the Earl of Warwick and Holland. My Lord had a paper of oranges, which he ate and offered to the actresses, joking with them. And Mrs. Bracegirdle, when my Lord Mohun said something rude, turned on him, and asked him what he did there, and whether he and his friends had come to stab anybody else, as they did poor Will Mountford? My Lord's dark face grew darker at this taunt, and wore a mischievous, fatal look. They that saw it remembered it, and said so afterward.

When the play was ended the two parties joined company; and my Lord Castlewood then proposed that they should go to a tavern and sup. Lockit's, the "Greyhound," in Charing Cross, was the house selected. All six marched together that way; the three lords going ahead, Lord Mohun's captain, and Colonel Westbury, and Harry Esmond walking behind them. As they walked, Westbury told Harry Esmond about his old friend Dick the Scholar, who had got promotion, and was Cornet of the Guards, and had wrote a book called the "Christian Hero," and had all the Guards to laugh at him for his pains, for the Christian Hero was breaking the commandments constantly, Westbury said, and had fought one or two duels already. And, in a lower tone, Westbury besought young Mr. Esmond to take no part in the quarrel. "There was no need for more seconds than one," said the Colonel, "and the Captain or Lord Warwick might easily withdraw." But Harry said no; he was bent on going through with the business. Indeed, he had a plan in his head, which, he thought, might prevent my Lord Viscount from engaging.

They went in at the bar of the tavern, and desired a private room and wine and cards, and when the drawer had brought these, they began to drink and call healths, and as long as the servants were in the room appeared very friendly.

Harry Esmond's plan was no other than to engage in talk with Lord Mohun, to insult him, and so get the first of the quarrel. So when cards were proposed he offered to play. "Psha!" says my Lord Mohun (whether wishing to save Harry, or not choosing to try the *botte de Jesuite*, it is not to be known); "young gentlemen from College should not play these stakes. You are too young."

"Who dares say I am too young?" broke out Harry. "Is your Lordship afraid?"

"Afraid!" cries out Mohun.

But my good Lord Viscount saw the move. "I'll play you for ten moidores, Mohun," says he. "You silly boy, we don't play for groats here as you do at Cambridge." And Harry, who had no such sum in his pocket (for his half-year's salary was always pretty well spent before it was due), fell back with rage and vexation in his heart that he had not money enough to stake.

"I'll stake the young gentleman a crown," says the Lord Mohun's captain.

"I thought crowns were rather scarce with the gentlemen of the army," says Harry.

"Do they birch at College?" says the Captain.

"They birch fools," says Harry, "and they cane bullies, and they fling puppies into the water'

"Faith, then, there's some escapes drowning," says the Captain, who was an Irishman; and all the gentlemen began to laugh, and made poor Harry only more angry.

My Lord Mohun presently snuffed a candle. It was when the drawers brought in fresh bottles and glasses and were in the room—on which my Lord Viscount said, "The deuce take you, Mohun, how damned awkward you are! Light the candle, you drawer."

"Damned awkward is a damned awkward expression, my Lord," says the other. "Town gentlemen don't use such words—or ask pardon if they do."

"I'm a country gentleman," says my Lord Viscount.

"I see it by your manner," says my Lord Mohun. "No man shall say damned awkward to me."

"I fling the words in your face, my Lord," says the other; "shall I send the cards too?"

"Gentlemen, gentlemen! before the servants?" cry out Colonel Westbury and my Lord Warwick in a breath. The drawers go out of the room hastily. They tell the people below of the quarrel upstairs.

"Enough has been said," says Colonel Westbury. "Will your Lordships meet to-morrow morning?"

"Will my Lord Castlewood withdraw his words?" asks the Earl of Warwick.

"My Lord Castlewood will be —— first," says Colonel Westbury.

"Then we have nothing for it. Take notice, gentlemen, there have been outrageous words—reparation asked and refused."

"And refused," says my Lord Castlewood, putting on his hat. "Where shall the meeting be? and when?"

"Since my Lord refuses me satisfaction, which I deeply regret, there is no time so good as now," says my Lord Mohun. "Let us have chairs and go to Leicester Field."

"Are your Lordship and I to have the honour of exchanging a pass or two?" says Colonel Westbury, with a low bow to my Lord of Warwick and Holland.

"It is an honour for me," says my Lord, with a profound congée, "to be matched with a gentleman who has been at Mons and Namur."

"Will your Reverence permit me to give you a lesson?" says the Captain.

"Nay, nay, gentlemen, two on a side are plenty," says Harry's patron. "Spare the boy, Captain Macartney," and he shook Harry's hand—for the last time, save one, in his life.

At the bar of the tavern all the gentlemen stopped, and my Lord Viscount said, laughing, to the barwoman, that those cards set people sadly a-quarrelling; but that the dispute was over now, and the parties were all going away to my Lord Mohun's house in Bow Street, to drink a bottle more before going to bed.

A half-dozen of chairs were now called, and the six gentlemen stepping into them, the word was privately given to the chairmen to go to Leicester Field, where the gentlemen were set down opposite the "Standard Tavern." It was midnight, and the town was a-bed by this time, and only a few lights in the windows of the houses; but the night was bright enough for the unhappy purpose which the disputants came about; and so all six entered into that fatal square, the chairmen standing without the railing and keeping the gate, lest any persons should disturb the meeting.

All that happened there hath been matter of public notoriety, and is recorded, for warning to lawless men, in the annals of our country. After being engaged for not more than a couple of minutes, as Harry Esmond thought (though being occupied at the time with his own adversary's point, which was active, he may not have taken a good note of time), a cry from the chairmen without, who were smoking their pipes, and leaning over the railings of the field as they watched the dim combat within, announced that some catastrophe had happened, which caused Esmond to drop his sword and look round, at which moment his enemy wounded him in the right hand. But the young man did not heed this hurt much, and ran up to the place where he saw his dear master was down.

My Lord Mohun was standing over him.

"Are you much hurt, Frank?" he asked in a hollow voice.

"I believe I'm a dead man," my Lord said from the ground.

"No, no, not so," says the other; "and I call God to witness, Frank Esmond, that I would have asked your pardon, had you but given me a chance. In—in the first cause of our falling out, I swear that no one was to blame but me, and—and that my Lady——"

"Hush!" says my poor Lord Viscount, lifting himself on his elbow and speaking faintly. "'Twas a dispute about the cards—the cursed cards. Harry my boy, are you wounded, too? God help thee! I loved thee, Harry, and thou must watch over my little Frank—and—and carry this little heart to my wife."

And here my dear Lord felt in his breast for a locket he wore there, and, in the act, fell back fainting.

We were all at this terrified, thinking him dead; but Esmond and Colonel Westbury bade the chairmen come into the field; and so my Lord was carried to one Mr. Aimes, a surgeon, in Long Acre, who kept a bath, and there the house was wakened up, and the victim of this quarrel carried in.

My Lord Viscount was put to bed, and his wound looked to by the surgeon, who seemed both kind and skilful. When he had looked to my Lord, he bandaged up Harry Esmond's hand (who, from loss of blood, had fainted too, in the house, and may have been some time unconscious); and when the young man came to himself, you may be sure he eagerly asked what news there was of his dear patron; on which the surgeon carried him to the room where the Lord Castlewood lay; who had already sent for a priest, and desired earnestly, they said, to speak with his kinsman. He was lying on a bed, very pale and ghastly, with that fixed, fatal look in his eyes, which betokens death; and faintly beckoning all the other persons away from him with his hand, and crying out "Only Harry Esmond," the hand fell powerless down on the coverlet, as Harry came forward, and knelt down and kissed it.

"Thou art all but a priest, Harry," my Lord Viscount gasped out, with a faint smile, and pressure of his cold hand. "Are they all gone? Let me make thee a death-bed confession."

And with sacred Death waiting, as it were, at the bed-foot, as an awful witness of his words, the poor dying soul gasped out his last wishes in respect of his family;—his humble profession of contrition for his faults;—and his charity towards the world he was leaving. Some things he said concerned Harry Esmond as much as they astonished him. And my Lord Viscount, sinking visibly, was in the midst of these strange confessions, when the ecclesiastic for whom my Lord had sent, Mr. Atterbury, arrived.

This gentleman had reached to no great church dignity as yet, but was only preacher at St. Bride's, drawing all the town thither by his eloquent sermons. He was godson to my Lord, who had been pupil to his father; had paid a visit to Castlewood from Oxford more than once; and it was by his advice, I think, that Harry Esmond was sent to Cambridge, rather than to Oxford, of which place Mr. Atterbury, though a distinguished member, spoke but ill.

Our messenger found the good priest already at his books at five o'clock in the morning, and he followed the man eagerly to the house where my poor Lord Viscount lay—Esmond watching him, and taking his dying words from his mouth.

My Lord, hearing of Mr. Atterbury's arrival, and squeezing Esmond's hand, asked to be alone with the priest; and Esmond left them there for this solemn interview. You may be sure that his own prayers and grief accompanied that dying benefactor. My Lord had said to him that which confounded the young man—informed him of a secret which greatly concerned him. Indeed, after hearing it, he had had good cause for doubt and dismay; for mental anguish as well as resolution. While the colloquy between Mr. Atterbury and his dying penitent took place within, an immense contest of perplexity was agitating Lord Castlewood's young companion.

At the end of an hour—it may be more—Mr. Atterbury came out of the room, looking very hard at Esmond, and holding a paper.

"He is on the brink of God's awful judgment," the priest whispered. "He has made his breast clean to me. He forgives and believes, and makes restitution. Shall it be in public? Shall we call a witness to sign it?"

"God knows," sobbed out the young man, "my dearest Lord has only done me kindness all his life."

The priest put the paper into Esmond's hand. He looked at it. It swam before his eyes.

"'Tis a confession," he said.

"'Tis as you please," said Mr. Atterbury.

There was a fire in the room, where the cloths were drying for the baths, and there lay a heap in a corner, saturated with the blood of my dear Lord's body. Esmond went to the fire, and threw the paper into it. 'Twas a great chimney with glazed Dutch tiles. How we remember such trifles in such awful moments!—the scrap of the book that we have read in a great grief—the taste of that last dish that we have eaten before a duel, or some such supreme meeting or parting. On the Dutch tiles at the bagnio was a rude picture representing Jacob in hairy gloves, cheating Isaac of Esau's birthright. The burning paper lighted it up.

"'Tis only a confession, Mr. Atterbury," said the young man. He leaned his head against the mantelpiece: a burst of tears came to his eyes. They were the first he had shed as he sat by his lord, scared by this calamity, and more yet by what the poor dying gentleman had told him, and shocked to think that he should be the agent of bringing this double misfortune on those he loved best.

"Let us go to him," said Mr. Esmond. And accordingly they went into the next chamber, where by this time the dawn had broke, which showed my Lord's poor pale face and wild appealing eyes, that wore that awful fatal look of coming dissolution. The surgeon was with him. He went into the chamber as Atterbury came out thence. My Lord Viscount turned round his sick eyes towards Esmond. It choked the other to hear that rattle in his throat.

"My Lord Viscount," says Mr. Atterbury, "Mr. Esmond wants no witnesses, and hath burned the paper."

"My dearest master!" Esmond said, kneeling down, and taking his hand and kissing it.

My Lord Viscount sprang up in his bed, and flung his arms round Esmond. "God bl—bless——" was all he said. The blood rushed from his mouth, deluging the young man. My dearest Lord was no more. He was gone with a blessing on his lips, and love and repentance and kindness in his manly heart.

"Benedicti benedicentes," says Mr. Atterbury, and the young man, kneeling at the bedside, groaned out an "Amen."

"Who shall take the news to her?" was Mr. Esmond's next thought. And on this he besought Mr. Atterbury to bear the tidings to Castlewood. He could not face his mistress himself with those dreadful news. Mr. Atterbury complying kindly, Esmond writ a hasty note on his table-book to my Lord's man, bidding him get the horses for Mr. Atterbury, and ride with him, and send Esmond's own valise to the Gatehouse prison, whither he resolved to go and give himself up.

BOOK II

CONTAINS MR. ESMOND'S MILITARY LIFE, AND OTHER MATTERS APPERTAINING TO THE ESMOND FAMILY

CHAPTER I

I AM IN PRISON, AND VISITED, BUT NOT CONSOLED THERE

THOSE may imagine, who have seen death untimely strike down persons revered and beloved, and know how unavailing consolation is, what was Harry Esmond's anguish after being an actor in that ghastly midnight scene of blood and homicide. He could not, he felt, have faced his dear mistress, and told her that story. He was thankful that kind Atterbury consented to break the sad news to her; but, besides his grief, which he took into prison with him, he had that in his heart which secretly cheered and consoled him.

A great secret had been told to Esmond by his unhappy stricken kinsman, lying on his death-bed. Were he to disclose it, as in equity and honour he might do, the discovery would but bring greater grief upon those whom he loved best in the world, and who were sad enough already. Should he bring down shame and perplexity upon all those beings to whom he was attached by so many tender ties of affection and gratitude? degrade his father's widow? impeach and sully his father's and kinsman's honour? and for what? For a barren title, to be worn at the expense of an innocent boy, the son of his dearest benefactress. He had debated this matter in his conscience, whilst his poor lord was making his dying confession. On one side were ambition, temptation, justice even; but love, gratitude, and fidelity pleaded on the other. And when the struggle was over in Harry's mind, a glow of righteous happiness filled it; and it was with grateful tears in his eyes that he returned thanks to God for that decision which he had been enabled to make.

"When I was denied by my own blood," thought he, "these dearest friends received and cherished me. When I was a nameless orphan myself, and needed a protector, I found one in yonder kind soul, who has gone to his account repenting of the innocent wrong he has done."

And with this consoling thought he went away to give himself up at the prison, after kissing the cold lips of his benefactor.

It was on the third day after he had come to the Gatehouse prison (where he lay in no small pain from his wound, which inflamed and ached severely), and with those thoughts and resolutions that have been just spoke of, to depress, and yet to console him, that H. Esmond's keeper came and told him that a visitor was asking for him, and though he could not see her face, which was enveloped in a black hood, her whole figure, too, being veiled and covered with the deepest mourning, Esmond knew at once that his visitor was his dear mistress.

He got up from his bed, where he was lying, being very weak; and advancing towards her as the retiring keeper shut the door upon him and his guest in that sad place, he put forward his left hand (for the right was wounded and bandaged), and he would have taken that kind one of his mistress, which had done so many offices of friendship for him for so many years.

But the Lady Castlewood went back from him, putting back her hood, and leaning against the great stanchioned door which the gaoler had just closed upon them. Her face was ghastly white, as Esmond saw it, looking from the hood; and her eyes, ordinarily so sweet and tender, were fixed on him with such a tragic glance of woe and anger, as caused the young man, unaccustomed to unkindness from that person, to avert his own glances from her face.

"And this, Mr. Esmond," she said, "is where I see you; and 'tis to this you have brought me!"

"You have come to console me in my calamity, madam," said he (though, in truth, he scarce knew how to address her, his emotions at beholding her so overpowered him).

She advanced a little, but stood silent and trembling, looking out at him from her black draperies, with her small white hands clasped together, and quivering lips and hollow eyes.

"Not to reproach me," he continued after a pause. "My grief is sufficient as it is."

"Take back your hand—do not touch me with it!" she cried. "Look! there's blood on it!"

"I wish they had taken it all," said Esmond; "if you are unkind to me."

"Where is my husband?" she broke out. "Give me back my husband, Henry! Why did you stand by at midnight and see him murdered? Why did the traitor escape who did it? You, the champion of our house, who offered to die for us! You that he loved and trusted, and to whom I confided him—you that vowed devotion and gratitude, and I believed you—yes, I believed you—why are you here, and my noble Francis gone? Why did you come among us? You have only brought us grief and sorrow; and repentance, bitter, bitter repentance, as a return for our love and kindness. Did I ever do you a wrong, Henry? You were but an orphan child when I first saw you—when *he* first saw you, who was so good, and noble, and trusting. He would have had you sent away, but, like a foolish woman, I besought him to let you stay. And you pretended to love us, and we believed you—and you made our house wretched, and my husband's heart went from me: and I lost him through you—I lost him—the husband of my youth, I say. I worshipped him: you know I worshipped him—and he was changed to me. He was no more my Francis of old—my dear, dear soldier. He loved me before he saw you; and I loved him. Oh, God is my witness how I loved him! Why did he not send you from among us? 'Twas only his kindness, that could refuse me nothing then. And, young as you were—yes, and weak and alone—there was evil, I knew there was evil in keeping you. I read it in your face and eyes. I saw that they boded harm to us—and it came, I knew it would. Why did you not die when you had the smallpox—and I came myself and watched you, and you didn't know me in your delirium—and you called out for me, though I was there at your side? All that has happened since was a just judgment on my wicked heart—my wicked jealous heart. Oh, I am punished—awfully punished! My husband lies in his blood—murdered for defending me, my kind, kind, generous lord—and you were by, and you let him die, Henry!"

These words, uttered in the wildness of her grief by one who was ordinarily quiet, and spoke seldom except with a gentle smile and a soothing tone, rung in Esmond's ear; and 'tis said that he repeated many of them in the fever into which he now fell from his wound, and perhaps from the emotion which such passionate, undeserved upbraidings caused him. It seemed as if his very sacrifices and love for this lady and her family were to turn to evil and reproach: as if his presence amongst them was indeed a cause of grief, and the continuance of his life but woe and bitterness to theirs. As the Lady Castlewood spoke bitterly, rapidly, without a tear, he never offered a word of appeal or remonstrance: but sat at the foot of his prison-bed, stricken only with the more pain at thinking it was that soft and beloved hand which should stab him so cruelly, and powerless against her fatal sorrow. Her words as she spoke struck the chords of all his memory, and the whole of his boyhood and youth passed within him; whilst his lady, so fond and gentle but yesterday—this good angel whom he had loved and worshipped—stood before him, pursuing him with keen words and aspect malign.

"I wish I were in my Lord's place," he groaned out. "It was not my fault that I was not there, madam. But Fate is stronger than all of us, and willed what has come to pass. It had been better for me to have died when I had the illness."

"Yes, Henry," said she—and as she spoke she looked at him with a glance that was at once so fond and so sad, that the young man, tossing up his arms, wildly fell back, hiding his head in the coverlet of the bed. As he turned he struck against the wall with his wounded hand, displacing the ligature; and he felt the blood rushing again from the wound. He remembered feeling a secret pleasure at the accident—and thinking, "Suppose I were to end now, who would grieve for me?"

This hemorrhage, or the grief and despair in which the luckless young man was at the time of the accident, must have brought on a deliquium presently; for he had scarce any recollection afterwards, save of some one, his mistress probably, seizing his hand—and then of the buzzing noise in his ears as he awoke, with two or three persons of the prison around his bed, whereon he lay in a pool of blood from his arm.

It was now bandaged up again by the prison surgeon, who happened to be in the place; and the governor's wife and servant, kind people both, were with the patient. Esmond saw his mistress still in the room when he awoke from his trance; but she went away without a word; though the governor's wife told him that she sat in her room for some time afterward, and did not leave the prison until she heard that Esmond was likely to do well.

Days afterwards, when Esmond was brought out of a fever which he had, and which attacked him that night pretty sharply, the honest keeper's wife brought her patient a handkerchief fresh washed and ironed, and at the corner of which he recognised his mistress's well-known cipher and viscountess's crown. "The lady had bound it round his arm when he fainted, and before she called for help," the keeper's wife said. "Poor lady! she took on sadly about her husband. He has been buried to-day, and a many of the coaches of the nobility went with him—my Lord Marlborough's and my Lord Sunderland's, and many of the officers of the Guards, in which he served in the old King's time; and my Lady has been with her two children to the King at Kensington, and asked for justice against my Lord Mohun, who is in hiding, and my Lord the Earl of Warwick and Holland, who is ready to give himself up and take his trial."

Such was the news, coupled with assertions about her own honesty and that of Molly her maid, who would never have stolen a certain trumpery gold sleeve-button of Mr. Esmond's that was missing after his fainting-fit, that the keeper's wife brought to her lodger. His thoughts followed to that untimely grave the brave heart, the kind friend, the gallant gentleman, honest of word and generous of thought if feeble of purpose (but are his betters much stronger than he?), who had given him bread and shelter when he had none; home and love when he needed them; and who, if he had kept one vital secret from him, had done that of which he repented ere dying—a wrong indeed, but one followed by remorse, and occasioned by almost irresistible temptation.

Esmond took the handkerchief when his nurse left him, and very likely kissed it, and looked at the bauble embroidered in the corner. "It has cost thee grief enough," he thought, "dear lady, so loving and so tender. Shall I take it from thee and thy children? No, never! Keep it, and wear it, my little Frank, my pretty boy! If I cannot make a name for myself, I can die without one. Some day, when my dear mistress sees my heart, I shall be righted; or if not here or now, why, elsewhere; where Honour doth not follow us, but where Love reigns perpetual."

'Tis needless to relate here, as the reports of the lawyers already have chronicled them, the particulars or issue of that trial which ensued upon my Lord Castlewood's melancholy homicide. Of the two lords engaged in that sad matter, the second, my Lord the Earl of Warwick and Holland, who had been engaged with Colonel Westbury, and wounded by him, was found not guilty by his peers, before whom he was tried (under the presidence of the Lord Steward, Lord Somers); and the principal, the Lord Mohun, being found guilty of the manslaughter (which, indeed, was forced upon him, and of which he repented most sincerely), pleaded his clergy, and so was discharged without any penalty. The widow of the slain nobleman, as it was told us in prison, showed an extraordinary spirit; and, though she had to wait for ten years before her son was old enough to compass it, declared she would have revenge of her husband's murderer. So much and suddenly had grief, anger, and misfortune appeared to change her. But fortune, good or ill, as I take it, does not change men and women. It but develops their character. As there are a thousand thoughts lying within a man that he does not know till he takes up the pen to write, so the heart is a secret even to him (or her) who has it in his own breast. Who hath not found himself surprised into revenge, or action, or passion, for good or evil, whereof the seeds lay within him, latent and unsuspected, until the occasion called them forth?

With the death of her lord, a change seemed to come over the whole conduct and mind of Lady Castlewood; but of this we shall speak in the right season and anon.

The lords being tried then before their peers at Westminster, according to their privilege, being brought from the Tower with state processions and barges, and accompanied by lieutenants and axemen, the commoners engaged in that melancholy fray took their trial at Newgate, as became them; and, being all found guilty, pleaded likewise their benefit of clergy. The sentence, as we all know in these cases, is, that the culprit lies a year in prison, or during the King's pleasure, and is burned in the hand, or only stamped with a cold iron; or this part of the punishment is altogether remitted at the grace of the Sovereign. So Harry Esmond found himself a criminal and a prisoner at two-and-twenty years old; as for the two colonels, his comrades, they took the matter very lightly. Duelling was a part of their business; and they could not in honour refuse any invitations of that sort.

But the case was different with Mr. Esmond. His life was changed by that stroke of the sword which destroyed his kind patron's. As he lay in prison, old Doctor Tusher fell ill and died; and Lady Castlewood appointed Thomas Tusher to the vacant living; about the filling of which she had a thousand times fondly talked to Harry Esmond: how they never should part; how he should educate her boy; how to be a country clergyman, like saintly George Herbert or pious Doctor Ken, was the happiest and greatest lot in life; how (if he were obstinately bent on it, though, for her part, she owned rather to holding Queen Bess's opinion, that a bishop should have no wife, and if not a bishop why a clergyman?) she would find a good wife for Harry Esmond; and so on, with a hundred pretty prospects told by fireside evenings, in fond prattle, as the children played about the hall. All these plans were overthrown now. Thomas Tusher wrote to Esmond, as he lay in prison, announcing that his patroness had conferred upon him the living his reverend father had held for many years; that she never, after the tragical events which had occurred (whereof Tom spoke with a very edifying horror), could see in the revered Tusher's pulpit, or at her son's table, the man who was answerable for the father's life; that her Ladyship bade him to say that she prayed for her kinsman's repentance and his worldly happiness; that he was free to command her aid for any scheme of life which he might propose to himself; but that on this side of the grave she would see him no more. And Tusher, for his own part, added that Harry should have his prayers as a friend of his youth, and commended him whilst he was in prison to read certain works of theology, which his Reverence pronounced to be very wholesome for sinners in his lamentable condition.

And this was the return for a life of devotion—this the end of years of affectionate intercourse and passionate fidelity! Harry would have died for his patron, and was held as little better than his murderer: he had sacrificed, she did not know how much, for his mistress, and she threw him aside; he had endowed her family with all they had, and she talked about giving him alms as to a menial! The grief for his patron's loss: the pains of his own present position, and doubts as to the future: all these were forgotten under the sense of the consummate outrage which he had to endure, and overpowered by the superior pang of that torture.

He writ back a letter to Mr. Tusher from his prison, congratulating his Reverence upon his appointment to the living of Castlewood: sarcastically bidding him to follow in the footsteps of his admirable father, whose gown had descended upon him; thanking her Ladyship for her offer of alms, which he said he should trust not to need; and beseeching her to remember that, if ever her determination should change towards him, he would be ready to give her proofs of a fidelity which had never wavered, and which ought never to have been questioned by that house. "And if we meet no more, or only as strangers in this world," Mr. Esmond concluded, "a sentence against the cruelty and injustice of which I disdain to appeal; hereafter she will know who was faithful to her, and whether she had any cause to suspect the love and devotion of her kinsman and servant."

After the sending of this letter, the poor young fellow's mind was more at ease than it had been previously. The blow had been struck, and he had borne it. His cruel goddess had shaken her wings and fled: and left him alone and friendless, but *virtute suâ*. And he had to bear him up, at once the sense of his right and the feeling of his wrongs, his honour and his misfortune. As I have seen men waking and running to arms at a sudden trumpet, before emergency a manly heart leaps up resolute; meets the threatening danger with undaunted countenance; and, whether conquered or conquering, faces it always. Ah! no man knows his strength or his weakness, till occasion proves them. If there be some thoughts and actions of his life from the memory of which a man shrinks with shame, sure there are some which he may be proud to own and remember: forgiven injuries, conquered temptations (now and then), and difficulties vanquished by endurance.

It was these thoughts regarding the living, far more than any great poignancy of grief respecting the dead, which affected Harry Esmond whilst in prison after his trial: but it may be imagined that he could take no comrade of misfortune into the confidence of his feelings, and they thought it was remorse and sorrow for his patron's loss which affected the young man, in error of which opinion he chose to leave them. As a companion he was so moody and silent that the two officers, his fellow-sufferers, left him to himself mostly, liked little very likely what they knew of him, consoled themselves with dice, cards, and the bottle, and whiled away their own captivity in their own way. It seemed to Esmond as if he lived years in that prison: and was changed and aged when he came out of it. At certain periods of life we live years of emotion in a few weeks—and look back on those times, as on great gaps between the old life and the new. You do not know how much you suffer in those critical maladies of the heart, until the disease is over and you look back on it afterwards. During the time, the suffering is at least sufferable. The day passes in more or less of pain, and the night wears away somehow. 'Tis only in after days that we see what the danger has been—as a man out a-hunting or riding for his life looks at a leap, and wonders how he should have survived the taking of it. O dark months of grief and rage! of wrong and cruel endurance! He is old now who recalls you. Long ago he has forgiven and blest the soft hand that wounded him: but the mark is there, and the wound is cicatrised only — no time, tears, caresses, or repentance can obliterate the scar. We are indocile to put up with grief, however. *Reficimus rates quassas:* we tempt the ocean again and again, and try upon new ventures. Esmond thought of his early time as a noviciate, and of this past trial as an initiation before entering into life—as our young Indians undergo tortures silently before they pass to the rank of warriors in the tribe.

The officers, meanwhile, who were not let into the secret of the grief which was gnawing at the side of their silent young friend, and being accustomed to such transactions, in which one comrade or another was daily paying the forfeit of the sword, did not, of course, bemoan themselves very inconsolably about the fate of their late companion in arms. This one told stories of former adventures of love, or war, or pleasure, in which poor Frank Esmond had been engaged; t'other recollected how a constable had been bilked, or a tavern-bully beaten: whilst my Lord's poor widow was sitting at his tomb worshipping him as an actual saint and spotless hero —so the visitors said who had news of Lady Castlewood; and Westbury and Macartney had pretty nearly had all the town to come and see them.

The duel, its fatal termination, the trial of the two peers and the three commoners concerned, had caused the greatest excitement in the town. The prints and news-letters were full of them. The three gentlemen in Newgate were almost as much crowded as the Bishops in the Tower, or a highwayman before execution. We were allowed to live in the Governor's house, as hath been said, both before trial and after condemnation, waiting the King's pleasure; nor was the real cause of the fatal quarrel known, so closely had my Lord and the two other persons who knew it kept the secret, but every one imagined that the origin of the meeting was a gambling dispute. Except fresh air, the prisoners had, upon payment, most things they could desire. Interest was made that they should not mix with the vulgar convicts, whose ribald choruses and loud laughter and curses could be heard from their own part of the prison, where they and the miserable debtors were confined pell-mell.

CHAPTER II

I COME TO THE END OF MY CAPTIVITY, BUT NOT OF MY TROUBLE

AMONG the company which came to visit the two officers was an old acquaintance of Harry Esmond; that gentleman of the Guards, namely, who had been so kind to Harry when Captain Westbury's troop had been quartered at Castlewood more than seven years before. Dick the Scholar was no longer Dick the Trooper now, but Captain Steele of Lucas's Fusileers, and secretary to my Lord Cutts, that famous officer of King William's, the bravest and most beloved man of the English army. The two jolly prisoners had been drinking with a party of friends (for our cellar, and that of the keepers of Newgate too, were supplied with endless hampers of burgundy and champagne that the friends of the Colonels sent in); and Harry, having no wish for their drink or their conversation, being too feeble in health for the one and too sad in spirits for the other, was sitting apart in his little room, reading such books as he had, one evening, when honest Colonel Westbury, flushed with liquor, and always good-humoured in and out of his cups, came laughing into Harry's closet and said, "Ho, young Killjoy! here's a friend come to see thee; he'll pray with thee, or he'll drink with thee; or he'll drink and pray turn about. Dick, my Christian hero, here's the little scholar of Castlewood."

Dick came up and kissed Esmond on both cheeks, imparting a strong perfume of burnt sack along with his caress to the young man.

"What! is this the little man that used to talk Latin and fetch our bowls? How tall thou art grown! I protest I should have known thee anywhere. And so you have turned ruffian and fighter; and wanted to measure swords with Mohun, did you? I protest that Mohun said at the Guard dinner yesterday, where there was a pretty company of us, that the young fellow wanted to fight him, and was the better man of the two."

"I wish we could have tried and proved it, Mr. Steele," says Esmond, thinking of his dead benefactor, and his eyes filling with tears.

With the exception of that one cruel letter which he had from his mistress, Mr. Esmond heard nothing from her, and she seemed determined to execute her resolve of parting from him and disowning him. But he had news of her, such as it was, which Mr. Steele assiduously brought him from the Prince's and Princess's Court, where our honest Captain had been advanced to the post of gentleman waiter. When off duty there, Captain Dick often came to console his friends in captivity; a good nature and a friendly disposition towards all who were in ill-fortune no doubt prompting him to make his visits, and good-fellowship and good wine to prolong them.

"Faith," says Westbury, "the little scholar was the first to begin the quarrel—I mind me of it now—at Lockit's. I always hated that fellow Mohun. What was the real cause of the quarrel betwixt him and poor Frank? I would wager 'twas a woman."

"'Twas a quarrel about play—on my word, about play," Harry said. "My poor lord lost great sums to his guest at Castlewood. Angry words passed between them; and though Lord Castlewood was the kindest and most pliable soul alive, his spirit was very high; and hence that meeting which has brought us all here," says Mr. Esmond, resolved never to acknowledge that there had ever been any other cause but cards for the duel.

"I do not like to use bad words of a nobleman," says Westbury; "but if my Lord Mohun were a commoner, I would say, 'twas a pity he was not hanged. He was familiar with dice and women at a time other boys are at school being birched; he was as wicked as the oldest rake, years ere he had done growing; and handled a sword and a foil, and a bloody one too, before he ever used a razor. He held poor Will Mountford in talk that night when bloody Dick Hill ran him through. He will come to a bad end, will that young lord; and no end is bad enough for him," says honest Mr. Westbury: whose prophecy was fulfilled twelve years after, upon that fatal day when Mohun fell, dragging down one of the bravest and greatest gentlemen in England in his fall.

From Mr. Steele, then, who brought the public rumour, as well as his own private intelligence, Esmond learned the movements of his unfortunate mistress. Steele's heart was of very inflammable composition; and the gentleman usher spoke in terms of boundless admiration both of the widow (that most beautiful woman, as he said) and of her daughter, who, in the Captain's eyes, was a still greater paragon. If the pale widow, whom Captain Richard, in his poetic rapture compared to a Niobe in tears—to a Sigismunda—to a weeping Belvidera—was an object the most lovely and pathetic which his eyes had ever beheld, or for which his heart had melted, even her ripened perfections and beauty were as nothing compared to the promise of that extreme loveliness which the good Captain saw in her daughter. It was *matre pulcra, filia pulcrior.* Steele composed sonnets whilst he was on duty in his Prince's antechamber, to the maternal and filial charms. He would speak for hours about them to Harry Esmond; and, indeed, he could have chosen few subjects more likely to interest the unhappy young man, whose heart was now as always devoted to these ladies; and who was thankful to all who loved them, or praised them, or wished them well.

Not that his fidelity was recompensed by any answering kindness, or show of relenting even, on the part of a mistress obdurate now after ten years of love and benefactions. The poor young man getting no answer, save Tusher's, to that letter which he had written, and being too proud to write more, opened a part of his heart to Steele, than whom no man, when unhappy, could find a kinder hearer, or more friendly emissary; described (in words which were no doubt pathetic, for they came *imo pectore*, and caused honest Dick to weep plentifully) his youth, his constancy, his fond devotion to that household which had reared him; his affection, how earned, and how tenderly requited until but yesterday, and (as far as he might) the circumstances and causes for which that sad quarrel had made of Esmond a prisoner under sentence, a widow and orphans of those whom in life he held dearest. In terms that might well move a harder-hearted man than young Esmond's confidant—for, indeed, the speaker's own heart was half broke as he uttered them—he described a part of what had taken place in that only sad interview which his mistress had granted him; how she had left him with anger and almost imprecation, whose words and thoughts until then had been only blessing and kindness; how she had accused him of the guilt of that blood, in exchange for which he would cheerfully have sacrificed his own (indeed, in this the Lord Mohun, the Lord Warwick, and all the gentlemen engaged, as well as the common rumour out of doors—Steele told him—bore out the luckless young man); and with all his heart, and tears, he besought Mr. Steele to inform his mistress of her kinsman's unhappiness, and to deprecate that cruel anger she showed him. Half frantic with grief at the injustice done him, and contrasting it with a thousand soft recollections of love and confidence gone by, that made his present misery inexpressibly more bitter, the poor wretch passed many a lonely day and wakeful night in a kind of powerless despair and rage against his iniquitous fortune. It was the softest hand that struck him, the gentlest and most compassionate nature that persecuted him. "I would as lief," he said, "have pleaded guilty to the murder, and have suffered for it like any other felon, as have to endure the torture to which my mistress subjects me."

Although the recital of Esmond's story, and his passionate appeals and remonstrances, drew so many tears from Dick who heard them, they had no effect upon the person whom they were designed to move. Esmond's ambassador came back from the mission with which the poor young gentleman had charged him, with a sad blank face and a shake of the head, which told that there was no hope for the prisoner; and scarce a wretched culprit in that prison of Newgate ordered for execution, and trembling for a reprieve, felt more cast down than Mr. Esmond, innocent and condemned.

As had been arranged between the prisoner and his counsel in their consultations, Mr. Steele had gone to the Dowager's house in Chelsey, where it has been said the widow and her orphans were, had seen my Lady Viscountess, and pleaded the cause of her unfortunate kinsman. "And I think I spoke well, my poor boy," says Mr. Steele; "for who would not speak well in such a cause, and before so beautiful a judge? I did not see the lovely Beatrix (sure her famous namesake of Florence was never half so beautiful), only the young Viscount was in the room with the Lord Churchill, my Lord of Marlborough's eldest son. But these young gentlemen went off to the garden; I could see them from the window tilting at each other with poles in a mimic tournament (grief touches the young but lightly, and I remember that I beat a drum at the coffin of my own father). My Lady Viscountess looked out at the two boys at their game and said, 'You see, sir, children are taught to use weapons of death as toys, and to make a sport of murder;' and as she spoke she looked so lovely, and stood there in herself so sad and beautiful an instance of that doctrine whereof I am a humble preacher, that had I not dedicated my little volume of the 'Christian Hero'—(I perceive, Harry, thou hast not cut the leaves of it. The sermon is good, believe me, though the preacher's life may not answer it)—I say, hadn't I dedicated the volume to Lord Cutts, I would have asked permission to place her Ladyship's name on the first page. I think I never saw such a beautiful violet as that of her eyes, Harry. Her complexion is of the pink of the blush-rose, she hath an exquisite turned wrist, and dimpled hand, and I make no doubt——"

"Did you come to tell me about the dimples on my Lady's hand?" broke out Mr. Esmond sadly.

"A lovely creature in affliction seems always doubly beautiful to me," says the poor Captain, who indeed was but too often in a state to see double, and so checked he resumed the interrupted thread of his story. "As I spoke my business," Mr. Steele said, "and narrated to your mistress what all the world knows, and the other side hath been eager to acknowledge—that you had tried to put yourself between the two lords, and to take your patron's quarrel on your own point; I recounted the general praises of your gallantry, besides my Lord Mohun's particular testimony to it; I thought the widow listened with some interest, and her eyes—I have never seen such a violet, Harry—looked up at mine once or twice. But after I had spoken on this theme for a while she suddenly broke away with a cry of grief. 'I would to God, sir,' she said, 'I had never heard that word gallantry which you use, or known the meaning of it. My Lord might have been here but for that; my home might be happy; my poor boy have a father. It was what you gentlemen call gallantry came into my home, and drove my husband on to the cruel sword that killed him. You should not speak the word to a Christian woman, sir, a poor widowed mother of orphans, whose home was happy until the world came into it—the wicked godless world, that takes the blood of the innocent, and lets the guilty go free.'

"As the afflicted lady spoke in this strain, sir," Mr. Steele continued, "it seemed as if indignation moved her, even more than grief. 'Compensation!' she went on passionately, her cheeks and eyes kindling; 'what compensation does your world give the widow for her husband, and the children for the murder of their father? The wretch who did the deed has not even a punishment. Conscience! what conscience has he, who can enter the house of a friend, whisper falsehood and insult to a woman that never harmed him, and stab the kind heart that trusted him? My Lord—my Lord Wretch's, my Lord Villain's, my Lord Murderer's peers meet to try him, and they dismiss him with a word or two of reproof, and send him into the world again, to pursue women with lust and falsehood, and to murder unsuspecting guests that harbour him. That day, my Lord—my Lord Murderer—(I will never name him)—was let loose, a woman was executed at Tyburn for stealing in a shop. But a man may rob another of his life, or a lady of her honour, and shall pay no penalty! I take my child, run to the throne, and on my knees ask for justice, and the King refuses me. The King! he is no king of mine—he never shall be. He, too, robbed the throne from the king his father—the true king—and he has gone unpunished, as the great do.'

"I then thought to speak for you," Mr. Steele continued, "and I interposed by saying, 'There was one, madam, who, at least, would have put his own breast between your husband's and my Lord Mohun's sword. Your poor young kinsman, Harry Esmond, hath told me that he tried to draw the quarrel on himself.'

"'Are you come from *him?*' asked the lady (so Mr. Steele went on), rising up with a great severity and stateliness. 'I thought you had come from the Princess. I saw Mr. Esmond in his prison, and bade him farewell. He brought misery into my house. He never should have entered it.'

"'Madam, madam, he is not to blame,' I interposed," continued Mr. Steele.

"'Do I blame him to you, sir?' asked the widow. 'If 'tis he who sent you, say that I have taken counsel, where'—she spoke with a very pallid cheek now, and a break in her voice—'where all who ask may have it;—and that it bids me to part from him, and to see him no more. We met in the prison for the last time—at least for years to come. It may be, in years hence, when—when our knees and our tears and our contrition have changed our sinful hearts, sir, and wrought our pardon, we may meet again—but not now. After what has passed, I could not bear to see him. I wish him well, sir; but I wish him farewell too; and if he has that—that regard towards us which he speaks of, I beseech him to prove it by obeying me in this.'

"'I shall break the young man's heart, madam, by this hard sentence,'" Mr. Steele said.

"The lady shook her head," continued my kind scholar. "'The hearts of young men, Mr. Steele, are not so made,' she said. 'Mr. Esmond will find other—other friends. The mistress of this house has relented very much towards the late lord's son,' she added with a blush, 'and has promised me,—that is, has promised that she will care for his fortune. Whilst I live in it, after the horrid, horrid deed which has passed, Castlewood must never be a home to him—never. Nor would I have him write to me—except—no—I would have him never write to me, nor see him more. Give him, if you will, my parting—— Hush! not a word of this before my daughter.'

"Here the fair Beatrix entered from the river, with her cheeks flushing with health, and looking only the more lovely and fresh for the mourning habiliments which she wore. And my Lady Viscountess said—

"'Beatrix, this is Mr. Steele, gentleman-usher to the Prince's Highness. When does your new comedy appear, Mr. Steele?' I hope thou wilt be out of prison for the first night, Harry."

The sentimental Captain concluded his sad tale, saying, "Faith, the beauty of *filia pulcrior* drove *pulcram matrem* out of my head! and yet as I came down the river, and thought about the pair, the pallid dignity and exquisite grace of the matron had the uppermost, and I thought her even more noble than the virgin!"

The party of prisoners lived very well in Newgate, and with comforts very different to those which were awarded to the poor wretches there (his insensibility to their misery, their gaiety still more frightful, their curses and blasphemy, hath struck with a kind of shame since—as proving how selfish, during his imprisonment, his own particular grief was, and how entirely the thoughts of it absorbed him): if the three gentlemen lived well under the care of the Warden of Newgate, it was because they paid well; and indeed the cost at the dearest ordinary or the grandest tavern in London could not have furnished a longer reckoning, than our host of the "Handcuff Inn"—as Colonel Westbury called it. Our rooms were the three in the gate over Newgate—on the second storey looking up Newgate Street towards Cheapside and Paul's Church. And we had leave to walk on the roof, and could see thence Smithfield and the Bluecoat Boys' School, Gardens, and the Chartreux, where, as Harry Esmond remembered, Dick the Scholar and his friend Tom Tusher had had their schooling.

Harry could never have paid his share of that prodigious heavy reckoning which my landlord brought to his guests once a week: for he had but three pieces in his pockets that fatal night before the duel, when the gentlemen were at cards, and offered to play five. But whilst he was yet ill at the Gatehouse, after Lady Castlewood had visited him there, and before his trial, there came one in an orange-tawny coat and blue lace, the livery which the Esmonds always wore, and brought a sealed packet for Mr. Esmond, which contained twenty guineas, and a note saying that a counsel had been appointed for him, and that more money would be forthcoming whenever he needed it.

'Twas a queer letter from the scholar as she was, or as she called herself: the Dowager Viscountess Castlewood, written in the strange barbarous French which she and many other fine ladies of that time—witness her Grace of Portsmouth—employed. Indeed, spelling was not an article of general commodity in the world then, and my Lord Marlborough's letters can show that he, for one, had but a little share of this part of grammar:—

"Mong Coussin," my Lady Viscountess Dowager wrote, "je scay que vous vous etes bravement batew et grievement bléssay—du costé de feu M. le Vicomte. M. le Compte de Varique ne se playt qua parlay de vous: M. de Moon auçy. Il di que vous avay voulew vous bastre avecque luy—que vous estes plus fort que luy fur l'ayscrimme—quil'y a surtout certaine Botte que vous scavay quil n'a jammay sceu pariay: et que c'en eut été fay de luy si vouseluy vous vous fussiay battews ansamb. Aincy ce pauv Vicompte est mort. Mort et peutayt—Mon coussin, mon coussin! jay dans la tayste que vous n'estes quung pety Monst—angcy que les Esmonds ong tousjours esté. La veuve est chay moy. J'ay recuilly cet' pauve famme. Elle est furieuse cont vous, allans tous les jours chercher ley Roy (d'icy) démandant à gran cri revanche pour son Mary. Elle ne veux voyre ni entende parlay de vous : pourtant elle ne fay qu'en parlay milfoy par jour. Quand vous seray hor prison venay me voyre. J'auray soing de vous. Si cette petite Prude veut se défaire de song pety Monste (Hélas je craing quil ne soy trotar !) je m'en chargeray. J'ay encor quelqu interay et quelques escus de costay.

"La Veuve se raccommode avec Miladi Marlboro qui est tout puiçante avecque la Princesse Anne. Cet dam sentéraysent pour la petite prude ; qui pourtant a un fi du mesme asge que vous savay.

"En sortant de prisong venez icy. Je ne puy vous recevoir chaymoy à cause des méchansetés du monde, may pre du moy vous aurez logement. ISABELLE, VISCOMTESSE D'ESMOND."

Marchioness of Esmond this lady sometimes called herself, in virtue of that patent which had been given by the late King James to Harry Esmond's father ; and in this state she had her train carried by a knight's wife, a cup and cover of assay to drink from, and fringed cloth.

He who was of the same age as little Francis, whom we shall henceforth call Viscount Castlewood here, was H.R.H. the Prince of Wales, born in the same year and month with Frank, and just proclaimed, at Saint Germains, King of Great Britain, France, and Ireland.

CHAPTER III

I TAKE THE QUEEN'S PAY IN QUIN'S REGIMENT

THE fellow in the orange-tawny livery with blue lace and facings was in waiting when Esmond came out of prison, and, taking the young gentleman's slender baggage, led the way out of that odious Newgate, and by Fleet Conduit, down to the Thames, where a pair of oars was called, and they went up the river to Chelsey. Esmond thought the sun had never shone so bright; nor the air felt so fresh and exhilarating. Temple Garden, as they rowed by, looked like the garden of Eden to him, and the aspect of the quays, wharves, and buildings by the river, Somerset House, and Westminster (where the splendid new bridge was just beginning), Lambeth tower and palace, and that busy shining scene of the Thames swarming with boats and barges, filled his heart with pleasure and cheerfulness—as well such a beautiful scene might to one who had been a prisoner so long, and with so many dark thoughts deepening the gloom of his captivity. They rowed up at length to the pretty village of Chelsey, where the nobility have many handsome country houses; and so came to my Lady Viscountess's house, a cheerful new house in the row facing the river, with a handsome garden behind it, and a pleasant look-out both towards Surrey and Kensington, where stands the noble ancient palace of the Lord Warwick, Harry's reconciled adversary.

Here in her Ladyship's saloon, the young man saw again some of those pictures which had been at Castlewood, and which she had removed thence on the death of her lord, Harry's father. Specially, and in the place of honour, was Sir Peter Lely's picture of the Honourable Mistress Isabella Esmond as Diana, in yellow satin, with a bow in her hand and a crescent in her forehead; and dogs frisking about her. 'Twas painted about the time when royal Endymions were said to find favour with this virgin huntress; and, as goddesses have youth perpetual, this one believed to the day of her death that she never grew older: and always persisted in supposing the picture was still like her.

After he had been shown to her room by the groom of the chamber, who filled many offices besides in her Ladyship's modest household, and after a proper interval, his elderly goddess Diana vouchsafed to appear to the young man. A blackamoor in a Turkish habit, with red boots and a silver collar, on which the Viscountess's arms were engraven, preceded her and bore her cushion; then came her gentlewoman; a little pack of spaniels barking and frisking about preceded the austere huntress—then, behold, the Viscountess herself "dropping odours." Esmond recollected from his childhood that rich aroma of musk which his mother-in-law (for she may be called so) exhaled. As the sky grows redder and redder towards sunset, so, in the decline of her years, the cheeks of my Lady Dowager blushed more deeply. Her face was illuminated with vermilion, which appeared the brighter from the white paint employed to set it off. She wore the ringlets which had been in fashion in King Charles's time; whereas the ladies of King William's had head-dresses like the towers of Cybele. Her eyes gleamed out from the midst of this queer structure of paint, dyes, and pomatums. Such was my Lady Viscountess, Mr. Esmond's father's widow.

He made her such a profound bow as her dignity and relationship merited, and advanced with the greatest gravity, and once more kissed that hand, upon the trembling knuckles of which glittered a score of rings—remembering old times when that trembling hand made him tremble. "Marchioness," says he, bowing, and on one knee, "is it only the hand I may have the honour of saluting?" For, accompanying that inward laughter, which the sight of such an astonishing old figure might well produce in the young man, there was good-will too, and the kindness of consanguinity. She had been his father's wife, and was his grandfather's daughter. She had suffered him in old day's, and was kind to him now after her fashion. And now that bar-sinister was removed from Esmond's thought, and that secret opprobrium no longer cast upon his mind, he was pleased to feel family ties and own them—perhaps secretly vain of the sacrifice he had made, and to think that he, Esmond, was really the chief of his house, and only prevented by his own magnanimity from advancing his claim.

At least, ever since he had learned that secret from his poor patron on his dying bed, actually as he was standing beside it, he had felt an independency which he had never known before, and which since did not desert him. So he called his old aunt Marchioness, but with an air as if he was the Marquis of Esmond who so addressed her.

Did she read in the young gentleman's eyes, which had now no fear of hers or their superannuated authority, that he knew or suspected the truth about his birth? She gave a start of surprise at his altered manner: indeed, it was quite a different bearing to that of the Cambridge student who had paid her a visit two years since, and whom she had dismissed with five pieces sent by the groom of the chamber. She eyed him, then trembled a little more than was her wont, perhaps, and said, "Welcome, cousin," in a frightened voice.

His resolution, as has been said before, had been quite different, namely, so to bear himself through life as if the secret of his birth was not known to him; but he suddenly and rightly determined on a different course. He asked that her Ladyship's attendants should be dismissed, and when they were private: "Welcome, nephew, at least, madam, it should be," he said. "A great wrong has been done to me and to you, and to my poor mother who is no more."

"I declare before Heaven that I was guiltless of it," she cried out, giving up her cause at once. "It was your wicked father who——"

"Who brought this dishonour on our family," says Mr. Esmond. "I know it full well. I want to disturb no one. Those who are in present possession have been my dearest benefactors, and are quite innocent of intentional wrong to me. The late lord, my dear patron, knew not the truth until a few months before his death, when Father Holt brought the news to him."

"The wretch! he had it in confession! he had it in confession!" cried out the Dowager Lady.

"Not so. He learned it elsewhere as well as in confession," Mr. Esmond answered. "My father, when wounded at the Boyne, told the truth to a French priest, who was in hiding after the battle, as well as to the priest there, at whose house he died. This gentleman did not think fit to divulge the story till he met with Mr. Holt at Saint Omer's. And the latter kept it back for his own purpose, and until he had learned whether my mother was alive or no. She is dead years since, my poor patron told me with his dying breath, and I doubt him not. I do not know even whether I could prove a marriage. I would not if I could. I do not care to bring shame on our name, or grief upon those whom I love, however hardly they may use me. My father's son, madam, won't aggravate the wrong my father did you. Continue to be his widow, and give me your kindness. 'Tis all I ask from you; and I shall never speak of this matter again."

"Mais vous êtes un noble jeune homme!" breaks out my Lady, speaking, as usual with her when she was agitated, in the French language.

"Noblesse oblige," says Mr. Esmond, making her a low bow.

"There are those alive to whom, in return for their love to me, I often fondly said I would give my life away. Shall I be their enemy now, and quarrel about a title? What matters who has it? 'Tis with the family still."

"What can there be in that little prude of a woman that makes men so *raffoler* about her?" cries out my Lady Dowager. "She was here for a month petitioning the King. She is pretty, and well conserved; but she has not the *bel air*. In his late Majesty's Court all the men pretended to admire her, and she was no better than a little wax doll. She is better now, and looks the sister of her daughter; but what mean you all by bepraising her? Mr. Steele, who was in waiting on Prince George, seeing her with her two children going to Kensington, writ a poem about her, and says he shall wear her colours, and dress in black for the future. Mr. Congreve says he will write a 'Mourning Widow,' that shall be better than his 'Mourning Bride.' Though their husbands quarrelled and fought when that wretch Churchill deserted the King (for which he deserved to be hung), Lady Marlborough has again gone wild about the little widow; insulted me in my own drawing-room, by saying that 'twas not the *old* widow, but the young Viscountess, she had come to see. Little Castlewood and little Lord Churchill are to be sworn friends, and have boxed each other twice or thrice like brothers already. 'Twas that wicked young Mohun who, coming back from the provinces last year, where he had disinterred her, raved about her all the winter; said she was a pearl set before swine; and killed poor stupid Frank. The quarrel was all about his wife. I know 'twas all about her. Was there anything between her and Mohun, nephew? Tell me now—was there anything? About yourself, I do not ask you to answer questions."

Mr. Esmond blushed up. "My Lady's virtue is like that of a saint in heaven," he cried out.

"Eh! mon neveu. Many saints get to heaven after having a deal to repent of. I believe you are like all the rest of the fools, and madly in love with her."

"Indeed, I loved and honoured her before all the world," Esmond answered. "I take no shame in that."

"And she has shut her door on you—given the living to that horrid young cub, son of that horrid old bear, Tusher, and says she will never see you more. Monsieur mon neveu—we are all like that. When I was a young woman, I'm positive that a thousand duels were fought about me. And when poor Monsieur de Souchy drowned himself in the canal at Bruges because I danced with Count Springbock, I couldn't squeeze out a single tear, but danced till five o'clock the next morning. 'Twas the Count—no, 'twas my Lord

Ormond that played the fiddles, and his Majesty did me the honour of dancing all night with me. How you are grown! You have got the *bel air*. You are a black man. Our Esmonds are all black. The little prude's son is fair; so was his father—fair and stupid. You were an ugly little wretch when you came to Castlewood—you were all eyes, like a young crow. We intended you should be a priest. That awful Father Holt—how he used to frighten me when I was ill! I have a comfortable director now—the Abbé Douillette—a dear man. We make meagre on Fridays always. My cook is a devout pious man. You, of course, are of the right way of thinking. They say the Prince of Orange is very ill indeed."

In this way the old Dowager rattled on remorselessly to Mr. Esmond, who was quite astounded with her present volubility, contrasting it with her former haughty behaviour to him. But she had taken him into favour for the moment, and chose not only to like him, as far as her nature permitted, but to be afraid of him; and he found himself to be as familiar with her now as a young man, as, when a boy, he had been timorous and silent. She was as good as her word respecting him. She introduced him to her company, of which she entertained a good deal—of the adherents of King James of course—and a great deal of loud intriguing took place over her card-tables. She presented Mr. Esmond as her kinsman to many persons of honour; she supplied him not illiberally with money, which he had no scruple in accepting from her, considering the relationship which he bore to her, and the sacrifices which he himself was making in behalf of the family. But he had made up his mind to continue at no woman's apron-strings longer; and perhaps had cast about how he should distinguish himself, and make himself a name, which his singular fortune had denied him. A discontent with his former bookish life and quietude,—a bitter feeling of revolt at that slavery in which he had chosen to confine himself for the sake of those whose hardness towards him made his heart bleed,—a restless wish to see men and the world,—led him to think of the military profession: at any rate, to desire to see a few campaigns, and accordingly he pressed his new patroness to get him a pair of colours; and one day had the honour of finding himself appointed an ensign in Colonel Quin's regiment of Fusileers on the Irish establishment.

Mr. Esmond's commission was scarce three weeks old when that accident befell King William which ended the life of the greatest, the wisest, the bravest, and most clement sovereign whom England ever knew. 'Twas the fashion of the hostile party to assail this great Prince's reputation during his life; but the joy which they and all his enemies in Europe showed at his death, is a proof of the terror in which they held him. Young as Esmond was, he was wise enough (and generous enough too, let it be said) to scorn that indecency of gratulation which broke out amongst the followers of King James in London, upon the death of this illustrious prince, this invincible warrior, this wise and moderate statesman. Loyalty to the exiled king's family was traditional, as has been said, in that house to which Mr. Esmond belonged. His father's widow had all her hopes, her sympathies, recollections, prejudices, engaged on King James's side; and was certainly as noisy a conspirator as ever asserted the King's rights, or abused his opponent's, over a quadrille table or a dish of bohea. Her Ladyship's house swarmed with ecclesiastics, in disguise and out; whilst tale-bearers from St. Germains; and quidnuncs that knew the last news from Versailles: nay, the exact force and number of the next expedition which the French King was to send from Dunkirk, and which was to swallow up the Prince of Orange, his army, and his court. She had received the Duke of Berwick when he landed here in '96. She kept the glass he drank from, vowing she never would use it till she drank King James the Third's health in it on his Majesty's return; she had tokens from the Queen, and relics of the saint who, if the story was true, had not always been a saint as far as she and many others were concerned. She believed in the miracles wrought at his tomb, and had a hundred authentic stories of wondrous cures effected by the blessed King's rosaries, the medals which he wore, the locks of his hair, or what not. Esmond remembered a score of marvellous tales which the credulous old woman told him. There was the Bishop of Autun, that was healed of a malady he had for forty years, and which left him after he said mass for the repose of the King's soul. There was Monsieur Marais, a surgeon in Auvergne, who had a palsy in both his legs, which was cured through the King's intercession. There was Philip Pitet, of the Benedictines, who had a suffocating cough, which well-nigh killed him, but he besought relief of Heaven through the merits and intercession of the blessed King, and he straightway felt a profuse sweat breaking out all over him, and was recovered perfectly. And there was the wife of Monsieur Lepervier, dancing-master to the Duke of Saxe Gotha, who was entirely eased of a rheumatism by the King's intercession, of which miracle there could be no doubt, for her surgeon and his apprentice had given their testimony, under oath, that they did not in any way contribute to the cure. Of these tales, and a thousand like them, Mr. Esmond believed as much as he chose. His kinswoman's greater faith had swallow for them all.

The English High Church party did not adopt these legends.

But truth and honour, as they thought, bound them to the exiled King's side; nor had the banished family any warmer supporter than that kind lady of Castlewood, in whose house Esmond was brought up. She influenced her husband, very much more perhaps than my Lord knew, who admired his wife prodigiously though he might be inconstant to her, and who, adverse to the trouble of thinking himself, gladly enough adopted the opinions which she chose for him. To one of her simple and faithful heart, allegiance to any sovereign but the one was impossible. To serve King William for interest's sake would have been a monstrous hypocrisy and treason. Her pure conscience could no more have consented to it than to a theft, a forgery, or any other base action. Lord Castlewood might have been won over, no doubt, but his wife never could: and he submitted his conscience to hers in this case as he did in most others, when he was not tempted too sorely. And it was from his affection and gratitude most likely, and from that eager devotion for his mistress which characterised all Esmond's youth, that the young man subscribed to this, and other articles of faith, which his fond benefactress sent him. Had she been a Whig, he had been one; had she followed Mr. Fox, and turned Quaker, no doubt he would have abjured ruffles and a periwig, and have forsworn swords, lace-coats, and clocked stockings. In the scholars' boyish disputes at the University, where parties ran very high, Esmond was noted as a Jacobite, and very likely from vanity as much as affection took the side of his family.

Almost the whole of the clergy of the country and more than a half of the nation were on this side. Ours is the most loyal people in the world surely; we admire our kings, and are faithful to them long after they have ceased to be true to us. 'Tis a wonder to any one who looks back at the history of the Stuart family to think how they kicked their crowns away from them; how they flung away chances after chances; what treasures of loyalty they dissipated, and how fatally they were bent on consummating their own ruin. If ever men had fidelity, 'twas they; if ever men squandered opportunity, 'twas they; and, of all the enemies they had, they themselves were the most fatal.*

When the Princess Anne succeeded, the wearied nation was glad enough to cry a truce from all these wars, controversies, and conspiracies, and to accept in the person of a Princess of the blood royal a compromise between the parties into which the country was divided. The Tories could serve under her with easy consciences;

* Ὢ πόποι, οἷον δή νυ θεοὺς βροτοὶ αἰτιόωνται·
ἐξ ἡμέων γάρ φασι κάκ' ἔμμεναι, οἱ δὲ καὶ αὐτοὶ
σφῇσιν ἀτασθαλίῃσιν ὑπὲρ μόρον ἄλγε' ἔχουσιν.

though a Tory herself, she represented the triumph of the Whig opinion. The people of England, always liking that their Princes should be attached to their own families, were pleased to think the Princess was faithful to hers; and up to the very last day and hour of her reign, and but for that fatality which he inherited from his fathers along with their claims to the English crown, King James the Third might have worn it. But he neither knew how to wait an opportunity, nor to use it when he had it; he was venturesome when he ought to have been cautious, and cautious when he ought to have dared everything. 'Tis with a sort of rage at his inaptitude that one thinks of his melancholy story. Do the Fates deal more specially with kings than with common men? One is apt to imagine so, in considering the history of that royal race, in whose behalf so much fidelity, so much valour, so much blood were desperately and bootlessly expended.

The King dead then, the Princess Anne (ugly Anne Hyde's daughter, our Dowager at Chelsey called her) was proclaimed by trumpeting heralds all over the town from Westminster to Ludgate Hill, amidst immense jubilations of the people.

Next week my Lord Marlborough was promoted to the Garter, and to be Captain-General of her Majesty's forces at home and abroad. This appointment only inflamed the Dowager's rage, or, as she thought it, her fidelity to her rightful sovereign. "The Princess is but a puppet in the hands of that fury of a woman, who comes into my drawing-room and insults me to my face. What can come to a country that is given over to such a woman?" says the Dowager. "As for that double-faced traitor, my Lord Marlborough, he has betrayed every man and every woman with whom he has had to deal, except his horrid wife, who makes him tremble. 'Tis all over with the country when it has got into the clutches of such wretches as these."

Esmond's old kinswoman saluted the new powers in this way; but some good fortune at last occurred to a family which stood in great need of it, by the advancement of these famous personages, who benefited humbler people that had the luck of being in their favour. Before Mr. Esmond left England in the month of August, and being then at Portsmouth, where he had joined his regiment, and was busy at drill, learning the practice and mysteries of the musket and pike, he heard that a pension on the Stamp Office had been got for his late beloved mistress, and that the young Mistress Beatrix was also to be taken into Court. So much good, at least, had come of the poor widow's visit to London, not revenge upon her husband's enemies, but reconcilement to old friends, who pitied, and seemed inclined to serve her. As for the comrades in prison and the late misfortune, Colonel Westbury was with the Captain-General gone to Holland; Captain Macartney was now at Portsmouth, with his regiment of Fusileers and the force under command of his Grace the Duke of Ormond, bound for Spain it was said; my Lord Warwick was returned home; and Lord Mohun, so far from being punished for the homicide which had brought so much grief and change into the Esmond family, was gone in company of my Lord Macclesfield's splendid embassy to the Elector of Hanover, carrying the Garter to his Highness, and a complimentary letter from the Queen.

CHAPTER IV

RECAPITULATIONS

FROM such fitful lights as could be cast upon his dark history by the broken narrative of his poor patron, torn by remorse and struggling in the last pangs of dissolution, Mr. Esmond had been made to understand so far, that his mother was long since dead; and so there could be no question as regarded her or her honour, tarnished by her husband's desertion and injury, to influence her son in any steps which he might take either for prosecuting or relinquishing his own just claims. It appeared from my poor Lord's hurried confession, that he had been made acquainted with the real facts of the case only two years since, when Mr. Holt visited him, and would have implicated him in one of those many conspiracies by which the secret leaders of King James's party in this country were ever endeavouring to destroy the Prince of Orange's life or power: conspiracies so like murder, so cowardly in the means used, so wicked in the end, that our nation has sure done well in throwing off all allegiance and fidelity to the unhappy family that could not vindicate its right except by such treachery—by such dark intrigue and base agents. There were designs against King William that were no more honourable than the ambushes of cut-throats and footpads. 'Tis humiliating to think that a great Prince, possessed of a great and sacred right, and upholder of a great cause, should have stooped to such baseness of assassination and treasons as are proved by the unfortunate King James's own warrant and sign-manual given to his supporters in this country. What he and they called levying war was, in truth, no better than instigating murder. The noble Prince of Orange burst magnanimously through those feeble meshes of conspiracy in which his enemies tried to envelop him: it seemed as if their cowardly daggers broke upon the breast of his undaunted resolution. After King James's death, the Queen and her people at St. Germains—priests and women for the most part—continued their intrigues in behalf of the young Prince, James the Third, as he was called in France and by his party here (this Prince, or Chevalier de St. George, was born in the same year with Esmond's young pupil Frank, my Lord Viscount's son); and the Prince's affairs, being in the hands of priests and women, were conducted as priests and women will conduct them,—artfully, cruelly, feebly, and to a certain bad issue. The moral of the Jesuits' story I think as wholesome a one as ever was writ: the artfullest, the wisest, the most toilsome and dexterous plot-builders in the world—there always comes a day when the roused public indignation kicks their flimsy edifice down, and sends its cowardly enemies a-flying. Mr. Swift hath finely described that passion for intrigue, that love of secrecy, slander, and lying, which belongs to weak people, hangers-on of weak courts. 'Tis the nature of such to hate and envy the strong, and conspire their ruin; and the conspiracy succeeds very well, and everything presages the satisfactory overthrow of the great victim; until one day Gulliver rouses himself, shakes off the little vermin of an enemy, and walks away unmolested. Ah! the Irish soldiers might well say after the Boyne, "Change kings with us, and we will fight it over again." Indeed, the fight was not fair between the two. 'Twas a weak, priest-ridden, woman-ridden man, with such puny allies and weapons as his own poor nature led him to choose, contending against the schemes, the generalship, the wisdom, and the heart of a hero.

On one of these many coward's errands then (for, as I view them now, I can call them no less), Mr. Holt had come to my Lord at Castlewood, proposing some infallible plan for the Prince of Orange's destruction, in which my Lord Viscount, loyalist as he was, had indignantly refused to join. As far as Mr. Esmond could gather from his dying words, Holt came to my Lord with a plan of insurrection, and offer of the renewal, in his person, of that marquis's title which King James had conferred on the preceding viscount; and on refusal of this bribe, a threat was made, on Holt's part, to upset my Lord Viscount's claim to his estate and title of Castlewood altogether. To back this astounding piece of intelligence, of which Henry Esmond's patron now had the first light, Holt came armed with the late lord's dying declaration, after the affair of the Boyne, at Trim, in Ireland, made both to the Irish priest and a French ecclesiastic of Holt's order, that was with King James's army. Holt showed, or pretended to show, the marriage certificate of the late Viscount Esmond with my mother, in the city of Brussels, in the year 1679, when the Viscount, then Thomas Esmond, was serving with the English army in Flanders; he could show, he said, that this Gertrude, deserted by her husband long since, was alive, and a professed nun in the year 1685, at Brussels, in which year Thomas Esmond married his uncle's daughter Isabella, now called Viscountess Dowager of Castlewood; and leaving him, for twelve hours, to consider this astounding news (so the poor dying lord said), disappeared with his papers in the mysterious way in which he came. Esmond knew how, well enough: by that window from which he had seen the Father issue:—but there was no need to explain to my poor Lord, only to gather from his parting lips the words which he would soon be able to utter no more.

Ere the twelve hours were over, Holt himself was a prisoner, implicated in Sir John Fenwick's conspiracy, and locked up at Hexton first, whence he was transferred to the Tower; leaving the poor Lord Viscount, who was not aware of the other's being taken, in daily apprehension of his return, when (as my Lord Castlewood declared, calling God to witness, and with tears in his dying eyes) it had been his intention at once to give up his estate and his title to their proper owner, and to retire to his own house at Walcote with his family. "And would to God I had done it," the poor lord said. "I would not be here now, wounded to death, a miserable, stricken man!"

My Lord waited day after day, and, as may be supposed, no messenger came; but at a month's end Holt got means to convey to him a message out of the Tower, which was to this effect: that he should consider all unsaid that had been said, and that things were as they were.

"I had a sore temptation," said my poor Lord. "Since I had come into this cursed title of Castlewood, which hath never prospered with me, I have spent far more than the income of that estate, and my paternal one too. I calculated all my means down to the last shilling, and found I never could pay you back, my poor Harry, whose fortune I had had for ten years. My wife and children must have gone out of the house dishonoured, and beggars. God knows, it hath been a miserable one for me and mine. Like a coward, I clung to that respite which Holt gave me. I kept the truth from Rachel and you. I tried to win money of Mohun, and only plunged deeper into debt; I scarce dared look thee in the face when I saw thee. This sword hath been hanging over my head these two years. I swear I felt happy when Mohun's blade entered my side."

After lying ten months in the Tower, Holt, against whom nothing could be found except that he was a Jesuit priest, known to be in King James's interest, was put on shipboard by the incorrigible forgiveness of King William, who promised him, however, a hanging if ever he should again set foot on English shore. More than once, whilst he was in prison himself, Esmond had thought where those papers could be which the Jesuit had shown to his patron, and which had such an interest for himself. They were not found on Mr. Holt's person when that Father was apprehended, for had such been the case my Lords of the Council had seen them, and this family history had long since been made public. However, Esmond cared not to seek the papers. His resolution being taken; his poor mother dead; what matter to him that documents existed proving his right to a title which he was determined not to claim, and of which he vowed never to deprive that family which he loved best in the world? Perhaps he took a greater pride out of his sacrifice than he would have had in those honours which he was resolved to forego. Again, as long as these titles were not forthcoming, Esmond's kinsman, dear young Francis, was the honourable and undisputed owner of the Castlewood estate and title. The mere word of a Jesuit could not overset Frank's right of occupancy, and so Esmond's mind felt actually at ease to think the papers were missing, and in their absence his dear mistress and her son the lawful Lady and Lord of Castlewood.

Very soon after his liberation, Mr. Esmond made it his business to ride to that village of Ealing where he had passed his earliest years in this country, and to see if his old guardians were still alive and inhabitants of that place. But the only relique which he found of old M. Pastoureau was a stone in the churchyard, which told that Athanasius Pastoureau, a native of Flanders, lay there buried, aged 87 years. The old man's cottage, which Esmond perfectly recollected, and the garden (where in his childhood he had passed many hours of play and reverie, and had many a beating from his termagant of a foster-mother) were now in the occupation of quite a different family; and it was with difficulty that he could learn in the village what had come of Pastoureau's widow and children. The clerk of the parish recollected her—the old man was scarce altered in the fourteen years that had passed since last Esmond set eyes on him. It appeared she had pretty soon consoled herself after the death of her old husband, whom she ruled over, by taking a new one younger than herself, who spent her money and ill-treated her and her children. The girl died; one of the boys 'listed; the other had gone apprentice. Old Mr. Rogers, the clerk, said he had heard that Mrs. Pastoureau was dead too. She and her husband had left Ealing this seven year; and so Mr. Esmond's hopes of gaining any information regarding his parentage from this family were brought to an end. He gave the old clerk a crown-piece for his news, smiling to think of the time when he and his little playfellows had slunk out of the churchyard or hidden behind the gravestones at the approach of this awful authority.

Who was his mother? What had her name been? When did she die? Esmond longed to find some one who could answer these questions to him, and thought even of putting them to his aunt the Viscountess, who had innocently taken the name which belonged of right to Henry's mother. But she knew nothing, or chose to know nothing, on this subject, nor, indeed, could Mr. Esmond press her much to speak on it. Father Holt was the only man who could enlighten him, and Esmond felt he must wait until some fresh chance or new intrigue might put him face to face with his old friend, or bring that restless indefatigable spirit back to England again.

The appointment to his ensigncy, and the preparations necessary for the campaign, presently gave the young gentleman other matters to think of. His new patroness treated him very kindly and liberally; she promised to make interest and pay money, too, to get him a company speedily; she bade him procure a handsome outfit, both of clothes and of arms, and was pleased to admire him when he made his first appearance in his laced scarlet coat, and to permit him to salute her on the occasion of this interesting investiture. "Red," says she, tossing up her old head, "hath always been the colour worn by the Esmonds." And so her Ladyship wore it on her own cheeks very faithfully to the last. She would have him be dressed, she said, as became his father's son, and paid cheerfully for his five-pound beaver, his black buckled periwig, and his fine holland shirts, and his swords, and his pistols mounted with silver. Since the day he was born, poor Harry had never looked such a fine gentleman: his liberal stepmother filled his purse with guineas too, some of which Captain Steele and a few choice spirits helped Harry to spend in an entertainment which Dick ordered (and, indeed, would have paid for, but that he had no money when the reckoning was called for; nor would the landlord give him any more credit) at the "Garter," over against the gate of the Palace, in Pall Mall.

The old Viscountess, indeed, if she had done Esmond any wrong formerly, seemed inclined to repair it by the present kindness of her behaviour: she embraced him copiously at parting, wept plentifully, bade him write by every packet, and gave him an inestimable relic, which she besought him to wear round his neck—a medal, blessed by I know not what pope, and worn by his late sacred Majesty King James. So Esmond arrived at his regiment with a better equipage than most young officers could afford. He was older than most of his seniors, and had a further advantage which belenged but to very few of the army gentlemen in his day—many of whom could do little more than write their names—that he had read much, both at home and at the University, was master of two or three languages, and had that further education which neither books nor years will give, but which some men get from the silent teaching of Adversity. She is a great schoolmistress, as many a poor fellow knows, that hath held his hand out to her ferule, and whimpered over his lesson before her awful chair.

CHAPTER V

I GO ON THE VIGO BAY EXPEDITION, TASTE SALT-WATER AND SMELL POWDER

THE first expedition in which Mr. Esmond had the honour to be engaged, rather resembled one of the invasions projected by the redoubted Captain Avory or Captain Kidd, than a war between crowned heads, carried on by generals of rank and honour. On the first day of July 1702, a great fleet, of a hundred and fifty sail, set sail from Spithead, under the command of Admiral Shovell, having on board 12,000 troops, with his Grace the Duke of Ormond as the Capt.-General of the expedition. One of these 12,000 heroes having never been to sea before, or, at least, only once in his infancy, when he made the voyage to England from that unknown country where he was born—one of those 12,000—the junior ensign of Colonel Quin's regiment of Fusileers—was in a quite unheroic state of corporal prostration a few hours after sailing; and an enemy, had he boarded the ship, would have had easy work of him. From Portsmouth we put into Plymouth, and took in fresh reinforcements. We were off Finisterre on the 31st of July, so Esmond's table-book informs him: and on the 8th of August made the rock of Lisbon. By this time the Ensign was grown as bold as an admiral, and a week afterwards had the fortune to be under fire for the first time—and under water too—his boat being swamped in the surf in Toros Bay, where the troops landed. The ducking of his new coat was all the harm the young soldier got in this expedition, for, indeed, the Spaniards made no stand before our troops, and were not in strength to do so.

But the campaign, if not very glorious, was very pleasant. New sights of nature, by sea and land—a life of action, beginning now for the first time—occupied and excited the young man. The many accidents and the routine of shipboard—the military duty—the new acquaintances, both of his comrades in arms and of the officers of the fleet—served to cheer and occupy his mind, and waken it out of that selfish depression into which his late unhappy fortunes had plunged him. He felt as if the ocean separated him from his past care, and welcomed the new era of life which was dawning for him. Wounds heal rapidly in a heart of two-and-twenty; hopes revive daily; and courage rallies in spite of a man. Perhaps, as Esmond thought of his late despondency and melancholy, and how irremediable it had seemed to him, as he lay in his prison a few months back, he was almost mortified in his secret mind at finding himself so cheerful.

To see with one's own eyes men and countries, is better than reading all the books of travel in the world: and it was with extreme delight and exultation that the young man found himself actually on his grand tour, and in the view of people and cities which he had read about as a boy. He beheld war for the first time—the pride, pomp, and circumstance of it, at least, if not much of the danger. He saw actually, and with his own eyes, those Spanish cavaliers and ladies whom he had beheld in imagination in that immortal story of Cervantes, which had been the delight of his youthful leisure. 'Tis forty years since Mr. Esmond witnessed those scenes, but they remain as fresh in his memory as on the day when first he saw them as a young man. A cloud, as of grief, that had lowered over him, and had wrapped the last years of his life in gloom, seemed to clear away from Esmond during this fortunate voyage and campaign. His energies seemed to awaken and to expand under a cheerful sense of freedom. Was his heart secretly glad to have escaped from that fond but ignoble bondage at home? Was it that the inferiority to which the idea of his base birth had compelled him, vanished with the knowledge of that secret, which though, perforce, kept to himself, was yet enough to cheer and console him? At any rate, young Esmond of the army was quite a different being to the sad little dependant of the kind Castlewood household, and the melancholy student of Trinity Walks; discontented with his fate, and with the vocation into which that drove him, and thinking, with a secret indignation, that the cassock and bands, and the very sacred office with which he had once proposed to invest himself, were, in fact, but marks of a servitude which was to continue all his life long. For, disguise it as he might to himself, he had all along felt that to be Castlewood's chaplain was to be Castlewood's inferior still, and that his life was but to be a long, hopeless servitude. So, indeed, he was far from grudging his old friend Tom Tusher's good fortune (as Tom, no doubt, thought it). Had it been a mitre and Lambeth which his friends offered him, and not a small living and a country parsonage, he would have felt as much a slave in one case as in the other, and was quite happy and thankful to be free.

The bravest man I ever knew in the army, and who had been present in most of King William's actions, as well as in the campaigns of the great Duke of Marlborough, could never be got to tell us of any achievement of his, except that once Prince Eugene ordered him up a tree to reconnoitre the enemy, which feat he could not achieve on account of the horseman's boots he wore; and on another day that he was very nearly taken prisoner because of these jackboots, which prevented him from running away. The present narrator shall imitate this laudable reserve, and doth not intend to dwell upon his military exploits, which were in truth not very different from those of a thousand other gentlemen. This first campaign of Mr. Esmond's lasted but a few days; and as a score of books have been written concerning it, it may be dismissed very briefly here.

When our fleet came within view of Cadiz, our commander sent a boat with a white flag and a couple of officers to the Governor of Cadiz, Don Scipio de Brancaccio, with a letter from his Grace, in which he hoped that as Don Scipio had formerly served with the Austrians against the French, 'twas to be hoped that his Excellency would now declare himself against the French King, and for the Austrian, in the war between King Philip and King Charles. But his Excellency, Don Scipio, prepared a reply, in which he announced that, having served his former king with honour and fidelity, he hoped to exhibit the same loyalty and devotion towards his present sovereign, King Philip V.; and by the time this letter was ready, the two officers had been taken to see the town, and the Alameda, and the theatre, where bull-fights are fought, and the convents, where the admirable works of Don Bartholomew Murillo inspired one of them with a great wonder and delight—such as he had never felt before—concerning this divine art of painting; and these sights over, and a handsome refection and chocolate being served to the English gentlemen, they were accompanied back to their shallop with every courtesy, and were the only two officers of the English army that saw at that time that famous city.

The general tried the power of another proclamation on the Spaniards, in which he announced that we only came in the interest of Spain and King Charles, and for ourselves wanted to make no conquest nor settlement in Spain at all. But all this eloquence was lost upon the Spaniards, it would seem: the Captain-General of Andalusia would no more listen to us than the Governor of Cadiz; and in reply to his Grace's proclamation, the Marquis of Villadarias fired off another, which those who knew the Spanish thought rather the best of the two; and of this number was Harry Esmond, whose kind Jesuit in old days had instructed him, and who now had the honour of translating for his Grace these harmless documents of war. There was a hard touch for his Grace, and, indeed, for other generals in her Majesty's service, in the concluding sentence of the Don: "That he and his council had the generous example of their ancestors to follow, who had never yet sought their elevation in the blood or in the flight of their kings. 'Mori pro patria' was his device, which the Duke might communicate to the Princess who governed England."

Whether the troops were angry at this repartee or no, 'tis certain something put them in a fury; for, not being able to get possession of Cadiz, our people seized upon Port St. Mary's and sacked it, burning down the merchants' storehouses, getting drunk with the famous wines there, pillaging and robbing quiet houses and convents, murdering and doing worse. And the only blood which Mr. Esmond drew in this shameful campaign, was the knocking down an English sentinel with a half-pike, who was offering insult to a poor trembling nun. Is she going to turn out a beauty? or a princess? or perhaps Esmond's mother that he had lost and never seen? Alas no: it was but a poor wheezy old dropsical woman, with a wart upon her nose. But having been early taught a part of the Roman religion, he never had the horror of it that some Protestants have shown, and seem to think to be a part of ours.

After the pillage and plunder of St. Mary's, and an assault upon a fort or two, the troops all took shipping, and finished their expedition, at any rate, more brilliantly than it had begun. Hearing that the French fleet with a great treasure was in Vigo Bay, our Admirals, Rooke and Hopson, pursued the enemy thither; the troops landed and carried the forts that protected the bay, Hopson passing the boom first on board his ship the *Torbay*, and the rest of the ships, English and Dutch, following him. Twenty ships were burned or taken in the port of Redondilla, and a vast deal more plunder than was ever accounted for; but poor men before that expedition were rich afterwards, and so often was it found and remarked that the Vigo officers came home with pockets full of money, that the notorious Jack Shafto, who made such a figure at the coffee-houses and gaming-tables in London, and gave out that he had been a soldier at Vigo, owned, when he was about to be hanged, that Bagshot Heath had been *his* Vigo, and that he only spoke of La Redondilla to turn away people's eyes from the real place where the booty lay. Indeed, Hounslow or Vigo—which matters much? The latter was a bad business, though Mr. Addison did sing its praises in Latin. That honest gentleman's muse had an eye to the main chance; and I doubt whether she saw much inspiration in the losing side.

But though Esmond, for his part, got no share of this fabulous booty, one great prize which he had out of the campaign was, that excitement of action and change of scene, which shook off a great deal of his previous melancholy. He learnt at any rate to bear his fate cheerfully. He brought back a browned face, a heart resolute enough, and a little pleasant store of knowledge and observation. from that expedition, which was over with the autumn, when the troops were back in England again; and Esmond giving up his post of secretary to General Lumley, whose command was over, and parting with that officer with many kind expressions of good-will on the General's side, had leave to go to London, to see if he could push his fortunes any way further, and found himself once more in his dowager aunt's comfortable quarters at Chelsey, and in greater favour than ever with the old lady. He propitiated her with a present of a comb, a fan, and a black mantle, such as the ladies of Cadiz wear, and which my Lady Viscountess pronounced became her style of beauty mightily. And she was greatly edified at hearing of that story of his rescue of the nun, and felt very little doubt but that her King James's relic, which he had always dutifully worn in his desk, had kept him out of danger, and averted the shot of the enemy. My Lady made feasts for him, introduced him to more company, and pushed his fortunes with such enthusiasm and success, that she got a promise of a company for him through the Lady Marlborough's interest, who was graciously pleased to accept of a diamond worth a couple of hundred guineas, which Mr. Esmond was enabled to present to her Ladyship through his aunt's bounty, and who promised that she would take charge of Esmond's fortune. He had the honour to make his appearance at the Queen's Drawing-room occasionally, and to frequent my Lord Marlborough's levées. The great man received the young one with very especial favour, so Esmond's comrades said, and deigned to say that he had received the best reports of Mr. Esmond, both for courage and ability, whereon you may be sure the young gentleman made a profound bow, and expressed himself eager to serve under the most distinguished captain in the world.

Whilst his business was going on thus prosperously, Esmond had his share of pleasure too, and made his appearance along with other young gentlemen at the coffee-houses, the theatres, and the Mall. He longed to hear of his dear mistress and her family: many a time, in the midst of the gaieties and pleasures of the town, his heart fondly reverted to them; and often, as the young fellows of his society were making merry at the tavern, and calling toasts (as the fashion of that day was) over their wine, Esmond thought of persons—of two fair women, whom he had been used to adore almost—and emptied his glass with a sigh.

By this time the elder Viscountess had grown tired again of the younger, and whenever she spoke of my Lord's widow, 'twas in terms by no means complimentary towards that poor lady: the younger woman not needing her protection any longer, the elder abused her. Most of the family quarrels that I have seen in life (saving always those arising from money-disputes, when a division of twopence halfpenny will often drive the dearest relatives into war and estrangement) spring out of jealousy and envy. Jack and Tom, born of the same family and to the same fortune, live very cordially together, not until Jack is ruined, when Tom deserts him, but until Tom makes a sudden rise in prosperity, which Jack can't forgive. Ten times to one 'tis the unprosperous man that is angry, not the other who is in fault. 'Tis Mrs. Jack, who can only afford a chair, that sickens at Mrs. Tom's new coach-and-six, cries out against her sister's airs, and sets her husband against his brother. 'Tis Jack who sees his brother shaking hands with a lord (with whom Jack would like to exchange snuffboxes himself), that goes home and tells his wife how poor Tom is spoiled, he fears, and no better than a sneak, parasite, and beggar on horseback. I remember how furious the coffee-house wits were with Dick Steele when he set up his coach and fine house at Bloomsbury; they began to forgive him when the bailiffs were after him, and abused Mr. Addison for selling Dick's country house. And yet Dick in the spunging-house, or Dick in the Park, with his four mares and plated harness, was exactly the same gentle, kindly, improvident, jovial Dick Steele: and yet Mr. Addison was perfectly right in getting the money which was his, and not giving up the amount of his just claim, to be spent by Dick upon champagne and fiddlers, laced clothes, fine furniture, and parasites, Jew and Christian, male and female, who clung to him. As, according to the famous maxim of Monsieur de Rochefoucault, "in our friends' misfortunes there's something secretly pleasant to us;" so, on the other hand, their good fortune is disagreeable. If 'tis hard for a man to bear his own good luck, 'tis harder still for his friends to bear it for him; and but few of them ordinarily can stand that trial: whereas one of the "precious uses" of adversity is, that it is a great reconciler; that it brings back averted kindness, disarms animosity, and causes yesterday's enemy to fling his hatred aside, and hold out a hand to the fallen friend of old days. There's pity and love, as well as envy, in the same heart and towards the same person. The rivalry stops when the competitor tumbles; and, as I view it, we should look at these agreeable and disagreeable qualities of our humanity humbly alike. They are consequent and natural, and our kindness and meanness both manly.

So you may either read the sentence, that the elder of Esmond's two kinswomen pardoned the younger her beauty, when that had lost somewhat of its freshness, perhaps; and forgot most her grievances against the other when the subject of them was no longer prosperous and enviable; or we may say more benevolently (but the sum comes to the same figures, worked either way), that Isabella repented of her unkindness towards Rachel, when Rachel was unhappy; and, bestirring herself in behalf of the poor widow and her children, gave them shelter and friendship. The ladies were quite good friends as long as the weaker one needed a protector. Before Esmond went away on his first campaign, his mistress was still on terms of friendship (though a poor little chit, a woman that had evidently no spirit in her, &c.) with the elder Lady Castlewood; and Mistress Beatrix was allowed to be a beauty.

But between the first year of Queen Anne's reign and the second, sad changes for the worse had taken place in the two younger ladies, at least in the elder's description of them. Rachel, Viscountess Castlewood, had no more face than a dumpling, and Mrs. Beatrix was grown quite coarse, and was losing all her beauty. Little Lord Blandford—(she never would call him Lord Blandford; his father was Lord Churchill—the King, whom he betrayed, had made him Lord Churchill, and he was Lord Churchill still)—might be making eyes at her; but his mother, that vixen of a Sarah Jennings, would never hear of such a folly. Lady Marlborough had got her to be a maid of honour at Court to the Princess, but she would repent of it. The widow Francis (she was but Mrs. Francis Esmond) was a scheming, artful, heartless hussy. She was spoiling her brat of a boy, and she would end by marrying her chaplain.

"What, Tusher!" cried Mr. Esmond, feeling a strange pang of rage and astonishment.

"Yes—Tusher, my maid's son; and who has got all the qualities of his father the lacquey in black, and his accomplished mamma the waiting-woman," cries my Lady. "What do you suppose that a sentimental widow, who will live down in that dingy dungeon of a Castlewood, where she spoils her boy, kills the poor with her drugs, has prayers twice a day, and sees nobody but the chaplain—what do you suppose she can do, mon cousin, but let the horrid parson, with his great square toes and hideous little green eyes, make love to her? Cela c'est vu, mon cousin. When I was a girl at Castlewood, all the chaplains fell in love with me—they've nothing else to do."

My Lady went on with more talk of this kind, though, in truth, Esmond had no idea of what she said further, so entirely did her first words occupy his thought. Were they true? Not all, nor half, nor a tenth part of what the garrulous old woman said, was true. Could this be so? No ear had Esmond for anything else, though his patroness chatted on for an hour.

Some young gentlemen of the town, with whom Esmond had made acquaintance, had promised to present him to that most charming of actresses, and lively and agreeable of women, Mrs. Bracegirdle, about whom Harry's old adversary Mohun had drawn swords, a few years before my poor Lord and he fell out. The famous Mr. Congreve had stamped with his high approval, to the which there was no gainsaying, this delightful person: and she was acting in Dick Steele's comedies and finally, and for twenty-four hours after beholding her, Mr. Esmond felt himself, or thought himself, to be as violently enamoured of this lovely brunette, as were a thousand other young fellows about the city. To have once seen her was to long to behold her again; and to be offered the delightful privilege of her acquaintance, was a pleasure the very idea of which set the young lieutenant's heart on fire. A man cannot live with comrades under the tents without finding out that he too is five-and-twenty. A young fellow cannot be cast down by grief and misfortune ever so severe but some night he begins to sleep sound, and some day when dinner-time comes to feel hungry for a beefsteak. Time, youth and good health, new scenes and the excitement of action and a campaign, had pretty well brought Esmond's mourning to an end; and his comrades said that Don Dismal, as they called him, was Don Dismal no more. So when a party was made to dine at the "Rose," and go to the playhouse afterward, Esmond was as pleased as another to take his share of the bottle and the play.

How was it that the old aunt's news, or it might be scandal, about Tom Tusher, caused such a strange and sudden excitement in Tom's old playfellow? Hadn't he sworn a thousand times in his own mind that the Lady of Castlewood, who had treated him with such kindness once, and then had left him so cruelly, was, and was to remain henceforth, indifferent to him for ever? Had his pride and his sense of justice not long since helped him to cure the pain of that desertion—was it even a pain to him now? Why, but last night as he walked across the fields and meadows to Chelsey from Pall Mall, had he not composed two or three stanzas of a song, celebrating Bracegirdle's brown eyes, and declaring them a thousand times more beautiful than the brightest blue ones that ever languished under the lashes of an insipid fair beauty! But Tom Tusher! Tom Tusher, the waiting-woman's son, raising up his little eyes to his mistress! Tom Tusher presuming to think of Castlewood's widow! Rage and contempt filled Mr. Harry's heart at the very notion; the honour of the family, of which he was the chief, made it his duty to prevent so monstrous an alliance, and to chastise the upstart who could dare to think of such an insult to their house. 'Tis true Mr. Esmond often boasted of republican principles, and could remember many fine speeches he had made at college and elsewhere, with *worth* and not *birth* for a text: but Tom Tusher to take the place of the noble Castlewood—faugh! 'twas as monstrous as King Hamlet's widow taking off her weeds for Claudius. Esmond laughed at all widows, all wives, all women; and were the banns about to be published, as no doubt they were, that very next Sunday at Walcote Church, Esmond swore that he would be present to shout No! in the face of the congregation, and to take a private revenge upon the ears of the bridegroom.

Instead of going to dinner then at the "Rose" that night, Mr. Esmond bade his servant pack a portmanteau and get horses, and was at Farnham, half-way on the road to Walcote, thirty miles off, before his comrades had got to their supper after the play. He bade his man give no hint to my Lady Dowager's household of the expedition on which he was going: and as Chelsey was distant from London, the roads bad, and infested by footpads, and Esmond often in the habit, when engaged in a party of pleasure, of lying at a friend's lodging in town, there was no need that his old aunt should be disturbed at his absence—indeed, nothing more delighted the old lady than to fancy that *mon cousin*, the incorrigible young sinner, was abroad boxing the watch, or scouring St. Giles's. When she was not at her books of devotion, she thought Etheredge and Sedley very good reading. She had a hundred pretty stories about Rochester, Harry Jermyn, and Hamilton; and if Esmond would but have run away with the wife even of a citizen, 'tis my belief she would have pawned her diamonds (the best of them went to our Lady of Chaillot) to pay his damages.

My Lord's little house of Walcote—which he inhabited before he took his title and occupied the house of Castlewood—lies about a mile from Winchester, and his widow had returned to Walcote after my Lord's death as a place always dear to her, and where her earliest and happiest days had been spent, cheerfuller than Castlewood, which was too large for her straitened means, and giving her, too, the protection of the ex-Dean, her father. The young Viscount had a year's schooling at the famous college there, with Mr. Tusher as his governor. So much news of them Mr. Esmond had had during the past year from the old Viscountess, his own father's widow; from the young one there had never been a word.

Twice or thrice in his benefactor's lifetime, Esmond had been to Walcote; and now, taking but a couple of hours' rest only at the inn on the road, he was up again long before daybreak, and made such good speed that he was at Walcote by two o'clock of the day. He rid to the end of the village, where he alighted and sent a man thence to Mr. Tusher, with a message that a gentleman from London would speak with him on urgent business. The messenger came back to say the Doctor was in town, most likely at prayers in the Cathedral. My Lady Viscountess was there too; she always went to Cathedral prayers every day.

The horses belonged to the post-house at Winchester. Esmond mounted again and rode on to the "George"; whence he walked, leaving his grumbling domestic at last happy with a dinner, straight to the Cathedral. The organ was playing, the winter's day was already growing grey, as he passed under the street-arch into the Cathedral yard, and made his way into the ancient solemn edifice.

CHAPTER VI

THE 29TH DECEMBER

THERE was scarce a score of persons in the Cathedral beside the Dean and some of his clergy, and the choristers, young and old, that performed the beautiful evening prayer. But Mr. Tusher was one of the officiants, and read from the eagle in an authoritative voice, and a great black periwig; and in the stalls, still in her black widow's hood, sat Esmond's dear mistress, her son by her side, very much grown, and indeed a noble-looking youth, with his mother's eyes, and his father's curling brown hair, that fell over his *point de Venise*—a pretty picture such as Vandyke might have painted. Monsieur Rigaud's portrait of my Lord Viscount, done at Paris afterwards, gives but a French version of his manly, frank, English face. When he looked up there were two sapphire beams out of his eyes such as no painter's palette has the colour to match, I think. On this day there was not much chance of seeing that particular beauty of my young Lord's countenance; for the truth is, he kept his eyes shut for the most part, and, the anthem being rather long, was asleep.

But the music ceasing, my Lord woke up, looking about him, and his eyes lighting on Mr. Esmond, who was sitting opposite him, gazing with no small tenderness and melancholy upon two persons who had so much of his heart for so many years, Lord Castlewood, with a start, pulled at his mother's sleeve (her face had scarce been lifted from her book), and said, "Look, mother!" so loud, that Esmond could hear on the other side of the church, and the old Dean on his throned stall. Lady Castlewood looked for an instant as her son bade her, and held up a warning finger to Frank; Esmond felt his whole face flush, and his heart throbbing, as that dear lady beheld him once more. The rest of the prayers were speedily over; Mr. Esmond did not hear them; nor did his mistress, very likely, whose hood went more closely over her face, and who never lifted her head again until the service was over, the blessing given, and Mr. Dean, and his procession of ecclesiastics, out of the inner chapel.

Young Castlewood came clambering over the stalls before the

clergy were fairly gone, and running up to Esmond, eagerly embraced him. "My dear, dearest old Harry!" he said, "are you come back? Have you been to the wars? You'll take me with you when you go again? Why didn't you write to us? Come to mother!"

Mr. Esmond could hardly say more than a "God bless you, my boy!" for his heart was very full and grateful at all this tenderness on the lad's part; and he was as much moved at seeing Frank as he was fearful about that other interview which was now to take place: for he knew not if the widow would reject him as she had done so cruelly a year ago.

"It was kind of you to come back to us, Henry," Lady Esmond said. "I thought you might come."

"We read of the fleet coming to Portsmouth. Why did you not come from Portsmouth?" Frank asked, or my Lord Viscount, as he now must be called.

Esmond had thought of that too. He would have given one of his eyes so that he might see his dear friends again once more; but believing that his mistress had forbidden him her house, he had obeyed her, and remained at a distance.

"You had but to ask, and you knew I would be here," he said.

She gave him her hand, her little fair hand; there was only her marriage ring on it. The quarrel was all over. The year of grief and estrangement was passed. They never had been separated. His mistress had never been out of his mind all that time. No, not once. No, not in the prison; nor in the camp; nor on shore before the enemy; nor at sea under the stars of solemn midnight; nor as he watched the glorious rising of the dawn: not even at the table, where he sat carousing with friends, or at the theatre yonder, where he tried to fancy that other eyes were brighter than hers. Brighter eyes there might be, and faces more beautiful, but none so dear—no voice so sweet as that of his beloved mistress, who had been sister, mother, goddess to him during his youth—goddess now no more, for he knew of her weaknesses; and by thought, by suffering, and that experience it brings, was older now than she; but more fondly cherished as woman perhaps than ever she had been adored as divinity. What is it? Where lies it? the secret which makes one little hand the dearest of all? Whoever can unriddle that mystery? Here she was, her son by his side, his dear boy. Here she was, weeping and happy. She took his hand in both hers; he felt her tears. It was a rapture of reconciliation.

"Here comes Squaretoes," says Frank. "Here's Tusher."

Tusher, indeed, now appeared, creaking on his great heels. Mr. Tom had divested himself of his alb or surplice, and came forward habited in his cassock and great black periwig. How had Esmond ever been for a moment jealous of this fellow?

"Give us thy hand, Tom Tusher," he said. The Chaplain made him a very low and stately bow. "I am charmed to see Captain Esmond," says he. "My Lord and I have read the *Reddas incolumem precor*, and applied it, I am sure, to you. You come back with Gaditanian laurels; when I heard you were bound thither, I wished, I am sure, I was another Septimius. My Lord Viscount, your Lordship remembers *Septimi, Gades aditure mecum?*"

"There's an angle of earth that I love better than Gades, Tusher," says Mr. Esmond "'Tis that one where your reverence hath a parsonage, and where our youth was brought up."

"A house that has so many sacred recollections to me," says Mr. Tusher (and Harry remembered how Tom's father used to flog him there)—"a house near to that of my respected patron, my most honoured patroness, must ever be a dear abode to me. But, madam, the verger waits to close the gates on your Ladyship."

"And Harry's coming home to supper. Huzzay! huzzay!" cries my Lord. "Mother, I shall run home and bid Beatrix put her ribands on. Beatrix is a maid of honour, Harry. Such a fine set-up minx!"

"Your heart was never in the Church, Harry," the widow said, in her sweet low tone, as they walked away together. (Now, it seemed they had never been parted, and again, as if they had been ages asunder.) "I always thought you had no vocation that way; and that 'twas a pity to shut you out from the world. You would but have pined and chafed at Castlewood: and 'tis better you should make a name for yourself. I often said so to my dear Lord. How he loved you! 'Twas my Lord that made you stay with us."

"I asked no better than to stay near you always," said Mr. Esmond.

"But to go was best, Harry. When the world cannot give peace, you will know where to find it; but one of your strong imagination and eager desires must try the world first before he tires of it. 'Twas not to be thought of, or if it once was, it was only by my selfishness, that you should remain as chaplain to a country gentleman and tutor to a little boy. You are of the blood of the Esmonds, kinsman; and that was always wild in youth. Look at Francis. He is but fifteen, and I scarce can keep him in my nest. His talk is all of war and pleasure, and he longs to serve in the next campaign. Perhaps he and the young Lord Churchill shall go the next. Lord Marlborough has been good to us. You know how kind they were in my misfortune. And so was your—your father's widow. No one knows how good the world is, till grief comes to try us. 'Tis through my Lady Marlborough's goodness that Beatrix hath her place at Court; and Frank is under my Lord Chamberlain. And the dowager lady, your father's widow, has promised to provide for you—has she not?"

Esmond said, "Yes. As far as present favour went, Lady Castlewood was very good to him. And should her mind change," he added gaily, "as ladies' minds will, I am strong enough to bear my own burden, and make my way somehow. Not by the sword very likely. Thousands have a better genius for that than I, but there are many ways in which a young man of good parts and education can get on in the world; and I am pretty sure, one way or other, of promotion!" Indeed, he had found patrons already in the army, and amongst persons very able to serve him too; and told his mistress of the flattering aspect of fortune. They walked as though they had never been parted, slowly, with the grey twilight closing round them.

"And now we are drawing near to home," she continued, "I knew you would come, Harry, if—if it was but to forgive me for having spoken unjustly to you after that horrid—horrid misfortune. I was half frantic with grief then when I saw you. And I know now—they have told me. That wretch, whose name I can never mention, even has said it: how you tried to avert the quarrel, and would have taken it on yourself, my poor child: but it was God's will that I should be punished, and that my dear lord should fall."

"He gave me his blessing on his deathbed," Esmond said. "Thank God for that legacy!"

"Amen, amen! dear Henry," said the lady, pressing his arm. "I knew it. Mr. Atterbury, of St. Bride's, who was called to him, told me so. And I thanked God, too, and in my prayers ever since remembered it."

"You had spared me many a bitter night, had you told me sooner," Mr. Esmond said.

"I know it, I know it," she answered, in a tone of such sweet humility, as made Esmond repent that he should ever have dared to reproach her. "I know how wicked my heart has been; and I have suffered too, my dear. I confessed to Mr. Atterbury—I must not tell any more. He—I said I would not write to you or go to you—and it was better even that, having parted, we should part. But I knew you would come back—I own that. That is no one's fault. And to-day, Henry, in the anthem, when they sang it, 'When the Lord turned the captivity of Zion, we were like them that dream,' I thought, yes, like them that dream—them that dream. And then it went, 'They that sow in tears shall reap in joy; and he that goeth forth and weepeth, shall doubtless come again with rejoicing, bringing his sheaves with him;' I looked up from the book, and saw you. I was not surprised when I saw you. I knew you would come, my dear, and saw the gold sunshine round your head."

She smiled an almost wild smile as she looked up at him. The moon was up by this time, glittering keen in the frosty sky. He could see, for the first time now clearly, her sweet careworn face.

"Do you know what day it is?" she continued. "It is the 29th of December—it is your birthday! But last year we did not drink it—no, no. My Lord was cold, and my Harry was likely to die: and my brain was in a fever; and we had no wine. But now—now you are come again, bringing your sheaves with you, my dear." She burst into a wild flood of weeping as she spoke; she laughed and sobbed on the young man's heart, crying out wildly, "bringing your sheaves with you—your sheaves with you!"

As he had sometimes felt, gazing up from the deck at midnight into the boundless starlit depths overhead, in a rapture of devout wonder at that endless brightness and beauty—in some such a way now, the depth of this pure devotion (which was, for the first time, revealed to him) quite smote upon him, and filled his heart with thanksgiving. Gracious God, who was he, weak and friendless creature, that such a love should be poured out upon him? Not in vain—not in vain has he lived—hard and thankless should he be to think so—that has such a treasure given him. What is ambition compared to that, but selfish vanity? To be rich, to be famous? What do these profit a year hence, when other names sound louder than yours, when you lie hidden away under the ground, along with idle titles engraven on your coffin? But only true love lives after you—follows your memory with secret blessing—or precedes you, and intercedes for you. *Non omnis moriar*—if dying, I yet live in a tender heart or two; nor am lost and hopeless living, if a sainted departed soul still loves and prays for me.

"If—if 'tis so, dear lady," Mr. Esmond said, "why should I ever leave you? If God hath given me this great boon—and near or far from me, as I know now, the heart of my dearest mistress follows me, let me have that blessing near me, nor ever part with it till death separate us. Come away—leave this Europe, this place which has so many sad recollections for you. Begin a new life in a new world. My good Lord often talked of visiting that land in Virginia which King Charles gave us—gave his ancestor. Frank will give us that. No man there will ask if there is a blot on my name, or inquire in the woods what my title is."

"And my children — and my duty — and my good father, Henry?" she broke out. "He has none but me now! for soon my sister will leave him, and the old man will be alone. He has conformed since the new Queen's reign; and here in Winchester, where they love him, they have found a church for him. When the children leave me, I will stay with him. I cannot follow them into the great world, where their way lies—it scares me. They will come and visit me; and you will, sometimes, Henry—yes, sometimes, as now, in the Holy Advent season, when I have seen and blessed you once more."

"I would leave all to follow you," said Mr. Esmond; "and can you not be as generous for me, dear lady?"

"Hush, boy!" she said, and it was with a mother's sweet plaintive tone and look that she spoke. "The world is beginning for you. For me I have been so weak and sinful that I must leave it, and pray out an expiation, dear Henry. Had we houses of religion as there were once, and many divines of our Church would have them again, I often think I would retire to one and pass my life in penance. But I would love you still—yes, there is no sin in such a love as mine now; and my dear lord in heaven may see my heart; and knows the tears that have washed my sin away—and now—now my duty is here, by my children whilst they need me, and by my poor old father, and——"

"And not by me?" Henry said.

"Hush!" she said again, and raised her hand up to his lip. "I have been your nurse. You could not see me, Harry, when you were in the smallpox, and I came and sat by you. Ah! I prayed that I might die, but it would have been in sin, Henry. Oh, it is horrid to look back to that time! It is over now and past, and it has been forgiven me. When you need me again, I will come ever so far. When your heart is wounded, then come to me, my dear. Be silent! let me say all. You never loved me, dear Henry—no, you do not now, and I thank Heaven for it. I used to watch you, and knew by a thousand signs that it was so. Do you remember how glad you were to go away to college? 'Twas I sent you. I told my papa that, and Mr. Atterbury too, when I spoke to him in London. And they both gave me absolution—both —and they are godly men, having authority to bind and to loose. And they forgave me, as my dear lord forgave me before he went to heaven."

"I think the angels are not all in heaven," Mr. Esmond said. And as a brother folds a sister to his heart; and as a mother cleaves to her son's breast—so for a few moments Esmond's beloved mistress came to him and blessed him.

CHAPTER VII

I AM MADE WELCOME AT WALCOTE

AS they came up to the house at Walcote, the windows from within were lighted up with friendly welcome; the supper-table was spread in the oak-parlour; it seemed as if forgiveness and love were awaiting the returning prodigal. Two or three familiar faces of domestics were on the look-out at the porch—the old housekeeper was there, and young Lockwood from Castlewood in my Lord's livery of tawny and blue. His dear mistress pressed his arm as they passed into the hall. Her eyes beamed out on him with affection indescribable. "Welcome!" was all she said, as she looked up, putting back her fair curls and black hood. A sweet rosy smile blushed on her face; Harry thought he had never seen her look so charming. Her face was lighted with a joy that was brighter than beauty—she took a hand of her son who was in the hall waiting his mother—she did not quit Esmond's arm.

"Welcome, Harry!" my young lord echoed after her. "Here, we are all come to say so. Here's old Pincot, hasn't she grown handsome?" and Pincot, who was older and no handsomer than usual, made a curtsey to the Captain, as she called Esmond, and told my Lord to "Have done, now!"

"And here's Jack Lockwood. He'll make a famous grenadier, Jack; and so shall I; we'll both 'list under you, cousin. As soon as I am seventeen, I go to the army—every gentleman goes to the army. Look who comes here!—ho, ho!" he burst into a laugh. "'Tis Mistress Trix, with a new riband; I knew she would put on one as soon as she heard a captain was coming to supper."

This laughing colloquy took place in the hall of Walcote House: in the midst of which is a staircase that leads from an open gallery, where are the doors of the sleeping chambers: and from one of these, a wax candle in her hand, and illuminating her, came Mistress Beatrix—the light falling indeed upon the scarlet riband which she wore, and upon the most brilliant white neck in the world.

Esmond had left a child and found a woman, grown beyond the common height; and arrived at such a dazzling completeness of beauty, that his eyes might well show surprise and delight at beholding her. In hers there was a brightness so lustrous and melting, that I have seen a whole assembly follow her as if by an attraction irresistible: and that night the great Duke was at the playhouse after Ramillies, every soul turned and looked (she chanced to enter at the opposite side of the theatre at the same moment) at her, and not at him. She was a brown beauty: that is, her eyes, hair, and eyebrows and eyelashes were dark: her hair curling with rich undulations, and waving over her shoulders; but her complexion was as dazzling white as snow in sunshine: except her cheeks, which were a bright red, and her lips, which were of a still deeper crimson. Her mouth and chin, they said, were too large and full, and so they might be for a goddess in marble, but not for a woman whose eyes were fire, whose look was love, whose voice was the sweetest low song, whose shape was perfect symmetry, health, decision, activity, whose foot as it planted itself on the ground was firm but flexible, and whose motion, whether rapid or slow, was always perfect grace —agile as a nymph, lofty as a queen—now melting, now imperious, now sarcastic—there was no single movement of hers but was beautiful. As he thinks of her, he who writes feels young again, and remembers a paragon.

So she came holding her dress with one fair rounded arm, and her taper before her, tripping down the stair to greet Esmond.

"She hath put on her scarlet stockings and white shoes," says my Lord, still laughing. "O my fine mistress! is this the way you set your cap at the Captain?" She approached, shining smiles upon Esmond, who could look at nothing but her eyes. She advanced holding forward her head, as if she would have him kiss her as he used to do when she was a child.

"Stop," she said, "I am grown too big! Welcome, Cousin Harry!" and she made him an arch curtsey, sweeping down to the ground almost, with the most gracious bend, looking up the while with the brightest eyes and sweetest smile. Love seemed to radiate from her. Harry eyed her with such a rapture as the first lover is described as having by Milton.

"N'est-ce pas?" says my Lady, in a low, sweet voice, still hanging on his arm.

Esmond turned round with a start and a blush, as he met his mistress's clear eyes. He had forgotten her, rapt in admiration of the *filia pulcrior*.

"Right foot forward, toe turned out, so: now drop the curtsey, and show the red stockings, Trix. They've silver clocks, Harry. The Dowager sent 'em. She went to put 'em on," cries my Lord.

"Hush, you stupid child!" says miss, smothering her brother with kisses; and then she must come and kiss her mamma, looking

BEATRIX.

all the while at Harry, over his mistress's shoulder. And if she did not kiss him, she gave him both her hands, and then took one of his in both hands, and said, "O Harry, we're so, *so* glad you're come!"

"There are woodcocks for supper," says my Lord. "Huzzay! It was such a hungry sermon."

"And it is the 29th of December; and our Harry has come home."

"Huzzay, old Pincot!" again says my Lord; and my dear lady's lips looked as if they were trembling with a prayer. She would have Harry lead in Beatrix to the supper-room, going herself with my young Lord Viscount; and to this party came Tom Tusher directly, whom four at least out of the company of five wished away. Away he went, however, as soon as the sweetmeats were put down, and then, by the great crackling fire, his mistress, or Beatrix with her blushing graces, filling his glass for him, Harry told the story of his campaign, and passed the most delightful night his life had ever known. The sun was up long ere he was, so deep, sweet, and refreshing was his slumber. He woke as if angels had been watching at his bed all night. I dare say one that was as pure and loving as an angel had blessed his sleep with her prayers.

Next morning the chaplain read prayers to the little household at Walcote, as the custom was; Esmond thought Mistress Beatrix did not listen to Tusher's exhortation much: her eyes were wandering everywhere during the service, at least whenever he looked up he met them. Perhaps he also was not very attentive to his Reverence the Chaplain. "This might have been my life," he was thinking; "this might have been my duty from now till old age. Well, were it not a pleasant one to be with these dear friends and part from 'em no more? Until—until the destined lover comes and takes away pretty Beatrix"—and the best part of Tom Tusher's exposition, which may have been very learned and eloquent, was quite lost to poor Harry by this vision of the destined lover, who put the preacher out.

All the while of the prayers, Beatrix knelt a little way before Harry Esmond. The red stockings were changed for a pair of grey, and black shoes, in which her feet looked to the full as pretty. All the roses of spring could not vie with the brightness of her complexion; Esmond thought he had never seen anything like the sunny lustre of her eyes. My Lady Viscountess look fatigued, as if with watching, and her face was pale.

Miss Beatrix remarked these signs of indisposition in her mother and deplored them. "I am an old woman," says my Lady, with a kind smile; "I cannot hope to look as young as you do, my dear."

"She'll never look as good as you do if she lives till she's a hundred," says my Lord, taking his mother by the waist, and kissing her hand.

"Do I look very wicked, cousin?" says Beatrix, turning full round on Esmond, with her pretty face so close under his chin, that the soft perfumed hair touched it. She laid her finger-tips on his sleeve as she spoke; and he put his other hand over hers.

"I'm like your looking-glass," says he, "and that can't flatter you."

"He means that you are always looking at him, my dear," says her mother archly. Beatrix ran away from Esmond at this, and flew to her mamma, whom she kissed, stopping my Lady's mouth with her pretty hand.

"And Harry is very good to look at," says my Lady, with her fond eyes regarding the young man.

"If 'tis good to see a happy face," says he, "you see that." My Lady said, "Amen," with a sigh; and Harry thought the memory of her dear lord rose up and rebuked her back again into sadness; for her face lost the smile, and resumed its look of melancholy.

"Why, Harry, how fine we look in our scarlet and silver, and our black periwig!" cries my Lord. "Mother, I am tired of my own hair. When shall I have a peruke? Where did you get your steenkirk, Harry?"

"It's some of my Lady Dowager's lace," says Harry; "she gave me this and a number of other fine things."

"My Lady Dowager isn't such a bad woman," my Lord continued.

"She's not so—so red as she's painted," says Miss Beatrix.

Her brother broke into a laugh. "I'll tell her you said so; by the Lord, Trix, I will!" he cries out.

"She'll know that you hadn't the wit to say it, my Lord," says Miss Beatrix.

"We won't quarrel the first day Harry's here, will we, mother?" said the young lord. "We'll see if we can get on to the new year without a fight. Have some of this Christmas pie. And here comes the tankard; no, it's Pincot with the tea."

"Will the Captain choose a dish?" asked Mistress Beatrix.

"I say, Harry," my Lord goes on, "I'll show thee my horses after breakfast; and we'll go a bird-netting to-night, and on Monday there's a cock-match at Winchester—do you love cock-fighting, Harry?—between the gentlemen of Sussex and the gentlemen of Hampshire, at ten pound the battle, and fifty pound the odd battle to show one-and-twenty cocks."

"And what will you do, Beatrix, to amuse our kinsman?" asks my Lady.

"I'll listen to him," says Beatrix. "I am sure he has a hundred things to tell us. And I'm jealous already of the Spanish ladies. Was that a beautiful nun at Cadiz that you rescued from the soldiers? Your man talked of it last night in the kitchen, and Mrs. Betty told me this morning as she combed my hair. And he says you must be in love, for you sat on deck all night, and scribbled verses all day in your table-book." Harry thought if he had wanted a subject for verses yesterday, to-day he had found one: and not all the Lindamiras and Ardelias of the poets were half so beautiful as this young creature; but he did not say so, though some one did for him.

This was his dear lady, who, after the meal was over, and the young people were gone, began talking of her children with Mr. Esmond, and of the characters of one and the other, and of her hopes and fears for both of them. "'Tis not while they are at home," she said, "and in their mother's nest, I fear for them—'tis when they are gone into the world, whither I shall not be able to follow them. Beatrix will begin her service next year. You may have heard a rumour about—about my Lord Blandford. They were both children; and it is but idle talk. I know my kinswoman would never let him make such a poor marriage as our Beatrix would be. There's scarce a princess in Europe that she thinks is good enough for him or for her ambition."

"There's not a princess in Europe to compare with her," says Esmond

"In beauty? No, perhaps not," answered my Lady. "She is most beautiful, isn't she? 'Tis not a mother's partiality that deceives me. I marked you yesterday when she came down the stair: and read it in your face. We look when you don't fancy us looking, and see better than you think, dear Harry: and just now, when they spoke about your poems—you writ pretty lines when you were but a boy—you thought Beatrix was a pretty subject for verse, did not you, Harry?" (The gentleman could only blush for a reply.) "And so she is—nor are you the first her pretty face has captivated. 'Tis quickly done. Such a pair of bright eyes as hers learn their power very soon, and use it very early." And, looking at him keenly with hers, the fair widow left him.

And so it is—a pair of bright eyes with a dozen glances suffice to subdue a man; to enslave him, and inflame him; to make him even forget; they dazzle him so that the past becomes straightway dim to him; and he so prizes them that he would give all his life to possess 'em. What is the fond love of dearest friends compared to this treasure? Is memory as strong as expectancy? fruition, as hunger? gratitude, as desire? I have looked at royal diamonds in the jewel-rooms in Europe, and thought how wars have been made about 'em; Mogul sovereigns deposed and strangled for them, or ransomed with them; millions expended to buy them; and daring lives lost in digging out the little shining toys that I value no more than the button in my hat. And so there are other glittering baubles (of rare water too) for which men have been set to kill and quarrel ever since mankind began; and which last but for a score of years, when their sparkle is over. Where are those jewels now that beamed under Cleopatra's forehead, or shone in the sockets of Helen?

The second day after Esmond's coming to Walcote, Tom Tusher had leave to take a holiday, and went off in his very best gown and bands to court the young woman whom his Reverence desired to marry, and who was not a viscount's widow, as it turned out, but a brewer's relict at Southampton, with a couple of thousand pounds to her fortune: for honest Tom's heart was under such excellent control, that Venus herself without a portion would never have caused it to flutter. So he rode away on his heavy-paced gelding to pursue his jogtrot loves, leaving Esmond to the society of his dear mistress and her daughter, and with his young lord for a companion, who was charmed, not only to see an old friend, but to have the tutor and his Latin books put out of the way.

The boy talked of things and people, and not a little about himself, in his frank artless way. 'Twas easy to see that he and his sister had the better of their fond mother, for the first place in whose affections, though they fought constantly, and though the kind lady persisted that she loved both equally, 'twas not difficult to understand that Frank was his mother's darling and favourite. He ruled the whole household (always excepting rebellious Beatrix) not less now than when he was a child marshalling the village boys in playing at soldiers, and caning them lustily too, like the sturdiest corporal. As for Tom Tusher, his Reverence treated the young lord with that politeness and deference which he always showed for a great man, whatever his age or his stature was. Indeed, with respect to this young one, it was impossible not to love him, so frank and winning were his manners, his beauty, his gaiety, the ring of his laughter, and the delightful tone of his voice. Wherever he went, he charmed and domineered. I think his old grandfather the Dean, and the grim old housekeeper, Mrs. Pincot, were as much his slaves as his mother was: and as for Esmond, he found himself presently submitting to a certain fascination the boy had, and slaving it like the rest of the family. The pleasure which he had in Frank's mere company and converse exceeded that which he ever enjoyed in the society of any other man, however delightful in talk, or famous for wit. His presence brought sunshine into a room, his laugh, his prattle, his noble beauty and brightness of look cheered and charmed indescribably. At the least tale of sorrow, his hands were in his purse, and he was eager with sympathy and bounty. The way in which women loved and petted him, when, a year or two afterwards, he came upon the world, yet a mere boy, and the follies which they did for him (as indeed he for them), recalled the career of Rochester, and outdid the successes of Grammont. His very creditors loved him; and the hardest usurers, and some of the rigid prudes of the other sex too, could deny him nothing. He was no more witty than another man, but what he said, he said and looked as no man else could say or look it. I have seen the women at the comedy at Bruxelles crowd round him in the lobby: and as he sat on the stage more people looked at him than at the actors, and watched him; and I remember at Ramillies, when he was hit and fell, a great big red-haired Scotch sergeant flung his halbert down, burst out a-crying like a woman, seizing him up as if he had been an infant, and carrying him out of the fire. This brother and sister were the most beautiful couple ever seen; though after he winged away from the maternal nest this pair were seldom together.

Sitting at dinner two days after Esmond's arrival (it was the last day of the year), and so happy a one to Harry Esmond, that to enjoy it was quite worth all the previous pain which he had endured and forgot, my young lord, filling a bumper, and bidding Harry take another, drank to his sister, saluting her under the title of "Marchioness."

"Marchioness!" says Harry, not without a pang of wonder, for he was curious and jealous already.

"Nonsense, my Lord," says Beatrix, with a toss of her head. My Lady Viscountess looked up for a moment at Esmond and cast her eyes down.

"The Marchioness of Blandford," says Frank. "Don't you know—hath not Rouge Dragon told you?" (My Lord used to call the Dowager of Chelsey by this and other names.) "Blandford has a lock of her hair: the Duchess found him on his knees to Mistress Trix, and boxed his ears, and said Dr. Hare should whip him."

"I wish Mr. Tusher would whip you too," says Beatrix.

My Lady only said, "I hope you will tell none of these silly stories elsewhere than at home, Francis."

"'Tis true, on my word," continues Frank. "Look at Harry scowling, mother, and see how Beatrix blushes as red as the silver-clocked stockings."

"I think we had best leave the gentlemen to their wine and their talk," says Mrs. Beatrix, rising up with the air of a young queen, tossing her rustling flowing draperies about her, and quitting the room, followed by her mother.

Lady Castlewood again looked at Esmond, as she stooped down and kissed Frank. "Do not tell those silly stories, child," she said: "do not drink much wine, sir; Harry never loved to drink wine." And she went away, too, in her black robes, looking back on the young man with her fair, fond face.

"Egad! it's true," says Frank, sipping his wine with the air of a lord. "What think you of this Lisbon—real Collares? 'Tis better than your heady port: we got it out of one of the Spanish ships that came from Vigo last year: my mother bought it at Southampton, as the ship was lying there—the *Rose*, Captain Hawkins."

"Why, I came home in that ship," says Harry.

"And it brought home a good fellow and good wine," says my Lord. "I say, Harry, I wish thou hadst not that cursed bar sinister."

"And why not the bar sinister?" asks the other.

"Suppose I go to the army and am killed—every gentleman goes to the army—who is to take care of the women? Trix will never stop at home; mother's in love with you,—yes, I think mother's in love with you. She was always praising you, and always talking about you; and when she went to Southampton, to see the ship, I found her out. But you see it is impossible: we are of the oldest blood in England; we came in with the Conqueror; we were only baronets,—but what then? we were forced into that. James the First forced our great-grandfather. We are above titles; we old English gentry don't want 'em; the Queen can make a duke any day. Look at Blandford's father, Duke Churchill, and Duchess Jennings, what were they, Harry? Damn it, sir, what are they, to turn up their noses at us? Where were they, when our ancestor rode with King Henry at Agincourt, and filled up the French King's cup after Poictiers? 'Fore George, sir, why shouldn't Blandford marry Beatrix? By G—! he *shall* marry Beatrix, or tell me the reason why. We'll marry with the best blood of England, and none but the best blood of England. You are an Esmond, and you can't help your birth, my boy. Let's have another bottle. What! no more? I've drunk three parts of this myself. I had many a night with my father; you stood to him like a man, Harry. You backed your blood; you can't help your misfortune, you know,—no man can help that."

The elder said he would go in to his mistress's tea-table. The young lad, with a heightened colour and voice, began singing a snatch of a song, and marched out of the room. Esmond heard him presently calling his dogs about him, and cheering and talking to them; and by a hundred of his looks and gestures, tricks of voice and gait, was reminded of the dead lord, Frank's father.

And so, the sylvester night passed away; the family parted long before midnight, Lady Castlewood remembering, no doubt, former New-Year's Eves, when healths were drunk, and laughter went round in the company of him, to whom years, past, and present, and future, were to be as one; and so cared not to sit with her children and hear the Cathedral bells ringing the birth of the year 1703. Esmond heard the chimes as he sat in his own chamber, ruminating by the blazing fire there, and listened to the last notes of them, looking out from his window towards the city, and the great grey towers of the Cathedral lying under the frosty sky, with the keen stars shining above.

The sight of these brilliant orbs no doubt made him think of other luminaries. "And so her eyes have already done execution," thought Esmond—"on whom?—who can tell me?" Luckily his kinsman was by, and Esmond knew he would have no difficulty in finding out Mistress Beatrix's history from the simple talk of the boy.

CHAPTER VIII

FAMILY TALK

WHAT Harry admired and submitted to in the pretty lad his kinsman was (for why should he resist it?) the calmness of patronage which my young lord assumed, as if to command was his undoubted right, and all the world (below his degree) ought to bow down to Viscount Castlewood.

"I know my place, Harry," he said. "I'm not proud—the boys at Winchester College say I'm proud: but I'm not proud. I am simply Francis James, Viscount Castlewood in the peerage of Ireland. I might have been (do you know that?) Francis James, Marquis and Earl of Esmond in that of England. The late lord refused the title which was offered to him by my godfather, his late Majesty. You should know that—you are of our family, you know—you cannot help your bar sinister, Harry my dear fellow; and you belong to one of the best families in England, in spite of that; and you stood by my father, and by G—! I'll stand by you. You shall never want a friend, Harry, while Francis James, Viscount Castlewood, has a shilling. It's now 1703—I shall come of age in 1709. I shall go back to Castlewood; I shall live at Castlewood; I shall build up the house. My property will be pretty well restored by then. The late viscount mismanaged my property, and left it in a very bad state. My mother is living close, as you see, and keeps me in a way hardly befitting a peer of these realms; for I have but a pair of horses, a governor, and a man that is valet and groom. But when I am of age, these things will be set right, Harry. Our house will be as it should be. You will always come to Castlewood, won't you? You shall always have your two rooms in the court kept for you; and if anybody slights you, d—— them! let them have a care of *me*. I shall marry early—Trix will be a duchess by that time, most likely: for a cannon-ball may knock over his Grace any day, you know."

"How?" says Harry.

"Hush, my dear!" says my Lord Viscount. "You are of the family—you are faithful to us, by George, and I tell you everything. Blandford will marry her—or——" and here he put his little hand on his sword—"you understand the rest. Blandford knows which of us two is the best weapon. At small-sword, or back-sword, or sword and dagger if he likes, I can beat him. I have tried him, Harry; and begad he knows I am a man not to be trifled with."

"But you do not mean," says Harry, concealing his laughter, but not his wonder, "that you can force my Lord Blandford, the son of the first man of this kingdom, to marry your sister at sword's point?"

"I mean to say that we are cousins by the mother's side, though that's nothing to boast of. I mean to say that an Esmond is as good as a Churchill; and when the King comes back, the Marquis of Esmond's sister may be a match for any nobleman's daughter in the kingdom. There are but two marquises in all England, William Herbert, Marquis of Powis, and Francis James, Marquis of Esmond; and hark you, Harry,—now swear you will never mention this. Give me your honour as a gentleman, for you *are* a gentleman, though you are a——"

"Well, well?" says Harry, a little impatient.

"Well, then, when after my late Viscount's misfortune, my mother went up with us to London, to ask for justice against you all (as for Mohun, I'll have his blood, as sure as my name is Francis, Viscount Esmond)—we went to stay with our cousin my Lady Marlborough, with whom we had quarrelled for ever so long. But when misfortune came, she stood by her blood;—so did the Dowager Viscountess stand by her blood;—so did you. Well, sir, whilst my mother was petitioning the late Prince of Orange—for I will never call him King—and while you were in prison, we lived at my Lord Marlborough's house, who was only a little there, being away with the army in Holland. And then . . . I say, Harry, you won't tell, now?"

Harry again made a vow of secrecy.

"Well, there used to be all sorts of fun, you know: my Lady Marlborough was very fond of us, and she said I was to be her page; and she got Trix to be a maid of honour, and while she was up in her room crying, we used to be always having fun, you know; and the Duchess used to kiss me, and so did her daughters, and Blandford fell tremendous in love with Trix, and she liked him; and one day he—he kissed her behind a door—he did though,—and the Duchess caught him, and she banged such a box of the ear both at Trix and Blandford—you should have seen it! And then she said that we must leave directly, and abused my mamma who was cognisant of the business; but she wasn't—never thinking about anything but father. And so we came down to Walcote.

Blandford being locked up, and not allowed to see Trix. But *I* got at him. I climbed along the gutter, and in through the window, where he was crying.

"'Marquis,' says I, when he had opened it and helped me in, 'you know I wear a sword,' for I had brought it.

"'O Viscount,' says he—'O my dearest Frank!' and he threw himself into my arms and burst out a-crying. 'I do love Mistress Beatrix so, that I shall die if I don't have her.'

"'My dear Blandford,' says I, 'you are young to think of marrying;' for he was but fifteen, and a young fellow of that age can scarce do so, you know.

"'But I'll wait twenty years, if she'll have me,' says he. 'I'll never marry—no, never, never, never marry anybody but her. No, not a princess, though they would have me do it ever so. If Beatrix will wait for me, her Blandford swears he will be faithful.' And he wrote a paper (it wasn't spelt right, for he wrote 'I'm ready to *sine with my blode*,' which, you know, Harry, isn't the way of spelling it), and vowing that he would marry none other but the Honourable Mistress Gertrude Beatrix Esmond, only sister of his dearest friend Francis James, fourth Viscount Esmond. And so I gave him a locket of her hair."

"A locket of her hair?" cries Esmond.

"Yes. Trix gave me one after the fight with the Duchess that very day. I am sure I didn't want it; and so I gave it him, and we kissed at parting, and said, 'Good-bye, brother!' And I got back through the gutter; and we set off home that very evening. And he went to King's College, in Cambridge, and *I'm* going to Cambridge soon; and if he doesn't stand to his promise (for he's only wrote once),—he knows I wear a sword, Harry. Come along, and let's go see the cocking-match at Winchester."

". . . But I say," he added, laughing, after a pause, "I don't think Trix will break her heart about him. La bless you! whenever she sees a man, she makes eyes at him; and young Sir Wilmot Crawley of Queen's Crawley, and Anthony Henley of Alresford, were at swords drawn about her, at the Winchester Assembly, a month ago."

That night Mr. Harry's sleep was by no means so pleasant or sweet as it had been on the first two evenings after his arrival at Walcote. "So the bright eyes have been already shining on another," thought he, "and the pretty lips, or the cheeks at any rate, have begun the work which they were made for. Here's a girl not sixteen, and one young gentleman is already whimpering over a lock of her hair, and two country squires are ready to cut each other's throats that they may have the honour of a dance with her. What a fool am I to be dallying about this passion, and singeing my wings in this foolish flame! Wings!—why not say crutches? There is but eight years' difference between us, to be sure; but in life I am thirty years older. How could I ever hope to please such a sweet creature as that, with my rough ways and glum face? Say that I have merit ever so much, and won myself a name, could she ever listen to me? She must be my Lady Marchioness, and I remain a nameless bastard. O my master, my master!" (Here he fell to thinking with a passionate grief of the vow which he had made to his poor dying lord.) "O my mistress, dearest and kindest, will you be contented with the sacrifice which the poor orphan makes for you, whom you love, and who so loves you?"

And then came a fiercer pang of temptation. "A word from me," Harry thought, "a syllable of explanation, and all this might be changed; but no, I swore it over the dying bed of my benefactor. For the sake of him and his; for the sacred love and kindness of old days; I gave my promise to him, and may kind Heaven enable me to keep my vow!"

The next day, although Esmond gave no sign of what was going on in his mind, but strove to be more than ordinarily gay and cheerful when he met his friends at the morning meal, his dear mistress, whose clear eyes it seemed no emotion of his could escape, perceived that something troubled him, for she looked anxiously towards him more than once during the breakfast, and when he went up to his chamber afterwards she presently followed him, and knocked at his door.

As she entered, no doubt the whole story was clear to her at once, for she found our young gentleman packing his valise, pursuant to the resolution which he had come to over-night of making a brisk retreat out of this temptation.

She closed the door very carefully behind her, and then leant against it, very pale, her hands folded before her, looking at the young man, who was kneeling over his work of packing. "Are you going so soon?" she said.

He rose up from his knees, blushing, perhaps, to be so discovered, in the very act, as it were, and took one of her fair little hands—it was that which had her marriage ring on—and kissed it.

"It is best that it should be so, dearest lady," he said.

"I knew you were going, at breakfast. I—I thought you might stay. What has happened? Why can't you remain longer with us? What has Frank told you—you were talking together late last night?"

"I had but three days' leave from Chelsey," Esmond said, as gaily as he could. "My aunt—she lets me call her aunt—is my mistress now! I owe her my lieutenancy and my laced coat. She has taken me into high favour; and my new General is to dine at Chelsey to-morrow—General Lumley, madam—who has appointed me his aide-de-camp, and on whom I must have the honour of waiting. See, here is a letter from the Dowager; the post brought it last night; and I would not speak of it, for fear of disturbing our last merry meeting."

My Lady glanced at the letter, and put it down with a smile that was somewhat contemptuous. "I have no need to read the letter," says she—(indeed, 'twas as well she did not; for the Chelsey missive, in the poor Dowager's usual French jargon, permitted him a longer holiday than he said. "Je vous donne," quoth her Ladyship, "oui jour, pour vous fatigay parfaictement de vos parens fatigans")—"I have no need to read the letter," says she. "What was it Frank told you last night?"

"He told me little I did not know," Mr. Esmond answered. "But I have thought of that little, and here's the result: I have no right to the name I bear, dear lady; and it is only by your sufferance that I am allowed to keep it. If I thought for an hour of what has perhaps crossed your mind too——"

"Yes, I did, Harry," said she; "I thought of it; and think of it. I would sooner call you my son than the greatest prince in Europe—yes, than the greatest prince. For who is there so good and so brave, and who would love her as you would? But there are reasons a mother can't tell."

"I know them," said Mr. Esmond, interrupting her with a smile. "I know there's Sir Wilmot Crawley of Queen's Crawley, and Mr. Anthony Henley of the Grange, and my Lord Marquis of Blandford, that seems to be the favoured suitor. You shall ask me to wear my Lady Marchioness's favours and to dance at her Ladyship's wedding."

"O Harry, Harry! it is none of these follies that frighten me," cried out Lady Castlewood. "Lord Churchill is but a child, his outbreak about Beatrix was a mere boyish folly. His parents would rather see him buried than married to one below him in rank. And do you think that I would stoop to sue for a husband for Francis Esmond's daughter; or submit to have my girl smuggled into that proud family to cause a quarrel between son and parents, and to be treated only as an inferior? I would disdain such a meanness. Beatrix would scorn it. Ah! Henry, 'tis not with you the fault lies, 'tis with her. I know you both, and love you: need I be ashamed of that love now? No, never, never, and 'tis not you, dear Harry, that is unworthy. 'Tis for my poor Beatrix I tremble — whose headstrong will frightens me; whose jealous temper (they say I was jealous too, but, pray God, I am cured of that sin) and whose vanity no words or prayers of mine can cure—only suffering, only experience, and remorse afterwards. O Henry, she will make no man happy who loves her. Go away, my son: leave her: love us always, and think kindly of us: and for me, my dear, you know that these walls contain all that I love in the world."

In after life, did Esmond find the words true which his fond mistress spoke from her sad heart? Warning he had: but I doubt others had warning before his time, and since: and he benefited by it as most men do.

My young Lord Viscount was exceeding sorry when he heard that Harry could not come to the cock-match with him, and must go to London, but no doubt my Lord consoled himself when the Hampshire cocks won the match; and he saw every one of the battles, and crowed properly over the conquered Sussex gentlemen.

As Esmond rode towards town his servant, coming up to him, informed him with a grin, that Mistress Beatrix had brought out a new gown and blue stockings for that day's dinner, in which she intended to appear, and had flown into a rage and given her maid a slap on the face soon after she heard he was going away. Mistress Beatrix's woman, the fellow said, came down to the servants' hall crying, and with the mark of a blow still on her cheek: but Esmond peremptorily ordered him to fall back and be silent, and rode on with thoughts enough of his own to occupy him—some sad ones, some inexpressibly dear and pleasant.

His mistress, from whom he had been a year separated, was his dearest mistress again. The family from which he had been parted, and which he loved with the fondest devotion, was his family once more. If Beatrix's beauty shone upon him, it was with a friendly lustre, and he could regard it with much such a delight as he brought away after seeing the beautiful pictures of the smiling Madonnas in the convent at Cadiz, when he was despatched thither with a flag; and as for his mistress, 'twas difficult to say with what a feeling he regarded her. 'Twas happiness to have seen her; 'twas no great pang to part; a filial tenderness, a love that was at once respect and protection, filled his mind as he thought of her; and near her or far from her, and from that day until now, and from now till death is past, and beyond it, he prays that sacred flame may ever burn.

CHAPTER IX

I MAKE THE CAMPAIGN OF 1704

MR. ESMOND rode up to London then, where, if the Dowager had been angry at the abrupt leave of absence he took, she was mightily pleased at his speedy return.

He went immediately and paid his court to his new general, General Lumley, who received him graciously, having known his father, and also, he was pleased to say, having had the very best accounts of Mr. Esmond from the officer whose aide-de-camp he had been at Vigo. During this winter Mr. Esmond was gazetted to a lieutenancy in Brigadier Webb's regiment of Fusileers, then with their colonel in Flanders; but being now attached to the suite of Mr. Lumley, Esmond did not join his own regiment until more than a year afterwards, and after his return from the campaign of Blenheim, which was fought the next year. The campaign began very early, our troops marching out of their quarters before the winter was almost over, and investing the city of Bonn, on the Rhine, under the Duke's command. His Grace joined the army in deep grief of mind, with crape on his sleeve, and his household in mourning; and the very same packet which brought the Commander-in-Chief over, brought letters to the forces which preceded him, and one from his dear mistress to Esmond, which interested him not a little.

The young Marquis of Blandford, his Grace's son, who had been entered in King's College in Cambridge (whither my Lord Viscount had also gone, to Trinity, with Mr. Tusher as his governor), had been seized with smallpox, and was dead at sixteen years of age, and so poor Frank's schemes for his sister's advancement were over, and that innocent childish passion nipped in the birth.

Esmond's mistress would have had him return, at least her letters hinted as much; but in the presence of the enemy this was impossible, and our young man took his humble share in the siege, which need not be described here, and had the good-luck to escape without a wound of any sort, and to drink his General's health after the surrender. He was in constant military duty this year, and did not think of asking for a leave of absence, as one or two of his less fortunate friends did, who were cast away in that tremendous storm which happened towards the close of November, that "which of late o'er pale Britannia past" (as Mr. Addison sang of it), and in which scores of our greatest ships and 15,000 of our seamen went down.

They said that our Duke was quite heartbroken by the calamity which had befallen his family; but his enemies found that he could subdue them, as well as master his grief. Successful as had been this great General's operations in the past year, they were far enhanced by the splendour of his victory in the ensuing campaign. His Grace the Captain-General went to England after Bonn, and our army fell back into Holland, where, in April 1704, his Grace again found the troops, embarking from Harwich and landing at Maesland Sluys: thence his Grace came immediately to the Hague, where he received the foreign ministers, general officers, and other people of quality. The greatest honours were paid to his Grace everywhere—at the Hague, Utrecht, Ruremonde, and Maestricht; the civil authorities coming to meet his coaches; salvoes of cannon saluting him, canopies of state being erected for him where he stopped, and feasts prepared for the numerous gentlemen following in his suite. His Grace reviewed the troops of the States-General between Liège and Maestricht, and afterwards the English forces, under the command of General Churchill, near Bois-le-Duc. Every preparation was made for a long march; and the army heard, with no small elation, that it was the Commander-in-Chief's intention to carry the war out of the Low Countries, and to march on the Mozelle. Before leaving our camp at Maestricht we heard that the French, under the Marshal Villeroy, were also bound towards the Mozelle.

Towards the end of May, the army reached Coblentz; and next day, his Grace, and the generals accompanying him, went to visit the Elector of Trèves at his Castle of Ehrenbreitstein, the horse and dragoons passing the Rhine whilst the Duke was entertained at a grand feast by the Elector. All as yet was novelty, festivity, and splendour—a brilliant march of a great and glorious army through a friendly country, and sure through some of the most beautiful scenes of nature which I ever witnessed.

The foot and artillery, following after the horse as quick as possible, crossed the Rhine under Ehrenbreitstein, and so to Castel, over against Mayntz, in which city his Grace, his generals, and his retinue were received at the landing-place by the Elector's coaches, carried to his Highness's palace amidst the thunder of cannon, and then once more magnificently entertained. Gidlingen, in Bavaria, was appointed as the general rendezvous of the army, and thither, by different routes, the whole forces of English, Dutch, Danes, and German auxiliaries took their way. The foot and artillery under General Churchill passed the Neckar, at Heidelberg; and Esmond had an opportunity of seeing that city and palace, once so famous and beautiful (though shattered and battered by the French, under Turenne, in the late war), where his grandsire had served the beautiful and unfortunate Electress-Palatine, the first King Charles's sister.

At Mindelsheim, the famous Prince of Savoy came to visit our commander, all of us crowding eagerly to get a sight of that brilliant and intrepid warrior; and our troops were drawn up in battalia before the Prince, who was pleased to express his admiration of this noble English army. At length we came in sight of the enemy between Dillingen and Lawingen, the Brentz lying between the two armies. The Elector, judging that Donauwort would be the point of his Grace's attack, sent a strong detachment of his best troops to Count Darcos, who was posted at Schellenberg, near that place, where great intrenchments were thrown up, and thousands of pioneers employed to strengthen the position.

On the 2nd of July his Grace stormed the post, with what success on our part need scarce be told. His Grace advanced with six thousand foot, English and Dutch, thirty squadrons, and three regiments of Imperial Cuirassiers, the Duke crossing the river at the head of the cavalry. Although our troops made the attack with unparalleled courage and fury—rushing up to the very guns of the enemy, and being slaughtered before their works—we were driven back many times, and should not have carried them, but that the Imperialists came up under the Prince of Baden, when the enemy could make no head against us: we pursued him into the trenches, making a terrible slaughter there, and into the very Danube, where a great part of his troops, following the example of their generals, Count Darcos and the Elector himself, tried to save themselves by swimming. Our army entered Donauwort, which the Bavarians evacuated; and where 'twas said the Elector purposed to have given us a warm reception, by burning us in our beds; the cellars of the houses, when we took possession of them, being found stuffed with straw. But though the links were there, the linkboys had run away. The townsmen saved their houses, and our General took possession of the enemy's ammunition in the arsenals, his stores, and magazines. Five days afterwards a great "Te Deum" was sung in Prince Lewis's army, and a solemn day of thanksgiving held in our own; the Prince of Savoy's compliments coming to his Grace the Captain-General during the day's religious ceremony, and concluding, as it were, with an Amen.

And now, having seen a great military march through a friendly country; the pomps and festivities of more than one German court; the severe struggle of a hotly contested battle, and the triumph of victory, Mr. Esmond beheld another part of military duty: our troops entering the enemy's territory, and putting all around them to fire and sword; burning farms, wasted fields, shrieking women, slaughtered sons and fathers, and drunken soldiery, cursing and carousing in the midst of tears, terror, and murder. Why does the stately Muse of History, that delights in describing the valour of heroes and the grandeur of conquest, leave out these scenes, so brutal, mean, and degrading, that yet form by far the greater part of the drama of war? You, gentlemen of England, who live at home at ease, and compliment yourselves in the songs of triumph with which our chieftains are bepraised — you, pretty maidens, that come tumbling down the stairs when the fife and drum call you, and huzzah for the British Grenadiers—do you take account that these items go to make up the amount of the triumph you admire, and form part of the duties of the heroes you fondle? Our chief, whom England and all Europe, saving only the Frenchmen, worshipped almost, had this of the godlike in him, that he was impassable before victory, before danger, before defeat. Before the greatest obstacle or the most trivial ceremony; before a hundred thousand men drawn in battalia, or a peasant slaughtered at the door of his burning hovel; before a carouse of drunken German lords, or a monarch's court, or a cottage table where his plans were laid, or an enemy's battery, vomiting flame and death, and strewing corpses round about him;—he was always cold, calm, resolute, like fate. He performed a treason or a court-bow, he told a falsehood as black as Styx, as easily as he paid a compliment or spoke about the weather. He took a mistress, and left her; he betrayed his benefactor, and supported him, or would have murdered him, with the same calmness always, and having no more remorse than Clotho when she weaves the thread, or Lachesis when she cuts it. In the hour of battle I have heard the Prince of Savoy's officers say, the Prince became possessed with a sort of warlike fury; his eyes lighted up; he rushed hither and thither, raging; he shrieked curses and encouragement, yelling and harking his bloody war-dogs on, and himself always at the first of the hunt. Our Duke was as calm at the mouth of the cannon as at the door of a drawing-room. Perhaps he could not have been the great man he was, had he had a heart either for love or hatred, or pity or fear, or regret or remorse. He achieved the highest deed of daring, or deepest calculation of thought, as he performed the very meanest action of which a man is capable; told a lie, or cheated a fond woman, or robbed a poor beggar of a halfpenny, with a like awful serenity and equal capacity of the highest and lowest acts of our nature.

His qualities were pretty well known in the army, where there were parties of all politics, and of plenty of shrewdness and wit; but there existed such a perfect confidence in him, as the first captain of the world, and such a faith and admiration in his prodigious genius and fortune, that the very men whom he notoriously cheated of their pay, the chiefs whom he used and injured—for he used all men, great and small, that came near him, as his instruments alike, and took something of theirs, either some quality or some property—the blood of a soldier, it might be, or a jewelled hat, or a hundred thousand crowns from a king, or a portion out of a starving sentinel's three-farthings; or (when he was young) a kiss from a woman, and the gold chain off her neck, taking all he could from woman or man, and having, as I have said, this of the godlike in him, that he could see a hero perish or a sparrow fall, with the same amount of sympathy for either. Not that he had no tears: he could always order up this reserve at the proper moment to battle; he could draw upon tears or smiles alike, and whenever need was for using this cheap coin. He would cringe to a shoeblack, as he would flatter a minister or a monarch; be haughty, be humble, threaten, repent, weep, grasp your hand (or stab you whenever he saw occasion).—But yet those of the army, who knew him best and had suffered most from him, admired him most of all: and as he rode along the lines to battle or galloped up in the nick of time to a battalion reeling from before the enemy's charge or shot, the fainting men and officers got new courage as they saw the splendid calm of his face, and felt that his will made them irresistible.

After the great victory of Blenheim the enthusiasm of the army for the Duke, even of his bitterest personal enemies in it, amounted to a sort of rage—nay, the very officers who cursed him in their hearts were among the most frantic to cheer him. Who could refuse his meed of admiration to such a victory and such a victor? Not he who writes: a man may profess to be ever so much a philosopher; but he who fought on that day must feel a thrill of pride as he recalls it.

The French right was posted near to the village of Blenheim, on the Danube, where the Marshal Tallard's quarters were; their line extending through, it may be a league and a half, before Lutzingen and up to a woody hill, round the base of which, and acting against the Prince of Savoy, were forty of his squadrons.

Here was a village that the Frenchmen had burned, the wood being, in fact, a better shelter and easier of guard than any village.

Before these two villages and the French lines ran a little stream, not more than two foot broad, through a marsh (that was mostly dried up from the heats of the weather), and this stream was the only separation between the two armies—ours coming up and ranging themselves in line of battle before the French, at six o'clock in the morning; so that our line was quite visible to theirs; and the whole of this great plain was black and swarming with troops for hours before the cannonading began.

On one side and the other this cannonading lasted many hours; the French guns being in position in front of their line, and doing severe damage among our horse especially, and on our right wing of Imperialists under the Prince of Savoy, who could neither advance his artillery nor his lines, the ground before him being cut up by ditches, morasses, and very difficult of passage for the guns.

It was past mid-day when the attack began on our left, where Lord Cutts commanded, the bravest and most beloved officer in the English army. And now, as if to make his experience in war complete, our young aide-de-camp having seen two great armies facing each other in line of battle, and had the honour of riding with orders from one end to other of the line, came in for a not uncommon accompaniment of military glory, and was knocked on the head, along with many hundred of brave fellows, almost at the very commencement of this famous day of Blenheim. A little after noon, the disposition for attack being completed with much delay and difficulty, and under a severe fire from the enemy's guns, that were better posted and more numerous than ours, a body of English and Hessians, with Major-General Wilkes commanding at the extreme left of our line, marched upon Blenheim, advancing with great gallantry, the Major-General on foot, with his officers, at the head of the column, and marching, with his hat off, intrepidly in the face of the enemy, who was pouring in a tremendous fire from his guns and musketry, to which our people were instructed not to reply, except with pike and bayonet when they reached the French palisades. To these Wilkes walked intrepidly, and struck the woodwork with his sword before our people charged it. He was shot down at the instant, with his colonel, major, and several officers; and our troops cheering and huzzaing, and coming on, as they did, with immense resolution and gallantry, were nevertheless stopped by the murderous fire from behind the enemy's defences, and then attacked in flank by a furious charge of French horse which swept out of Blenheim, and cut down our men in great numbers. Three fierce and desperate assaults of our foot were made and repulsed by the enemy; so that our columns of foot were quite shattered, and fell back, scrambling over the little rivulet, which we had crossed so resolutely an hour before, and pursued by the French cavalry, slaughtering us and cutting us down.

And now the conquerors were met by a furious charge of English horse under Esmond's general, General Lumley, behind whose squadrons the flying foot found refuge, and formed again, whilst Lumley drove back the French horse, charging up to the village of Blenheim and the palisades where Wilkes, and many hundred more gallant Englishmen, lay in slaughtered heaps. Beyond this moment, and of this famous victory Mr. Esmond knows nothing; for a shot brought down his horse and our young gentleman on it, who fell crushed and stunned under the animal, and came to his senses he knows not how long after, only to lose them again from pain and loss of blood. A dim sense, as of people groaning round about him, a wild incoherent thought or two for her who occupied so much of his heart now, and that here his career, and his hopes, and misfortunes were ended, he remembers in the course of these hours. When he woke up, it was with a pang of extreme pain, his breastplate was taken off, his servant was holding his head up, the good and faithful lad of Hampshire * was blubbering over his master, whom he found and had thought dead, and a surgeon was probing a wound in the shoulder, which he must have got at the same moment when his horse was shot and fell over him. The battle was over at this end of the field, by this time: the village was in possession of the English, its brave defenders prisoners, or fled, or drowned, many of them, in the neighbouring waters of Donau. But for honest Lockwood's faithful search after his master, there had no doubt been an end of Esmond here, and of this his story. The marauders were out rifling the bodies as they lay on the field, and Jack had brained one of these gentry with the club-end of his musket, who had eased Esmond of his hat and periwig, his purse, and fine silver-mounted pistols which the Dowager gave him, and was fumbling in his pockets for further treasure, when Jack Lockwood came up and put an end to the scoundrel's triumph.

Hospitals for our wounded were established at Blenheim, and here for several weeks Esmond lay in very great danger of his life; the wound was not very great from which he suffered, and the ball extracted by the surgeon on the spot where our young gentleman received it; but a fever set in next day, as he was lying in hospital, and that almost carried him away. Jack Lockwood said he talked in the wildest manner during his delirium; that he called himself the Marquis of Esmond, and seizing one of the surgeon's assistants who came to dress his wounds, swore that he was Madame Beatrix, and

* My mistress, before I went this campaign, sent me John Lockwood out of Walcote, who hath ever since remained with me.—H. E.

that he would make her a duchess if she would but say yes. He was passing the days in these crazy fancies, and *vana somnia*, whilst the army was singing "Te Deum" for the victory, and those famous festivities were taking place at which our Duke, now made a Prince of the Empire, was entertained by the King of the Romans and his nobility. His Grace went home by Berlin and Hanover, and Esmond lost the festivities which took place at those cities, and which his General shared in company of the other general officers who travelled with our great captain. When he could move, it was by the Duke of Würtemberg's city of Stuttgard that he made his way homewards, revisiting Heidelberg again, whence he went to Mannheim, and hence had a tedious but easy water journey down the river of Rhine, which he had thought a delightful and beautiful voyage indeed, but that his heart was longing for home, and something far more beautiful and delightful.

As bright and welcome as the eyes almost of his mistress shone the lights of Harwich, as the packet came in from Holland. It was not many hours ere he, Esmond, was in London, of that you may be sure, and received with open arms by the old Dowager of Chelsey, who vowed, in her jargon of French and English, that he had the *air noble*, that his pallor embellished him, that he was an Amadis and deserved a Gloriana; and oh! flames and darts! what was his joy at hearing that his mistress was come into waiting, and was now with her Majesty at Kensington! Although Mr. Esmond had told Jack Lockwood to get horses and they would ride for Winchester that night, when he heard this news he countermanded the horses at once; his business lay no longer in Hants; all his hope and desire lay within a couple of miles of him in Kensington Park wall. Poor Harry had never looked in the glass before so eagerly to see whether he had the *bel air*, and his paleness really did become him; he never took such pains about the curl of his periwig, and the taste of his embroidery and point-lace, as now, before Mr. Amadis presented himself to Madam Gloriana. Was the fire of the French lines half so murderous as the killing glances from her Ladyship's eyes? Oh! darts and raptures, how beautiful were they!

And as, before the blazing sun of morning, the moon fades away in the sky almost invisible, Esmond thought, with a blush perhaps, of another sweet pale face, sad and faint, and fading out of sight, with its sweet fond gaze of affection; such a last look it seemed to cast as Eurydice might have given, yearning after her lover, when Fate and Pluto summoned her, and she passed away into the shades.

CHAPTER X

AN OLD STORY ABOUT A FOOL AND A WOMAN

ANY taste for pleasure which Esmond had (and he liked to *desipere in loco*, neither more nor less than most young men of his age) he could now gratify to the utmost extent, and in the best company which the town afforded. When the army went into winter quarters abroad, those of the officers who had interest or money easily got leave of absence, and found it much pleasanter to spend their time in Pall Mall and Hyde Park, than to pass the winter away behind the fortifications of the dreary old Flanders towns, where the English troops were gathered. Yachts and packets passed daily between the Dutch and Flemish ports and Harwich; the roads thence to London and the great inns were crowded with army gentlemen; the taverns and ordinaries of the town swarmed with red-coats; and our great Duke's levées at St. James's were as thronged as they had been at Ghent and Brussels, where we treated him, and he us, with the grandeur and ceremony of a sovereign. Though Esmond had been appointed to a lieutenancy in the Fusileer regiment, of which that celebrated officer, Brigadier John Richmond Webb, was colonel, he had never joined the regiment, nor been introduced to its excellent commander, though they had made the same campaign together, and been engaged in the same battle. But being aide-de-camp to General Lumley, who commanded the division of horse, and the army marching to its point of destination on the Danube by different routes, Esmond had not fallen in, as yet, with his commander and future comrades of the fort; and it was in London, in Golden Square, where Major-General Webb lodged, that Captain Esmond had the honour of first paying his respects to his friend, patron, and commander of after days.

Those who remember this brilliant and accomplished gentleman may recollect his character, upon which he prided himself, I think, not a little, of being the handsomest man in the army; a poet who writ a dull copy of verses upon the battle of Oudenarde three years after, describing Webb, says:—

"To noble danger Webb conducts the way,
His great example all his troops obey;
Before the front the General sternly rides,
With such an air as Mars to battle strides:
Propitious Heaven must sure a hero save,
Like Paris handsome, and like Hector brave."

Mr. Webb thought these verses quite as fine as Mr. Addison's on the Blenheim Campaign, and, indeed, to be Hector *à la mode de Paris* was part of this gallant gentleman's ambition. It would have been difficult to find an officer in the whole army, or amongst the splendid courtiers and cavaliers of the Maison du Roy, that fought under Vendosme and Villeroy in the army opposed to ours, who was a more accomplished soldier and perfect gentleman, and either braver or better-looking. And if Mr. Webb believed of himself what the world said of him, and was deeply convinced of his own indisputable genius, beauty, and valour, who has a right to quarrel with him very much? This self-content of his kept him in general good-humour, of which his friends and dependants got the benefit.

He came of a very ancient Wiltshire family, which he respected above all families in the world: he could prove a lineal descent from King Edward the First, and his first ancestor, Roaldus de Richmond, rode by William the Conqueror's side on Hastings field. "We were gentlemen, Esmond," he used to say, "when the Churchills were horseboys." He was a very tall man, standing in his pumps six feet three inches (in his great jack-boots, with his tall fair periwig, and hat and feather, he could not have been less than eight feet high). "I am taller than Churchill," he would say, surveying himself in the glass, "and I am a better-made man; and if the women won't like a man that hasn't a wart on his nose, faith, I can't help myself, and Churchill has the better of me there." Indeed, he was always measuring himself with the Duke, and always asking his friends to measure them. And talking in this frank way, as he would do, over his cups, wags would laugh and encourage him; friends would be sorry for him; schemers and flatterers would egg him on, and tale-bearers carry the stories to headquarters, and widen the difference which already existed there between the great captain and one of the ablest and bravest lieutenants he ever had.

His rancour against the Duke was so apparent, that one saw it in the first half-hour's conversation with General Webb; and his lady, who adored her General, and thought him a hundred times taller, handsomer, and braver than a prodigal nature had made him, hated the great Duke with such an intensity as it becomes faithful wives to feel against their husbands' enemies. Not that my Lord Duke was so yet; Mr. Webb had said a thousand things against him, which his superior had pardoned; and his Grace, whose spies were everywhere, had heard a thousand things more that Webb had never said. But it cost this great man no pains to pardon; and he passed over an injury or a benefit alike easily.

Should any child of mine take the pains to read these his ancestor's memoirs, I would not have him judge of the great Duke * by what a contemporary has written of him. No man hath been so immensely lauded and decried as this great statesman and warrior; as, indeed, no man ever deserved better the very greatest praise and the strongest censure. If the present writer joins with the latter faction, very likely a private pique of his own may be the cause of his ill-feeling.

On presenting himself at the Commander-in-Chief's levée, his Grace had not the least remembrance of General Lumley's aide-de-camp, and though he knew Esmond's family perfectly well, having served with both lords (my Lord Francis and the Viscount Esmond's father) in Flanders, and in the Duke of York's Guard, the Duke of Marlborough, who was friendly and serviceable to the (so-styled) legitimate representatives of the Viscount Castlewood, took no sort of notice of the poor lieutenant who bore their name. A word of kindness or acknowledgment, or a single glance of approbation, might have changed Esmond's opinion of the great man; and instead of a satire, which his pen cannot help writing, who knows but that the humble historian might have taken the other side of panegyric? We have but to change the point of view, and the greatest action looks mean; as we turn the perspective-glass, and a giant appears a pigmy. You may describe, but who can tell whether your sight is clear or not, or your means of information accurate? Had the great man said but a word of kindness to the small one (as he would have stepped out of his gilt chariot to shake hands with Lazarus in rags and sores, if he thought Lazarus could have been of any service to him), no doubt Esmond would have fought for him with pen and sword to the utmost of his might; but my lord the lion did not want master mouse at this moment, and so Muscipulus went off and nibbled in opposition.

So it was, however, that a young gentleman, who, in the eyes of his family, and in his own, doubtless, was looked upon as a consummate hero, found that the great hero of the day took no

* This passage in the Memoirs of Esmond is written on a leaf inserted into the MS. book, and dated 1744, probably after he had heard of the Duchess's death.

more notice of him than of the smallest drummer in his Grace's army. The Dowager of Chelsey was furious against this neglect of her family, and had a great battle with Lady Marlborough (as Lady Castlewood insisted on calling the Duchess). Her Grace was now Mistress of the Robes to her Majesty, and one of the greatest personages in this kingdom, as her husband was in all Europe, and the battle between the two ladies took place in the Queen's drawing-room.

The Duchess, in reply to my aunt's eager clamour, said haughtily, that she had done her best for the legitimate branch of the Esmonds, and could not be expected to provide for the bastard brats of the family.

"Bastards!" says the Viscountess, in a fury. "There are bastards among the Churchills, as your Grace knows, and the Duke of Berwick is provided for well enough."

"Madam," says the Duchess, "you know whose fault it is that there are no such dukes in the Esmond family too, and how that little scheme of a certain lady miscarried."

Esmond's friend, Dick Steele, who was in waiting on the Prince, heard the controversy between the ladies at Court. "And faith," says Dick, "I think, Harry, thy kinswoman had the worst of it."

He could not keep the story quiet; 'twas all over the coffee-houses ere night; it was printed in a news-letter before a month was over, and "The reply of her Grace the Duchess of M–rlb–r–gh to a Popish Lady of the Court, once a favourite of the late K— J–m–s," was printed in half-a-dozen places, with a note stating that "this Duchess, when the head of this lady's family came by his death lately in a fatal duel, never rested until she got a pension for the orphan heir, and widow, from her Majesty's bounty." The squabble did not advance poor Esmond's promotion much, and indeed made him so ashamed of himself that he dared not show his face at the Commander-in-Chief's levées again.

During those eighteen months which had passed since Esmond saw his dear mistress, her good father, the old Dean, quitted this life, firm in his principles to the very last, and enjoining his family always to remember that the Queen's brother, King James the Third, was their rightful sovereign. He made a very edifying end, as his daughter told Esmond, and not a little to her surprise, after his death (for he had lived always very poorly) my Lady found that her father had left no less a sum than £3000 behind him, which he bequeathed to her.

With this little fortune Lady Castlewood was enabled, when her daughter's turn at Court came, to come to London, where she took a small genteel house at Kensington, in the neighbourhood of the Court, bringing her children with her, and here it was that Esmond found his friends.

As for the young lord, his university career had ended rather abruptly. Honest Tusher, his governor, had found my young gentleman quite ungovernable. My Lord worried his life away with tricks; and broke out, as home-bred lads will, into a hundred youthful extravagances, so that Doctor Bentley, the new Master of Trinity, thought fit to write to the Viscountess Castlewood, my Lord's mother, and beg her to remove the young nobleman from a college where he declined to learn, and where he only did harm by his riotous example. Indeed, I believe he nearly set fire to Nevil's Court, that beautiful new quadrangle of our college, which Sir Christopher Wren had lately built. He knocked down a proctor's man that wanted to arrest him in a midnight prank; he gave a dinner-party on the Prince of Wales's birthday, which was within a fortnight of his own, and the twenty young gentlemen then present sallied out after their wine, having toasted King James's health with open windows, and sung cavalier songs, and shouted "God save the King!" in the great court, so that the Master came out of his lodge at midnight, and dissipated the riotous assembly.

This was my Lord's crowning freak, and the Rev. Thomas Tusher, Domestic Chaplain to the Right Honourable the Lord Viscount Castlewood, finding his prayers and sermons of no earthly avail to his Lordship, gave up his duties of governor; went and married his brewer's widow at Southampton, and took her and her money to his parsonage house at Castlewood.

My Lady could not be angry with her son for drinking King James's health, being herself a loyal Tory, as all the Castlewood family were, and acquiesced with a sigh, knowing, perhaps, that her refusal would be of no avail to the young lord's desire for a military life. She would have liked him to be in Mr. Esmond's regiment, hoping that Harry might act as a guardian and adviser to his wayward young kinsman; but my young lord would hear of nothing but the Guards, and a commission was got for him in the Duke of Ormond's regiment: so Esmond found my Lord ensign and lieutenant when he returned from Germany after the Blenheim campaign.

The effect produced by both Lady Castlewood's children when they appeared in public was extraordinary, and the whole town speedily rang with their fame: such a beautiful couple, it was declared, never had been seen; the young maid of honour was toasted at every table and tavern, and as for my young lord, his good looks were even more admired than his sister's. A hundred songs were written about the pair, and as the fashion of that day was, my young lord was praised in these Anacreontics as warmly as Bathyllus. You may be sure that he accepted very complacently the town's opinion of him, and acquiesced with that frankness and charming good-humour he always showed in the idea that he was the prettiest fellow in all London.

The old Dowager at Chelsey, though she could never be got to acknowledge that Mistress Beatrix was any beauty at all (in which opinion, as it may be imagined, a vast number of the ladies agreed with her), yet, on the very first sight of young Castlewood, she owned she fell in love with him; and Henry Esmond, on his return to Chelsey, found himself quite superseded in her favour by her younger kinsman. The feat of drinking the King's health at Cambridge would have won her heart, she said, if nothing else did. "How had the dear young fellow got such beauty?" she asked. "Not from his father—certainly not from his mother. How had he come by such noble manners, and the perfect *bel air?* That countrified Walcote widow could never have taught him." Esmond had his own opinion about the countrified Walcote widow, who had a quiet grace and serene kindness, that had always seemed to him the perfection of good breeding, though he did not try to argue this point with his aunt. But he could agree in most of the praises which the enraptured old Dowager bestowed on my Lord Viscount, than whom he never beheld a more fascinating and charming gentleman. Castlewood had not wit so much as enjoyment. "The lad looks good things," Mr. Steele used to say; "and his laugh lights up a conversation as much as ten repartees from Mr. Congreve. I would as soon sit over a bottle with him as with Mr. Addison; and rather listen to his talk than hear Nicolini. Was ever man so gracefully drunk as my Lord Castlewood? I would give anything to carry my wine" (though, indeed, Dick bore his very kindly, and plenty of it, too) "like this incomparable young man. When he is sober he is delightful; and when tipsy, perfectly irresistible." And referring to his favourite, Shakspeare (who was quite out of fashion until Steele brought him back into the mode), Dick compared Lord Castlewood to Prince Hal, and was pleased to dub Esmond as Ancient Pistol.

The Mistress of the Robes, the greatest lady in England after the Queen, or even before her Majesty, as the world said, though she never could be got to say a civil word to Beatrix, whom she had promoted to her place as maid of honour, took her brother into instant favour. When young Castlewood, in his new uniform, and looking like a prince out of a fairy tale, went to pay his duty to her Grace, she looked at him for a minute in silence, the young man blushing and in confusion before her, then fairly burst out a-crying, and kissed him before her daughters and company. "He was my boy's friend," she said, through her sobs. "My Blandford might have been like him." And everybody saw, after this mark of the Duchess's favour, that my young Lord's promotion was secure, and people crowded round the favourite's favourite, who became vainer and gayer, and more good-humoured than ever.

Meanwhile Madame Beatrix was making her conquests on her own side, and amongst them was one poor gentleman, who had been shot by her young eyes two years before, and had never been quite cured of that wound; he knew, to be sure, how hopeless any passion might be, directed in that quarter, and had taken that best, though ignoble, *remedium amoris*, a speedy retreat from before the charmer, and a long absence from her; and not being dangerously smitten in the first instance, Esmond pretty soon got the better of his complaint, and if he had it still, did not know he had it, and bore it easily. But when he returned after Blenheim, the young lady of sixteen, who had appeared the most beautiful object his eyes had ever looked on two years back, was now advanced to a perfect ripeness and perfection of beauty, such as instantly enthralled the poor devil, who had already been a fugitive from her charms. Then he had seen her but for two days, and fled; now he beheld her day after day, and when she was at Court watched after her; when she was at home, made one of the family party; when she went abroad, rode after her mother's chariot; when she appeared in public places, was in the box near her, or in the pit looking at her; when she went to church was sure to be there, though he might not listen to the sermon, and be ready to hand her to her chair, if she deigned to accept of his services, and select him from a score of young men who were always hanging round about her. When she went away, accompanying her Majesty to Hampton Court, a darkness fell over London. Gods, what nights has Esmond passed, thinking of her, rhyming about her, talking about her! His friend Dick Steele was at this time courting the young lady, Mrs. Scurlock, whom he married; she had a lodging in Kensington Square, hard by my Lady Castlewood's house there. Dick and Harry, being on the same errand, used to meet constantly at Kensington. They were always prowling about that place, or dismally walking thence, or eagerly running thither. They emptied scores of bottles at the "King's Arms," each man prating of his love, and allowing the other to talk on condition that he might have his own turn as a listener. Hence arose an intimacy between them, though to all the rest of their friends they must have been insufferable. Esmond's verses to "Gloriana at the Harpsichord," to "Gloriana's Nosegay," to "Gloriana at Court," appeared this year in the *Observator*.—Have you never read them? They were thought pretty poems, and attributed by some to Mr. Prior.

This passion did not escape—how should it?—the clear eyes of Esmond's mistress: he told her all; what will a man not do when frantic with love? To what baseness will he not demean himself? What pangs will he not make others suffer, so that he may ease his selfish heart of a part of its own pain? Day after day he would seek his dear mistress, pour insane hopes, supplications, rhapsodies, raptures, into her ear. She listened, smiled, consoled, with untiring pity and sweetness. Esmond was the eldest of her children, so she was pleased to say; and as for her kindness, who ever had or would look for aught else from one who was an angel of goodness and pity? After what has been said, 'tis needless almost to add that poor Esmond's suit was unsuccessful. What was a nameless, penniless lieutenant to do, when some of the greatest in the land were in the field? Esmond never so much as thought of asking permission to hope so far above his reach as he knew this prize was—and passed his foolish, useless life in mere abject sighs and impotent longing. What nights of rage, what days of torment, of passionate unfulfilled desire, of sickening jealousy can he recall! Beatrix thought no more of him than of the lacquey that followed her chair. His complaints did not touch her in the least; his raptures rather fatigued her; she cared for his verses no more than for Dan Chaucer's, who's dead these ever so many hundred years; she did not hate him; she rather despised him, and just suffered him.

One day, after talking to Beatrix's mother, his dear, fond, constant mistress—for hours—for all day long—pouring out his flame and his passion, his despair and rage, returning again and again to the theme, pacing the room, tearing up the flowers on the table, twisting and breaking into bits the wax out of the stand-dish, and performing a hundred mad freaks of passionate folly; seeing his mistress at last quite pale and tired out with sheer weariness of compassion, and watching over his fever for the hundredth time, Esmond seized up his hat and took his leave. As he got into Kensington Square, a sense of remorse came over him for the wearisome pain he had been inflicting upon the dearest and kindest friend ever man had. He went back to the house, where the servant still stood at the open door, ran up the stairs, and found his mistress where he had left her in the embrasure of the window, looking over the fields towards Chelsey. She laughed, wiping away at the same time the tears which were in her kind eyes; he flung himself down on his knees, and buried his head in her lap. She had in her hand the stalk of one of the flowers, a pink, that he had torn to pieces. "Oh, pardon me, pardon me, my dearest and kindest," he said; "I am in hell, and you are the angel that brings me a drop of water."

"I am your mother, you are my son, and I love you always," she said, holding her hands over him: and he went away comforted and humbled in mind, as he thought of that amazing and constant love and tenderness with which this sweet lady ever blessed and pursued him.

CHAPTER XI

THE FAMOUS MR. JOSEPH ADDISON

THE gentlemen-ushers had a table at Kensington and the Guard a very splendid dinner daily at St. James's, at either of which ordinaries Esmond was free to dine. Dick Steele liked the Guard-table better than his own at the gentlemen-ushers', where there was less wine and more ceremony; and Esmond had many a jolly afternoon in company of his friend, and a hundred times at least saw Dick into his chair. If there is verity in wine, according to the old adage, what an amiable-natured character Dick's must have been! In proportion as he took in wine he overflowed with kindness. His talk was not witty so much as charming. He never said a word that could anger anybody, and only became the more benevolent the more tipsy he grew. Many of the wags derided the poor fellow in his cups, and chose him as a butt for their satire: but there was a kindness about him, and a sweet playful fancy, that seemed to Esmond far more charming than the pointed talk of the brightest wits with their elaborate repartees and affected severities. I think Steele shone rather than sparkled. Those famous *beaux-esprits* of the coffee-houses (Mr. William Congreve, for instance, when his gout and his grandeur permitted him to come among us) would make many brilliant hits—half-a-dozen in a night sometimes—but, like sharpshooters, when they had fired their shot, they were obliged to retire under cover till their pieces were loaded again, and wait till they got another chance at their enemy; whereas Dick never thought that his bottle companion was a butt to aim at—only a friend to shake by the hand. The poor fellow had half the town in his confidence; everybody knew everything about his loves and his debts, his creditors or his mistress's obduracy. When Esmond first came on to the town, honest Dick was all flames and raptures for a young lady, a West India fortune, whom he married. In a couple of years the lady was dead, the fortune was all but spent, and the honest widower was as eager in pursuit of a new paragon of beauty as if he had never courted and married and buried the last one.

Quitting the Guard-table one Sunday afternoon, when by chance

Dick had a sober fit upon him, he and his friend were making their way down Germain Street, and Dick all of a sudden left his companion's arm, and ran after a gentleman who was poring over a folio volume at the book-shop near to St. James's Church. He was a fair, tall man, in a snuff-coloured suit, with a plain sword, very sober and almost shabby in appearance—at least when compared to Captain Steele, who loved to adorn his jolly round person with the finest of clothes, and shone in scarlet and gold lace. The Captain rushed up, then, to the student of the book-stall, took him in his arms, hugged him, and would have kissed him—for Dick was always hugging and bussing his friends—but the other stepped back with a flush on his pale face, seeming to decline this public manifestation of Steele's regard.

"My dearest Joe, where hast thou hidden thyself this age?" cries the Captain, still holding both his friend's hands; "I have been languishing for thee this fortnight."

"A fortnight is not an age, Dick," says the other, very good-humouredly. (He had light-blue eyes, extraordinary bright, and a face perfectly regular and handsome, like a tinted statue.) "And I have been hiding myself—where do you think?"

"What! not across the water, my dear Joe?" says Steele, with a look of great alarm: "thou knowest I have always——"

"No," says his friend, interrupting him with a smile: "we are not come to such straits as that, Dick. I have been hiding, sir, at a place where people never think of finding you—at my own lodgings, whither I am going to smoke a pipe now and drink a glass of sack: will your honour come?"

"Harry Esmond, come hither," cries out Dick. "Thou hast heard me talk over and over again of my dearest Joe, my guardian angel?"

"Indeed," says Mr. Esmond, with a bow, "it is not from you only that I have learnt to admire Mr. Addison. We loved good poetry at Cambridge as well as at Oxford; and I have some of yours by heart, though I have put on a red coat. . . . 'O qui canoro blandius Orpheo vocale ducis carmen;' shall I go on, sir?" says Mr. Esmond, who, indeed, had read and loved the charming Latin poems of Mr. Addison, as every scholar of that time knew and admired them.

"This is Captain Esmond who was at Blenheim," says Steele.

"Lieutenant Esmond," says the other, with a low bow, "at Mr. Addison's service."

"I have heard of you," says Mr. Addison, with a smile; as, indeed, everybody about town had heard that unlucky story about Esmond's dowager aunt and the Duchess.

"We were going to the 'George' to take a bottle before the play," says Steele: "wilt thou be one, Joe?"

Mr. Addison said his own lodgings were hard by, where he was still rich enough to give a good bottle of wine to his friends; and invited the two gentlemen to his apartment in the Haymarket, whither we accordingly went.

"I shall get credit with my landlady," says he, with a smile, "when she sees two such fine gentlemen as you come up my stair." And he politely made his visitors welcome to his apartment, which was indeed but a shabby one, though no grandee of the land could receive his guests with a more perfect and courtly grace than this gentleman. A frugal dinner, consisting of a slice of meat and a penny loaf, was awaiting the owner of the lodgings. "My wine is better than my meat," says Mr. Addison; "my Lord Halifax sent me the burgundy." And he set a bottle and glasses before his friends, and ate his simple dinner in a very few minutes, after which the three fell to and began to drink. "You see," says Mr. Addison, pointing to his writing-table, whereon was a map of the action at Hochstedt, and several other gazettes and pamphlets relating to the battle, "that I, too, am busy about your affairs, Captain. I am engaged as a poetical gazetteer, to say truth, and am writing a poem on the campaign."

So Esmond, at the request of his host, told him what he knew about the famous battle, drew the river on the table *aliquo mero*, and with the aid of some bits of tobacco-pipe showed the advance of the left wing, where he had been engaged.

A sheet or two of the verses lay already on the table beside our bottles and glasses, and Dick having plentifully refreshed himself from the latter, took up the pages of manuscript, writ out with scarce a blot or correction, in the author's slim, neat handwriting, and began to read therefrom with great emphasis and volubility. At pauses of the verse, the enthusiastic reader stopped and fired off a great salvo of applause.

Esmond smiled at the enthusiasm of Addison's friend. "You are like the German Burghers," says he, "and the Princes on the Mozelle: when our army came to a halt, they always sent a deputation to compliment the chief, and fired a salute with all their artillery from their walls."

"And drunk the great chief's health afterward, did not they?" says Captain Steele, gaily filling up a bumper;—he never was tardy at that sort of acknowledgment of a friend's merit.

"And the Duke, since you will have me act his Grace's part," says Mr. Addison, with a smile, and something of a blush, "pledged his friends in return. Most Serene Elector of Covent Garden, I drink to your Highness's health," and he filled himself a glass. Joseph required scarce more pressing than Dick to that sort of amusement; but the wine never seemed at all to fluster Mr. Addison's brains; it only unloosed his tongue: whereas Captain Steele's head and speech were quite overcome by a single bottle.

No matter what the verses were, and, to say truth, Mr. Esmond found some of them more than indifferent, Dick's enthusiasm for his chief never faltered, and in every line from Addison's pen Steele found a master-stroke. By the time Dick had come to that part of the poem wherein the bard describes as blandly as though he were recording a dance at the opera, or a harmless bout of bucolic cudgelling at a village fair, that bloody and ruthless part of our campaign, with the remembrance whereof every soldier who bore a part in it must sicken with shame—when we were ordered to ravage and lay waste the Elector's country; and with fire and murder, slaughter and crime, a great part of his dominions was overrun;—when Dick came to the lines—

> " In vengeance roused the soldier fills his hand
> With sword and fire, and ravages the land,
> In crackling flames a thousand harvests burn,
> A thousand villages to ashes turn.
> To the thick woods the woolly flocks retreat,
> And mixed with bellowing herds confusedly bleat.
> Their trembling lords the common shade partake,
> And cries of infants sound in every brake.
> The listening soldier fixed in sorrow stands,
> Loth to obey his leader's just commands.
> The leader grieves, by generous pity swayed,
> To see his just commands so well obeyed;"—

by this time wine and friendship had brought poor Dick to a perfectly maudlin state, and he hiccupped out the last line with a tenderness that set one of his auditors a-laughing.

"I admire the licence of your poets," says Esmond to Mr. Addison. (Dick, after reading of the verses, was fain to go off, insisting on kissing his two dear friends before his departure, and reeling away with his periwig over his eyes.) "I admire your art: the murder of the campaign is done to military music, like a battle at the opera, and the virgins shriek in harmony as our victorious grenadiers march into their villages. Do you know what a scene it was?"—(by this time, perhaps, the wine had warmed Mr. Esmond's head too)—"what a triumph you are celebrating? what scenes of shame and horror were enacted, over which the commander's genius presided, as calm as though he didn't belong to our sphere? "You talk of the 'listening soldier fixed in sorrow,' the 'leader's grief swayed by generous pity:' to my belief the leader cared no more for bleating flocks than he did for infants' cries, and many of our ruffians butchered one or the other with equal alacrity. I was ashamed of my trade when I saw those horrors perpetrated which came under every man's eyes. You hew out of your polished verses a stately image of smiling victory: I tell you 'tis an uncouth, distorted, savage idol; hideous, bloody, and barbarous. The rites performed before it are shocking to think of. You great poets should show it as it is—ugly and horrible, not beautiful and serene. O sir, had you made the campaign, believe me, you never would have sung it so."

During this little outbreak, Mr. Addison was listening, smoking out of his long pipe, and smiling very placidly. "What would you have?" says he. "In our polished days, and according to the rules of art, 'tis impossible that the Muse should depict tortures or begrime her hands with the horrors of war. These are indicated rather than described; as in the Greek tragedies, that, I dare say, you have read (and sure there can be no more elegant specimens of composition), Agamemnon is slain, or Medea's children destroyed, away from the scene;—the chorus occupying the stage and singing of the action to pathetic music. Something of this I attempt, my dear sir, in my humble way: 'tis a panegyric I mean to write, and not a satire. Were I to sing as you would have me, the town would tear the poet in pieces, and burn his book by the hands of the common hangman. Do you not use tobacco? Of all the weeds grown on earth, sure the nicotian is the most soothing and salutary. We must paint our great Duke," Mr. Addison went on, "not as a man, which no doubt he is, with weaknesses like the rest of us, but as a hero. 'Tis in a triumph, not a battle, that your humble servant is riding his sleek Pegasus. We college poets trot, you know, on very easy nags; it hath been, time out of mind, part of the poet's profession to celebrate the actions of heroes in verse, and to sing the deeds which you men of war perform. I must follow the rules of my art, and the composition of such a strain as this must be harmonious and majestic, not familiar, or too near the vulgar truth. Si parva licet: if Virgil could invoke the divine Augustus, a humbler poet from the banks of the Isis may celebrate a victory and a conqueror of our own nation, in whose triumphs every Briton has a share, and whose glory and genius contributes to every citizen's individual honour. When hath there been, since our Henrys' and Edwards' days, such a great feat of arms as that from which you yourself have brought away marks of distinction? If 'tis in my power to sing that song worthily, I will do so, and be thankful to my Muse. If I fail as a poet, as a Briton at least I will show my loyalty, and fling up my cap and huzzah for the conqueror:

> "'. . . Rheni pacator et Istri,
> Omnis in hoc uno variis discordia cessit
> Ordinibus; lætatur eques, plauditque senator,
> Votaque patricio certant plebeia favori.'"

"There were as brave men on that field," says Mr. Esmond (who never could be made to love the Duke of Marlborough, nor to forget those stories which he used to hear in his youth regarding that great chief's selfishness and treachery)—"There were men at Blenheim as good as the leader, whom neither knights nor senators applauded, nor voices plebeian or patrician favoured, and who lie there forgotten, under the clods. What poet is there to sing them?"

"To sing the gallant souls of heroes sent to Hades!" says Mr. Addison, with a smile. "Would you celebrate them all? If I may venture to question anything in such an admirable work, the catalogue of the ships in Homer hath always appeared to me as somewhat wearisome: what had the poem been, supposing the writer had chronicled the names of captains, lieutenants, rank and file? One of the greatest of a great man's qualities is success; 'tis the result of all the others; 'tis a latent power in him which compels the favour of the gods, and subjugates fortune. Of all his gifts I admire that one in the great Marlborough. To be brave? every man is brave. But in being victorious, as he is, I fancy there is something divine. In presence of the occasion, the great soul of the leader shines out, and the god is confessed. Death itself respects him, and passes by him to lay others low. War and carnage flee before him to ravage other parts of the field, as Hector from before the divine Achilles. You say he hath no pity: no more have the gods, who are above it, and superhuman. The fainting battle gathers strength at his aspect; and, wherever he rides, victory charges with him."

A couple of days after, when Mr. Esmond revisited his poetic friend, he found this thought, struck out in the fervour of conversation, improved and shaped into those famous lines, which are in truth the noblest in the poem of the "Campaign." As the two gentlemen sat engaged in talk, Mr. Addison solacing himself with his customary pipe, the little maid-servant that waited on his lodging came up, preceding a gentleman in fine laced clothes, that had evidently been figuring at Court or a great man's levée. The courtier coughed a little at the smoke of the pipe, and looked round the room curiously, which was shabby enough, as was the owner in his worn snuff-coloured suit and plain tie-wig.

"How goes on the magnum opus, Mr. Addison?" says the Court gentleman on looking down at the papers that were on the table.

"We were but now over it," says Addison (the greatest courtier in the land could not have a more splendid politeness, or greater dignity of manner). "Here is the plan," says he, "on the table: hâc ibat Simois, here ran the little river Nebel: hic est Sigeia tellus, here are Tallard's quarters, at the bowl of this pipe, at the attack of which Captain Esmond was present. I have the honour to introduce him to Mr. Boyle; and Mr. Esmond was but now depicting aliquo prœlia mixta mero, when you came in." In truth, the two gentlemen had been so engaged when the visitor arrived, and Addison in his smiling way, speaking of Mr. Webb, colonel of Esmond's regiment (who commanded a brigade in the action, and greatly distinguished himself there), was lamenting that he could find never a suitable rhyme for Webb, otherwise the brigade should have had a place in the poet's verses. "And for you, you are but a lieutenant," says Addison, "and the Muse can't occupy herself with any gentleman under the rank of a field officer."

Mr. Boyle was all impatient to hear, saying that my Lord Treasurer and my Lord Halifax were equally anxious; and Addison, blushing, began reading of his verses, and, I suspect, knew their weak parts as well as the most critical hearer. When he came to the lines describing the angel, that

"Inspired repulsed battalions to engage,
And taught the doubtful battle where to rage,

he read with great animation, looking at Esmond, as much as to say, "You know where that simile came from—from our talk, and our bottle of burgundy, the other day."

The poet's two hearers were caught with enthusiasm, and applauded the verses with all their might. The gentleman of the Court sprang up in great delight. "Not a word more, my dear sir," says he. "Trust me with the papers—I'll defend them with my life. Let me read them over to my Lord Treasurer, whom I am appointed to see in half-an-hour. I venture to promise, the verses shall lose nothing by my reading, and then, sir, we shall see whether Lord Halifax has a right to complain that his friend's pension is no longer paid." And without more ado, the courtier in lace seized the manuscript pages, placed them in his breast with his ruffled hand over his heart, executed a most gracious wave of the hat with the disengaged hand, and smiled and bowed out of the room, leaving an odour of pomander behind him.

"Does not the chamber look quite dark?" says Addison, surveying it, "after the glorious appearance and disappearance of that gracious messenger? Why, he illuminated the whole room. Your scarlet, Mr. Esmond, will bear any light; but this threadbare old coat of mine, how very worn it looked under the glare of that splendour! I wonder whether they will do anything for me," he continued. "When I came out of Oxford into the world, my patrons promised me great things; and you see where their promises have landed me, in a lodging up two pair of stairs, with a sixpenny dinner from the cook's shop. Well, I suppose this promise will go after the others, and Fortune will jilt me, as the jade has been doing any time these seven years. 'I puff the prostitute away,'" says he, smiling, and blowing a cloud out of his pipe. There is no hardship in poverty, Esmond, that is not bearable; no hardship even in honest dependence that an honest man may not put up with. I came out of the lap of Alma Mater, puffed up with her praises of me, and thinking to make a figure in the world with the parts and learning which had got me no small name in our college. The world is the ocean, and Isis and Charwell are but little drops, of which the sea takes no account. My reputation ended a mile beyond Maudlin Tower; no one took note of me; and I learned this at least, to bear up against evil fortune with a cheerful heart. Friend Dick hath made a figure in the world, and has passed me in the race long ago. What matters a little name or a little fortune? There is no fortune that a philosopher cannot endure. I have been not unknown as a scholar, and yet forced to live by turning bear-leader, and teaching a boy to spell. What then? The life was not pleasant, but possible—the bear was bearable. Should this venture fail, I will go back to Oxford; and some day, when you are a general, you shall find me a curate in a cassock and bands, and I shall welcome your honour to my cottage in the country, and to a mug of penny ale. 'Tis not poverty that's the hardest to bear, or the least happy lot in life," says Mr. Addison, shaking the ash out of his pipe. "See, my pipe is smoked out. Shall we have another bottle? I have still a couple in the cupboard, and of the right sort. No more? Let us go abroad and take a turn on the Mall, or look in at the theatre and see Dick's comedy. 'Tis not a masterpiece of wit; but Dick is a good fellow, though he doth not set the Thames on fire."

Within a month after this day, Mr. Addison's ticket had come up a prodigious prize in the lottery of life. All the town was in an uproar of admiration of his poem, the "Campaign," which Dick Steele was spouting at every coffee-house in Whitehall and Covent Garden. The wits on the other side of Temple Bar saluted him at once as the greatest poet the world had seen for ages; the people huzzahed for Marlborough and for Addison, and, more than this, the party in power provided for the meritorious poet, and Mr. Addison got the appointment of Commissioner of Excise, which the famous Mr. Locke vacated, and rose from this place to other dignities and honours; his prosperity from henceforth to the end of his life being scarce ever interrupted. But I doubt whether he was not happier in his garret in the Haymarket, than ever he was in his splendid palace at Kensington; and I believe the fortune that came to him in the shape of the countess his wife, was no better than a shrew and a vixen.

Gay as the town was, 'twas but a dreary place for Mr. Esmond, whether his charmer was in or out of it, and he was glad when his General gave him notice that he was going back to his division of the army which lay in winter quarters at Bois-le-Duc. His dear mistress bade him farewell with a cheerful face; her blessing he knew he had always, and wheresoever fate carried him. Mistress Beatrix was away in attendance on her Majesty at Hampton Court, and kissed her fair finger-tips to him, by way of adieu, when he rode thither to take his leave. She received her kinsman in a waiting-room where there were half-a-dozen more ladies of the Court, so that his high-flown speeches, had he intended to make any (and very likely he did), were impossible; and she announced to her friends that her cousin was going to the army, in as easy a manner as she would have said he was going to a chocolate house. He asked with a rather rueful face if she had any orders for the army? and she was pleased to say that she would like a mantle of Mechlin lace. She made him a saucy curtsey in reply to his own dismal bow. She deigned to kiss her finger-tips from the window, where she stood laughing with the other ladies, and chanced to see him as he made his way to the "Toy." The Dowager at Chelsey was not sorry to part with him this time. "Mon cher, vous êtes triste comme un sermon," she did him the honour to say to him; indeed, gentlemen in his condition are by no means amusing companions, and besides, the fickle old woman had now found a much more amiable favourite, and *raffolé'd* for her darling lieutenant of the Guard. Frank remained behind for a while, and did not join the army till later, in the suite of his Grace the Commander-in-Chief. His dear mother, on the last day before Esmond went away, and when the three dined together, made Esmond promise to befriend her boy, and besought Frank to take the example of his kinsman as of a loyal gentleman and brave soldier, so she was pleased to say; and at parting, betrayed not the least sign of faltering or weakness, though, God knows, that fond heart was fearful enough when others were concerned, though so resolute in bearing its own pain.

Esmond's General embarked at Harwich. 'Twas a grand sight to see Mr. Webb dressed in scarlet on the deck, waving his hat as our yacht put off, and the guns saluted from the shore. Harry did not see his Viscount again, until three months after, at Bois-le-Duc, when his Grace the Duke came to take the command, and Frank brought a budget of news from home: how he had supped with this actress, and got tired of that; how he had got the better of Mr. St. John, both over the bottle, and with Mrs. Mountford, of the Haymarket Theatre (a veteran charmer of fifty, with whom the young scapegrace chose to fancy himself in love); how his sister was always at her tricks, and had jilted a young baron for an old earl. "I can't make out Beatrix," he said; "she cares for none of us—she only thinks about herself; she is never happy unless she is quarrelling; but as for my mother—my mother, Harry, is an angel." Harry tried to impress on the young fellow the necessity of doing everything in his power to please that angel: not to drink too much; not to go into debt; not to run after the pretty Flemish girls, and so forth, as became a senior speaking to a lad. "But Lord bless thee!" the boy said; "I may do what I like, and I know she will love me all the same;" and so, indeed, he did what he liked. Everybody spoiled him, and his grave kinsman as much as the rest.

CHAPTER XII

I GET A COMPANY IN THE CAMPAIGN OF 1706

ON Whit Sunday, the famous 23rd of May 1706, my young lord first came under the fire of the enemy, whom we found posted in order of battle, their lines extending three miles or more, over the high ground behind the little Gheet river, and having on his left the little village of Anderkirk or Autre-église, and on his right Ramillies, which has given its name to one of the most brilliant and disastrous days of battle that history ever hath recorded.

Our Duke here once more met his old enemy of Blenheim, the Bavarian Elector and the Maréchal Villeroy, over whom the Prince of Savoy had gained the famous victory of Chiari. What Englishman or Frenchman doth not know the issue of that day? Having chosen his own ground, having a force superior to the English, and besides the excellent Spanish and Bavarian troops, the whole Maison-du-Roy with him, the most splendid body of horse in the world,—in an hour (and in spite of the prodigious gallantry of the French Royal Household, who charged through the centre of our line and broke it) this magnificent army of Villeroy was utterly routed by troops that had been marching for twelve hours, and by the intrepid skill of a commander who did, indeed, seem in the presence of the enemy to be the very Genius of Victory.

I think it was more from conviction than policy, though that policy was surely the most prudent in the world, that the great Duke always spoke of his victories with an extraordinary modesty, and as if it was not so much his own admirable genius and courage which achieved these amazing successes, but as if he was a special and fatal instrument in the hands of Providence, that willed irresistibly the enemy's overthrow. Before his actions he always had the Church service read solemnly, and professed an undoubting belief that our Queen's arms were blessed and our victory sure. All the letters which he writ after his battles show awe rather than exultation ; and he attributes the glory of these achievements, about which I have heard mere petty officers and men bragging with a pardonable vain-glory, in nowise to his own bravery or skill, but to the superintending protection of Heaven, which he ever seemed to think was our especial ally. And our army got to believe so, and the enemy learnt to think so too; for we never entered into a battle without a perfect confidence that it was to end in a victory; nor did the French, after the issue of Blenheim, and that astonishing triumph of Ramillies, ever meet us without feeling that the game was lost before it was begun to be played, and that our General's fortune was irresistible. Here, as at Blenheim, the Duke's charger was shot, and 'twas thought for a moment he was dead. As he mounted another, Binfield, his master of the horse, kneeling to hold his Grace's stirrup, had his head shot away by a cannon-ball. A French gentleman of the Royal Household, that was a prisoner with us, told the writer that at the time of the charge of the Household, when their horse and ours were mingled, an Irish officer recognised the Prince-Duke, and calling out "Marlborough, Marlborough!" fired his pistol at him *à bout-portant*, and that a score more carbines and pistols were discharged at him. Not one touched him: he rode through the French Cuirassiers sword in hand, and entirely unhurt, and calm and smiling, rallied the German Horse, that was reeling before the enemy, brought these and twenty squadrons of Orkney's back upon them, and drove the French across the river, again leading the charge himself, and defeating the only dangerous move the French made that day.

Major-General Webb commanded on the left of our line, and had his own regiment under the orders of their beloved colonel. Neither he nor they belied their character for gallantry on this occasion; but it was about his dear young lord that Esmond was anxious, never having sight of him save once, in the whole course of the day, when he brought an order from the Commander-in-Chief to Mr. Webb. When our horse, having charged round the right flank of the enemy by Overkirk, had thrown him into entire confusion, a general advance was made, and our whole line of foot, crossing the little river and the morass, ascended the high ground where the French were posted, cheering as they went, the enemy retreating before them. 'Twas a service of more glory than danger, the French battalions never waiting to exchange push of pike or bayonet with ours; and the gunners flying from their pieces, which our line left behind us as they advanced, and the French fell back.

At first it was a retreat orderly enough; but presently the retreat became a rout, and a frightful slaughter of the French ensued on this panic: so that an army of sixty thousand men was utterly crushed and destroyed in the course of a couple of hours. It was as if a hurricane had seized a compact numerous fleet, flung it all to the winds, shattered, sunk, and annihilated it: *afflavit Deus, et dissipati sunt.* The French army of Flanders was gone; their artillery, their standards, their treasure, provisions, and ammunition were all left behind them: the poor devils had even fled without their soup-kettles, which are as much the palladia of the French infantry as of the Grand Seignior's Janissaries, and round which they rally even more than round their lilies.

The pursuit, and a dreadful carnage which ensued (for the dregs of a battle, however brilliant, are ever a base residue of rapine, cruelty, and drunken plunder), was carried far beyond the field of Ramillies.

Honest Lockwood, Esmond's servant, no doubt wanted to be among the marauders himself and take his share of the booty; for when, the action over, and the troops got to their ground for the night, the Captain bade Lockwood get a horse, he asked, with a very rueful countenance, whether his honour would have him come too; but his honour only bade him go about his own business, and Jack hopped away quite delighted as soon as he saw his master mounted. Esmond made his way, and not without danger and difficulty, to his Grace's headquarters, and found for himself very quickly where the aides-de-camp's quarters were, in an outbuilding of a farm, where several of these gentlemen were seated, drinking and singing, and at supper. If he had any anxiety about his boy, 'twas relieved at once. One of the gentlemen was singing a song to a tune that Mr. Farquhar and Mr. Gay both had used in their admirable comedies, and very popular in the army of that day; and after the song came a chorus, "Over the hills and far away;" and Esmond heard Frank's fresh voice, soaring, as it were, over the songs of the rest of the young men—a voice that had always a certain artless, indescribable pathos with it, and indeed which caused Mr. Esmond's eyes to fill with tears now, out of thankfulness to God the child was safe and still alive to laugh and sing.

When the song was over, Esmond entered the room, where he knew several of the gentlemen present, and there sat my young lord, having taken off his cuirass, his waistcoat open, his face flushed, his long yellow hair hanging over his shoulders, drinking with the rest; the youngest, gayest, handsomest there. As soon as he saw Esmond, he clapped down his glass, and running towards his friend, put both his arms round him and embraced him. The other's voice trembled with joy as he greeted the lad; he had thought but now as he stood in the courtyard under the clear-shining moonlight: "Great God! what a scene of murder is here within a mile of us; what hundreds and thousands have faced danger to-day; and here are these lads singing over their cups, and the same moon that is shining over yonder horrid field is looking down on Walcote very likely, while my Lady sits and thinks about her boy that is at the war." As Esmond embraced his young pupil now, 'twas with a feeling of quite religious thankfulness and an almost paternal pleasure that he beheld him.

Round his neck was a star with a striped riband, that was made of small brilliants and might be worth a hundred crowns. "Look," says he, "won't that be a pretty present for mother?"

"Who gave you the Order?" says Harry, saluting the gentlemen: "did you win it in battle?"

"I won it," cried the other, "with my sword and my spear. There was a mousquetaire that had it round his neck—such a big mousquetaire, as big as General Webb. I called out to him to surrender, and that I'd give him quarter: he called me a *petit polisson* and fired his pistol at me, and then sent it at my head with a curse. I rode at him, sir, drove my sword right under his armhole, and broke it in the rascal's body. I found a purse in his holster with sixty-five Louis in it, and a bundle of love-letters, and a flask of Hungary-water. *Vive la guerre!* there are the ten pieces you lent me. I should like to have a fight every day;" and he pulled at his little moustache and bade a servant bring a supper to Captain Esmond.

Harry fell to with a very good appetite: he had tasted nothing since twenty hours ago, at early dawn. Master Grandson, who read this, do you look for the history of battles and sieges? Go, find them in the proper books; this is only the story of your grandfather and his family. Far more pleasant to him than the victory, though for that too he may say *meminisse juvat*, it was to find that the day was over, and his dear young Castlewood was unhurt.

And would you, sirrah, wish to know how it was that a sedate Captain of Foot, a studious and rather solitary bachelor of eight or nine and twenty years of age, who did not care very much for the jollities which his comrades engaged in, and was never known to lose his heart in any garrison-town—should you wish to know why such a man had so prodigious a tenderness, and tended so fondly a boy of eighteen, wait, my good friend, until thou art in love with thy schoolfellow's sister, and then see how mighty tender thou wilt be towards him. Esmond's General and his Grace the Prince-Duke were notoriously at variance, and the former's friendship was in nowise likely to advance any man's promotion of whose services Webb spoke well; but rather likely to injure him, so the army said, in the favour of the greater man. However, Mr. Esmond had the good fortune to be mentioned very advantageously by Major-General Webb in his report after the action; and the major of his regiment and two of the captains having been killed upon the day of Ramillies, Esmond, who was second of the lieutenants, got his company, and had the honour of serving as Captain Esmond in the next campaign.

My Lord went home in the winter, but Esmond was afraid to follow him. His dear mistress wrote him letters more than once, thanking him, as mothers know how to thank, for his care and protection of her boy, extolling Esmond's own merits with a great deal more praise than they deserved; for he did his duty no better than any other officer; and speaking sometimes, though gently and cautiously, of Beatrix. News came from home of at least half-a-dozen grand matches that the beautiful maid of honour was about to make. She was engaged to an earl, our gentleman of St. James's said, and then jilted him for a duke, who, in his turn, had drawn off. Earl or duke it might be who should win this Helen, Esmond knew she would never bestow herself on a poor captain. Her conduct, it was clear, was little satisfactory to her mother, who scarcely mentioned her, or else the kind lady thought it was best to say nothing, and leave time to work out its cure. At any rate, Harry was best away from the fatal object which always wrought him so much mischief; and so he never asked for leave to go home, but remained with his regiment that was garrisoned in Brussels, which city fell into our hands when the victory of Ramillies drove the French out of Flanders.

CHAPTER XIII

I MEET AN OLD ACQUAINTANCE IN FLANDERS, AND FIND MY MOTHER'S GRAVE AND MY OWN CRADLE THERE

BEING one day in the Church of St. Gudule, at Brussels, admiring the antique splendour of the architecture (and always entertaining a great tenderness and reverence for the Mother Church, that hath been as wickedly persecuted in England as ever she herself persecuted in the days of her prosperity), Esmond saw kneeling at a side altar an officer in a green uniform coat, very deeply engaged in devotion. Something familiar in the figure and posture of the kneeling man struck Captain Esmond, even before he saw the officer's face. As he rose up, putting away into his pocket a little black breviary, such as priests use, Esmond beheld a countenance so like that of his friend and tutor of early days, Father Holt, that he broke out into an exclamation of astonishment and advanced a step towards the gentleman, who was making his way out of church. The German officer too looked surprised when he saw Esmond, and his face from being pale grew suddenly red. By this mark of recognition the Englishman knew that he could not be mistaken; and though the other did not stop, but on the contrary rather hastily walked away towards the door, Esmond pursued him and faced him once more, as the officer, helping himself to holy water, turned mechanically towards the altar, to bow to it ere he quitted the sacred edifice.

"My Father!" says Esmond in English.

"Silence! I do not understand. I do not speak English," says the other in Latin.

Esmond smiled at this sign of confusion, and replied in the same language, "I should know my Father in any garment, black or white, shaven or bearded;" for the Austrian officer was habited quite in the military manner, and had as warlike a mustachio as any Pandour.

He laughed—we were on the church steps by this time, passing through the crowd of beggars that usually is there holding up little trinkets for sale and whining for alms. "You speak Latin," says he, "in the English way, Harry Esmond; you have forsaken the old true Roman tongue you once knew." His tone was very frank, and quite friendly; the kind voice of fifteen years back; he gave Esmond his hand as he spoke.

"Others have changed their coats too, my Father," says Esmond, glancing at his friend's military decoration.

"Hush! I am Mr. or Captain von Holtz, in the Bavarian Elector's service, and on a mission to his Highness the Prince of Savoy. You can keep a secret I know from old times."

"Captain von Holtz," says Esmond, "I am your very humble servant."

"And you, too, have changed your coat," continues the other in his laughing way. "I have heard of you at Cambridge and afterwards: we have friends everywhere; and I am told that Mr. Esmond at Cambridge was as good a fencer as he was a bad theologian." (So, thinks Esmond, my old *maître d'armes* was a Jesuit, as they said.)

"Perhaps you are right," says the other, reading his thoughts quite as he used to do in old days; "you were all but killed at Hochstedt of a wound in the left side. You were before that at Vigo, aide-de-camp to the Duke of Ormonde. You got your company the other day after Ramillies; your General and the Prince-Duke are not friends; he is of the Webbs of Lydiard Tregoze, in the county of York, a relation of my Lord St. John. Your cousin, M. de Castlewood, served his first campaign this year in the Guard. Yes, I do know a few things, as you see."

Captain Esmond laughed in his turn. "You have indeed a curious knowledge," he says. A foible of Mr. Holt's, who did know more about books and men than, perhaps, almost any person Esmond had ever met, was omniscience; thus in every point he here professed to know, he was nearly right, but not quite. Esmond's wound was in the right side, not the left; his first general was General Lumley; Mr. Webb came out of Wiltshire, not out of Yorkshire; and so forth. Esmond did not think fit to correct his old master in these trifling blunders, but they served to give him a knowledge of the other's character, and he smiled to think that this was his oracle of early days; only now no longer infallible or divine.

"Yes," continues Father Holt, or Captain von Holtz, "for a man who has not been in England these eight years, I know what goes on in London very well. The old Dean is dead, my Lady Castlewood's father. Do you know that your recusant bishops wanted to consecrate him Bishop of Southampton, and that Collier is Bishop of Thetford by the same imposition? The Princess Anne has the gout and eats too much; when the King returns, Collier will be an archbishop."

"Amen!" says Esmond, laughing; "and I hope to see your Eminence no longer in jackboots, but red stockings, at Whitehall."

"You are always with us—I know that—I heard of that when you were at Cambridge; so was the late lord; so is the young viscount."

"And so was my father before me," said Mr. Esmond, looking calmly at the other, who did not, however, show the least sign of intelligence in his impenetrable grey eyes—how well Harry remembered them and their look! only crows'-feet were wrinkled round them—marks of black old Time had settled there.

Esmond's face chose to show no more sign of meaning than the Father's. There may have been on the one side and the other just the faintest glitter of recognition, as you see a bayonet shining out of an ambush; but each party fell back, when everything was again dark.

"And you, mon capitaine, where have you been?" says Esmond, turning away the conversation from this dangerous ground, where neither chose to engage.

"I may have been in Pekin," says he, "or I may have been in Paraguay—who knows where? I am now Captain von Holtz, in the service of his Electoral Highness, come to negotiate exchange of prisoners with his Highness of Savoy."

'Twas well known that very many officers in our army were well affected towards the young King at St. Germains, whose right to the throne was undeniable, and whose accession to it, at the death of his sister, by far the greater part of the English people would have preferred, to the having a petty German prince for a sovereign, about whose cruelty, rapacity, boorish manners, and odious foreign ways, a thousand stories were current. It wounded our English pride to think that a shabby High-Dutch duke, whose revenues were not a tithe as great as those of many of the princes of our ancient English nobility, who could not speak a word of our language, and whom we chose to represent as a sort of German boor, feeding on train-oil and sour-crout with a bevy of mistresses in a barn, should come to reign over the proudest and most polished people in the world. Were we, the conquerors of the Grand Monarch, to submit to that ignoble domination? What did the Hanoverian's Protestantism matter to us? Was it not notorious (we were told and led to believe so) that one of the daughters of this Protestant hero was being bred up with no religion at all, as yet, and ready to be made Lutheran or Roman, according as the husband might be whom her parents should find for her? This talk, very idle and abusive much of it was, went on at a hundred mess-tables in the army; there was scarce an ensign that did not hear it, or join in it, and everybody knew, or affected to know, that the Commander-in-Chief himself had relations with his nephew, the Duke of Berwick ('twas by an Englishman, thank God, that we were beaten at Almanza), and that his Grace was most anxious to restore the royal race of his benefactors, and to repair his former treason.

This is certain, that for a considerable period no officer in the Duke's army lost favour with the Commander-in-Chief for entertaining or proclaiming his loyalty towards the exiled family. When the Chevalier de St. George, as the King of England called himself, came with the dukes of the French blood royal, to join the French army under Vendosme, hundreds of ours saw him and cheered him, and we all said he was like his father in this, who, seeing the action of La Hogue fought between the French ships and ours, was on the side of his native country during the battle. But this at least the Chevalier knew, and every one knew, that, however well our troops and their general might be inclined towards the Prince personally, in the face of the enemy there was no question at all. Wherever my Lord Duke found a French army, he would fight and beat it, as he did at Oudenarde, two years after Ramillies, where his Grace achieved another of his transcendent victories; and the noble young Prince, who charged gallantly along with the magnificent Maison-du-Roy, sent to compliment his conquerors after the action.

In this battle, where the young Electoral Prince of Hanover behaved himself very gallantly, fighting on our side, Esmond's dear General Webb distinguished himself prodigiously, exhibiting consummate skill and coolness as a general, and fighting with the personal bravery of a common soldier. Esmond's good-luck again attended him; he escaped without a hurt, although more than a third of his regiment was killed, had again the honour to be favourably mentioned in his commander's report, and was advanced to the rank of major. But of this action there is little need to speak, as it hath been related in every Gazette, and talked of in every hamlet in this country. To return from it to the writer's private affairs, which here, in his old age, and at a distance, he narrates for his children who come after him. Before Oudenarde, after that chance rencontre with Captain von Holtz at Brussels, a space of more than a year elapsed, during which the captain of Jesuits and the Captain of Webb's Fusileers were thrown very much together. Esmond had no difficulty in finding out (indeed, the other made no secret of it to him, being assured from old times of his pupil's fidelity) that the negotiator of prisoners was an agent from St. Germains, and that he carried intelligence between great personages in our camp and that of the French. "My business," said he—"and I tell you, both because I can trust you and your keen eyes have already discovered it—is between the King of England and his subjects here engaged in fighting the French King. As between you and them, all the Jesuits in the world will not prevent your quarrelling: fight it out, gentlemen. St. George for England, I say—and you know who says so, wherever he may be."

I think Holt loved to make a parade of mystery, as it were, and would appear and disappear at our quarters as suddenly as he used to return and vanish in the old days at Castlewood. He had passes between both armies, and seemed to know (but with that inaccuracy which belonged to the good Father's omniscience) equally well what passed in the French camp and in ours. One day he would give Esmond news of a great feste that took place in the French quarters, of a supper of Monsieur de Rohan's where there was play and violins, and then dancing and masques; the King drove thither in Marshal Villars' own guinguette. Another day he had the news of his Majesty's ague: the King had not had a fit these ten days, and might be said to be well. Captain Holtz made a visit to England during this time, so eager was he about negotiating prisoners; and 'twas on returning from this voyage that he began to open himself more to Esmond, and to make him, as occasion served, at their various meetings, several of those confidences which are here set down all together.

The reason of his increased confidence was this: upon going to London, the old director of Esmond's aunt, the Dowager, paid her Ladyship a visit at Chelsey, and there learnt from her that Captain Esmond was acquainted with the secret of his family, and was determined never to divulge it. The knowledge of this fact raised Esmond in his old tutor's eyes, so Holt was pleased to say, and he admired Harry very much for his abnegation.

"The family at Castlewood have done far more for me than my own ever did," Esmond said. "I would give my life for them. Why should I grudge the only benefit that 'tis in my power to confer on them?" The good Father's eyes filled with tears at this speech, which to the other seemed very simple: he embraced Esmond, and broke out into many admiring expressions; he said he was a *noble cœur*, that he was proud of him, and fond of him as his pupil and friend—regretted more than ever that he had lost him, and been forced to leave him in those early times, when he might have had an influence over him, have brought him into that only true Church to which the Father belonged, and enlisted him in the noblest army in which a man ever engaged—meaning his own Society of Jesus, which numbers (says he) in its troops the greatest heroes the world ever knew:—warriors brave enough to dare or endure anything, to encounter any odds, to die any death;—soldiers that have won triumphs a thousand times more brilliant than those of the greatest general; that have brought nations on their knees to their sacred banner, the Cross; that have achieved glories and palms incomparably brighter than those awarded to the most splendid earthly conquerors—crowns of immortal light, and seats in the high places of heaven.

Esmond was thankful for his old friend's good opinion, however little he might share the Jesuit Father's enthusiasm. "I have thought of that question, too," says he, "dear Father," and he took the other's hand—"thought it out for myself, as all men must, and contrive to do the right, and trust to Heaven as devoutly in my way as you in yours. Another six months of you as a child, and I had desired no better. I used to weep upon my pillow at Castlewood as I thought of you, and I might have been a brother of your order; and who knows," Esmond added with a smile, "a priest in full orders, and with a pair of mustachios, and a Bavarian uniform?"

"My son," says Father Holt, turning red, "in the cause of religion and loyalty all disguises are fair."

"Yes," broke in Esmond, "all disguises are fair, you say; and all uniforms, say I, black or red,—a black cockade or a white one —or a laced hat, or a sombrero, with a tonsure under it. I cannot believe that Saint Francis Xavier sailed over the sea in a cloak, or raised the dead—I tried, and very nearly did once, but cannot. Suffer me to do the right, and to hope for the best in my own way.'

Esmond wished to cut short the good Father's theology, and succeeded; and the other, sighing over his pupil's invincible ignorance, did not withdraw his affection from him, but gave him his utmost confidence—as much, that is to say, as a priest can give: more than most do; for he was naturally garrulous, and too eager to speak.

Holt's friendship encouraged Captain Esmond to ask, what he long wished to know, and none could tell him, some history of the poor mother whom he had often imagined in his dreams, and whom he never knew. He described to Holt those circumstances which are already put down in the first part of this story—the promise he had made to his dear lord, and that dying friend's confession; and he besought Mr. Holt to tell him what he knew regarding the poor woman from whom he had been taken.

"She was of this very town," Holt said, and took Esmond to see the street where her father lived, and where, as he believed, she was born. "In 1679, when your father came hither in the retinue of the late King, then Duke of York, and banished hither in disgrace, Captain Thomas Esmond became acquainted with your mother, pursued her, and made a victim of her; he hath told me in many subsequent conversations, which I felt bound to keep private then, that she was a woman of great virtue and tenderness, and in all respects a most fond, faithful creature. He called himself Captain Thomas, having good reason to be ashamed of his conduct towards her, and hath spoken to me many times with sincere remorse for that, as with fond love for her many amiable qualities. He owned to having treated her very ill: and that at this time his life was one of profligacy, gambling, and poverty. She became with child of you; was cursed by her own parents at that discovery; though she never upbraided, except by her involuntary tears, and the misery depicted on her countenance, the author of her wretchedness and ruin.

"Thomas Esmond—Captain Thomas, as he was called—became engaged in a gaming-house brawl, of which the consequence was a duel, and a wound so severe that he never—his surgeon said—could outlive it. Thinking his death certain, and touched with remorse, he sent for a priest of the very Church of St. Gudule where I met you; and on the same day, after his making submission to our Church, was married to your mother a few weeks before you were born. My Lord Viscount Castlewood, Marquis of Esmond, by King James's patent, which I myself took to your father, your Lordship was christened at St. Gudule by the same curé who married your parents, and by the name of Henry Thomas, son of E. Thomas, officier Anglois, and Gertrude Maes. You see you belong to us from your birth, and why I did not christen you when you became my dear little pupil at Castlewood.

"Your father's wound took a favourable turn—perhaps his conscience was eased by the right he had done—and to the surprise of the doctors he recovered. But as his health came back, his wicked nature, too, returned. He was tired of the poor girl whom he had ruined; and receiving some remittance from his uncle, my Lord the old Viscount, then in England, he pretended business, promised return, and never saw your poor mother more.

"He owned to me, in confession first, but afterwards in talk before your aunt, his wife, else I never could have disclosed what I now tell you, that on coming to London he writ a pretended confession to poor Gertrude Maes—Gertrude Esmond—of his having been married in England previously, before uniting himself with her; said that his name was not Thomas; that he was about to quit Europe for the Virginian plantations, where, indeed, your family had a grant of land from King Charles the First; sent her a supply of money, the half of the last hundred guineas he had, entreated her pardon, and bade her farewell.

"Poor Gertrude never thought that the news in this letter might be untrue as the rest of your father's conduct to her. But though a young man of her own degree, who knew her history, and whom she liked before she saw the English gentleman who was the cause of all her misery, offered to marry her, and to adopt you as his own child, and give you his name, she refused him. This refusal only angered her father, who had taken her home; she never held up her head there, being the subject of constant unkindness after her fall; and some devout ladies of her acquaintance offering to pay a little pension for her, she went into a convent, and you were put out to nurse.

"A sister of the young fellow who would have adopted you as his son was the person who took charge of you. Your mother and this person were cousins. She had just lost a child of her own, which you replaced, your own mother being too sick and feeble to feed you; and presently your nurse grew so fond of you, that she even grudged letting you visit the convent where your mother was, and where the nuns petted the little infant, as they pitied and loved its unhappy parent. Her vocation became stronger every day, and at the end of two years she was received as a sister of the house.

"Your nurse's family were silk-weavers out of France, whither they returned to Arras in French Flanders, shortly before your mother took her vows, carrying you with them, then a child of three years old. 'Twas a town, before the late vigorous measures of the French King, full of Protestants, and here your nurse's father, old Pastoureau, he with whom you afterwards lived at Ealing, adopted the reformed doctrines, perverting all his house with him. They were expelled thence by the edict of his Most Christian Majesty, and came to London, and set up their looms in Spittlefields. The old man brought a little money with him, and carried on his trade, but in a poor way. He was a widower; by this time his daughter, a widow too, kept house for him, and his son and he laboured together at their vocation. Meanwhile your father had publicly owned his conversion just before King Charles's death (in whom our Church had much such another convert), was reconciled to my Lord Viscount Castlewood, and married, as you know, to his daughter.

"It chanced that the younger Pastoureau, going with a piece of brocade to the mercer who employed him, on Ludgate Hill, met his old rival coming out of an ordinary there. Pastoureau knew your father at once, seized him by the collar, and upbraided him as a villain, who had seduced his mistress, and afterwards deserted her and her son. Mr. Thomas Esmond also recognised Pastoureau at once, besought him to calm his indignation, and not to bring a crowd round about them; and bade him to enter into the tavern, out of which he had just stepped, when he would give him any explanation. Pastoureau entered, and heard the landlord order the drawer to show Captain Thomas to a room; it was by his Christian name that your father was familiarly called at his tavern haunts, which, to say the truth, were none of the most reputable.

"I must tell you that Captain Thomas, or my Lord Viscount afterwards, was never at a loss for a story, and could cajole a woman or a dun with a volubility, and an air of simplicity at the same time, of which many a creditor of his has been the dupe. His tales used to gather verisimilitude as he went on with them. He strung together fact after fact with a wonderful rapidity and coherence. It required, saving your presence, a very long habit of acquaintance with your father to know when his Lordship was l——, —telling the truth or no.

"He told me with rueful remorse when he was ill—for the fear of death set him instantly repenting, and with shrieks of laughter when he was well, his Lordship having a very great sense of humour—how in half-an-hour's time, and before a bottle was drunk, he had completely succeeded in biting poor Pastoureau. The seduction he owned to: that he could not help: he was quite ready with tears at a moment's warning, and shed them profusely to melt his credulous listener. He wept for your mother even more than Pastoureau did, who cried very heartily, poor fellow, as my Lord informed me; he swore upon his honour that he had twice sent money to Brussels, and mentioned the name of the merchant with whom it was lying for poor Gertrude's use. He did not even know whether she had a child or no, or whether she was alive or dead; but got these facts easily out of honest Pastoureau's answers to him. When he heard that she was in a convent, he said he hoped to end his days in one himself, should he survive his wife, whom he hated, and had been forced by a cruel father to marry; and when he was told that Gertrude's son was alive, and actually in London, 'I started,' says he; 'for then, damme, my wife was expecting to lie-in, and I thought should this old Put, my father-in-law, run rusty, here would be a good chance to frighten him.'

"He expressed the deepest gratitude to the Pastoureau family for the care of the infant: you were now near six years old; and on Pastoureau bluntly telling him, when he proposed to go that instant and see the darling child, that they never wished to see his ill-omened face again within their doors; that he might have the boy, though they should all be very sorry to lose him; and that they would take his money, they being poor, if he gave it; or bring him up, by God's help, as they had hitherto done, without: he acquiesced in this at once, with a sigh, said, 'Well, 'twas better that the dear child should remain with friends who had been so admirably kind to him;' and in his talk to me afterwards, honestly praised and admired the weaver's conduct and spirit; owned that the Frenchman was a right fellow, and he, the Lord have mercy upon him, a sad villain.

"Your father," Mr. Holt went on to say, "was good-natured with his money when he had it; and having that day received a supply from his uncle, gave the weaver ten pieces with perfect freedom, and promised him further remittances. He took down eagerly Pastoureau's name and place of abode in his table-book, and when the other asked him for his own, gave, with the utmost readiness, his name as Captain Thomas, New Lodge, Penzance, Cornwall; he said he was in London for a few days only on business connected with his wife's property; described her as a shrew, though a woman of kind disposition; and depicted his father as a Cornish squire, in an infirm state of health, at whose death he hoped for something handsome, when he promised richly to reward the admirable protector of his child, and to provide for the boy. 'And by Gad, sir,' he said to me in his strange laughing way, 'I ordered a piece of brocade of the very same pattern as that which the fellow was carrying, and presented it to my wife for a morning wrapper, to receive company after she lay-in of our little boy.'

"Your little pension was paid regularly enough; and when your father became Viscount Castlewood on his uncle's demise, I was employed to keep a watch over you, and 'twas at my instance that you were brought home. Your foster-mother was dead; her father made acquaintance with a woman whom he married, who quarrelled with his son. The faithful creature came back to Brussels to be near the woman he loved, and died, too, a few months before her. Will you see her cross in the convent cemetery? The Superior is an old penitent of mine, and remembers Sœur Marie Madeleine fondly still."

Esmond came to this spot in one sunny evening of spring, and saw, amidst a thousand black crosses, casting their shadows across the grassy mounds, that particular one which marked his mother's resting-place. Many more of those poor creatures that lay there had adopted that same name, with which sorrow had rebaptized her, and which fondly seemed to hint their individual story of love and grief. He fancied her in tears and darkness, kneeling at the foot of her cross, under which her cares were buried. Surely he knelt down, and said his own prayer there, not in sorrow so much as in awe (for even his memory had no recollection of her), and in pity for the pangs which the gentle soul in life had been made to suffer. To this cross she brought them; for this heavenly bridegroom she exchanged the husband who had wooed her, the traitor who had left her. A thousand such hillocks lay round about, the gentle daisies springing out of the grass over them, and each bearing its cross and requiescat. A nun, veiled in black, was kneeling hard by, at a sleeping sister's bedside (so fresh made, that the spring had scarce had time to spin a coverlid for it); beyond the cemetery walls you had glimpses of life and the world, and the spires and gables of the city. A bird came down from a roof opposite, and lit first on a cross, and then on the grass below it, whence it flew away presently with a leaf in its mouth: then came a sound as of chanting, from the chapel of the sisters hard by; others had long since filled the place which poor Mary Magdalene once had there, were kneeling at the same stall, and hearing the same hymns and prayers in which her stricken heart had found consolation. Might she sleep in peace—might she sleep in peace; and we, too, when our struggles and pains are over! But the earth is the Lord's as the heaven is; we are alike His creatures here and yonder. I took a little flower off the hillock and kissed it, and went my way, like the bird that had just lighted on the cross by me, back into the world again. Silent receptacle of death; tranquil depth of calm, out of reach of tempest and trouble! I felt as one who had been walking below the sea, and treading amidst the bones of shipwrecks.

CHAPTER XIV

THE CAMPAIGN OF 1707, 1708

DURING the whole of the year which succeeded that in which the glorious battle of Ramillies had been fought, our army made no movement of importance, much to the disgust of very many of our officers remaining inactive in Flanders, who said that his Grace the Captain-General had had fighting enough, and was all for money now, and the enjoyment of his five thousand a year and his splendid palace at Woodstock, which was now being built. And his Grace had sufficient occupation fighting his enemies at home this year, where it began to be whispered that his favour was decreasing, and his Duchess losing her hold on the Queen, who was transferring her royal affections to the famous Mrs. Masham, and Mrs. Masham's humble servant, Mr. Harley. Against their intrigues, our Duke passed a great part of his time intriguing. Mr. Harley was got out of office, and his Grace, in so far, had a victory. But her Majesty, convinced against her will, was of that opinion still, of which the poet says people are when so convinced, and Mr. Harley before long had his revenge.

Meanwhile the business of fighting did not go on any way to the satisfaction of Marlborough's gallant lieutenants. During all 1707, with the French before us, we had never so much as a battle; our army in Spain was utterly routed at Almanza by the gallant Duke of Berwick; and we of Webb's, which regiment the young Duke had commanded before his father's abdication, were a little proud to think that it was our colonel who had achieved this victory. "I think if I had had Galway's place, and my Fusileers," says our General, "we would not have laid down our arms, even to our old colonel, as Galway did;" and Webb's officers swore if we had had Webb, at least we would not have been taken prisoners. Our dear old General talked incautiously of himself and of others; a braver or a more brilliant soldier never lived than he; but he blew his honest trumpet rather more loudly than became a commander of his station, and, mighty man of valour as he was, shook his great spear and blustered before the army too fiercely.

Mysterious Mr. Holtz went off on a secret expedition in the

early part of 1708, with great elation of spirits and a prophecy to Esmond that a wonderful something was about to take place. This secret came out on my friend's return to the army, whither he brought a most rueful and dejected countenance, and owned that the great something he had been engaged upon had failed utterly. He had been indeed with that luckless expedition of the Chevalier de St. George, who was sent by the French King with ships and an army from Dunkirk, and was to have invaded and conquered Scotland. But that ill wind which ever opposed all the projects upon which the Prince ever embarked, prevented the Chevalier's invasion of Scotland, as 'tis known, and blew poor Monsieur von Holtz back into our camp again, to scheme and foretell, and to pry about as usual. The Chevalier (the King of England, as some of us held him) went from Dunkirk to the French army to make the campaign against us. The Duke of Burgundy had the command this year, having the Duke of Berry with him, and the famous Mareschal Vendosme and the Duke of Matignon to aid him in the campaign. Holtz, who knew everything that was passing in Flanders and France (and the Indies for what I know), insisted that there would be no more fighting in 1708 than there had been in the previous year, and that our commander had reasons for keeping him quiet. Indeed, Esmond's General, who was known as a grumbler, and to have a hearty mistrust of the great Duke, and hundreds more officers besides, did not scruple to say that these private reasons came to the Duke in the shape of crown-pieces from the French King, by whom the Generalissimo was bribed to avoid a battle. There were plenty of men in our lines, quidnuncs, to whom Mr. Webb listened only too willingly, who could specify the exact sums the Duke got, how much fell to Cadogan's share, and what was the precise fee given to Doctor Hare.

And the successes with which the French began the campaign of 1708 served to give strength to these reports of treason, which were in everybody's mouth. Our General allowed the enemy to get between us and Ghent, and declined to attack him though for eight-and-forty hours the armies were in presence of each other. Ghent was taken, and on the same day Monsieur de la Mothe summoned Bruges; and these two great cities fell into the hands of the French without firing a shot. A few days afterwards La Mothe seized upon the fort of Plashendall: and it began to be supposed that all Spanish Flanders, as well as Brabant, would fall into the hands of the French troops; when the Prince Eugene arrived from the Mozelle, and then there was no more shilly-shallying.

The Prince of Savoy always signalised his arrival at the army by a great feast (my Lord Duke's entertainments were both seldom and shabby); and I remember our General returning from this dinner with the two Commanders-in-Chief; his honest head a little excited by wine, which was dealt out much more liberally by the Austrian than by the English commander:—"Now," says my General, slapping the table, with an oath, "he must fight; and when he is forced to it, d—— it, no man in Europe can stand up against Jack Churchill." Within a week the battle of Oudenarde was fought, when, hate each other as they might, Esmond's General and the Commander-in-Chief were forced to admire each other, so splendid was the gallantry of each upon this day.

The brigade commanded by Major-General Webb gave and received about as hard knocks as any that were delivered in that action, in which Mr. Esmond had the fortune to serve at the head of his own company in his regiment, under the command of their own Colonel as Major-General; and it was his good luck to bring the regiment out of action as commander of it, the four senior officers above him being killed in the prodigious slaughter which happened on that day. I like to think that Jack Haythorn, who sneered at me for being a bastard and a parasite of Webb's, as he chose to call me, and with whom I had had words, shook hands with me the day before the battle begun. Three days before, poor Brace, our Lieutenant-Colonel, had heard of his elder brother's death, and was heir to a baronetcy in Norfolk, and four thousand a year. Fate, that had left him harmless through a dozen campaigns, seized on him just as the world was worth living for, and he went into action knowing, as he said, that the luck was going to turn against him. The Major had just joined us—a creature of Lord Marlborough, put in much to the dislike of the other officers, and to be a spy upon us, as it was said. I know not whether the truth was so, nor who took the tattle of our mess to headquarters, but Webb's regiment, as its Colonel, was known to be in the Commander-in-Chief's black books: "And if he did not dare to break it up at home," our gallant old chief used to say, "he was determined to destroy it before the enemy;" so that poor Major Proudfoot was put into a post of danger.

Esmond's dear young Viscount, serving as aide-de-camp to my Lord Duke, received a wound, and won an honourable name for himself in the Gazette; and Captain Esmond's name was sent in for promotion by his General, too, whose favourite he was. It made his heart beat to think that certain eyes at home, the brightest in the world, might read the page on which his humble services were recorded; but his mind was made up steadily to keep out of their dangerous influence, and to let time and absence conquer that passion he had still lurking about him. Away from Beatrix, it did not trouble him; but he knew as certain that if he returned home, his fever would break out again, and avoided Walcote as a Lincolnshire man avoids returning to his fens, where he is sure that the ague is lying in wait for him.

We of the English party in the army, who were inclined to sneer at everything that came out of Hanover, and to treat as little better than boors and savages the Elector's Court and family, were yet forced to confess that, on the day of Oudenarde, the young Electoral Prince, then making his first campaign, conducted himself with the spirit and courage of an approved soldier. On this occasion his Electoral Highness had better luck than the King of England, who was with his cousins in the enemy's camp, and had to run with them at the ignominious end of the day. With the most consummate generals in the world before them, and an admirable commander on their own side, they chose to neglect the counsels, and to rush into a combat with the former, which would have ended in the utter annihilation of their army but for the great skill and bravery of the Duke of Vendosme, who remedied, as far as courage and genius might, the disasters occasioned by the squabbles and follies of his kinsmen, the legitimate princes of the blood royal.

"If the Duke of Berwick had but been in the army, the fate of the day would have been very different," was all that poor Mr. von Holtz could say; "and you would have seen that the hero of Almanza was fit to measure swords with the conqueror of Blenheim."

The business relative to the exchange of prisoners was always going on, and was at least that ostensible one which kept Mr. Holtz perpetually on the move between the forces of the French and the Allies. I can answer for it, that he was once very near hanged as a spy by Major-General Wayne, when he was released and sent on to headquarters by a special order of the Commander-in-chief. He came and went, always favoured, wherever he was, by some high though occult protection. He carried messages between the Duke of Berwick and his uncle, our Duke. He seemed to know as well what was taking place in the Prince's quarter as our own: he brought the compliments of the King of England to some of our officers, the gentlemen of Webb's among the rest, for their behaviour on that great day; and after Wynendael, when our General was chafing at the neglect of our Commander-in Chief, he said he knew how that action was regarded by the chiefs of the French army, and that the stand made before Wynendael wood was the passage by which the Allies entered Lille.

"Ah!" says Holtz (and some folks were very willing to listen to him), "if the King came by his own, how changed the conduct of affairs would be! His Majesty's very exile has this advantage, that he is enabled to read England impartially, and to judge honestly of all the eminent men. His sister is always in the hand of one greedy favourite or another, through whose eyes she sees, and to whose flattery or dependants she gives away everything. Do you suppose that his Majesty, knowing England so well as he does, would neglect such a man as General Webb? He ought to be in the House of Peers as Lord Lydiard. The enemy and all Europe know his merit; it is that very reputation which certain great people, who hate all equality and independence, can never pardon." It was intended that these conversations should be carried to Mr. Webb. They were welcome to him, for great as his services were, no man could value them more than John Richmond Webb did himself, and the differences between him and Marlborough being notorious, his Grace's enemies in the army and at home began to court Webb, and set him up against the all-grasping, domineering chief. And soon after the victory of Oudenarde, a glorious opportunity fell into General Webb's way, which that gallant warrior did not neglect, and which gave him the means of immensely increasing his reputation at home.

After Oudenarde, and against the counsels of Marlborough, it was said, the Prince of Savoy sat down before Lille, the capital of French Flanders, and commenced that siege, the most celebrated of our time, and almost as famous as the siege of Troy itself for the feats of valour performed in the assault and the defence. The enmity of the Prince of Savoy against the French King was a furious personal hate, quite unlike the calm hostility of our great English General, who was no more moved by the game of war than that of billiards, and pushed forward his squadrons, and drove his red battalions hither and thither, as calmly as he would combine a stroke or make a cannon with the balls. The game over (and he played it so as to be pretty sure to win it), not the least animosity against the other party remained in the breast of this consummate tactician. Whereas between the Prince of Savoy and the French it was *guerre à mort*. Beaten off in one quarter, as he had been in Toulon in the last year, he was back again on another frontier of France, assailing it with his indefatigable fury. When the Prince came to the army, the smouldering fires of war were lighted up and burst out into a flame. Our phlegmatic Dutch allies were made to advance at a quick march—our calm Duke forced into action. The Prince was an army in himself against the French; the energy of his hatred, prodigious, indefatigable—infectious over hundreds of thousands of men. The Emperor's General was repaying, and with a vengeance, the slight the French King had put upon the fiery little Abbé of Savoy. Brilliant and famous as a leader himself, and beyond all measure daring and intrepid, and enabled to cope with almost the best of those famous men of war who commanded the armies of the French King, Eugene had a weapon, the equal of which could not be found in France since the cannon-shot of Sasbach laid low the noble Turenne, and could hurl Marlborough at the heads of the French host, and crush them as with a rock, under which all the gathered strength of their strongest captains must go down.

The English Duke took little part in that vast siege of Lille, which the Imperial Generalissimo pursued with all his force and vigour, further than to cover the besieging lines from the Duke of Burgundy's army, between which and the Imperialists our Duke lay. Once, when Prince Eugene was wounded, our Duke took his Highness's place in the trenches; but the siege was with the Imperialists, not with us. A division under Webb and Rantzau was detached into Artois and Picardy upon the most painful and odious service that Mr. Esmond ever saw in the course of his military life. The wretched towns of the defenceless provinces, whose young men had been drafted away into the French armies, which year after year the insatiable war devoured, were left at our mercy; and our orders were to show them none. We found places garrisoned by invalids, and children and women; poor as they were, and as the costs of this miserable war had made them, our commission was to rob these almost starving wretches—to tear the food out of their granaries, and strip them of their rags. 'Twas an expedition of rapine and murder we were sent on: our soldiers did deeds such as an honest man must blush to remember. We brought back money and provisions in quantity to the Duke's camp; there had been no one to resist us, and yet who dares to tell with what murder and violence, with what brutal cruelty, outrage, insult, that ignoble booty had been ravished from the innocent and miserable victims of the war?

Meanwhile, gallantly as the operations before Lille had been conducted, the Allies had made but little progress, and 'twas said when we returned to the Duke of Marlborough's camp, that the siege would never be brought to a satisfactory end, and that the Prince of Savoy would be forced to raise it. My Lord Marlborough gave this as his opinion openly; those who mistrusted him, and Mr. Esmond owns himself to be of the number, hinted that the Duke had his reasons why Lille should not be taken, and that he was paid to that end by the French King. If this was so, and I believe it,

General Webb had now a remarkable opportunity of gratifying his hatred of the Commander-in-chief, of balking that shameful avarice, which was one of the basest and most notorious qualities of the famous Duke, and of showing his own consummate skill as a commander. And when I consider all the circumstances preceding the event which will now be related, that my Lord Duke was actually offered certain millions of crowns provided that the siege of Lille should be raised; that the Imperial army before it was without provisions and ammunition, and must have decamped but for the supplies that they received; that the march of the convoy destined to relieve the siege was accurately known to the French; and that the force covering it was shamefully inadequate to that end, and by six times inferior to Count de la Mothe's army, which was sent to intercept the convoy; when 'tis certain that the Duke of Berwick, De la Mothe's chief, was in constant correspondence with his uncle, the English Generalissimo: I believe on my conscience that 'twas my Lord Marlborough's intention to prevent those supplies, of which the Prince of Savoy stood in absolute need, from ever reaching his Highness; that he meant to sacrifice the little army which covered this convoy, and to betray it as he had betrayed Tollemache at Brest; as he had betrayed every friend he had, to further his own schemes of avarice or ambition. But for the miraculous victory which Esmond's General won over an army six or seven times greater than his own, the siege of Lille must have been raised; and it must be remembered that our gallant little force was under the command of a general whom Marlborough hated, that he was furious with the conqueror, and tried afterwards by the most open and shameless injustice to rob him of the credit of his victory.

CHAPTER XV

GENERAL WEBB WINS THE BATTLE OF WYNENDAEL

BY the besiegers and besieged of Lille, some of the most brilliant feats of valour were performed that ever illustrated any war. On the French side (whose gallantry was prodigious, the skill and bravery of Marshal Boufflers actually eclipsing those of his conqueror, the Prince of Savoy) may be mentioned that daring action of Messieurs de Luxembourg and Tournefort, who, with a body of horse and dragoons, carried powder into the town, of which the besieged were in extreme want, each soldier bringing a bag with forty pounds of powder behind him; with which perilous provision they engaged our own horse, faced the fire of the foot brought out to meet them: and though half of the men were blown up in the dreadful errand they rode on, a part of them got into the town with the succours of which the garrison was so much in want. A French officer, Monsieur du Bois, performed an act equally daring, and perfectly successful. The Duke's great army lying at Helchin, and covering the siege, and it being necessary for M. de Vendosme to get news of the condition of the place, Captain du Bois performed his famous exploit: not only passing through the lines of the siege, but swimming afterwards no less than seven moats and ditches: and coming back the same way, swimming with his letters in his mouth.

By these letters Monsieur de Boufflers said that he could undertake to hold the place till October; and that if one of the convoys of the Allies could be intercepted, they must raise the siege altogether.

Such a convoy as hath been said was now prepared at Ostend, and about to march for the siege; and on the 27th September we (and the French too) had news that it was on its way. It was composed of 700 waggons, containing ammunition of all sorts, and was escorted out of Ostend by 2000 infantry and 300 horse. At the same time M. de la Mothe quitted Bruges, having with him five-and-thirty battalions, and upwards of sixty squadrons and forty guns, in pursuit of the convoy.

Major-General Webb had meanwhile made up a force of twenty

battalions and three squadrons of dragoons at Turout, whence he moved to cover the convoy and pursue La Mothe: with whose advanced guard ours came up upon the great plain of Turout, and before the little wood and castle of Wynendael; behind which the convoy was marching.

As soon as they came in sight of the enemy, our advanced troops were halted, with the wood behind them, and the rest of our force brought up as quickly as possible, our little body of horse being brought forward to the opening of the plain, as our General said, to amuse the enemy. When M. de la Mothe came up, he found us posted in two lines in front of the wood; and formed his own army in battle facing ours, in eight lines, four of infantry in front, and dragoons and cavalry behind.

The French began the action, as usual, with a cannonade which lasted three hours, when they made their attack, advancing in eight lines, four of foot and four of horse, upon the allied troops in the wood where we were posted. Their infantry behaved ill: they were ordered to charge with the bayonet, but, instead, began to fire, and almost at the very first discharge from our men, broke and fled. The cavalry behaved better; with these alone, who were three or four times as numerous as our whole force, Monsieur de la Mothe might have won victory: but only two of our battalions were shaken in the least; and these speedily rallied: nor could the repeated attacks of the French horse cause our troops to budge an inch from the position in the wood in which our General had placed them.

After attacking for two hours, the French retired at nightfall entirely foiled. With all the loss we had inflicted upon him, the enemy was still three times stronger than we: and it could not be supposed that our General could pursue M. de la Mothe, or do much more than hold our ground about the wood, from which the Frenchmen had in vain attempted to dislodge us. La Mothe retired behind his forty guns, his cavalry protecting them better than it had been able to annoy us; and meanwhile the convoy, which was of more importance than all our little force, and the safe passage of which we would have dropped to the last man to accomplish, marched away in perfect safety during the action, and joyfully reached the besieging camp before Lille.

Major-General Cadogan, my Lord Duke's Quartermaster-General (and between whom and Mr. Webb there was no love lost), accompanied the convoy, and joined Mr. Webb with a couple of hundred horse just as the battle was over, and the enemy in full retreat. He offered, readily enough, to charge with his horse upon the French as they fell back; but his force was too weak to inflict any damage upon them; and Mr. Webb, commanding as Cadogan's senior, thought enough was done in holding our ground before an enemy that might still have overwhelmed us had we engaged him in the open territory, and in securing the safe passage of the convoy. Accordingly, the horse brought up by Cadogan did not draw a sword; and only prevented, by the good countenance they showed, any disposition the French might have had to renew the attack on us. And no attack coming, at nightfall General Cadogan drew off with his squadron, being bound for headquarters, the two Generals at parting grimly saluting each other.

"He will be at Roncq time enough to lick my Lord Duke's trenchers at supper," says Mr. Webb.

Our own men lay out in the woods of Wynendael that night, and our General had his supper in the little castle there.

"If I was Cadogan, I would have a peerage for this day's work," General Webb said; "and, Harry, thou shouldst have a regiment. Thou hast been reported in the last two actions; thou wert near killed in the first. I shall mention thee in my despatch to his Grace the Commander-in-Chief, and recommend thee to poor Dick Harwood's vacant majority. Have you ever a hundred guineas to give Cardonnel? Slip them into his hand to-morrow, when you go to headquarters with my report."

In this report the Major-General was good enough to mention Captain Esmond's name with particular favour; and that gentleman carried the despatch to headquarters the next day, and was not a little pleased to bring back a letter by his Grace's secretary, addressed to Lieutenant-General Webb. The Dutch officer despatched by Count Nassau Woudenbourg, Vælt-Mareschal Auverquerque's son, brought back also a complimentary letter to his commander, who had seconded Mr. Webb in the action with great valour and skill.

Esmond, with a low bow and a smiling face, presented his despatch, and saluted Mr. Webb as Lieutenant-General, as he gave it in. The gentlemen round about him—he was riding with his suite on the road to Menin as Esmond came up with him—gave a cheer, and he thanked them, and opened the despatch with rather a flushed, eager face.

He slapped it down on his boot in a rage after he had read it. "'Tis not even writ with his own hand. Read it out, Esmond." And Esmond read it out:—

"SIR,—Mr. Cadogan is just now come in, and has acquainted me with the success of the action you had yesterday in the afternoon against the body of troops commanded by M. de la Mothe, at

Wynendael, which must be attributed chiefly to your good conduct and resolution. You may be sure I shall do you justice at home, and be glad on all occasions to own the service you have done in securing this convoy.—Yours, &c., M."

"Two lines by that d——d Cardonnel, and no more, for the taking of Lille—for beating five times our number—for an action as brilliant as the best he ever fought," says poor Mr. Webb. "Lieutenant-General! That's not his doing. I was the oldest major-general. By ——, I believe he had been better pleased if I had been beat."

The letter to the Dutch officer was in French, and longer and more complimentary than that to Mr. Webb.

"And this is the man," he broke out, "that's gorged with gold—that's covered with titles and honours that we won for him—and that grudges even a line of praise to a comrade in arms! Hasn't he enough? Don't we fight that he may roll in riches? Well, well, wait for the *Gazette*, gentlemen. The Queen and the country will do us justice if his Grace denies it us." There were tears of rage in the brave warrior's eyes as he spoke; and he dashed them off his face on to his glove. He shook his fist in the air. "Oh, by the Lord!" says he, "I know what I had rather have than a peerage!"

"And what is that, sir?" some of them asked.

"I had rather have a quarter of an hour with John Churchill, on a fair green field, and only a pair of rapiers between my shirt and his——"

"Sir!" interposes one.

"Tell him so! I know that's what you mean. I know every word goes to him that's dropped from every general officer's mouth. I don't say he's not brave. Curse him! he's brave enough; but we'll wait for the *Gazette*, gentlemen. God save her Majesty! she'll do us justice."

The *Gazette* did not come to us till a month afterwards; when my General and his officers had the honour to dine with Prince Eugene in Lille; his Highness being good enough to say that we had brought the provisions, and ought to share in the banquet. 'Twas a great banquet. His Grace of Marlborough was on his Highness's right, and on his left the Mareschal de Boufflers, who had so bravely defended the place. The chief officers of either army were present; and you may be sure Esmond's General was splendid this day: his tall noble person, and manly beauty of face, made him remarkable anywhere; he wore, for the first time, the star of the Order of Generosity, that his Prussian Majesty had sent to him for his victory. His Highness the Prince of Savoy called a toast to the conqueror of Wynendael. My Lord Duke drank it with rather a sickly smile. The aides-de-camp were present; and Harry Esmond and his dear young lord were together, as they always strove to be when duty would permit: they were over against the table where the generals were, and could see all that passed pretty well. Frank laughed at my Lord Duke's glum face: the affair of Wynendael, and the Captain-General's conduct to Webb, had been the talk of the whole army. When his Highness spoke, and gave, "Le vainqueur de Wynendael; son armée et sa victoire," adding, "qui nous font dîner à Lille aujourd'huy"—there was a great cheer through the hall; for Mr. Webb's bravery, generosity, and very weaknesses of character caused him to be beloved in the army.

"Like Hector, handsome, and like Paris, brave!" whispers Frank Castlewood. "A Venus, an elderly Venus, couldn't refuse him a pippin. Stand up, Harry! See, we are drinking the army of Wynendael. Ramillies is nothing to it. Huzzay! huzzay!"

At this very time, and just after our General had made his acknowledgment, some one brought in an English *Gazette*—and was passing it from hand to hand down the table. Officers were eager enough to read it; mothers and sisters at home must have sickened over it. There scarce came out a *Gazette* for six years that did not tell of some heroic death or some brilliant achievement.

"Here it is—Action of Wynendael—here you are, General," says Frank, seizing hold of the little dingy paper that soldiers love to read so; and, scrambling over from our bench, he went to where the General sat, who knew him, and had seen many a time at his table his laughing, handsome face, which everybody loved who saw. The Generals in their great perukes made way for him. He handed the paper over General Dohna's buff-coat to our General on the opposite side.

He came hobbling back, and blushing at his feat: "I thought he'd like it, Harry," the young fellow whispered. "Didn't I like to read my name after Ramillies, in the *London Gazette?*—Viscount, Castlewood serving a volunteer—— I say, what's yonder?"

Mr. Webb, reading the *Gazette*, looked very strange—slapped it down on the table—then sprang up in his place, and began, "Will your Highness please to——"

His Grace the Duke of Marlborough here jumped up too—"There's some mistake, my dear General Webb."

"Your Grace had better rectify it," says Mr. Webb, holding out the letter; but he was five off his Grace the Prince Duke, who, besides, was higher than the General (being seated with the Prince of Savoy, the Electoral Prince of Hanover, and the envoys of Prussia and Denmark, under a baldaquin), and Webb could not reach him, tall as he was.

"Stay," says he, with a smile, as if catching at some idea, and then, with a perfect courtesy, drawing his sword, he ran the *Gazette* through with the point, and said, "Permit me to hand it to your Grace.

The Duke looked very black. "Take it," says he, to his Master of the Horse, who was waiting behind him.

The Lieutenant-General made a very low bow, and retired and finished his glass. The *Gazette* in which Mr. Cardonnel, the Duke's secretary, gave an account of the victory of Wynendael, mentioned Mr. Webb's name, but gave the sole praise and conduct of the action to the Duke's favourite, Mr. Cadogan.

There was no little talk and excitement occasioned by this strange behaviour of General Webb, who had almost drawn a sword upon the Commander-in-Chief; but the General, after the first outbreak of his anger, mastered it outwardly altogether; and, by his subsequent behaviour, had the satisfaction of even more angering the Commander-in-Chief, than he could have done by any public exhibition of resentment.

On returning to his quarters, and consulting with his chief adviser, Mr. Esmond, who was now entirely in the General's confidence, and treated by him as a friend, and almost a son, Mr. Webb writ a letter to his Grace the Commander-in-Chief, in which he said:—

"Your Grace must be aware that the sudden perusal of the *London Gazette*, in which your Grace's secretary, Mr. Cardonnel, hath mentioned Major-General Cadogan's name as the officer commanding in the late action of Wynendael, must have caused a feeling of anything but pleasure to the General who fought that action.

"Your Grace must be aware that Mr. Cadogan was not even present at the battle, though he arrived with squadrons of horse at its close, and put himself under the command of his superior officer. And as the result of the battle of Wynendael, in which Lieutenant-General Webb had the good fortune to command, was the capture of Lille, the relief of Brussels, then invested by the enemy under the Elector of Bavaria, the restoration of the great cities of Ghent and Bruges, of which the enemy (by treason within the walls) had got possession in the previous year, Mr. Webb cannot consent to forego the honours of such a success and service, for the benefit of Mr. Cadogan, or any other person.

"As soon as the military operations of the year are over, Lieutenant-General Webb will request permission to leave the army, and return to his place in Parliament, where he gives notice to his Grace the Commander-in-Chief, that he shall lay his case before the House of Commons, the country, and her Majesty the Queen.

"By his eagerness to rectify that false statement of the *Gazette*, which had been written by his Grace's secretary, Mr. Cardonnel, Mr. Webb, not being able to reach his Grace the Commander-in-Chief on account of the gentlemen seated between them, placed the paper containing the false statement on his sword, so that it might more readily arrive in the hands of his Grace the Duke of Marlborough, who surely would wish to do justice to every officer of his army.

"Mr. Webb knows his duty too well to think of insubordination to his superior officer, or of using his sword in a campaign against any but the enemies of her Majesty. He solicits permission to return to England immediately the military duties will permit, and take with him to England Captain Esmond, of his regiment, who acted as his aide-de-camp, and was present during the entire action, and noted by his watch the time when Mr. Cadogan arrived at its close."

The Commander-in-Chief could not but grant his permission, nor could he take notice of Webb's letter, though it was couched in terms the most insulting. Half the army believed that the cities of Ghent and Bruges were given up by a treason, which some in our army very well understood; that the Commander-in-Chief would not have relieved Lille, if he could have helped himself; that he would not have fought that year had not the Prince of Savoy forced him. When the battle once began, then, for his own renown, my Lord Marlborough would fight as no man in the world ever fought better; and no bribe on earth could keep him from beating the enemy.*

* Our grandfather's hatred of the Duke of Marlborough appears all through his account of these campaigns. He always persisted that the Duke was the greatest traitor and soldier history ever told of: and declared that he took bribes on all hands during the war. My Lord Marquis (for so we may call him here, though he never went by any other name than Colonel Esmond) was in the habit of telling many stories which he did not set down in his memoirs, and which he had from his friend the Jesuit, who was not always correctly informed, and who persisted that Marlborough was looking for a bribe of two millions of crowns before the campaign of Ramillies.

And our grandmother used to tell us children, that on his first presentation to my Lord Duke, the Duke turned his back upon my grandfather; and said to the Duchess, who told my Lady Dowager at Chelsey, who afterwards told Colonel Esmond: "Tom Esmond's bastard has been to my levée: he has the hangdog look of his rogue of a father"—an expression which my grandfather never forgave. He was as constant in his dislikes as in his attachments; and exceedingly partial to Webb, whose side he took against the more celebrated general. We have General Webb's portrait now at Castlewood, Va.

But the matter was taken up by the subordinates; and half the army might have been by the ears, if the quarrel had not been stopped. General Cadogan sent an intimation to General Webb to say that he was ready if Webb liked, and would meet him. This was a kind of invitation our stout old General was always too ready to accept, and 'twas with great difficulty we got the General to reply that he had no quarrel with Mr. Cadogan, who had behaved with perfect gallantry, but only with those at headquarters, who had belied him. Mr. Cardonnel offered General Webb reparation; Mr. Webb said he had a cane at the service of Mr. Cardonnel, and the only satisfaction he wanted from him was one he was not likely to get, namely, the truth. The officers in our staff of Webb's, and those in the immediate suite of the General, were ready to come to blows; and hence arose the only affair in which Mr. Esmond ever engaged as principal, and that was from a revengeful wish to wipe off an old injury.

My Lord Mohun, who had a troop in Lord Macclesfield's regiment of the Horse Guards, rode this campaign with the Duke. He had sunk by this time to the very worst reputation; he had had another fatal duel in Spain; he had married, and forsaken his wife; he was a gambler, a profligate, and debauchee. He joined just before Oudenarde; and, as Esmond feared, as soon as Frank Castlewood heard of his arrival, Frank was for seeking him out, and killing him. The wound my Lord got at Oudenarde prevented their meeting, but that was nearly healed, and Mr. Esmond trembled daily lest any chance should bring his boy and this known assassin together. They met at the mess-table of Handyside's regiment at Lille; the officer commanding not knowing of the feud between the two noblemen.

Esmond had not seen the hateful handsome face of Mohun for nine years, since they had met on that fatal night in Leicester Field. It was degraded with crime and passion now; it wore the anxious look of a man who has three deaths, and who knows how many hidden shames, and lusts, and crimes on his conscience. He bowed with a sickly low bow, and slunk away when our host presented us round to one another. Frank Castlewood had not known him till then, so changed was he. He knew the boy well enough.

'Twas curious to look at the two—especially the young man, whose face flushed up when he heard the hated name of the other; and who said in his bad French and his brave boyish voice, "He had long been anxious to meet my Lord Mohun." The other only bowed, and moved away from him. To do him justice, he wished to have no quarrel with the lad.

Esmond put himself between them at table. "D—— it," says

Frank, "why do you put yourself in the place of a man who is above you in degree? My Lord Mohun should walk after me. I want to sit by my Lord Mohun."

Esmond whispered to Lord Mohun, that Frank was hurt in the leg at Oudenarde; and besought the other to be quiet. Quiet enough he was for some time; disregarding the many taunts which young Castlewood flung at him, until after several healths, when my Lord Mohun got to be rather in liquor.

"Will you go away, my Lord?" Mr. Esmond said to him, imploring him to quit the table.

"No, by G—," says my Lord Mohun. "I'll not go away for any man;" he was quite flushed with wine by this time.

The talk got round to the affairs of yesterday. Webb had offered to challenge the Commander-in-Chief: Webb had been ill-used: Webb was the bravest, handsomest, vainest man in the army. Lord Mohun did not know that Esmond was Webb's aide-de-camp. He began to tell some stories against the General; which, from t'other side of Esmond, young Castlewood contradicted.

"I can't bear any more of this," says my Lord Mohun.

"Nor can I, my Lord," says Mr. Esmond, starting up. "The story my Lord Mohun has told respecting General Webb is false, gentlemen—false, I repeat," and making a low bow to Lord Mohun, and without a single word more, Esmond got up and left the dining-room. These affairs were common enough among the military of those days. There was a garden behind the house, and all the party turned instantly into it; and the two gentlemen's coats were off and their points engaged within two minutes after Esmond's words had been spoken. If Captain Esmond had put Mohun out of the world, as he might, a villain would have been punished and spared further villainies—but who is one man to punish another? I declare upon my honour that my only thought was to prevent Lord Mohun from mischief with Frank, and the end of this meeting was, that after half-a-dozen passes my Lord went home with a hurt which prevented him from lifting his right arm for three months.

"O Harry! why didn't you kill the villain?" young Castlewood asked. "I can't walk without a crutch: but I could have met him on horseback with sword and pistol." But Harry Esmond said, "'Twas best to have no man's life on one's conscience, not even that villain's." And this affair, which did not occupy three minutes, being over, the gentlemen went back to their wine, and my Lord Mohun to his quarters, where he was laid up with a fever which had spared mischief had it proved fatal. And very soon after this affair Harry Esmond and his General left the camp for London; whither a certain reputation had preceded the Captain, for my Lady Castlewood of Chelsey received him as if he had been a conquering hero. She gave a great dinner to Mr. Webb, where the General's chair was crowned with laurels; and her Ladyship called Esmond's health in a toast, to which my kind General was graciously pleased to bear the strongest testimony: and took down a mob of at least forty coaches to cheer our General as he came out of the House of Commons, the day when he received the thanks of Parliament for his action. The mob huzza'd and applauded him, as well as the fine company: it was splendid to see him waving his hat, and bowing, and laying his hand upon his Order of Generosity. He introduced Mr. Esmond to Mr. St. John and the Right Honourable Robert Harley, Esquire, as he came out of the House walking between them; and was pleased to make many flattering observations regarding Mr. Esmond's behaviour during the three last campaigns.

Mr. St. John (who had the most winning presence of any man I ever saw, excepting always my peerless young Frank Castlewood) said he had heard of Mr. Esmond before from Captain Steele, and how he had helped Mr. Addison to write his famous poem of the "Campaign."

"'Twas as great an achievement as the victory of Blenheim itself," Mr. Harley said, who was famous as a judge and patron of letters, and so, perhaps, it may be—though for my part I think there are twenty beautiful lines, but all the rest is commonplace, and Mr. Addison's hymn worth a thousand such poems.

All the town was indignant at my Lord Duke's unjust treatment of General Webb, and applauded the vote of thanks which the House of Commons gave to the General for his victory at Wynendael. 'Tis certain that the capture of Lille was the consequence of that lucky achievement, and the humiliation of the old French King, who was said to suffer more at the loss of this great city, than from any of the former victories our troops had won over him. And, I think, no small part of Mr. Webb's exultation at his victory arose from the idea that Marlborough had been disappointed of a great bribe the French King had promised him, should the siege be raised. The very sum of money offered to him was mentioned by the Duke's enemies; and honest Mr. Webb chuckled at the notion, not only of beating the French, but of beating Marlborough too, and intercepting a convoy of three millions of French crowns, that were on their way to the Generalissimo's insatiable pockets. When the General's lady went to the Queen's drawing-room, all the Tory women crowded round her with congratulations, and made her a train greater than the Duchess of Marlborough's own. Feasts were given to the General by all the chiefs of the Tory party, who vaunted him as the Duke's equal in military skill; and perhaps used the worthy soldier as their instrument, whilst he thought they were but acknowledging his merits as a commander. As the General's aide-de-camp and favourite officer, Mr. Esmond came in for a share of his chief's popularity, and was presented to her Majesty, and advanced to the rank of Lieutenant-Colonel, at the request of his grateful chief.

We may be sure there was one family in which any good fortune that happened to Esmond caused such a sincere pride and pleasure, that he, for his part, was thankful he could make them so happy. With these fond friends Blenheim and Oudenarde seemed to be mere trifling incidents of the war; and Wynendael was its crowning victory. Esmond's mistress never tired to hear accounts of the battle; and I think General Webb's lady grew jealous of her, for the General was for ever at Kensington, and talking on that delightful theme. As for his aide-de-camp, though, no doubt, Esmond's own natural vanity was pleased at the little share of reputation which his good fortune had won him, yet it was chiefly precious to him (he may say so, now that he hath long since outlived it) because it pleased his mistress, and, above all, because Beatrix valued it.

As for the old Dowager of Chelsey, never was an old woman in all England more delighted nor more gracious than she. Esmond had his quarters in her Ladyship's house, where the domestics were instructed to consider him as their master. She bade him give entertainments, of which she defrayed the charges, and was charmed when his guests were carried away tipsy in their coaches. She must have his picture taken; and accordingly he was painted by Mr. Jervas, in his red coat, and smiling upon a bombshell, which was bursting at the corner of the piece. She vowed that unless he made a great match, she should never die easy, and was for ever bringing young ladies to Chelsey, with pretty faces and pretty fortunes, at the disposal of the Colonel. He smiled to think how times were altered with him, and of the early days in his father's lifetime, when a trembling page he stood before her, with her Ladyship's basin and ewer, or crouched in her coach-step. The only fault she found with him was, that he was more sober than an Esmond ought to be; and would neither be carried to bed by his valet, nor lose his heart to any beauty, whether of St. James's or Covent Garden.

What is the meaning of fidelity in love, and whence the birth of it? 'Tis a state of mind that men fall into, and depending on the man rather than the woman. We love being in love, that's the truth on't. If we had not met Joan, we should have met Kate, and adored her. We know our mistresses are no better than many other women, nor no prettier, nor no wiser, nor no wittier. 'Tis not for these reasons we love a woman, or for any special quality or charm I know of; we might as well demand that a lady should be the tallest woman in the world, like the Shropshire giantess,* as that she should be a paragon in any other character, before we began to love her. Esmond's mistress had a thousand faults beside her charms; he knew both perfectly well! She was imperious, she was light minded, she was flighty, she was false, she had no reverence in her character; she was in everything, even in beauty, the contrast of her mother, who was the most devoted and the least selfish of women. Well, from the very first moment he saw her on the stairs at Walcote, Esmond knew he loved Beatrix. There might be better women—he wanted that one. He cared for none other. Was it because she was gloriously beautiful? Beautiful as she was, he had heard people say a score of times in their company that Beatrix's mother looked as young, and was the handsomer of the two. Why did her voice thrill in his ear so? She could not sing near so well as Nicolini or Mrs. Tofts; nay, she sang out of tune, and yet he liked to hear her better than St. Cecilia. She had not a finer complexion than Mrs. Steele (Dick's wife, whom he had now got, and who ruled poor Dick with a rod of pickle), and yet to see her dazzled Esmond; he would shut his eyes, and the thought of her dazzled him all the same. She was brilliant and lively in talk, but not so incomparably witty as her mother, who, when she was cheerful, said the finest things; but yet to hear her, and to be with her, was Esmond's greatest pleasure. Days passed away between him and these ladies, he scarce knew how. He poured his heart out to them, so as he never could in any other company, where he hath generally passed for being moody, or supercilious and silent. This society† was more delightful than that of the greatest wits to him. May Heaven pardon him the lies he told the Dowager at Chelsey in order to get a pretext for going away to Kensington: the business at the Ordnance which he invented; the interviews with his General, the courts and statesmen's levées which he *didn't* frequent, and described; who wore a new suit on Sunday at St. James's or at the Queen's birthday; how many coaches filled the street at Mr. Harley's levée; how many bottles he had had the honour to drink over-night with Mr. St. John at the "Cocoa-Tree," or at the "Garter" with Mr. Walpole and Mr. Steele.

Mistress Beatrix Esmond had been a dozen times on the point of making great matches, so the Court scandal said; but for his

* 'Tis not thus *woman loves:* Col. E. hath owned to this folly for a *score of women* besides.—R.

† And, indeed, so was his to them, a thousand thousand times more charming, for where was his equal?—R.

part Esmond never would believe the stories against her; and came back, after three years' absence from her, not so frantic as he had been perhaps, but still hungering after her and no other; still hopeful, still kneeling, with his heart in his hand for the young lady to take. We were now got to 1709. She was near twenty-two years old, and three years at Court, and without a husband.

"'Tis not for want of being asked," Lady Castlewood said, looking into Esmond's heart, as she could, with that perceptiveness affection gives. "But she will make no mean match, Harry; she will not marry as I would have her; the person whom I should like to call my son, and Henry Esmond knows who that is, is best served by my not pressing his claim. Beatrix is so wilful, that what I would urge on her, she would be sure to resist. The man who would marry her will not be happy with her, unless he be a great person, and can put her in a great position. Beatrix loves admiration more than love; and longs, beyond all things, for command. Why should a mother speak so of her child? You are my son, too, Harry. You should know the truth about your sister. I thought you might cure yourself of your passion," my Lady added fondly. "Other people can cure themselves of that folly, you know. But I see you are still as infatuated as ever. When we read your name in the *Gazette*, I pleaded for you, my poor boy. Poor boy, indeed! You are growing a grave old gentleman, now, and I am an old woman. She likes your fame well enough, and she likes your person. She says you have wit, and fire, and good-breeding, and are more natural than the fine gentlemen of the Court. But this is not enough. She wants a commander-in-chief, and not a colonel. Were a duke to ask her, she would leave an earl whom she had promised. I told you so before. I know not how my poor girl is so worldly."

"Well," says Esmond, "a man can but give his best and his all. She has that from me. What little reputation I have won, I swear I cared for it because I thought Beatrix would be pleased with it. What care I to be a colonel or a general? Think you 'twill matter a few score years hence, what our foolish honours to-day are? I would have had a little fame, that she might wear it in her hat. If I had anything better, I would endow her with it. If she wants my life, I would give it her. If she marries another, I will say God bless him. I make no boast, nor no complaint. I think my fidelity is folly, perhaps. But so it is. I cannot help myself. I love her. You are a thousand times better: the fondest, the fairest, the dearest of women. Sure, my dear lady, I see all Beatrix's faults as well as you do. But she is my fate. 'Tis endurable. I shall not die for not having her. I think I should be no happier if I won her. Que voulez-vous? as my Lady of Chelsey would say. Je l'aime."

"I wish she would have you," said Harry's fond mistress, giving a hand to him. He kissed the fair hand ('twas the prettiest dimpled little hand in the world, and my Lady Castlewood, though now almost forty years old, did not look to be within ten years of her age). He kissed and kept her fair hand as they talked together.

"Why," says he, "should she hear me? She knows what I would say. Far or near, she knows I'm her slave. I have sold myself for nothing, it may be. Well, 'tis the price I choose to take. I am worth nothing, or I am worth all."

"You are such a treasure," Esmond's mistress was pleased to say, "that the woman who has your love, shouldn't change it away against a kingdom, I think. I am a country-bred woman, and cannot say but the ambitions of the town seem mean to me. I never was awe-stricken by my Lady Duchess's rank and finery, or afraid," she added, with a sly laugh, "of anything but her temper. I hear of Court ladies who pine because her Majesty looks cold on them; and great noblemen who would give a limb that they might wear a garter on the other. This worldliness, which I can't comprehend, was born with Beatrix, who, on the first day of her waiting, was a perfect courtier. We are like sisters, and she the elder sister, somehow. She tells me I have a mean spirit. I laugh, and say she adores a coach-and-six. I cannot reason her out of her ambition. 'Tis natural to her, as to me to love quiet, and be indifferent about rank and riches. What are they, Harry? and for how long do they last? Our home is not here." She smiled as she spoke, and looked like an angel that was only on earth on a visit. "Our home is where the just are, and where our sins and sorrows enter not. My father used to rebuke me, and say that I was too hopeful about heaven. But I cannot help my nature, and grow obstinate as I grow to be an old woman; and as I love my children so, sure our Father loves us with a thousand and a thousand times greater love. It must be that we shall meet yonder, and be happy. Yes, you—and my children, and my dear lord. Do you know, Harry, since his death, it has always seemed to me as if his love came back to me, and that we are parted no more. Perhaps he is here now, Harry—I think he is. Forgiven I am sure he is: even Mr. Atterbury absolved him, and he died forgiving. Oh, what a noble heart he had! How generous he was! I was but fifteen and a child when he married me. How good he was to stoop to me! He was always good to the poor and humble." She stopped, then presently, with a peculiar expression, as if her eyes were looking into heaven, and saw my Lord there, she smiled, and gave a little laugh. "I laugh to see you, sir," she says; "when you come, it seems as if you never were away." One may put her words down, and remember them, but how describe her sweet tones, sweeter than music!

My young lord did not come home at the end of the campaign, and wrote that he was kept at Bruxelles on military duty. Indeed, I believe he was engaged in laying siege to a certain lady, who was of the suite of Madame de Soissons, the Prince of Savoy's mother, who was just dead, and who, like the Flemish fortresses, was taken and retaken a great number of times during the war, and occupied by French, English, and Imperialists. Of course, Mr. Esmond did not think fit to enlighten Lady Castlewood regarding the young scapegrace's doings; nor had he said a word about the affair with Lord Mohun, knowing how abhorrent that man's name was to his mistress. Frank did not waste much time or money on pen and ink; and, when Harry came home with his General, only writ two lines to his mother, to say his wound in the leg was almost healed, that he would keep his coming of age next year—that the duty aforesaid would keep him at Bruxelles, and that Cousin Harry would tell all the news.

But from Bruxelles, knowing how the Lady Castlewood always liked to have a letter about the famous 29th of December, my Lord writ her a long and full one, and in this he must have described the affair with Mohun; for when Mr. Esmond came to visit his mistress one day, early in the new year, to his great wonderment, she and her daughter both came up and saluted him, and after them the Dowager of Chelsey, too, whose chairman had just brought her Ladyship from her village to Kensington across the fields. After this honour, I say, from the two ladies of Castlewood, the Dowager came forward in great state, with her grand tall head-dress of King James's reign, that she never forsook, and said, "Cousin Henry, all our family have met; and we thank you, cousin, for your noble conduct towards the head of our house." And pointing to her blushing cheek, she made Mr. Esmond aware that he was to enjoy the rapture of an embrace there. Having saluted one cheek, she turned to him the other. "Cousin Harry," said both the other ladies, in a little chorus, "we thank you for your noble conduct;" and then Harry became aware that the story of the Lille affair had come to his kinswomen's ears. It pleased him to hear them all saluting him as one of their family.

The tables of the dining-room were laid for a great entertainment; and the ladies were in gala dresses—my Lady of Chelsey in her highest tour, my Lady Viscountess out of black, and looking fair and happy à ravir; and the Maid of Honour attired with that splendour which naturally distinguished her, and wearing on her beautiful breast the French officer's star which Frank had sent home after Ramillies.

"You see, 'tis a gala day with us," says she, glancing down to the star complacently, "and we have our orders on. Does not mamma look charming? 'Twas I dressed her!" Indeed, Esmond's dear mistress, blushing as he looked at her, with her beautiful fair hair, and an elegant dress, according to the *mode*, appeared to have the shape and complexion of a girl of twenty.

On the table was a fine sword, with a red velvet scabbard, and a beautiful chased silver handle, with a blue riband for a sword-knot. "What is this?" says the Captain, going up to look at this pretty piece.

Mrs. Beatrix advanced towards it. "Kneel down," says she: "we dub you our knight with this"—and she waved the sword over his head. "My Lady Dowager hath given the sword; and I give the riband, and mamma hath sewn on the fringe.

"Put the sword on him, Beatrix," says her mother. "You are our knight, Harry—our true knight. Take a mother's thanks and prayers for defending her son, my dear, dear friend. She could say no more, and even the Dowager was affected, for a couple of rebellious tears made sad marks down those wrinkled old roses which Esmond had just been allowed to salute.

"We had a letter from dearest Frank," his mother said, "three days since, whilst you were on your visit to your friend Captain Steele, at Hampton. He told us all that you had done, and how nobly you had put yourself between him and that—that wretch."

"And I adopt you from this day," says the Dowager; "and I wish I was richer, for your sake, son Esmond," she added with a wave of her hand; and as Mr. Esmond dutifully went down on his knee before her Ladyship, she cast her eyes up to the ceiling (the gilt chandelier, and the twelve wax-candles in it, for the party was numerous), and invoked a blessing from that quarter upon the newly adopted son.

"Dear Frank," says the other Viscountess, "how fond he is of his military profession! He is studying fortification very hard. I wish he were here. We shall keep his coming of age at Castlewood next year."

"If the campaign permit us," says Mr. Esmond.

"I am never afraid when he is with you," cries the boy's mother. "I am sure my Henry will always defend him."

"But, there will be a peace before next year; we know it for certain," cries the Maid of Honour. "Lord Marlborough will be dismissed, and that horrible Duchess turned out of all her places. Her Majesty won't speak to her now. Did you see her at Bushy, Harry? She is furious, and she ranges about the Park like a lioness, and tears people's eyes out."

"And the Princess Anne will send for somebody," says my Lady of Chelsey, taking out her medal and kissing it.

"Did you see the King at Oudenarde, Harry?" his mistress asked. She was a staunch Jacobite, and would no more have thought of denying her King than her God.

"I saw the young Hanoverian only," Harry said. "The Chevalier de St. George——"

"The King, sir, the King!" said the ladies and Miss Beatrix; and she clapped her pretty hands, and cried, "Vive le Roy!"

By this time there came a thundering knock, that drove in the doors of the house almost. It was three o'clock, and the company were arriving; and presently the servant announced Captain Steele and his lady.

Captain and Mrs. Steele, who were the first to arrive, had driven to Kensington from their country house, the Hovel at Hampton Wick. "Not from our mansion in Bloomsbury Square," as Mrs. Steele took care to inform the ladies. Indeed Harry had ridden away from Hampton that very morning, leaving the couple by the ears; for from the chamber where he lay, in a bed that was none of the cleanest, and kept awake by the company which he had in his own bed, and the quarrel which was going on in the next room, he could hear both night and morning the curtain lecture which Mrs. Steele was in the habit of administering to poor Dick.

At night it did not matter so much for the culprit; Dick was fuddled, and when in that way no scolding could interrupt his benevolence. Mr. Esmond could hear him coaxing and speaking in that maudlin manner, which punch and claret produce, to his beloved Prue, and beseeching her to remember that there was a *distiwisht officer ithe rex roob*, who would overhear her. She went on, nevertheless, calling him a drunken wretch, and was only interrupted in her harangues by the Captain's snoring.

In the morning, the unhappy victim awoke to a headache and consciousness, and the dialogue of the night was resumed. "Why do you bring captains home to dinner when there's not a guinea in the house? How am I to give dinners when you leave me without a shilling? How am I to go trapesing to Kensington in my yellow satin sack before all the fine company? I've nothing fit to put on; I never have:" and so the dispute went on—Mr. Esmond interrupting the talk when it seemed to be growing too intimate by blowing his nose as loudly as ever he could, at the sound of which trumpet there came a lull. But Dick was charming, though his wife was odious, and 'twas to give Mr. Steele pleasure that the ladies of Castlewood, who were ladies of no small fashion, invited Mrs. Steele.

Besides the Captain and his lady there was a great and notable assemblage of company: my Lady of Chelsey having sent her lacqueys and liveries to aid the modest attendance at Kensington. There was Lieutenant-General Webb, Harry's kind patron, of whom the Dowager took possession, and who resplended in velvet and gold lace; there was Harry's new acquaintance, the Right Honourable Henry St. John, Esquire, the General's kinsman, who was charmed with the Lady Castlewood, even more than with her daughter; there was one of the greatest noblemen in the kingdom, the Scots Duke of Hamilton, just created Duke of Brandon in England; and two other noble Lords of the Tory party, my Lord Ashburnham, and another I have forgot; and for ladies, her Grace the Duchess of Ormonde and her daughters, the Lady Mary and the Lady Betty, the former one of Mistress Beatrix's colleagues in waiting on the Queen.

"What a party of Tories!" whispered Captain Steele to Esmond, as we were assembled in the parlour before dinner. Indeed, all the company present, save Steele, were of that faction.

Mr. St. John made his special compliments to Mrs. Steele, and so charmed her that she declared she would have Steele a Tory too.

"Or will you have me a Whig?" says Mr. St. John. "I think, madam, you could convert a man to anything."

"If Mr. St. John ever comes to Bloomsbury Square I will teach him what I know," says Mrs. Steele, dropping her handsome eyes. "Do you know Bloomsbury Square?"

"Do I know the Mall? Do I know the Opera? Do I know the reigning toast? Why, Bloomsbury is the very height of the mode," says Mr. St. John. "'Tis *rus in urbe*. You have gardens all the way to Hampstead, and palaces round about you—Southampton House and Montague House."

"Where you wretches go and fight duels," cries Mrs. Steele.

"Of which the ladies are the cause!" says her entertainer. "Madam, is Dick a good swordsman? How charming the *Tatler* is! We all recognised your portrait in the 49th number, and I have been dying to know you ever since I read it. 'Aspâsia must be allowed to be the first of the beauteous order of love.' Doth not the passage run so? 'In this accomplished lady love is the constant effect, though it is never the design; yet though her mien carries much more invitation than command, to behold her is an immediate check to loose behaviour, and to love her is a liberal education.' "

"Oh, indeed!" says Mrs. Steele, who did not seem to understand a word of what the gentleman was saying.

"Who could fail to be accomplished under such a mistress?" says Mr. St. John, still gallant and bowing.

"Mistress! upon my word, sir!" cries the lady. "If you mean me, sir, I would have you know that I am the Captain's wife."

"Sure we all know it," answers Mr. St. John, keeping his countenance very gravely; and Steele broke in saying, "'Twas not about Mrs. Steele I writ that paper—though I am sure she is worthy of any compliment I can pay her—but of the Lady Elizabeth Hastings."

"I hear Mr. Addison is equally famous as a wit and a poet," says Mr. St. John. "Is it true that his hand is to be found in your *Tatler*, Mr. Steele?"

"Whether 'tis the sublime or the humorous, no man can come near him," cries Steele.

"A fig, Dick, for your Mr. Addison!" cries out his lady: "a gentleman who gives himself such airs and holds his head so high now. I hope your Ladyship thinks as I do: I can't bear those very fair men with white eyelashes—a black man for me." (All the black men at table applauded, and made Mrs. Steele a bow for this compliment.) "As for this Mr. Addison," she went on, "he comes to dine with the Captain sometimes, never says a word to me, and then they walk upstairs, both tipsy, to a dish of tea. I remember your Mr. Addison when he had but one coat to his back, and that with a patch at the elbow."

"Indeed—a patch at the elbow! You interest me," says Mr. St. John. "'Tis charming to hear of one man of letters from the charming wife of another."

"La, I could tell you ever so much about 'em," continues the voluble lady. "What do you think the Captain has got now?—a little hunchback fellow—a little hop-o'-my-thumb creature that he calls a poet—a little Popish brat!"

"Hush! there are two in the room," whispers her companion.

"Well, I call him Popish because his name is Pope," says the lady. "'Tis only my joking way. And this little dwarf of a fellow has wrote a pastoral poem—all about shepherds and shepherdesses, you know."

"A shepherd should have a little crook," says my mistress, laughing from her end of the table: on which Mrs. Steele said, "She did not know, but the Captain brought home this queer little creature when she was in bed with her first boy, and it was a mercy he had come no sooner; and Dick raved about his *genus*, and was always raving about some nonsense or other."

"Which of the *Tatlers* do you prefer, Mrs. Steele?" asked Mr. St. John.

"I never read but one, and think it all a pack of rubbish, sir," says the lady. "Such stuff about Bickerstaffe, and Distaff, and Quarterstaff, as it all is! There's the Captain going on still with the burgundy—I know he'll be tipsy before he stops—Captain Steele!"

"I drink to your eyes, my dear," says the Captain, who seemed to think his wife charming, and to receive as genuine all the satiric compliments which Mr. St. John paid her.

All this while the Maid of Honour had been trying to get Mr. Esmond to talk, and no doubt voted him a dull fellow. For, by some mistake, just as he was going to pop into the vacant place, he was placed far away from Beatrix's chair, who sat between his Grace and my Lord Ashburnham, and shrugged her lovely white shoulders, and cast a look as if to say, "Pity me," to her cousin. My Lord Duke and his young neighbour were presently in a very animated and close conversation. Mrs. Beatrix could no more help using her eyes than the sun can help shining, and setting those it shines on a-burning. By the time the first course was done the dinner seemed long to Esmond; by the time the soup came he fancied they must have been hours at table; and as for the sweets and jellies he thought they never would be done.

At length the ladies rose, Beatrix throwing a Parthian glance at her duke as she retreated; a fresh bottle and glasses were fetched, and toasts were called. Mr. St. John asked his Grace the Duke of Hamilton and the company to drink to the health of his Grace the Duke of Brandon. Another lord gave General Webb's health, "and may he get the command the bravest officer in the world deserves." Mr. Webb thanked the company, complimented his aide-de-camp, and fought his famous battle over again.

"Il est fatiguant," whispers Mr. St. John, "avec sa trompette de Wynendael."

Captain Steele, who was not of our side, loyally gave the health of the Duke of Marlborough, the greatest general of the age.

"I drink to the greatest general with all my heart," says Mr. Webb; "there can be no gainsaying that character of him. My glass goes to the General, and not to the Duke, Mr. Steele." And the stout old gentleman emptied his bumper; to which Dick replied by filling and emptying a pair of brimmers, one for the General and one for the Duke.

And now his Grace of Hamilton, rising up with flashing eyes (we had all been drinking pretty freely), proposed a toast to the lovely, to the incomparable Mrs. Beatrix Esmond; we all drank it with cheers, and my Lord Ashburnham especially, with a shout of enthusiasm.

"What a pity there is a Duchess of Hamilton!" whispers St. John, who drank more wine and yet was more steady than most of the others, and we entered the drawing-room where the ladies were at their tea. As for poor Dick, we were obliged to leave him alone at the dining-table, where he was hiccupping out the lines from the "Campaign," in which the greatest poet had celebrated the greatest general in the world; and Harry Esmond found him, half-an-hour afterwards, in a more advanced stage of liquor, and weeping about the treachery of Tom Boxer.

The drawing-room was all dark to poor Harry, in spite of the grand illumination. Beatrix scarce spoke to him. When my Lord Duke went away, she practised upon the next in rank, and plied my young Lord Ashburnham with all the fire of her eyes and the fascinations of her wit. Most of the party were set to cards, and Mr. St. John, after yawning in the face of Mrs. Steele, whom he did not care to pursue any more, and talking in his most brilliant animated way to Lady Castlewood, whom he pronounced to be beautiful, of a far higher order of beauty than her daughter, presently took his leave, and went his way. The rest of the company speedily followed, my Lord Ashburnham the last, throwing fiery glances at the smiling young temptress, who had bewitched more hearts than his in her thrall.

No doubt, as a kinsman of the house, Mr. Esmond thought fit to be the last of all in it; he remained after the coaches had rolled away—after his dowager aunt's chair and flambeaux had marched off in the darkness towards Chelsey, and the town's people had gone to bed, who had been drawn into the square to gape at the unusual assemblage of chairs and chariots, lacqueys, and torchmen. The poor mean wretch lingered yet for a few minutes, to see whether the girl would vouchsafe him a smile, or a parting word of consolation. But her enthusiasm of the morning was quite died out, or she chose to be in a different mood. She fell to joking about the dowdy appearance of Lady Betty, and mimicked the vulgarity of Mrs. Steele; and then she put up her little hand to her mouth and yawned, lighted a taper, and shrugged her shoulders, and dropping Mr. Esmond a saucy curtsey, sailed off to bed.

"The day began so well, Henry, that I had hoped it might have ended better," was all the consolation that poor Esmond's fond mistress could give him; and as he trudged home through the dark alone, he thought with bitter rage in his heart, and a feeling of almost revolt against the sacrifice he had made :—"She would have me," thought he, "had I but a name to give her. But for my promise to her father, I might have my rank and my mistress too."

I suppose a man's vanity is stronger than any other passion in him; for I blush, even now, as I recall the humiliation of those distant days, the memory of which still smarts, though the fever of balked desire has passed away more than a score of years ago. When the writer's descendants come to read this memoir, I wonder will they have lived to experience a similar defeat and shame? Will they ever have knelt to a woman, who has listened to them, and played with them, and laughed with them—who beckoning them with lures and caresses, and with Yes smiling from her eyes, has tricked them on to their knees, and turned her back and left them? All this shame Mr. Esmond had to undergo; and he submitted, and revolted, and presently came crouching back for more.

After this feste, my young Lord Ashburnham's coach was for ever rolling in and out of Kensington Square; his lady-mother came to visit Esmond's mistress, and at every assembly in the town, wherever the Maid of Honour made her appearance, you might be pretty sure to see the young gentleman in a new suit every week, and decked out in all the finery that his tailor or embroiderer could furnish for him. My Lord was for ever paying Mr. Esmond compliments; bidding him to dinner, offering him horses to ride, and giving him a thousand uncouth marks of respect and good-will. At last, one night at the coffee-house, whither my Lord came considerably flushed and excited with drink, he rushes up to Mr. Esmond, and cries out, "Give me joy, my dearest Colonel; I am the happiest of men."

"The happiest of men needs no dearest colonel to give him joy," says Mr. Esmond. "What is the cause of this supreme felicity?"

"Haven't you heard?" says he. "Don't you know? I thought the family told you everything: the adorable Beatrix hath promised to be mine."

"What!" cries out Mr. Esmond, who had spent happy hours with Beatrix that very morning—had writ verses for her, that she had sung at the harpsichord.

"Yes," says he; "I waited on her to-day. I saw you walking towards Knightsbridge as I passed in my coach; and she looked so lovely, and spoke so kind, that I couldn't help going down on my knees, and—and—sure I am the happiest of men in all the world; and I'm very young; but she says I shall get older: and you know I shall be of age in four months; and there's very little difference between us; and I'm so happy, I should like to treat the company to something. Let us have a bottle—a dozen bottles—and drink the health of the finest woman in England."

Esmond left the young lord tossing off bumper after bumper, and strolled away to Kensington to ask whether the news was true. 'Twas only too sure: his mistress's sad, compassionate face told him the story; and then she related what particulars of it she knew, and how my young lord had made his offer, half-an-hour after Esmond went away that morning, and in the very room where the song lay yet on the harpischord, which Esmond had writ, and they had sung together.

BOOK III

CONTAINING THE END OF MR. ESMOND'S ADVENTURES IN ENGLAND

CHAPTER I

I COME TO AN END OF MY BATTLES AND BRUISES

THAT feverish desire to gain a little reputation which Esmond had had, left him now perhaps that he had attained some portion of his wish, and the great motive of his ambition was over. His desire for military honour was that it might raise him in Beatrix's eyes. 'Twas, next to nobility and wealth, the only kind of rank she valued. It was the stake quickest won or lost too; for law is a very long game that requires a life to practise; and to be distinguished in letters or the Church would not have forwarded the poor gentleman's plans in the least. So he had no suit to play but the red one, and he played it; and this, in truth, was the reason of his speedy promotion; for he exposed himself more than most gentlemen do, and risked more to win more. Is he the only man that hath set his life against a stake which may be not worth the winning? Another risks his life (and his honour, too, sometimes) against a bundle of bank-notes, or a yard of blue riband, or a seat in Parliament; and some for the mere pleasure and excitement of the sport; as a field of a hundred huntsmen will do, each out-bawling and out-galloping the other at the tail of a dirty fox, that is to be the prize of the foremost happy conqueror.

When he heard this news of Beatrix's engagement in marriage, Colonel Esmond knocked under to his fate, and resolved to surrender his sword, that could win him nothing now he cared for; and in this dismal frame of mind he determined to retire from the regiment, to the great delight of the captain next in rank to him, who happened to be a young gentleman of good fortune, who eagerly paid Mr. Esmond a thousand guineas for his majority in Webb's regiment, and was knocked on the head the next campaign. Perhaps

Esmond would not have been sorry to share his fate. He was more the Knight of the Woeful Countenance than ever he had been. His moodiness must have made him perfectly odious to his friends under the tents, who like a jolly fellow, and laugh at a melancholy warrior always sighing after Dulcinea at home.

Both the ladies of Castlewood approved of Mr. Esmond quitting the army, and his kind General coincided in his wish of retirement and helped in the transfer of his commission, which brought a pretty sum into his pocket. But when the Commander-in-Chief came home, and was forced, in spite of himself, to appoint Lieutenant-General Webb to the command of a division of the army in Flanders, the Lieutenant-General prayed Colonel Esmond so urgently to be his aide-de-camp and military secretary, that Esmond could not resist his kind patron's entreaties, and again took the field, not attached to any regiment, but under Webb's orders. What must have been the continued agonies of fears * and apprehensions which racked the gentle breasts of wives and matrons in those dreadful days, when every *Gazette* brought accounts of deaths and battles, and when, the present anxiety over, and the beloved person escaped, the doubt still remained that a battle might be fought, possibly, of which the next Flanders letter would bring the account; so they, the poor tender creatures, had to go on sickening and trembling through the whole campaign. Whatever these terrors were on the part of Esmond's mistress (and that tenderest of women must have felt them most keenly for both her sons, as she called them), she never allowed them outwardly to appear, but hid her apprehension as she did her charities and devotion. 'Twas only by chance that Esmond, wandering in Kensington, found his mistress coming out of a mean cottage there, and heard that she had a score of poor retainers, whom she visited and comforted in their sickness and poverty, and who blessed her daily. She attended the early church daily (though of a Sunday, especially, she encouraged and advanced all sorts of cheerfulness and innocent gaiety in her little household): and by notes entered into a table-book of hers at this time, and devotional compositions writ with a sweet artless fervour, such as the best divines could not surpass, showed how fond her heart was, how humble and pious her spirit, what pangs of apprehension she endured silently, and with what a faithful reliance she committed the care of those she loved to the awful Dispenser of death and life.

As for her Ladyship at Chelsey, Esmond's newly adopted mother, she was now of an age when the danger of any second party doth not disturb the rest much. She cared for trumps more than for most things in life. She was firm enough in her own

* What indeed? Psm. xci. 2, 3, 7.—R. E.

faith, but no longer very bitter against ours. She had a very good-natured, easy French director, Monsieur Gauthier by name, who was a gentleman of the world, and would take a hand of cards with Dean Atterbury, my Lady's neighbour at Chelsey, and was well with all the High Church party. No doubt Monsieur Gauthier knew what Esmond's peculiar position was, for he corresponded with Holt, and always treated Colonel Esmond with particular respect and kindness; but for good reasons the Colonel and the Abbé never spoke on this matter together, and so they remained perfect good friends.

All the frequenters of my Lady of Chelsey's house were of the Tory and High Church party. Madam Beatrix was as frantic about the King as her elderly kinswoman: she wore his picture on her heart; she had a piece of his hair; she vowed he was the most injured, and gallant, and accomplished, and unfortunate, and beautiful of princes. Steele, who quarrelled with very many of his Tory friends, but never with Esmond, used to tell the Colonel that his kinswoman's house was a rendezvous of Tory intrigues; that Gauthier was a spy; that Atterbury was a spy; that letters were constantly going from that house to the Queen at St. Germains; on which Esmond, laughing, would reply, that they used to say in the army the Duke of Marlborough was a spy too, and as much in correspondence with that family as any Jesuit. And without entering very eagerly into the controversy, Esmond had frankly taken the side of his family. It seemed to him that King James the Third was undoubtedly King of England by right: and at his sister's death it would be better to have him than a foreigner over us. No man admired King William more; a hero and a conqueror, the bravest, justest, wisest of men—but 'twas by the sword he conquered the country, and held and governed it by the very same right that the great Cromwell held it, who was truly and greatly a sovereign. But that a foreign despotic prince, out of Germany, who happened to be descended from King James the First, should take possession of this empire, seemed to Mr. Esmond a monstrous injustice—at least, every Englishman had a right to protest, and the English prince, the heir-at-law, the first of all. What man of spirit with such a cause would not back it? What man of honour with such a crown to win would not fight for it? But that race was destined. That Prince had himself against him, an enemy he could not overcome. He never dared to draw his sword, though he had it. He let his chances slip by as he lay in the lap of opera-girls, or snivelled at the knees of priests, asking pardon; and the blood of heroes, and the devotedness of honest hearts, and endurance, courage, fidelity, were all spent for him in vain.

But let us return to my Lady of Chelsey, who, when her son Esmond announced to her Ladyship that he proposed to make the ensuing campaign, took leave of him with perfect alacrity, and was down to piquet with her gentlewoman before he had well quitted the room on his last visit. "Tierce to a king" were the last words he ever heard her say: the game of life was pretty nearly over for the good lady, and three months afterwards she took to her bed, where she flickered out without any pain, so the Abbé Gauthier wrote over to Mr. Esmond, then with his General on the frontier of France. The Lady Castlewood was with her at her ending, and had written too, but these letters must have been taken by a privateer in the packet that brought them; for Esmond knew nothing of their contents until his return to England.

My Lady Castlewood had left everything to Colonel Esmond, "as a reparation for the wrong done to him;" 'twas writ in her will. But her fortune was not much, for it never had been large, and the honest Viscountess had wisely sunk most of the money she had upon an annuity which terminated with her life. However, there was the house and furniture, plate and pictures at Chelsey, and a sum of money lying at her merchant's, Sir Josiah Child, which altogether would realise a sum of near three hundred pounds per annum, so that Mr. Esmond found himself, if not rich, at least easy for life. Likewise there were the famous diamonds which had been said to be worth fabulous sums, though the goldsmith pronounced they would fetch no more than four thousand pounds. These diamonds, however, Colonel Esmond reserved, having a special use for them; but the Chelsey house, plate, goods, &c., with the exception of a few articles which he kept back, were sold by his orders; and the sums resulting from the sale invested in the public securities so as to realise the aforesaid annual income of three hundred pounds.

Having now something to leave, he made a will and despatched it home. The army was now in presence of the enemy; and a great battle expected every day. 'Twas known that the General-in-Chief was in disgrace, and the parties at home strong against him, and there was no stroke this great and resolute player would not venture to recall his fortune when it seemed desperate. Frank Castlewood was with Colonel Esmond; his General having gladly taken the young nobleman on to his staff. His studies of fortification at Bruxelles were over by this time. The fort he was besieging had yielded, I believe, and my Lord had not only marched in with flying colours, but marched out again. He used to tell his boyish wickednesses with admirable humour, and was the most charming young scapegrace in the army.

'Tis needless to say that Colonel Esmond had left every penny of his little fortune to this boy. It was the Colonel's firm conviction that the next battle would put an end to him: for he felt aweary of the sun, and quite ready to bid that and the earth farewell. Frank would not listen to his comrade's gloomy forebodings, but swore they would keep his birthday at Castlewood that autumn, after the campaign. He had heard of the engagement at home. "If Prince Eugene goes to London," says Frank, "and Trix can get hold of him, she'll jilt Ashburnham for his Highness. I tell you, she used to make eyes at the Duke of Marlborough, when she was only fourteen, and ogling poor little Blandford. *I* wouldn't marry her, Harry—no, not if her eyes were twice as big. I'll take my fun. I'll enjoy for the next three years every possible pleasure. I'll sow my wild oats then, and marry some quiet, steady, modest, sensible Viscountess; hunt my harriers; and settle down at Castlewood. Perhaps I'll represent the county —no, damme, *you* shall represent the county. You have the brains of the family. By the Lord, my dear old Harry, you have the best head and the kindest heart in all the army; and every man says so—and when the Queen dies, and the King comes back, why shouldn't you go to the House of Commons, and be a Minister, and be made a Peer, and that sort of thing? *You* be shot in the next action! I wager a dozen of burgundy you are not touched. Mohun is well of his wound. He is always with Corporal John now. As soon as ever I see his ugly face I'll spit in it. I took lessons of Father—of Captain Holt at Bruxelles. What a man that is! He knows everything." Esmond bade Frank have a care; that Father Holt's knowledge was rather dangerous; not, indeed, knowing as yet how far the Father had pushed his instructions with his young pupil.

The gazetteers and writers, both of the French and English side, have given accounts sufficient of that bloody battle of Blaregnies or Malplaquet, which was the last and the hardest earned of the victories of the great Duke of Marlborough. In that tremendous combat near upon two hundred and fifty thousand men were engaged, more than thirty thousand of whom were slain or wounded (the Allies lost twice as many men as they killed of the French, whom they conquered): and this dreadful slaughter very likely took place because a great General's credit was shaken at home, and he thought to restore it by a victory. If such were the motives which induced the Duke of Marlborough to venture that prodigious stake, and desperately sacrifice thirty thousand brave lives, so that he might figure once more in a *Gazette*, and hold his places and pensions a little longer, the event defeated the dreadful and selfish design, for the victory was purchased at a cost which no nation, greedy of glory as it might be, would willingly pay for any triumph. The gallantry of the French was as remarkable as the furious bravery of their assailants. We took a few score of their flags, and a few pieces of their artillery; but we left twenty thousand of the bravest soldiers of the world round about the intrenched lines, from which the enemy was driven. He retreated in perfect good order; the panic-spell seemed to be broke under which the French had laboured ever since the disaster of Hochstedt; and, fighting now on the threshold of their country, they showed an heroic ardour of resistance, such as had never met us in the course of their aggressive war. Had the battle been more successful, the conqueror might have got the price for which he waged it. As it was (and justly, I think), the party adverse to the Duke in England were indignant at the lavish extravagance of slaughter, and demanded more eagerly than ever the recall of a chief whose cupidity and desperation might urge him further still. After this bloody fight of Malplaquet, I can answer for it, that in the Dutch quarters and our own, and amongst the very regiments and commanders whose gallantry was most conspicuous upon this frightful day of carnage, the general cry was, that there was enough of the war. The French were driven back into their own boundary, and all their conquests and booty of Flanders disgorged. As for the Prince of Savoy, with whom our Commander-in-Chief, for reasons of his own, consorted more closely than ever, 'twas known that he was animated not merely by a political hatred, but by personal rage against the old French King: the Imperial Generalissimo never forgot the slight put by Lewis upon the Abbé de Savoie; and in the humiliation or ruin of his most Christian Majesty, the Holy Roman Emperor found his account. But what were these quarrels to us, the free citizens of England and Holland? Despot as he was, the French monarch was yet the chief of European civilisation, more venerable in his age and misfortunes than at the period of his most splendid successes; whilst his opponent was but a semi-barbarous tyrant, with a pillaging, murderous horde of Croats and Pandours, composing a half of his army, filling our camp with their strange figures, bearded like the miscreant Turks their neighbours, and carrying into Christian warfare their native heathen habits of rapine, lust, and murder. Why should the best blood in England and France be shed in order that the Holy Roman and Apostolic master of these ruffians should have his revenge over the Christian King? And it was to this end we were fighting; for this that every village and family in England was deploring the death of beloved sons and fathers. We dared not speak to each other, even at table, of Malplaquet, so frightful were the gaps left in our army by the cannon of that bloody action. 'Twas heartrending for an officer who had a heart to look down his line on a parade-day afterwards, and miss hundreds of faces of comrades—humble or of high rank—that had gathered but yesterday full of courage and cheerfulness round the torn and blackened flags. Where were our friends? As the great Duke reviewed us, riding along our lines with his fine suite of prancing aides-de-camp and generals, stopping here and there to thank an officer with those eager smiles and bows of which his Grace was always lavish, scarce a huzzah could be got for him, though Cadogan, with an oath, rode up and cried, "D—— you, why don't you cheer?" But the men had no heart for that: not one of them but was thinking, "Where's my comrade?—where's my brother that fought by me, or my dear captain that led me yesterday?" 'Twas the most gloomy pageant I ever looked on; and the "Te Deum" sung by our chaplains, the most woeful and dreary satire.

Esmond's General added one more to the many marks of honour which he had received in the front of a score of battles, and got a wound in the groin, which laid him on his back; and you may be sure he consoled himself by abusing the Commander-in-Chief, as he lay groaning: "Corporal John's as fond of me," he used to say, "as King David was of General Uriah; and so he always gives me the post of danger." He persisted, to his dying day, in believing that the Duke intended he should be beat at Wynendael, and sent him purposely with a small force, hoping that he might be knocked on the head there. Esmond and Frank Castlewood both escaped without hurt, though the division which our General commanded suffered even more than any other, having to sustain not only the fury of the enemy's cannonade, which was very hot and well served, but the furious and repeated charges of the famous Maison du Roy, which we had to receive and beat off again and again, with volleys of shot and hedges of iron, and our four lines of musqueteers and pikemen. They said the King of England charged us no less than twelve times that day, along with the French Household. Esmond's late regiment, General Webb's own Fusileers, served in the division which their Colonel commanded. The General was thrice in the centre of the square of the Fusileers, calling the fire at the French charges, and, after the action, his Grace the Duke of Berwick sent his compliments to his old regiment and their Colonel for their behaviour on the field.

We drank my Lord Castlewood's health and majority, the 25th of September, the army being then before Mons: and here Colonel Esmond was not so fortunate as he had been in actions much more dangerous, and was hit by a spent ball just above the place where his former wound was, which caused the old wound to open again, fever, spitting of blood, and other ugly symptoms, to ensue; and, in a word, brought him near to death's door. The kind lad, his kinsman, attended his elder comrade with a very praiseworthy affectionateness and care until he was pronounced out of danger by the doctors, when Frank went off, passed the winter at Bruxelles, and besieged, no doubt, some other fortress there. Very few lads would have given up their pleasures so long and so gaily as Frank did; his cheerful prattle soothed many long days of Esmond's pain and languor. Frank was supposed to be still at his kinsman's bedside for a month after he had left it, for letters came from his mother at home full of thanks to the younger gentleman for his care of his elder brother (so it pleased Esmond's mistress now affectionately to style him); nor was Mr. Esmond in a hurry to undeceive her, when the good young fellow was gone for his Christmas holiday. It was as pleasant to Esmond on his couch to watch the young man's pleasure at the idea of being free, as to note his simple efforts to disguise his satisfaction on going away. There are days when a flask of champagne at a cabaret, and a red-cheeked partner to share it, are too strong temptations for any young fellow of spirit. I am not going to play the moralist, and cry "Fie!" For ages past, I know how old men preach, and what young men practise; and that patriarchs have had their weak moments too, long since Father Noah toppled over after discovering the vine. Frank went off, then, to his pleasures at Bruxelles, in which capital many young fellows of our army declared they found infinitely greater diversion even than in London: and Mr. Henry Esmond remained in his sick-room, where he writ a fine comedy, that his mistress pronounced to be sublime, and that was acted no less than three successive nights in London in the next year.

Here, as he lay nursing himself, ubiquitous Mr. Holt reappeared, and stopped a whole month at Mons, where he not only won over Colonel Esmond to the King's side in politics (that side being always held by the Esmond family); but where he endeavoured to re-open the controversial question between the Churches once more, and to recall Esmond to that religion in which, in his infancy, he had been baptized. Holt was a casuist, both dexterous and learned, and presented the case between the English Church and his own in such a way that those who granted his premises ought certainly to allow his conclusions. He touched on Esmond's delicate state of health, chance of dissolution, and so forth; and enlarged upon the immense benefits that the sick man was likely to forego—benefits which the Church of England did not deny to those of the Roman Communion, as how should she, being derived from that Church, and only an offshoot from it? But Mr. Esmond said that his Church was the Church of his country, and to that he chose to remain faithful: other people were welcome to worship and to subscribe any other set of articles, whether at Rome or at Augsburg. But if the good Father meant that Esmond should join the Roman communion for fear of consequences, and that all England ran the risk of being damned for heresy, Esmond, for one, was perfectly willing to take his chance of the penalty along with the countless millions of his fellow-countrymen, who were bred in the same faith, and along with some of the noblest, the truest, the purest, the wisest, the most pious and learned men and women in the world.

As for the political question, in that Mr. Esmond could agree with the Father much more readily, and had come to the same conclusion, though, perhaps, by a different way. The right divine, about which Dr. Sacheverel and the High Church party in England were just now making a bother, they were welcome to hold as they chose. If Richard Cromwell and his father before him had been crowned and anointed (and bishops enough would have been found to do it), it seemed to Mr. Esmond that they would have had the right divine just as much as any Plantagenet, or Tudor, or Stuart. But the desire of the country being unquestionably for an hereditary monarchy, Esmond thought an English king out of St. Germains was better and fitter than a German prince from Herrenhausen, and that if he failed to satisfy the nation, some other Englishman might be found to take his place; and so, though with no frantic enthusiasm, or worship of that monstrous pedigree which the Tories chose to consider divine, he was ready to say, "God save King James!" when Queen Anne went the way of kings and commoners.

"I fear, Colonel, you are no better than a republican at heart," says the priest with a sigh.

"I am an Englishman," says Harry, "and take my country as I find her. The will of the nation being for Church and King, I am for Church and King too; but English Church and English King; and that is why your Church isn't mine, though your King is."

Though they lost the day at Malplaquet, it was the French who were elated by that action, whilst the conquerors were dispirited by it; and the enemy gathered together a larger army than ever, and made prodigious efforts for the next campaign. Marshal Berwick was with the French this year; and we heard that Mareschal Villars was still suffering of his wound, was eager to bring our Duke to action, and vowed he would fight us in his coach. Young Castlewood came flying back from Bruxelles as soon as he heard that fighting was to begin; and the arrival of the Chevalier de St. George was announced about May. "It's the King's third campaign, and it's mine," Frank liked saying. He was come back a greater Jacobite than ever, and Esmond suspected that some fair conspirators at Bruxelles had been inflaming the young man's ardour. Indeed, he owned that he had a message from the Queen, Beatrix's godmother, who had given her name to Frank's sister the year before he and his sovereign were born.

However desirous Mareschal Villars might be to fight, my Lord Duke did not seem disposed to indulge him this campaign. Last year his Grace had been all for the Whigs and Hanoverians; but finding, on going to England, his country cold towards himself, and the people in a ferment of High Church loyalty, the Duke comes back to his army cooled towards the Hanoverians, cautious with the Imperialists, and particularly civil and polite towards the Chevalier de St. George. 'Tis certain that messengers and letters were continually passing between his Grace and his brave nephew, the Duke of Berwick, in the opposite camp. No man's caresses were more opportune than his Grace's, and no man ever uttered expressions of regard and affection more generously. He professed to Monsieur de Torcy, so Mr. St. John told the writer, quite an eagerness to be cut in pieces for the exiled Queen and her family; nay more, I believe, this year he parted with a portion of the most precious part of himself—his money—which he sent over to the royal exiles. Mr. Tunstal, who was in the Prince's service, was twice or thrice in and out of our camp; the French, in theirs of Arlieu and about Arras. A little river, the Canihe I think 'twas called (but this is writ away from books and Europe; and the only map the writer hath of these scenes of his youth, bears no mark of this little stream), divided our picquets from the enemy's. Our sentries talked across the stream, when they could make themselves understood to each other, and when they could not, grinned, and handed each other their brandy-flasks or their pouches of tobacco. And one fine day of June, riding thither with the officer who visited the outposts (Colonel Esmond was taking an airing on horseback, being too weak for military duty), they came to this river, where a number of English and Scots were assembled, talking to the good-natured enemy on the other side.

Esmond was especially amused with the talk of one long fellow, with a great curling red moustache, and blue eyes, that was half-a-dozen inches taller than his swarthy little comrades on the French side of the stream, and being asked by the Colonel, saluted him, and said that he belonged to the Royal Cravats.

From his way of saying "Royal Cravat," Esmond at once knew that the fellow's tongue had first wagged on the banks of the Liffey, and not the Loire; and the poor soldier—a deserter probably—did not like to venture very deep into French conversation, lest his unlucky brogue should peep out. He chose to restrict himself to such few expressions in the French language as he thought he had mastered easily; and his attempt at disguise was infinitely amusing. Mr. Esmond whistled Lillibullero, at which Teague's eyes began to twinkle, and then flung him a dollar, when the poor boy broke out with a "God bless—that is, Dieu bénisse votre honor," that would infallibly have sent him to the provost-marshal had he been on our side of the river.

Whilst this parley was going on, three officers on horseback, on the French side, appeared at some little distance, and stopped as if eyeing us, when one of them left the other two, and rode close up to us who were by the stream. "Look, look!" says the Royal Cravat, with great agitation, "pas lui, that's he; not him, l'autre," and pointed to the distant officer on a chestnut horse, with a cuirass shining in the sun, and over it a broad blue riband.

"Please to take Mr. Hamilton's services to my Lord Marlborough—my Lord Duke," says the gentleman in English; and looking to see that the party were not hostilely disposed, he added, with a smile, "There's a friend of yours, gentlemen, yonder; he bids me to say that he saw some of your faces on the 11th of September last year."

As the gentleman spoke, the other two officers rode up, and came quite close. We knew at once who it was. It was the King, then two-and-twenty years old, tall and slim, with deep-brown eyes, that looked melancholy, though his lips wore a smile. We took off our hats and saluted him. No man, sure, could see for the first time, without emotion, the youthful inheritor of so much fame and misfortune. It seemed to Mr. Esmond that the Prince was not unlike young Castlewood, whose age and figure he resembled. The Chevalier de St. George acknowledged the salute, and looked at us hard. Even the idlers on our side of the river set up a hurrah. As for the Royal Cravat, he ran to the Prince's stirrup, knelt down and kissed his boot, and bawled and looked a hundred ejaculations and blessings. The Prince bade the aide-de-camp give him a piece of money; and when the party saluting us had ridden away, Cravat spat upon the piece of gold by way of benediction, and swaggered away, pouching his coin and twirling his honest carroty moustache.

The officer in whose company Esmond was, the same little captain of Handyside's regiment, Mr. Sterne, who had proposed the garden at Lille, when my Lord Mohun and Esmond had their affair, was an Irishman too, and as brave a little soul as ever wore a sword. "Bedad," says Roger Sterne, "that long fellow spoke French so beautiful that I shouldn't have known he wasn't a foreigner, till he broke out with his hulla-ballooing, and only an Irish calf can bellow like that." And Roger made another remark in his wild way, in which there was sense as well as absurdity: "If that young gentleman," says he, "would but ride over to our camp, instead of Villars's, toss up his hat and say, 'Here am I, the King, who'll follow me?' by the Lord, Esmond, the whole army would rise and carry him home again, and beat Villars, and take Paris by the way."

The news of the Prince's visit was all through the camp quickly, and scores of ours went down in hopes to see him. Major Hamilton, whom we had talked with, sent back by a trumpet several silver pieces for officers with us. Mr. Esmond received one of these; and that medal, and a recompense not uncommon amongst Princes, were the only rewards he ever had from a Royal person whom he endeavoured not very long after to serve

Esmond quitted the army almost immediately after this, following his General home; and, indeed, being advised to travel in the fine weather and attempt to take no further part in the campaign. But he heard from the army, that of the many who crowded to see the Chevalier de St. George, Frank Castlewood had made himself most conspicuous: my Lord Viscount riding across the little stream bareheaded to where the Prince was, and dismounting and kneeling before him to do him homage. Some said that the Prince had actually knighted him, but my Lord denied that statement, though he acknowledged the rest of the story, and said: "From having been out of favour with Corporal John," as he called the Duke, "before, his Grace warned him not to commit those follies, and smiled on him cordially ever after."

"And he was so kind to me," Frank writ, "that I thought I would put in a good word for Master Harry, but when I mentioned your name he looked as black as thunder, and said he had never heard of you."

CHAPTER II

I GO HOME, AND HARP ON THE OLD STRING

AFTER quitting Mons and the army, and as he was waiting for a packet at Ostend, Esmond had a letter from his young kinsman Castlewood at Bruxelles, conveying intelligence whereof Frank besought him to be the bearer to London, and which caused Colonel Esmond no small anxiety.

The young scapegrace, being one-and-twenty years old, and being anxious to sow his "wild otes," as he wrote, had married Mademoiselle de Wertheim, daughter of Count de Wertheim, Chamberlain to the Emperor, and having a post in the Household of the Governor of the Netherlands "*P.S.*," the young gentleman wrote: "Clotilda is *older than me*, which perhaps may be objected to her: but I am so *old a raik* that the age makes no difference, and I am *determined* to reform. We were married at St. Gudule, by Father Holt. She is heart and soul for the *good cause.* And here the cry is *Vif-le-Roy*, which my mother will *join in*, and Trix *too.* Break this news to 'em gently: and tell Mr. Finch, my agent, to press the people for their rents, and send me the *ryno* anyhow. Clotilda sings, and plays on the spinet *beautifully.* She is a fair beauty. And if it's a son, you shall stand *Godfather.* I'm going to leave the army, having had *enuf of soldering;* and my Lord Duke *recommends* me. I shall pass the winter here: and stop at least until Clo's lying-in. I call her *old Clo*, but nobody else shall. She is the cleverest woman in all Bruxelles: understanding painting, music, poetry, and perfect at *cookery and puddens.* I borded with the Count, that's how I came to know her. There are four Counts her brothers. One an Abbey—three with the Prince's army. They have a lawsuit for *an immence fortune:* but are now in *a pore way.* Break this to mother, who'll take anything from *you.* And write, and bid Finch write *amediately.* Hostel de l'Aigle Noire, Bruxelles, Flanders."

So Frank had married a Roman Catholic lady, and an heir was expected, and Mr. Esmond was to carry this intelligence to his mistress at London. 'Twas a difficult embassy; and the Colonel felt not a little tremor as he neared the capital.

He reached his inn late, and sent a messenger to Kensington to announce his arrival and visit the next morning. The messenger brought back news that the Court was at Windsor, and the fair Beatrix absent and engaged in her duties there. Only Esmond's mistress remained in her house at Kensington. She appeared in Court but once in the year; Beatrix was quite the mistress and ruler of the little mansion, inviting the company thither, and engaging in every conceivable frolic of town pleasure; whilst her mother, acting as the young lady's protectress and elder sister, pursued her own path, which was quite modest and secluded.

As soon as ever Esmond was dressed (and he had been awake long before the town), he took a coach for Kensington, and reached it so early that he met his dear mistress coming home from morning prayers. She carried her prayer-book, never allowing a footman to bear it, as everybody else did: and it was by this simple sign Esmond knew what her occupation had been. He called to the coachman to stop, and jumped out as she looked towards him. She wore her hood as usual, and she turned quite pale when she saw him. To feel that kind little hand near to his heart seemed to give him strength. They were soon at the door of her Ladyship's house—and within it.

With a sweet sad smile she took his hand and kissed it.

"How ill you have been: how weak you look, my dear Henry!" she said.

'Tis certain the Colonel did look like a ghost, except that ghosts do not look very happy, 'tis said. Esmond always felt so on returning to her after absence, indeed whenever he looked in her sweet kind face.

"I am come back to be nursed by my family," says he. "If Frank had not taken care of me after my wound, very likely I should have gone altogether."

"Poor Frank, good Frank!" says his mother. "You'll always be kind to him, my Lord," she went on. "The poor child never knew he was doing you a wrong."

"My Lord!" cries out Colonel Esmond. "What do you mean, dear lady?"

"I am no lady," says she; "I am Rachel Esmond, Francis Esmond's widow, my Lord. I cannot bear that title. Would we never had taken it from him who has it now. But we did all in our power, Henry: we did all in our power; and my Lord and I—that is——"

"Who told you this tale, dearest lady?" asked the Colonel.

"Have you not had the letter I writ you? I writ to you at Mons directly I heard it," says Lady Esmond.

"And from whom?" again asked Colonel Esmond—and his mistress then told him that on her deathbed the Dowager Countess, sending for her, had presented her with this dismal secret as a legacy. "'Twas very malicious of the Dowager," Lady Esmond said, "to have had it so long, and to have kept the truth from me." "Cousin Rachel," she said—and Esmond's mistress could not forbear smiling as she told the story—"Cousin Rachel," cries the Dowager, "I have sent for you, as the doctors say I may go off any day in this dysentery; and to ease my conscience of a great load that has been on it. You always have been a poor creature and unfit for great honour, and what I have to say won't, therefore, affect you so much. You must know, Cousin Rachel, that I have left my house, plate, and furniture, three thousand pounds in money, and my diamonds that my late revered Saint and Sovereign, King James, presented me with, to my Lord Viscount Castlewood."

"To my Frank?" says Lady Castlewood: "I was in hopes——"

"To Viscount Castlewood, my dear; Viscount Castlewood and Baron Esmond of Shandon in the Kingdom of Ireland, Earl and Marquis of Esmond under patent of his Majesty King James the Second, conferred upon my husband the late Marquis—for I am Marchioness of Esmond before God and man."

"And have you left poor Harry nothing, dear Marchioness?" asks Lady Castlewood (she hath told me the story completely since with her quiet arch way; the most charming any woman ever had: and I set down the narrative here at length, so as to have done with it). "And have you left poor Harry nothing?" asks my dear lady: "for you know, Henry," she says with her sweet smile, "I used always to pity Esau—and I think I am on his side—though papa tried very hard to convince me the other way."

"Poor Harry!" says the old lady. "So you want something left to poor Harry: he,—he! (reach me the drops, cousin). Well, then, my dear, since you want poor Harry to have a fortune, you must understand that ever since the year 1691, a week after the battle of the Boyne, where the Prince of Orange defeated his royal sovereign and father, for which crime he is now suffering in flames (ugh! ugh!), Henry Esmond hath been Marquis of Esmond and Earl of Castlewood in the United Kingdom, and Baron and Viscount Castlewood of Shandon in Ireland, and a Baronet—and his eldest son will be, by courtesy, styled Earl of Castlewood—he! he! What do you think of that, my dear?"

"Gracious mercy! how long have you known this?" cries the other lady (thinking perhaps that the old Marchioness was wandering in her wits).

"My husband, before he was converted, was a wicked wretch," the sick sinner continued. "When he was in the Low Countries he seduced a weaver's daughter; and added to his wickedness by marrying her. And then he came to this country and married me—a poor girl—a poor innocent young thing—I say,"—"though she was past forty, you know, Harry, when she married: and as for being innocent——" "Well," she went on, "I knew nothing of my Lord's wickedness for three years after our marriage, and after the burial of our poor little boy I had it done over again, my dear: I had myself married by Father Holt in Castlewood chapel, as soon as ever I heard the creature was dead—and having a great illness then, arising from another sad disappointment I had, the priest came and told me that my Lord had a son before our marriage, and that the child was at nurse in England; and I consented to let the brat be brought home, and a queer little melancholy child it was when it came.

"Our intention was to make a priest of him: and he was bred for this, until you perverted him from it, you wicked woman. And I had again hopes of giving an heir to my Lord, when he was called away upon the King's business, and died fighting gloriously at the Boyne water.

"Should I be disappointed—I owed your husband no love, my dear, for he had jilted me in the most scandalous way—I thought there would be time to declare the little weaver's son for the true heir. But I was carried off to prison, where your husband was so kind to me—urging all his friends to obtain my release, and using all his credit in my favour—that I relented towards him, especially as my director counselled me to be silent; and that it was for the good of the King's service that the title of our family should continue with your husband the late Viscount, whereby his fidelity would be always secured to the King. And a proof of this is, that a year before your husband's death, when he thought of taking a place under the Prince of Orange, Mr. Holt went to him, and told him what the state of the matter was, and obliged him to raise a large sum for his Majesty, and engaged him in the true cause so heartily, that we were sure of his support on any day when it should be considered advisable to attack the usurper. Then his sudden death came; and there was a thought of declaring the truth. But 'twas determined to be best for the King's service to let the title still go with the younger branch; and there's no sacrifice a Castlewood wouldn't make for that cause, my dear.

"As for Colonel Esmond, he knew the truth already." ("And then, Harry," my mistress said, "she told me of what had happened at my dear husband's deathbed.") "He doth not intend to take the title, though it belongs to him. But it eases my conscience that you should know the truth, my dear. And your son is lawfully Viscount Castlewood so long as his cousin doth not claim the rank."

This was the substance of the Dowager's revelation. Dean Atterbury had knowledge of it, Lady Castlewood said, and Esmond very well knows how: that divine being the clergyman for whom the late lord had sent on his deathbed; and when Lady Castlewood would instantly have written to her son, and conveyed the truth to him, the Dean's advice was that a letter should be writ to Colonel Esmond rather; that the matter should be submitted to his decision, by which alone the rest of the family were bound to abide.

"And can my dearest lady doubt what that will be?" says the Colonel.

"It rests with you, Harry, as the head of our house."

"It was settled twelve years since, by my dear lord's bedside," says Colonel Esmond. "The children must know nothing of this. Frank and his heirs after him must bear our name. 'Tis his rightfully: I have not even a proof of that marriage of my father and mother, though my poor lord, on his deathbed, told me that Father Holt had brought such a proof to Castlewood. I would not seek it when I was abroad. I went and looked at my poor mother's grave in her convent. What matter to her now? No court of law on earth, upon my mere word, would deprive my Lord Viscount and set me up. I am the head of the house, dear lady; but Frank is Viscount of Castlewood still. And rather than disturb him, I would turn monk, or disappear in America."

As he spoke so to his dearest mistress, for whom he would have been willing to give up his life, or to make any sacrifice any day, the fond creature flung herself down on her knees before him, and kissed both his hands in an outbreak of passionate love and gratitude, such as could not but melt his heart, and make him feel very proud and thankful that God had given him the power to show his love for her, and to prove it by some little sacrifice on his own part. To be able to bestow benefits or happiness on those one loves is sure the greatest blessing conferred upon a man—and what wealth or name, or gratification of ambition or vanity, could compare with the pleasure Esmond now had of being able to confer some kindness upon his best and dearest friends?

"Dearest saint," says he—"purest soul, that has had so much to suffer, that has blest the poor lonely orphan with such a treasure of love! 'Tis for me to kneel, not for you; 'tis for me to be thankful that I can make you happy. Hath my life any other aim? Blessed be God that I can serve you! What pleasure, think you, could all the world give me compared to that?"

"Don't raise me," she said, in a wild way, to Esmond, who would have lifted her. "Let me kneel—let me kneel, and—and—worship you."

Before such a partial judge as Esmond's dear mistress owned herself to be, any cause which he might plead was sure to be given in his favour; and accordingly he found little difficulty in reconciling her to the news whereof he was bearer, of her son's marriage to a foreign lady, Papist though she was. Lady Castlewood never could be brought to think so ill of that religion as other people in England thought of it: she held that ours was undoubtedly a branch of the Catholic Church, but that the Roman was one of the main stems on which, no doubt, many errors had been grafted (she was, for a woman, extraordinarily well versed in this controversy, having acted, as a girl, as secretary to her father, the late Dean, and written many of his sermons, under his dictation); and if Frank had chosen to marry a lady of the Church of South Europe, as she would call the Roman communion, there was no need why she should not welcome her as a daughter-in-law: and accordingly she wrote to her new daughter a very pretty, touching letter (as Esmond thought, who had cognisance of it before it went), in which the only hint of reproof was a gentle remonstrance that her son had not written to herself, to ask a fond mother's blessing for that step which he was about taking. "Castlewood knew very well," so she wrote to her son, "that she never denied him anything in her power to give, much less would she think of opposing a marriage that was to make his happiness, as she trusted, and keep him out of wild courses, which had alarmed her a good deal:" and she besought him to come quickly to England, to settle down in his family house of Castlewood ("It is his family house," says she to Colonel Esmond, "though only his own house by your forbearance") and to receive the accompt of her stewardship during his ten years' minority. By care and frugality, she had got the estate into a better condition than ever it had been since the Parliamentary wars; and my Lord was now master of a pretty, small income, not encumbered of debts, as it had been during his father's ruinous time. "But in saving my son's fortune," says she, "I fear I have lost a great part of my hold on him." And, indeed, this was the case: her Ladyship's daughter complaining that their mother did all for Frank, and nothing for her; and Frank himself being dissatisfied at the narrow, simple way of his mother's living at Walcote, where he had been brought up more like a poor parson's son than a young nobleman that was to make a figure in the world. 'Twas this mistake in his early training, very likely, that set him so eager upon pleasure when he had it in his power; nor is he the first lad that has been spoiled by the over-careful fondness of women. No training is so useful for children, great or small, as the company of their betters in rank or natural parts; in whose society they lose the overweening sense of their own importance, which stay-at-home people very commonly learn.

But, as a prodigal that's sending in a schedule of his debts to his friends, never puts all down, and, you may be sure, the rogue keeps back some immense swingeing bill, that he doesn't dare to own; so the poor Frank had a very heavy piece of news to break to his mother, and which he hadn't the courage to introduce into his first confession. Some misgivings Esmond might have, upon receiving Frank's letter, and knowing into what hands the boy had fallen; but whatever these misgivings were, he kept them to himself, not caring to trouble his mistress with any fears that might be groundless.

However, the next mail which came from Bruxelles, after Frank had received his mother's letters there, brought back a joint composition from himself and his wife, who could spell no better than her young scapegrace of a husband, full of expressions of thanks, love, and duty to the Dowager Viscountess, as my poor lady now was styled; and along with this letter (which was read in a family council, namely, the Viscountess, Mistress Beatrix, and the writer of this memoir, and which was pronounced to be vulgar by the Maid of Honour, and felt to be so by the other two) there came a private letter for Colonel Esmond from poor Frank, with another dismal commission for the Colonel to execute, at his best opportunity; and this was to announce that Frank had seen fit, "by the exhortation of Mr. Holt, the influence of his Clotilda, and the blessing of Heaven and the saints," says my Lord demurely, "to change his religion, and be received into the bosom of that Church of which his sovereign, many of his family, and the greater part of the civilised world, were members." And his Lordship added a postscript, of which Esmond knew the inspiring genius very well, for it had the genuine twang of the Seminary, and was quite unlike poor Frank's ordinary style of writing and thinking; in which he reminded Colonel Esmond that he too was, by birth, of that Church; and that his mother and sister should have his Lordship's prayers to the saints (an inestimable benefit, truly!) for their conversion.

If Esmond had wanted to keep this secret, he could not; for a day or two after receiving this letter, a notice from Bruxelles appeared in the *Post-Boy* and other prints, announcing that "a young Irish lord, the Viscount C–stlew—d, just come to his majority, and who had served the last campaigns with great credit, as aide-de-camp to his Grace the Duke of Marlborough, had declared for the Popish religion at Bruxelles, and had walked in a procession barefoot, with a wax-taper in his hand." The notorious Mr. Holt, who had been employed as a Jacobite agent during the last reign, and many times pardoned by King William, had been, the *Post-Boy* said, the agent of this conversion.

The Lady Castlewood was as much cast down by this news as Miss Beatrix was indignant at it. "So," says she, "Castlewood is no longer a home for us, mother. Frank's foreign wife will bring her confessor, and there will be frogs for dinner; and all Tusher's and my grandfather's sermons are flung away upon my brother. I used to tell you that you killed him with the Catechism, and that he would turn wicked as soon as he broke from his mammy's leading-strings. O mother, you would not believe that the young scapegrace was playing you tricks, and that sneak of a Tusher was not a fit guide for him. Oh, those parsons, I hate 'em all!" says Mistress Beatrix, clapping her hands together; "yes, whether they wear cassocks and buckles, or beards and bare feet. There's a horrid Irish wretch who never misses a Sunday at Court, and who pays me compliments there, the horrible man; and if you want to know what parsons are, you should see his behaviour, and hear him talk of his own cloth. They're all the same, whether they're bishops, or bonzes, or Indian fakirs. They try to domineer, and they frighten us with kingdom come; and they wear a sanctified air in public, and expect us to go down on our knees and ask their blessing; and they intrigue, and they grasp, and they backbite, and they slander worse than the worst courtier or the wickedest old woman. I heard this Mr. Swift sneering at my Lord Duke of Marlborough's courage the other day. He! that Teague from Dublin! because his Grace is not in favour, dares to say this of him; and he says this that it may get to her Majesty's ear, and to coax and wheedle Mrs. Masham. They say the Elector of Hanover has a dozen of mistresses in his Court at Herrenhausen, and if he comes to be king over us, I wager that the bishops and Mr. Swift, that wants to be one, will coax and wheedle them. Oh, those priests and their grave airs! I'm sick of their square toes and their rustling cassocks. I should like to go to a country where there was not one, or turn Quaker, and get rid of 'em; and I would, only the dress is not becoming, and I've much too pretty a figure to hide it. Haven't I, cousin?" and here she glanced at her person and the looking-glass, which told her rightly that a more beautiful shape and face never were seen.

"I made that onslaught on the priests," says Miss Beatrix, afterwards, "in order to divert my poor dear mother's anguish about Frank. Frank is as vain as a girl, cousin. Talk of us girls being vain, what are *we* to you? It was easy to see that the first woman who chose would make a fool of him, or the first robe—I count a priest and a woman all the same. We are always caballing; we are not answerable for the fibs we tell; we are always cajoling and coaxing, or threatening; and we are always making mischief, Colonel Esmond—mark my word for that, who know the world, sir, and have to make my way in it. I see as well as possible how Frank's marriage hath been managed. The Count, our papa-in-law, is always away at the coffee-house. The Countess, our mother, is always in the kitchen looking after the dinner. The Countess, our sister, is at the spinet. When my Lord comes to say he is going on the campaign, the lovely Clotilda bursts into tears, and faints—so; he catches her in his arms—no, sir, keep your distance, cousin, if you please—she cries on his shoulder, and he says, 'O my divine, my adored, my beloved Clotilda, are you sorry to part with me?' 'O my Francisco,' says she, 'O my Lord!' and at this very instant mamma and a couple of young brothers, with moustaches and long rapiers, come in from the kitchen, where they have been eating bread and onions. Mark my word, you will have all this woman's relations at Castlewood three months after she has arrived there. The old count and countess, and the young counts, and all the little countesses her sisters. Counts! every one of these wretches says he is a count. Guiscard, that stabbed Mr. Harvey, said he was a count; and I believe he was a barber. All Frenchmen are barbers—Fiddledee! don't contradict me—or else dancing-masters, or else priests." And so she rattled on.

"Who was it taught *you* to dance, Cousin Beatrix?" says the Colonel.

She laughed out the air of a minuet, and swept a low curtsey, coming up to the recover with the prettiest little foot in the world pointed out. Her mother came in as she was in this attitude; my Lady had been in her closet, having taken poor Frank's conversion in a very serious way; the madcap girl ran up to her mother, put her arms round her waist, kissed her, tried to make her dance, and said, "Don't be silly, you kind little mamma, and cry about Frank turning Papist. What a figure he must be, with a white sheet and a candle, walking in a procession barefoot!" And she kicked off her little slippers (the wonderfullest little shoes with wonderful tall red heels: Esmond pounced upon one as it fell close beside him), and she put on the drollest little *moue*, and marched up and down the room holding Esmond's cane by way of taper. Serious as her mood was, Lady Castlewood could not refrain from laughing; and as for Esmond he looked on with that delight with which the sight of this fair creature always inspired him: never had he seen any woman so arch, so brilliant, and so beautiful.

Having finished her march, she put out her foot for her slipper. The Colonel knelt down: "If you will be Pope I will turn Papist," says he; and her Holiness gave him gracious leave to kiss the little stockinged foot before he put the slipper on.

Mamma's feet began to pat on the floor during this operation, and Beatrix, whose bright eyes nothing escaped, saw that little mark of impatience. She ran up and embraced her mother, with her usual cry of, "O you silly little mamma: your feet are quite as pretty as mine," says she: "they are, cousin, though she hides 'em; but the shoemaker will tell you that he makes for both off the same last."

"You are taller than I am, dearest," says her mother, blushing over her whole sweet face—"and—and it is your hand, my dear, and not your foot he wants you to give him;" and she said it with a hysteric laugh, that had more of tears than laughter in it; laying her head on her daughter's fair shoulder, and hiding it there. They made a very pretty picture together, and looked like a pair of sisters—the sweet simple matron seeming younger than her years, and her daughter, if not older, yet somehow, from a commanding manner and grace which she possessed above most women, her mother's superior and protectress.

"But oh!" cries my mistress, recovering herself after this scene, and returning to her usual sad tone, "'tis a shame that we should laugh and be making merry on a day when we ought to be down on our knees and asking pardon."

"Asking pardon for what?" says saucy Mrs. Beatrix—"because Frank takes it into his head to fast on Fridays and worship images? You know if you had been born a Papist, mother, a Papist you would have remained till the end of your days? 'Tis the religion of the King and of some of the best quality. For my part, I'm no enemy to it, and think Queen Bess was not a penny better than Queen Mary."

"Hush, Beatrix! Do not jest with sacred things, and remember of what parentage you come," cries my Lady. Beatrix was ordering her ribands, and adjusting her tucker, and performing a dozen provokingly pretty ceremonies before the glass. The girl was no hypocrite at least. She never at that time could be brought to think but of the world and her beauty; and seemed to have no more sense of devotion than some people have of music, that cannot distinguish one air from another. Esmond saw this fault in her, as he saw many others—a bad wife would Beatrix Esmond make, he thought, for any man under the degree of a prince. She was born to shine in great assemblies, and to adorn palaces, and to command everywhere—to conduct an intrigue of politics, or to glitter in a queen's train. But to sit at a homely table, and mend the stockings of a poor man's children! that was no fitting duty for her, or at least one that she wouldn't have broke her heart in trying to do. She was a princess, though she had scarce a shilling to her fortune; and one of her subjects—the most abject and devoted wretch, sure, that ever drivelled at a woman's knees—was this unlucky gentleman; who bound his good sense, and reason, and independence, hand and foot, and submitted them to her.

And who does not know how ruthlessly women will tyrannise when they are let to domineer? and who does not know how useless advice is? I could give good counsel to my descendants, but I know they'll follow their own way, for all their grandfather's sermon. A man gets his own experience about women, and will take nobody's hearsay; nor, indeed, is the young fellow worth a fig that would. 'Tis I that am in love with my mistress, not my old grandmother that counsels me: 'tis I that have fixed the value of the thing I would have, and know the price I would pay for it. It may be worthless to you, but 'tis all my life to me. Had Esmond possessed the Great Mogul's crown and all his diamonds, or all the Duke of Marlborough's money, or all the ingots sunk at Vigo, he would have given them all for this woman. A fool he was, if you will; but so is a sovereign a fool, that will give half a principality for a little crystal as big as a pigeon's egg, and called a diamond: so is a wealthy nobleman a fool, that will face danger or death, and spend half his life, and all his tranquillity, caballing for a blue riband; so is a Dutch merchant a fool, that hath been known to pay ten thousand crowns for a tulip. There's some particular prize we all of us value, and that every man of spirit will venture his life for. With this, it may be to achieve a great reputation for learning; with that, to be a man of fashion, and the admiration of the town; with another, to consummate a great work of art or poetry, and go to immortality that way; and with another, for a certain time of his life, the sole object and aim is a woman.

Whilst Esmond was under the domination of this passion, he remembers many a talk he had with his intimates, who used to rally Our Knight of the Rueful Countenance at his devotion, whereof he made no disguise, to Beatrix; and it was with replies such as the above he met his friends' satire. "Granted, I am a fool," says he, "and no better than you; but you are no better than I. You have your folly you labour for; give me the charity of mine. What flatteries do you, Mr. St. John, stoop to whisper in the ears of a queen's favourite? What nights of labour doth not the laziest man in the world endure, foregoing his bottle, and his boon companions, foregoing Lais, in whose lap he would like to be yawning, that he may prepare a speech full of lies, to cajole three hundred stupid country-gentlemen in the House of Commons, and get the hiccupping cheers of the October Club! What days will you spend in your jolting chariot" (Mr. Esmond often rode to Windsor, and especially, of later days, with the Secretary). "What hours will you pass on your gouty feet—and how humbly will you kneel down to present a despatch—you, the proudest man in the world, that has not knelt to God since you were a boy, and in that posture whisper, flatter, adore almost, a stupid woman, that's often boozy with too much meat and drink, when Mr. Secretary goes for his audience! If my pursuit is vanity, sure yours is too." And then the Secretary would fly out in such a rich flow of eloquence as this pen cannot pretend to recall; advocating his scheme of ambition, showing the great good he would do for his country when he was the undisputed chief of it; backing his opinion with a score of pat sentences from Greek and Roman authorities (of which kind of learning he made rather an ostentatious display), and scornfully vaunting the very arts and meannesses by which fools were to be made to follow him, opponents to be bribed or silenced, doubters converted, and enemies overawed.

"I am Diogenes," says Esmond, laughing, "that is taken up for a ride in Alexander's chariot. I have no desire to vanquish Darius or to tame Bucephalus. I do not want what you want, a great name or a high place: to have them would bring me no pleasure. But my moderation is taste, not virtue; and I know that what I do want is as vain as that which you long after. Do not grudge me my vanity, if I allow yours; or rather, let us laugh at both indifferently, and at ourselves, and at each other."

"If your charmer holds out," says St. John, "at this rate she may keep you twenty years besieging her, and surrender by the time you are seventy, and she is old enough to be a grandmother. I do not say the pursuit of a particular woman is not as pleasant a pastime as any other kind of hunting," he added; "only, for my part, I find the game won't run long enough. They knock under too soon—that's the fault I find with 'em."

"The game which you pursue is in the habit of being caught, and used to being pulled down," says Mr. Esmond.

"But Dulcinea del Toboso is peerless, eh?" says the other. "Well, honest Harry, go and attack windmills—perhaps thou art not more mad than other people," St. John added, with a sigh.

CHAPTER III

A PAPER OUT OF THE "SPECTATOR"

DOTH any young gentleman of my progeny, who may read his old grandfather's papers, chance to be presently suffering under the passion of Love? There is a humiliating cure, but one that is easy and almost specific for the malady—which is, to try an alibi. Esmond went away from his mistress and was cured a half-dozen times; he came back to her side, and instantly fell ill again of the fever. He vowed that he could leave her and think no more of her, and so he could pretty well, at least, succeed in quelling that rage and longing he had whenever he was with her; but as soon as he returned he was as bad as ever again. Truly a ludicrous and pitiable object, at least exhausting everybody's pity but his dearest mistress's, Lady Castlewood's, in whose tender breast he reposed all his dreary confessions, and who never tired of hearing him and pleading for him.

Sometimes Esmond would think there was hope. Then again he would be plagued with despair, at some impertinence or coquetry of his mistress. For days they would be like brother and sister, or the dearest friends—she, simple, fond, and charming—he, happy beyond measure at her good behaviour. But this would all vanish on a sudden. Either he would be too pressing, and hint his love, when she would rebuff him instantly, and give his vanity a box on the ear; or he would be jealous, and with perfect good reason, of some new admirer that had sprung up, or some rich young gentleman newly arrived in the town, that this incorrigible flirt would set her nets and baits to draw in. If Esmond remonstrated, the little rebel would say, "Who are you? I shall go my own way, sirrah, and that way is towards a husband, and I don't want *you* on the way. I am for your betters, Colonel, for your betters: do you hear that? You might do if you had an estate and were younger: only eight years older than I, you say! pish, you are a hundred years older. You are an old, old Graveairs, and I should make you miserable, that would be the only comfort I should have in marrying you. But you have not money enough to keep a cat decently after you have paid your man his wages, and your landlady her bill. Do you think I am going to live in a lodging, and turn the mutton on a string whilst your honour nurses the baby? Fiddlestick, and why did you not get this nonsense knocked out of your head when you were in the wars? You are come back more dismal and dreary than ever. You and mamma are fit for each other. You might be Darby and Joan, and play cribbage to the end of your lives."

"At least you own to your wordliness, my poor Trix," says her mother.

"Worldliness! O my pretty lady! Do you think that I am a child in the nursery, and to be frightened by Bogey? Worldliness, to be sure; and pray, madam, where is the harm of wishing to be comfortable? When you are gone, you dearest old woman, or when I am tired of you and have run away from you, where shall I go? Shall I go and be head nurse to my Popish sister-in-law, take the children their physic, and whip 'em, and put 'em to bed when they are naughty? Shall I be Castlewood's upper servant, and perhaps marry Tom Tusher? *Merci!* I have been long enough Frank's humble servant. Why am I not a man? I have ten times his brains, and had I worn the—well, don't let your Ladyship be frightened—had I worn a sword and periwig instead of this mantle and commode to which nature has condemned me—(though 'tis a pretty stuff, too—Cousin Esmond! you will go to the Exchange to-morrow, and get the exact counterpart of this riband, sir; do you hear?)—I would have made our name talked about. So would Graveairs here have made something out of our name if he had represented it. My Lord Graveairs would have done very well. Yes, you have a very pretty way, and would have made a very decent, grave speaker." And here she began to imitate Esmond's way of carrying himself and speaking to his face, and so ludicrously that his mistress burst out a-laughing, and even he himself could see there was some likeness in the fantastical malicious caricature.

"Yes," says she, "I solemnly vow, own, and confess, that I want a good husband. Where's the harm of one? My face is my fortune. Who'll come?—buy, buy, buy! I cannot toil, neither can I spin, but I can play twenty-three games on the cards. I can dance the last dance, I can hunt the stag, and I think I could shoot flying. I can talk as wicked as any woman of my years, and know enough stories to amuse a sulky husband for at least one thousand and one nights. I have a pretty taste for dress, diamonds, gambling, and old China. I love sugar-plums, Malines lace (that you brought me, cousin, is very pretty), the opera, and everything that is useless and costly. I have got a monkey and a little black boy—Pompey, sir, go and give a dish of chocolate to Colonel

Graveairs—and a parrot and a spaniel, and I must have a husband. Cupid, you hear?"

"Iss, missis!" says Pompey, a little grinning negro Lord Peterborow gave her, with a bird of paradise in his turbant, and a collar with his mistress' name on it.

"Iss, missis!" says Beatrix, imitating the child. "And if husband not come, Pompey must go fetch one."

And Pompey went away grinning with his chocolate tray as Miss Beatrix ran up to her mother and ended her sally of mischief in her common way, with a kiss—no wonder that upon paying such a penalty her fond judge pardoned her.

When Mr. Esmond came home, his health was still shattered; and he took a lodging near to his mistresses, at Kensington, glad enough to be served by them, and to see them day after day. He was enabled to see a little company—and of the sort he liked best. Mr. Steele and Mr. Addison both did him the honour to visit him; and drank many a glass of good claret at his lodging, whilst their entertainer, through his wound, was kept to diet drink and gruel. These gentlemen were Whigs, and great admirers of my Lord Duke of Marlborough; and Esmond was entirely of the other party. But their different views of politics did not prevent the gentlemen from agreeing in private, nor from allowing, on one evening when Esmond's kind old patron, Lieutenant-General Webb, with a stick and a crutch, hobbled up to the Colonel's lodging (which was prettily situate at Knightsbridge, between London and Kensington, and looking over the Gardens), that the Lieutenant-General was a noble and gallant soldier—and even that he had been hardly used in the Wynendael affair. He took his revenge in talk, that must be confessed; and if Mr. Addison had had a mind to write a poem about Wynendael, he might have heard from the commander's own lips the story a hundred times over.

Mr. Esmond, forced to be quiet, betook himself to literature for a relaxation, and composed his comedy, whereof the prompter's copy lieth in my walnut escritoire, sealed up and docketed, "The Faithful Fool, a Comedy, as it was performed by her Majesty's Servants." 'Twas a very sentimental piece; and Mr. Steele, who had more of that kind of sentiment than Mr. Addison, admired it, whilst the other rather sneered at the performance; though he owned that, here and there, it contained some pretty strokes. He was bringing out his own play of "Cato" at the time, the blaze of which quite extinguished Esmond's farthing candle; and his name was never put to the piece, which was printed as by a Person of Quality. Only nine copies were sold, though Mr. Dennis, the great critic, praised it, and said 'twas a work of great merit; and Colonel Esmond had the whole impression burned one day in a rage, by Jack Lockwood, his man.

All this comedy was full of bitter satiric strokes against a certain young lady. The plot of the piece was quite a new one. A young woman was represented with a great number of suitors, selecting a pert fribble of a peer, in place of the hero (but ill acted, I think, by Mr. Wilks, the Faithful Fool), who persisted in admiring her. In the fifth act, Teraminta was made to discover the merits of Eugenio (the F. F.), and to feel a partiality for him too late; for he announced that he had bestowed his hand and estate upon Rosaria, a country lass, endowed with every virtue. But it must be owned that the audience yawned through the play; and that it perished on the third night, with only half-a-dozen persons to behold its agonies. Esmond and his two mistresses came to the first night, and Miss Beatrix fell asleep; whilst her mother, who had not been to a play since King James the Second's time, thought the piece, though not brilliant, had a very pretty moral.

Mr. Esmond dabbled in letters, and wrote a deal of prose and verse at this time of leisure. When displeased with the conduct of Miss Beatrix, he would compose a satire, in which he relieved his mind. When smarting under the faithlessness of women, he dashed off a copy of verses, in which he held the whole sex up to scorn. One day, in one of these moods, he made a little joke, in which (swearing him to secrecy) he got his friend Dick Steele to help him; and, composing a paper, he had it printed exactly like Steele's paper, and by his printer, and laid on his mistress' breakfast-table the following—

"SPECTATOR.

"No. 341. "*Tuesday, April* 1, 1712.

Mutato nomine de te Fabula narratur.—HORACE.
Thyself the moral of the Fable see.—CREECH.

"Jocasta is known as a woman of learning and fashion, and as one of the most amiable persons of this court and country. She is at home two mornings of the week, and all the wits and a few of the beauties of London flock to her assemblies. When she goes abroad to Tunbridge or the Bath, a retinue of adorers rides the journey with her; and besides the London beaux, she has a crowd of admirers at the Wells, the polite amongst the natives of Sussex and Somerset pressing round her tea-tables, and being anxious for a nod from her chair. Jocasta's acquaintance is thus very numerous. Indeed, 'tis one smart writer's work to keep her visiting-book—

a strong footman is engaged to carry it; and it would require a much stronger head even than Jocasta's own to remember the names of all her dear friends.

"Either at Epsom Wells or Tunbridge (for of this important matter Jocasta cannot be certain) it was her Ladyship's fortune to become acquainted with a young gentleman, whose conversation was so sprightly, and manners amiable, that she invited the agreeable young spark to visit her if ever he came to London, where her house in Spring Garden should be open to him. Charming as he was, and without any manner of doubt a pretty fellow, Jocasta hath such a regiment of the like continually marching round her standard, that 'tis no wonder her attention is distracted amongst them. And so, though this gentleman made a considerable impression upon her, and touched her heart for at least three-and-twenty minutes, it must be owned that she has forgotten his name. He is a dark man, and may be eight-and-twenty years old. His dress is sober, though of rich materials. He has a mole on his forehead over his left eye; has a blue riband to his cane and sword, and wears his own hair.

"Jocasta was much flattered by beholding her admirer (for that everybody admires who sees her is a point which she never can for a moment doubt) in the next pew to her at St. James's Church last Sunday; and the manner in which he appeared to go to sleep during the sermon—though from under his fringed eyelids it was evident he was casting glances of respectful rapture towards Jocasta—deeply moved and interested her. On coming out of church he found his way to her chair, and made her an elegant bow as she stepped into it. She saw him at Court afterwards, where he carried himself with a most distinguished air, though none of her acquaintances knew his name; and the next night he was at the play, where her Ladyship was pleased to acknowledge him from the side-box.

"During the whole of the comedy she racked her brains so to remember his name that she did not hear a word of the piece: and having the happiness to meet him once more in the lobby of the playhouse, she went up to him in a flutter, and bade him remember that she kept two nights in the week, and that she longed to see him at Spring Garden.

"He appeared on Tuesday, in a rich suit, showing a very fine taste both in the tailor and wearer; and though a knot of us were gathered round the charming Jocasta, fellows who pretended to know every face upon the town, not one could tell the gentleman's name in reply to Jocasta's eager inquiries, flung to the right and left of her as he advanced up the room with a bow that would become a duke.

"Jocasta acknowledged this salute with one of those smiles and curtseys of which that lady hath the secret. She curtseys with a languishing air, as if to say, 'You are come at last. I have been pining for you:' and then she finishes her victim with a killing look, which declares: 'O Philander! I have no eyes but for you.' Camilla hath as good a curtsey perhaps, and Thalestris much such another look; but the glance and the curtsey together belong to Jocasta of all the English beauties alone.

"'Welcome to London, sir,' says she. 'One can see you are from the country by your looks.' She would have said 'Epsom,' or 'Tunbridge,' had she remembered rightly at which place she had met the stranger; but, alas! she had forgotten.

"The gentleman said, 'he had been in town but three days; and one of his reasons for coming hither was to have the honour of paying his court to Jocasta.'

"She said, 'the waters had agreed with her but indifferently.'

"'The waters were for the sick,' the gentleman said: 'the young and beautiful came but to make them sparkle. And as the clergyman read the service on Sunday,' he added, 'your Ladyship reminded me of the angel that visited the pool.' A murmur of approbation saluted this sally. Manilio, who is a wit when he is not at cards, was in such a rage that he revoked when he heard it.

"Jocasta was an angel visiting the waters; but at which of the Bethesdas? She was puzzled more and more; and, as her way always is, looked the more innocent and simple, the more artful her intentions were.

"'We were discoursing,' says she, 'about spelling of names and words when you came. Why should we say goold and write gold, and call china chayney, and Cavendish Candish, and Cholmondeley Chumley? If we call Pulteney Poltney, why shouldn't we call poultry pultry—and——'

"'Such an enchantress as your Ladyship,' says he, 'is mistress of all sorts of spells.' But this was Dr. Swift's pun, and we all knew it.

"'And—and how do you spell your name?' says she, coming to the point at length; for this sprightly conversation had lasted much longer than is here set down, and been carried on through at least three dishes of tea.

"'Oh, madam,' says he, '*I spell my name with the y.*' And laying down his dish, my gentleman made another elegant bow, and was gone in a moment.

"Jocasta hath had no sleep since this mortification, and the stranger's disappearance. If balked in anything she is sure to lose her health and temper; and we, her servants, suffer, as usual, during the angry fits of our Queen. Can you help us, Mr. Spectator, who know everything, to read this riddle for her, and set at rest all our minds? We find in her list, Mr. Berty, Mr. Smith, Mr. Pike, Mr. Tyler—who may be Mr. Bertie, Mr. Smyth, Mr. Pyke, Mr. Tiler, for what we know. She hath turned away the clerk of her visiting-book, a poor fellow with a great family of children. Read me this riddle, good Mr. Shortface, and oblige your admirer —ŒDIPUS."

"THE TRUMPET COFFEE-HOUSE, WHITEHALL.

"MR. SPECTATOR,—I am a gentleman but little acquainted with the town, though I have had a university education, and passed some years serving my country abroad, where my name is better known than in the coffee-houses and St. James's.

"Two years since my uncle died, leaving me a pretty estate in the county of Kent; and being at Tunbridge Wells last summer, after my mourning was over, and on the look-out, if truth must be told, for some young lady who would share with me the solitude of my great Kentish house, and be kind to my tenantry (for whom a woman can do a great deal more good than the best-intentioned man can), I was greatly fascinated by a young lady of London, who was the toast of all the company at the Wells. Every one knows Saccharissa's beauty; and I think, Mr. Spectator, no one better than herself.

"My table-book informs me that I danced no less than seven-and-twenty sets with her at the Assembly. I treated her to the fiddles twice. I was admitted on several days to her lodging, and received by her with a great deal of distinction, and, for a time, was entirely her slave. It was only when I found, from common talk of the company at the Wells, and from narrowly watching one, who I once thought of asking the most sacred question a man can put to a woman, that I became aware how unfit she was to be a country gentleman's wife; and that this fair creature was but a heartless worldly jilt, playing with affections that she never meant to return, and, indeed, incapable of returning them. 'Tis admiration such women want, not love that touches them; and I can conceive, in her old age, no more wretched creature than this lady will be, when her beauty hath deserted her, when her admirers have left her, and she hath neither friendship nor religion to console her.

"Business calling me to London, I went to St. James's Church last Sunday, and there opposite me sat my beauty of the Wells. Her behaviour during the whole service was so pert, languishing, and absurd; she flirted her fan, and ogled and eyed me in a manner so indecent, that I was obliged to shut my eyes, so as actually not to see her, and whenever I opened them beheld hers (and very bright they are) still staring at me. I fell in with her afterwards at Court, and at the play-house; and here nothing would satisfy her but she must elbow through the crowd and speak to me, and invite me to the assembly, which she holds at her house, not very far from Ch–r–ng Cr–ss.

"Having made her a promise to attend, of course I kept my promise; and found the young widow in the midst of a half-dozen of card-tables, and a crowd of wits and admirers. I made the best bow I could, and advanced towards her; and saw by a peculiar puzzled look in her face, though she tried to hide her perplexity, that she had forgotten even my name.

"Her talk, artful as it was, convinced me that I had guessed aright. She turned the conversation most ridiculously upon the spelling of names and words; and I replied with as ridiculous fulsome compliments as I could pay her: indeed, one in which I compared her to an angel visiting the sick wells, went a little too far; nor should I have employed it, but that the allusion came from the Second Lesson last Sunday, which we both had heard, and I was pressed to answer her.

"Then she came to the question, which I knew was awaiting me, and asked how I *spelt* my name? 'Madam,' says I, turning on my heel, 'I spell it with a *y*.' And so I left her, wondering at the light-heartedness of the town-people, who forget and make friends so easily, and resolved to look elsewhere for a partner for your constant reader. CYMON WYLDOATS."

"You know my real name, Mr. Spectator, in which there is no such letter as *hupsilon*. But if the lady, whom I have called Saccharissa, wonders that I appear no more at the tea-tables, she is hereby respectfully informed the reason *y*."

The above is a parable, whereof the writer will now expound the meaning. Jocasta was no other than Miss Esmond, Maid of Honour to her Majesty. She had told Mr. Esmond this little story of having met a gentleman somewhere, and forgetting his name, when the gentleman, with no such malicious intentions as those of "Cymon" in the above fable, made the answer simply as above; and we all laughed to think how little Mistress Jocasta-Beatrix had profited by her artifice and precautions.

As for Cymon he was intended to represent yours and her very humble servant, the writer of the apologue and of this story, which we had printed on a *Spectator* paper at Mr. Steele's office, exactly as those famous journals were printed, and which was laid on the table at breakfast in place of the real newspaper. Mistress Jocasta, who had plenty of wit, could not live without her *Spectator* to her tea; and this sham *Spectator* was intended to convey to the young woman that she herself was a flirt, and that Cymon was a gentleman of honour and resolution, seeing all her faults, and determined to break the chains once and for ever.

For though enough hath been said about this love business already—enough, at least, to prove to the writer's heirs what a silly fond fool their old grandfather was, who would like them to consider him as a very wise old gentleman; yet not near all has been told concerning this matter, which, if it were allowed to take in Esmond's journal the space it occupied in his time, would weary his kinsmen and women of a hundred years' time beyond all endurance; and form such a diary of folly and drivelling, raptures and rage, as no man of ordinary vanity would like to leave behind him.

The truth is, that, whether she laughed at him or encouraged him; whether she smiled or was cold, and turned her smiles on another; worldly and ambitious as he knew her to be; hard and careless, as she seemed to grow with her Court life, and a hundred admirers that came to her and left her; Esmond, do what he would, never could get Beatrix out of his mind; thought of her constantly at home or away. If he read his name in a *Gazette*, or escaped the shot of a cannon-ball or a greater danger in the campaign, as has happened to him more than once, the instant thought after the honour achieved or the danger avoided, was, "What will *she* say of it?" "Will this distinction or the idea of this peril elate her or touch her, so as to be better inclined towards me?" He could no more help this passionate fidelity of temper than he could help the eyes he saw with—one or the other seemed a part of his nature; and knowing every one of her faults as well as the keenest of her detractors, and the folly of an attachment to such a woman, of which the fruition could never bring him happiness for above a week, there was yet a charm about this Circe from which the poor deluded gentleman could not free himself; and for a much longer period than Ulysses (another middle-aged officer, who had travelled much, and been in the foreign wars), Esmond felt himself enthralled and besotted by the wiles of this enchantress. Quit her! He could no more quit her, as the Cymon of this story was made to quit his false one, than he could lose his consciousness of yesterday. She had but to raise her finger, and he would come back from ever so far; she had but to say I have discarded such and such an adorer, and the poor infatuated wretch would be sure to come and *rôder* about her mother's house, willing to be put on the ranks of suitors, though he knew he might be cast off the next week. If he were like Ulysses in his folly, at least she was in so far like Penelope that she had a crowd of suitors, and undid day after day and night after night the handiwork of fascination and the web of coquetry with which she was wont to allure and entertain them.

Part of her coquetry may have come from her position about the Court, where the beautiful Maid of Honour was the light about which a thousand beaux came and fluttered; where she was sure to have a ring of admirers round her, crowding to listen to her repartees as much as to admire her beauty; and where she spoke and listened to much free talk, such as one never would have thought the lips or ears of Rachel Castlewood's daughter would have uttered or heard. When in waiting at Windsor or Hampton, the Court ladies and gentlemen would be making riding parties together; Mrs. Beatrix in a horseman's coat and hat, the foremost after the staghounds and over the park fences, a crowd of young fellows at her heels. If the English country ladies at this time were the most pure and modest of any ladies in the world—the English town and Court ladies permitted themselves words and behaviour that were neither modest nor pure; and claimed, some of them, a freedom which those who love that sex most would never wish to grant them. The gentlemen of my family that follow after me (for I don't encourage the ladies to pursue any such studies) may read in the works of Mr. Congreve, and Dr. Swift and others, what was the conversation and what the habits of our time.

The most beautiful woman in England in 1712, when Esmond returned to this country, a lady of high birth, and though of no fortune to be sure, with a thousand fascinations of wit and manners, Beatrix Esmond was now six-and-twenty years old, and Beatrix Esmond still. Of her hundred adorers she had not chosen one for a husband; and those who had asked had been jilted by her; and more still had left her. A succession of near ten years' crops of beauties had come up since her time, and had been reaped by proper *husband*men, if we may make an agricultural simile, and had been housed comfortably long ago. Her own contemporaries were sober mothers by this time; girls with not a tithe of her charms, or her wit, having made good matches, and now claiming precedence over the spinster who but lately had derided and outshone them. The young beauties were beginning to look down on Beatrix as an old maid, and sneer, and call her one of Charles the Second's ladies, and ask whether her portrait was not in the Hampton Court Gallery? But still she reigned, at least in one man's opinion, superior over all the little misses that were the toasts of the young lads; and in Esmond's eyes was ever perfectly lovely and young.

Who knows how many were nearly made happy by possessing

her, or, rather, how many were fortunate in escaping this siren? 'Tis a marvel to think that her mother was the purest and simplest woman in the whole world, and that this girl should have been born from her. I am inclined to fancy, my mistress, who never said a harsh word to her children (and but twice or thrice only to one person), must have been too fond and pressing with the maternal authority; for her son and her daughter both revolted early; nor after their first flight from the nest could they ever be brought back quite to the fond mother's bosom. Lady Castlewood, and perhaps it was as well, knew little of her daughter's life and real thoughts. How was she to apprehend what passes in Queen's ante-chambers and at Court tables? Mrs. Beatrix asserted her own authority so resolutely that her mother quickly gave in. The Maid of Honour had her own equipage; went from home and came back at her own will: her mother was alike powerless to resist her or to lead her, or to command or to persuade her.

She had been engaged once, twice, thrice, to be married, Esmond believed. When he quitted home, it hath been said, she was promised to my Lord Ashburnham, and now, on his return, behold his Lordship was just married to Lady Mary Butler, the Duke of Ormonde's daughter, and his fine houses, and twelve thousand a year of fortune, for which Miss Beatrix had rather coveted him, were out of her power. To her Esmond could say nothing in regard to the breaking of this match; and, asking his mistress about it, all Lady Castlewood answered was: "Do not speak to me about it, Harry. I cannot tell you how or why they parted, and I fear to inquire. I have told you before, that with all her kindness, and wit, and generosity, and that sort of splendour of nature she has, I can say but little good of poor Beatrix, and look with dread at the marriage she will form. Her mind is fixed on ambition only, and making a great figure; and, this achieved, she will tire of it as she does of everything. Heaven help her husband, whoever he shall be! My Lord Ashburnham was a most excellent young man, gentle and yet manly, of very good parts, so they told me, and as my little conversation would enable me to judge: and a kind temper—kind and enduring I'm sure he must have been, from all that he had to endure. But he quitted her at last, from some crowning piece of caprice or tyranny of hers; and now he has married a young woman that will make him a thousand times happier than my poor girl ever could."

The rupture, whatever its cause was (I heard the scandal, but indeed shall not take pains to repeat at length in this diary the trumpery coffee-house story), caused a good deal of low talk; and Mr. Esmond was present at my Lord's appearance at the Birthday with his bride, over whom the revenge that Beatrix took was to look so imperial and lovely that the modest downcast young lady could not appear beside her, and Lord Ashburnham, who had his reasons for wishing to avoid her, slunk away quite shamefaced, and very early. This time his Grace the Duke of Hamilton, whom Esmond had seen about her before, was constant at Miss Beatrix's side: he was one of the most splendid gentlemen of Europe, accomplished by books, by travel, by long command of the best company, distinguished as a statesman, having been ambassador in King William's time, and a noble speaker in the Scots' Parliament, where he had led the party that was against the Union, and though now five or six-and-forty years of age, a gentleman so high in stature, accomplished in wit, and favoured in person, that he might pretend to the hand of any Princess in Europe.

"Should you like the Duke for a cousin?" says Mr. Secretary St. John, whispering to Colonel Esmond in French; "it appears that the widower consoles himself."

But to return to our little *Spectator* paper and the conversation which grew out of it. Miss Beatrix at first was quite *bit* (as the phrase of that day was) and did not "smoke" the authorship of the story; indeed Esmond had tried to imitate as well as he could Mr. Steele's manner (as for the other author of the *Spectator*, his prose style I think is altogether inimitable); and Dick, who was the idlest and best-natured of men, would have let the piece pass into his journal and go to posterity as one of his own lucubrations, but that Esmond did not care to have a lady's name whom he loved sent forth to the world in a light so unfavourable. Beatrix pished and psha'd over the paper; Colonel Esmond watching with no little interest her countenance as she read it.

"How stupid your friend Mr. Steele becomes!" cries Miss Beatrix. "Epsom and Tunbridge! Will he never have done with Epsom and Tunbridge, and with beaux at church, and Jocastas and Lindamiras? Why does he not call women Nelly and Betty, as their godfathers and godmothers did for them in their baptism?"

"Beatrix, Beatrix!" says her mother, "speak gravely of grave things."

"Mamma thinks the Church Catechism came from heaven, I believe," says Beatrix, with a laugh, "and was brought down by a bishop from a mountain. Oh, how I used to break my heart over it! Besides, I had a Popish godmother, mamma; why did you give me one?"

"I gave you the Queen's name," says her mother, blushing. "And a very pretty name it is," said somebody else.

Beatrix went on reading: "Spell my name with a *y*—why, you

wretch," says she, turning round to Colonel Esmond, "you have been telling my story to Mr. Steele—or stop—you have written the paper yourself to turn me into ridicule. For shame, sir!"

Poor Mr. Esmond felt rather frightened, and told a truth, which was nevertheless an entire falsehood. "Upon my honour," says he, "I have not even read the *Spectator* of this morning." Nor had he, for that was not the *Spectator*, but a sham newspaper put in its place.

She went on reading: her face rather flushed as she read. "No," she says, "I think you couldn't have written it. I think it must have been Mr. Steele when he was drunk—and afraid of his horrid vulgar wife. Whenever I see an enormous compliment to a woman, and some outrageous panegyric about female virtue, I always feel sure that the Captain and his better half have fallen out over-night, and that he has been brought home tipsy, or has been found out in——"

"Beatrix!" cries the Lady Castlewood.

"Well, mamma! Do not cry out before you are hurt. I am not going to say anything wrong. I won't give you more annoyance than I can help, you pretty, kind mamma. Yes, and your little Trix is a naughty little Trix, and she leaves undone those things which she ought to have done, and does those things which she ought not to have done, and there's—— well now—I won't go on. Yes, I will, unless you kiss me." And with this the young lady lays aside her paper, and runs up to her mother and performs a variety of embraces with her Ladyship, saying as plain as eyes could speak to Mr. Esmond, "There, sir: would not *you* like to play the very same pleasant game?"

"Indeed, madam, I would," says he.

"Would what?" asked Miss Beatrix.

"What you meant when you looked at me in that provoking way," answers Esmond.

"What a confessor!" cries Beatrix, with a laugh.

"What is it Henry would like, my dear?" asks her mother, the kind soul, who was always thinking what we would like, and how she could please us.

The girl runs up to her. "O you silly, kind mamma," she says, kissing her again, "that's what Harry would like;" and she broke out into a great joyful laugh; and Lady Castlewood blushed as bashful as a maid of sixteen.

"Look at her, Harry," whispers Beatrix, running up, and speaking in her sweet low tones. "Doesn't the blush become her? Isn't she pretty? She looks younger than I am, and I am sure she is a hundred thousand million times better."

Esmond's kind mistress left the room, carrying her blushes away with her.

"If we girls at Court could grow such roses as that," continues Beatrix, with her laugh, "what wouldn't we do to preserve 'em? We'd clip their stalks and put 'em in salt and water. But those flowers don't bloom at Hampton Court and Windsor, Henry." She paused for a minute, and the smile fading away from her April face, gave place to a menacing shower of tears. "Oh, how good she is, Harry!" Beatrix went on to say. "Oh, what a saint she is! Her goodness frightens me. I'm not fit to live with her. I should be better, I think, if she were not so perfect. She has had a great sorrow in her life, and a great secret; and repented of it. It could not have been my father's death. She talks freely about that; nor could she have loved him very much—though who knows what we women do love, and why."

"What, and why, indeed!" says Mr. Esmond.

"No one knows," Beatrix went on, without noticing this interruption except by a look, "what my mother's life is. She hath been at early prayer this morning: she passes hours in her closet; if you were to follow her thither, you would find her at prayers now. She tends the poor of the place—the horrid dirty poor! She sits through the curate's sermons—oh, those dreary sermons! And you see, *on a beau dire;* but good as they are, people like her are not fit to commune with us of the world. There is always, as it were, a third person present, even when I and my mother are alone. She can't be frank with me quite; who is always thinking of the next world, and of her guardian angel, perhaps that's in company. O Harry, I'm jealous of that guardian angel!" here broke out Mistress Beatrix. "It's horrid, I know; but my mother's life is all for heaven, and mine—all for earth. We can never be friends quite; and then she cares more for Frank's little finger than she does for me—I know she does: and she loves you, sir, a great deal too much; and I hate you for it. I would have had her all to myself; but she wouldn't. In my childhood, it was my father she loved—(oh, how could she? I remember him kind and handsome, but so stupid, and not being able to speak after drinking wine). And then it was Frank; and now, it is heaven and the clergyman. How I would have loved her! From a child I used to be in a rage that she loved anybody but me; but she loved you all better—all, I know she did. And now, she talks of the blessed consolation of religion. Dear soul! she thinks she is happier for believing, as she must, that we are all of us wicked and miserable sinners; and this world is only a *pied-à-terre* for the good, where they stay for a night, as we do, coming from Walcote, at that great, dreary, uncomfortable Hounslow Inn, in those horrid beds—oh, do you remember those horrid beds?—and the chariot comes and fetches them to heaven the next morning."

"Hush, Beatrix!" says Mr. Esmond.

"Hush, indeed. You are a hypocrite, too, Henry, with your grave airs and your glum face. We are all hypocrites. Oh dear me! We are all alone, alone, alone," says poor Beatrix, her fair breast heaving with a sigh.

"It was I that writ every line of that paper, my dear," says Mr. Esmond. "You are not so worldly as you think yourself, Beatrix, and better than we believe you. The good we have in us we doubt of; and the happiness that's to our hand we throw away. You bend your ambition on a great marriage and establishment—and why? You'll tire of them when you win them; and be no happier with a coronet on your coach——"

"Than riding pillion with Lubin to market," says Beatrix. "Thank you, Lubin!"

"I'm a dismal shepherd, to be sure," answers Esmond, with a blush; "and require a nymph that can tuck my bed-clothes up, and make me water-gruel. Well, Tom Lockwood can do that. He took me out of the fire upon his shoulders, and nursed me through my illness as love will scarce ever do. Only good wages, and a hope of my clothes, and the contents of my portmanteau. How long was it that Jacob served an apprenticeship for Rachel?"

"For mamma?" says Beatrix. "It is mamma your honour wants, and that I should have the happiness of calling you papa?"

Esmond blushed again. "I spoke of a Rachel that a shepherd courted five thousand years ago; when shepherds were longer lived than now. And my meaning was, that since I saw you first after our separation—a child you were then . . ."

"And I put on my best stockings to captivate you, I remember, sir . . ."

"You have had my heart ever since then, such as it was; and such as you were, I cared for no other woman. What little reputation I have won, it was that you might be pleased with it: and indeed, it is not much; and I think a hundred fools in the army have got and deserved quite as much. Was there something in the air of that dismal old Castlewood that made us all gloomy, and dissatisfied, and lonely under its ruined old roof? We were all so, even when together and united, as it seemed, following our separate schemes, each as we sat round the table."

"Dear, dreary old place!" cries Beatrix. "Mamma hath never had the heart to go back thither since we left it, when—never mind how many years ago." And she flung back her curls, and looked over her fair shoulder at the mirror superbly, as if she said, "Time, I defy you."

"Yes," says Esmond, who had the art, as she owned, of divining many of her thoughts. "You can afford to look in the glass still; and only be pleased by the truth it tells you. As for me, do you know what my scheme is? I think of asking Frank to give me the Virginian estate King Charles gave our grandfather." (She gave a superb curtsey, as much as to say, "Our grandfather, indeed! Thank you, Mr. Bastard.") "Yes, I know you are thinking of my bar sinister, and so am I. A man cannot get over it in this country; unless, indeed, he wears it across a king's arms, when 'tis a highly honourable coat; and I am thinking of retiring into the plantations, and building myself a wigwam in the woods, and perhaps, if I want company, suiting myself with a squaw. We will send your Ladyship furs over for the winter; and, when you are old, we will provide you with tobacco. I am not quite clever enough, or not rogue enough—I know not which—for the Old World. I may make a place for myself in the New, which is not so full; and found a family there. When you are a mother yourself, and a great lady, perhaps I shall send you over from the plantation some day a little barbarian that is half Esmond half Mohock, and you will be kind to him for his father's sake, who was, after all, your kinsman; and whom you loved a little."

"What folly you are talking, Harry!" says Miss Beatrix, looking with her great eyes.

"'Tis sober earnest," says Esmond. And, indeed, the scheme had been dwelling a good deal in his mind for some time past, and especially since his return home, when he found how hopeless, and even degrading to himself, his passion was. "No," says he, then: "I have tried half-a-dozen times now. I can bear being away from you well enough; but being with you is intolerable" (another low-curtsey on Mistress Beatrix's part), "and I will go. I have enough to buy axes and guns for my men, and beads and blankets for the savages; and I'll go and live amongst them."

"*Mon ami*," she says, quite kindly, and taking Esmond's hand, with an air of great compassion, "you can't think that in our position anything more than our present friendship is possible. You are our elder brother—as such we view you, pitying your misfortune, not rebuking you with it. Why, you are old enough and grave enough to be our father. I always thought you a hundred years old, Harry, with your solemn face and grave air. I feel as a sister to you, and can no more. Isn't that enough, sir?" And she put her face quite close to his—who knows with what intention?

"It's too much," says Esmond, turning away. "I can't bear

this life, and shall leave it. I shall stay, I think, to see you married, and then freight a ship, and call it the *Beatrix*, and bid you all——"

Here the servant, flinging the door open, announced his Grace the Duke of Hamilton, and Esmond started back with something like an imprecation on his lips, as the nobleman entered, looking splendid in his star and green riband. He gave Mr. Esmond just that gracious bow which he would have given to a lacquey who fetched him a chair or took his hat, and seated himself by Miss Beatrix, as the poor Colonel went out of the room with a hangdog look.

Esmond's mistress was in the lower room as he passed downstairs. She often met him as he was coming away from Beatrix; and she beckoned him into the apartment.

"Has she told you, Harry?" Lady Castlewood said.

"She has been very frank—very," says Esmond.

"But—but about what is going to happen?"

"What is going to happen?" says he, his heart beating.

"His Grace the Duke of Hamilton has proposed to her," says my Lady. "He made his offer yesterday. They will marry as soon as his mourning is over; and you have heard his Grace is appointed Ambassador to Paris; and the Ambassadress goes with him."

CHAPTER IV

BEATRIX'S NEW SUITOR

THE gentleman whom Beatrix had selected was, to be sure, twenty years older than the Colonel, with whom she quarrelled for being too old; but this one was but a nameless adventurer, and the other the greatest Duke in Scotland, with pretensions even to a still higher title. My Lord Duke of Hamilton had, indeed, every merit belonging to a gentleman, and he had had the time to mature his accomplishments fully, being upwards of fifty years old when Madam Beatrix selected him for a bridegroom. Duke Hamilton, then Earl of Arran, had been educated at the famous Scottish University of Glasgow, and, coming to London, became a great favourite of Charles the Second, who made him a lord of his bedchamber, and afterwards appointed him ambassador to the French King, under whom the Earl served two campaigns as his Majesty's aide-de-camp; and he was absent on this service when King Charles died.

King James continued my Lord's promotion—made him Master of the Wardrobe and Colonel of the Royal Regiment of Horse; and his Lordship adhered firmly to King James, being of the small company that never quitted that unfortunate monarch till his departure out of England; and then it was, in 1688 namely, that he made the friendship with Colonel Francis Esmond, that had always been, more or less, maintained in the two families.

The Earl professed a great admiration for King William always, but never could give him his allegiance; and was engaged in more than one of the plots in the late great King's reign which always ended in the plotters' discomfiture, and generally in their pardon, by the magnanimity of the King. Lord Arran was twice prisoner in the Tower during this reign, undauntedly saying, when offered his release, upon parole not to engage against King William, that he would not give his word, because "he was sure he could not keep it"; but, nevertheless, he was both times discharged without any trial; and the King bore this noble enemy so little malice, that when his mother, the Duchess of Hamilton, of her own right, resigned her claim on her husband's death, the Earl was, by patent signed at Loo, 1690, created Duke of Hamilton, Marquis of Clydesdale, and Earl of Arran, with precedency from the original creation. His Grace took the oaths and his seat in the Scottish parliament in 1700: was famous there for his patriotism and eloquence, especially in the debates about the Union Bill, which Duke Hamilton opposed with all his strength, though he would not go the length of the Scottish gentry, who were for resisting it by force of arms. 'Twas said he withdrew his opposition all of a sudden, and in consequence of letters from the King at St. Germains, who entreated him on his allegiance not to thwart the Queen his sister in this measure; and the Duke, being always bent upon effecting the King's return to his kingdom through a reconciliation between his Majesty and Queen Anne, and quite averse to his landing with arms and French troops, held aloof, and kept out of Scotland during the time when the Chevalier de St. George's descent from Dunkirk was projected, passing his time in England in his great estate in Staffordshire.

When the Whigs went out of office in 1710, the Queen began to show his Grace the very greatest marks of her favour. He was created Duke of Brandon and Baron of Dutton in England; having the Thistle already originally bestowed on him by King James the Second, his Grace was now promoted to the honour of the Garter—a distinction so great and illustrious, that no subject hath ever borne them hitherto together. When this objection was made to her Majesty, she was pleased to say, "Such a subject as the Duke of Hamilton has a pre-eminent claim to every mark of distinction which a crowned head can confer. I will henceforth wear both orders myself."

At the Chapter held at Windsor in October 1712, the Duke and other knights, including Lord-Treasurer, the new-created Earl of Oxford and Mortimer, were installed; and a few days afterwards his Grace was appointed Ambassador-Extraordinary to France, and his equipages, plate, and liveries commanded, of the most sumptuous kind, not only for his Excellency the Ambassador, but for her Excellency the Ambassadress, who was to accompany him. Her arms were already quartered on the coach panels, and her brother was to hasten over on the appointed day to give her away.

His Lordship was a widower, having married, in 1698, Elizabeth, daughter of Digby Lord Gerard, by which marriage great estates came into the Hamilton family; and out of these estates came, in part, that tragic quarrel which ended the Duke's career.

From the loss of a tooth to that of a mistress there's no pang that is not bearable. The apprehension is much more cruel than the certainty; and we make up our mind to the misfortune when 'tis irremediable, part with the tormentor, and mumble our crust on t'other side of the jaws. I think Colonel Esmond was relieved when a ducal coach and six came and whisked his charmer away out of his reach, and placed her in a higher sphere. As you have seen the nymph in the opera-machine go up to the clouds at the end of the piece where Mars, Bacchus, Apollo, and all the divine company of Olympians are seated, and quaver out her last song as a goddess: so when this portentous elevation was accomplished in the Esmond family, I am not sure that every one of us did not treat the divine Beatrix with special honours; at least the saucy little beauty carried her head with a toss of supreme authority, and assumed a touch-me-not air, which all her friends very good-humouredly bowed to.

An old army acquaintance of Colonel Esmond's, honest Tom Trett, who had sold his company, married a wife, and turned merchant in the City, was dreadfully gloomy for a long time, though living in a fine house on the river, and carrying on a great trade to all appearance. At length Esmond saw his friend's name in the *Gazette* as a bankrupt; and a week after this circumstance my bankrupt walks into Mr. Esmond's lodging with a face perfectly radiant with good-humour, and as jolly and careless as when they had sailed from Southampton ten years before for Vigo. "This bankruptcy," says Tom, "has been hanging over my head these three years; the thought hath prevented my sleeping, and I have looked at poor Polly's head on t'other pillow, and then towards my razor on the table, and thought to put an end to myself, and so give my woes the slip. But now we are bankrupts: Tom Trett pays as many shillings in the pound as he can; his wife has a little cottage at Fulham, and her fortune secured to herself. I am afraid neither of bailiff nor of creditor: and for the last six nights have slept easy." So it was that when Fortune shook her wings and left him, honest Tom cuddled himself up in his ragged virtue, and fell asleep.

Esmond did not tell his friend how much his story applied to Esmond too; but he laughed at it, and used it; and having fairly struck his docket in this love transaction, determined to put a cheerful face on his bankruptcy. Perhaps Beatrix was a little offended at his gaiety. "Is this the way, sir, that you receive the announcement of your misfortune?" says she, "and do you come smiling before me as if you were glad to be rid of me?"

Esmond would not be put off from his good-humour, but told her the story of Tom Trett and his bankruptcy. "I have been hankering after the grapes on the wall," says he, "and lost my temper because they were beyond my reach: was there any wonder? They're gone now, and another has them—a taller man than your humble servant has won them." And the Colonel made his cousin a low bow

"A taller man, Cousin Esmond!" says she. "A man of spirit would have scaled the wall, sir, and seized them! A man of courage would have fought for 'em, not gaped for 'em."

"A Duke has but to gape and they drop into his mouth," says Esmond, with another low bow.

"Yes, sir," says she, "a Duke *is* a taller man than you. And why should I not be grateful to one such as his Grace, who gives me his heart and his great name? It is a great gift he honours me with; I know 'tis a bargain between us; and I accept it, and will do my utmost to perform my part of it. 'Tis no question of sighing and philandering between a nobleman of his Grace's age, and a girl who hath little of that softness in her nature. Why should I not own that I am ambitious, Harry Esmond; and if it be no sin in a man to covet honour, why should a woman too not desire it? Shall I be frank with you, Harry, and say that if you had not been down on your knees, and so humble, you might have fared better with me? A woman of my spirit, cousin, is to be won by gallantry, and not by sighs and rueful faces. All the time you are worshipping and singing hymns to me, I know very well I am no goddess, and grow weary of the incense. So would you have been weary of the goddess too—when she was called Mrs. Esmond, and got out of humour because she had not pin-money enough, and was forced to go about in an old gown. Eh! cousin, a goddess in a mob-cap, that has to make her husband's gruel, ceases to be divine—I am sure of it. I should have been sulky and scolded; and of all the proud wretches in the world Mr. Esmond is the proudest, let me tell him that. You never fall into a passion; but you never forgive, I think. Had you been a great man, you might have been good-humoured; but being nobody, sir, you are too great a man for me; and I'm afraid of you, cousin—there! and I won't worship you, and you'll never be happy except with a woman who will. Why, after I belonged to you, and after one of my tantrums, you would have put the pillow over my head some night, and smothered me, as the black man does the woman in the play that you're so fond of. What's the creature's name?—Desdemona. You would, you little black-dyed Othello!"

"I think I should, Beatrix," says the Colonel.

"And I want no such ending. I intend to live to be a hundred, and to go to ten thousand routs and balls, and to play cards every night of my life till the year eighteen hundred. And I like to be the first of my company, sir; and I like flattery and compliments, and you give me none: and I like to be made to laugh, sir, and who's to laugh at *your* dismal face, I should like to know? and I like a coach-and-six or a coach-and-eight; and I like diamonds, and a new gown every week; and people to say, 'That's the Duchess. How well her Grace looks! Make way for Madame l'Ambassadrice d'Angleterre. Call her Excellency's people'—that's what I like. And as for you, you want a woman to bring your slippers and cap, and to sit at your feet, and cry, 'O caro! O bravo!' whilst you read your Shakspeares and Miltons and stuff. Mamma would have been the wife for you, had you been a little older, though you look ten years older than she does—you do, you glum-faced, blue-bearded little old man! You might have sat, like Darby and Joan, and flattered each other; and billed and cooed like a pair of old pigeons on a perch. I want my wings and to use them, sir." And she spread out her beautiful arms, as if indeed she could fly off like the pretty "Gawrie," whom the man in the story was enamoured of.

"And what will your Peter Wilkins say to your flight?" says Esmond, who never admired this fair creature more than when she rebelled and laughed at him.

"A duchess knows her place," says she, with a laugh. "Why, I have a son already made for me, and thirty years old (my Lord Arran), and four daughters. How they will scold, and what a rage they will be in, when I come to take the head of the table! But I give them only a month to be angry; at the end of that time they shall love me every one, and so shall Lord Arran, and so shall all his Grace's Scots vassals and followers in the Highlands. I'm bent on it; and when I take a thing in my head, 'tis done. His Grace is the greatest gentleman in Europe, and I'll try and make him happy; and, when the King comes back, you may count on my protection, Cousin Esmond—for come back the King will and shall; and I'll bring him back from Versailles, if he comes under my hoop."

"I hope the world will make you happy, Beatrix," says Esmond, with a sigh. "You'll be Beatrix till you are my Lady Duchess—will you not? I shall then make your Grace my very lowest bow."

"None of these sighs and this satire, cousin," she says. "I take his Grace's great bounty thankfully—yes, thankfully; and will wear his honours becomingly. I do not say he hath touched my heart; but he has my gratitude, obedience, admiration—I have told him that, and no more; and with that his noble heart is content. I have told him all—even the story of that poor creature that I was engaged to—and that I could not love; and I gladly gave his word back to him, and jumped for joy to get back my own. I am twenty-five years old."

"Twenty-six, my dear," says Esmond.

"Twenty-five, sir—I choose to be twenty-five; and in eight years no man hath ever touched my heart. Yes—you did once, for a little, Harry, when you came back after Lille, and engaging with that murderer Mohun, and saving Frank's life. I thought I could like you; and mamma begged me hard, on her knees, and I did—for a day. But the old chill came over me, Henry, and the old fear of you and your melancholy; and I was glad when you went away, and engaged with my Lord Ashburnham, that I might hear no more of you, that's the truth. You are too good for me, somehow. I could not make you happy, and should break my heart in trying, and not being able to love you. But if you had asked me when we gave you the sword, you might have had me, sir, and we both should have been miserable by this time. I talked with that silly lord all night just to vex you and mamma, and I succeeded, didn't I? How frankly we can talk of these things! It seems a thousand years ago: and, though we are here sitting in the same room, there is a great wall between us. My dear, kind, faithful, gloomy old cousin! I can like now, and admire you too, sir, and say that you are brave, and very kind, and very true, and a fine gentleman for all—for all your little mishap at your birth," says she, wagging her arch head.

"And now, sir," says she, with a curtsey, "we must have no more talk except when mamma is by, or his Grace is with us; for he does not half like you, cousin, and is jealous as the black man in your favourite play."

Though the very kindness of the words stabbed Mr. Esmond with the keenest pang, he did not show his sense of the wound by any look of his (as Beatrix, indeed, afterwards owned to him), but said, with a perfect command of himself and an easy smile, "The interview must not end yet, my dear, until I have had my last word. Stay, here comes your mother" (indeed she came in here with her sweet anxious face, and Esmond going up kissed her hand respectfully). "My dear lady may hear, too, the last words, which are no secrets, and are only a parting benediction accompanying a present for your marriage from an old gentleman your guardian; for I feel as if I was the guardian of all the family, and an old fellow that is fit to be the grandfather of you all; and in this character let me make my Lady Duchess her wedding present. They are the diamonds my father's widow left me. I had thought Beatrix might have had them a year ago; but they are good enough for a Duchess, though not bright enough for the handsomest woman in the world." And he took the case out of his pocket in which the jewels were, and presented them to his cousin.

She gave a cry of delight, for the stones were indeed very handsome, and of great value; and the next minute the necklace was where Belinda's cross is in Mr. Pope's admirable poem, and glittering on the whitest and most perfectly-shaped neck in all England.

The girl's delight at receiving these trinkets was so great, that after rushing to the looking-glass and examining the effect they produced upon that fair neck which they surrounded, Beatrix was running back with her arms extended, and was perhaps for paying her cousin with a price that he would have liked no doubt to receive from those beautiful rosy lips of hers, but at this moment the door opened, and his Grace the bridegroom elect was announced.

He looked very black upon Mr. Esmond, to whom he made a very low bow indeed, and kissed the hand of each lady in his most ceremonious manner. He had come in his chair from the palace hard by, and wore his two stars of the Garter and the Thistle.

"Look, my Lord Duke," says Mistress Beatrix, advancing to him, and showing the diamonds on her breast.

"Diamonds," says his Grace. "Hm! they seem pretty."

"They are a present on my marriage," says Beatrix.

"From her Majesty?" asks the Duke. "The Queen is very good."

"From my Cousin Henry—from our Cousin Henry," cry both the ladies in a breath.

"I have not the honour of knowing the gentleman. I thought that my Lord Castlewood had no brother: and that on your Ladyship's side there were no nephews."

"From our cousin, Colonel Henry Esmond, my Lord," says Beatrix, taking the Colonel's hand very bravely, "who was left guardian to us by our father, and who has a hundred times shown his love and friendship for our family."

"The Duchess of Hamilton receives no diamonds but from her husband, madam," says the Duke; "may I pray you to restore these to Mr. Esmond?'

"Beatrix Esmond may receive a present from our kinsman and benefactor, my Lord Duke," says Lady Castlewood, with an air of great dignity. "She is my daughter yet: and if her mother sanctions the gift—no one else hath the right to question it."

"Kinsman and benefactor!" says the Duke. "I know of no kinsman: and I do not choose that my wife should have for benefactor a——"

"My Lord!" says Colonel Esmond.

"I am not here to bandy words," says his Grace; "frankly I tell you that your visits to this house are too frequent, and that I

choose no presents for the Duchess of Hamilton from gentlemen that bear a name they have no right to."

"My Lord!" breaks out Lady Castlewood, "Mr. Esmond hath the best right to that name of any man in the world: and 'tis as old and as honourable as your Grace's."

My Lord Duke smiled, and looked as if Lady Castlewood was mad, that was so talking to him.

"If I called him benefactor," said my mistress, "it is because he has been so to us—yes, the noblest, the truest, the bravest, the dearest of benefactors. He would have saved my husband's life from Mohun's sword. He did save my boy's, and defended him from that villain. Are those no benefits?"

"I ask Colonel Esmond's pardon," says his Grace, if possible more haughty than before. "I would say not a word that should give him offence, and thank him for his kindness to your Ladyship's family. My Lord Mohun and I are connected, you know, by marriage—though neither by blood nor friendship; but I must repeat what I said, that my wife can receive no presents from Colonel Esmond."

"My daughter may receive presents from the Head of our House; my daughter may thankfully take kindness from her father's, her mother's, her brother's dearest friend; and be grateful for one more benefit besides the thousand we owe him," cries Lady Castlewood. "What is a string of diamond stones compared to that affection he hath given us—our dearest preserver and benefactor? We owe him not only Frank's life, but our all—yes, our all," says my mistress, with a heightened colour and a trembling voice. "The title we bear is his, if he would claim it. 'Tis we who have no right to our name: not he that's too great for it. He sacrificed his name at my dying lord's bedside—sacrificed it to my orphan children; gave up rank and honour because he loved us so nobly. His father was Viscount of Castlewood and Marquis of Esmond before him; and he is his father's lawful son and true heir, and we are the recipients of his bounty, and he the chief of a house that's as old as your own. And if he is content to forego his name that my child may bear it, we love him and honour him and bless him under whatever name he bears"—and here the fond and affectionate creature would have knelt to Esmond again, but that he prevented her; and Beatrix, running up to her with a pale face and a cry of alarm, embraced her and said, "Mother, what is this?"

"'Tis a family secret, my Lord Duke," says Colonel Esmond: "poor Beatrix knew nothing of it; nor did my Lady till a year ago. And I have as good a right to resign my title as your Grace's mother to abdicate hers to you."

"I should have told everything to the Duke of Hamilton," said my mistress, "had his Grace applied to me for my daughter's hand, and not to Beatrix. I should have spoken with you this very day in private, my Lord, had not your words brought about this sudden explanation—and now 'tis fit Beatrix should hear it; and know, as I would have all the world know, what we owe to our kinsman and patron."

And then, in her touching way, and having hold of her daughter's hand, and speaking to her rather than my Lord Duke, Lady Castlewood told the story which you know already—lauding up to the skies her kinsman's behaviour. On his side Mr. Esmond explained the reasons that seemed quite sufficiently cogent with him, why the succession in the family, as at present it stood, should not be disturbed; and he should remain as he was, Colonel Esmond.

"And Marquis of Esmond, my Lord," says his Grace, with a low bow. "Permit me to ask your Lordship's pardon for words that were uttered in ignorance; and to beg for the favour of your friendship. To be allied to you, sir, must be an honour under whatever name you are known" (so his Grace was pleased to say); "and in return for the splendid present you make my wife, your kinswoman, I hope you will please to command any service that James Douglas can perform. I shall never be easy until I repay you a part of my obligations at least; and ere very long, and with the mission her Majesty hath given me," says the Duke, "that may perhaps be in my power. I shall esteem it as a favour, my Lord, if Colonel Esmond will give away the bride."

"And if he will take the usual payment in advance, he is welcome," says Beatrix, stepping up to him; and, as Esmond kissed her, she whispered, "Oh, why didn't I know you before?"

My Lord Duke was as hot as a flame at this salute, but said never a word: Beatrix made him a proud curtsey, and the two ladies quitted the room together.

"When does your Excellency go for Paris?" asks Colonel Esmond.

"As soon after the ceremony as may be," his Grace answered. "'Tis fixed for the first of December: it cannot be sooner. The equipage will not be ready till then. The Queen intends the embassy should be very grand—and I have law business to settle. That ill-omened Mohun has come, or is coming, to London again: we are in a lawsuit about my late Lord Gerard's property; and he hath sent to me to meet him."

CHAPTER V

MOHUN APPEARS FOR THE LAST TIME IN THIS HISTORY

BESIDES my Lord Duke of Hamilton and Brandon, who for family reasons had kindly promised his protection and patronage to Colonel Esmond, he had other great friends in power now, both able and willing to assist him, and he might, with such allies, look forward to as fortunate advancement in civil life at home as he had got rapid promotion abroad. His Grace was magnanimous enough to offer to take Mr. Esmond as secretary on his Paris embassy, but no doubt he intended that proposal should be rejected; at any rate, Esmond could not bear the thoughts of attending his mistress farther than the church-door after her marriage, and so declined that offer which his generous rival made him.

Other gentlemen in power were liberal at least of compliments and promises to Colonel Esmond. Mr. Harley, now become my Lord Oxford and Mortimer, and installed Knight of the Garter on the same day as his Grace of Hamilton had received the same honour, sent to the Colonel to say that a seat in Parliament should be at his disposal presently, and Mr. St. John held out many flattering hopes of advancement to the Colonel when he should enter the House. Esmond's friends were all successful, and the most successful and triumphant of all was his dear old commander, General Webb, who was now appointed Lieutenant-General of the Land Forces, and received with particular honour by the Ministry, by the Queen, and the people out of doors, who huzza'd the brave chief when they used to see him in his chariot going to the House or to the Drawing-room, or hobbling on foot to his coach from St. Stephen's upon his glorious old crutch and stick, and cheered him as loud as they had ever done Marlborough.

That great Duke was utterly disgraced; and honest old Webb dated all his Grace's misfortunes from Wynendael, and vowed that Fate served the traitor right. Duchess Sarah had also gone to ruin; she had been forced to give up her keys, and her places, and her pensions:—"Ah, ah!" says Webb, "she would have locked up three millions of French crowns with her keys had I but been knocked on the head, but I stopped that convoy at Wynendael."

Our enemy Cardonnel was turned out of the House of Commons (along with Mr. Walpole) for malversation of public money. Cadogan lost his place of Lieutenant of the Tower. Marlborough's daughters resigned their posts of ladies of the bedchamber; and so complete was the Duke's disgrace, that his son-in-law, Lord Bridgewater, was absolutely obliged to give up his lodgings at St. James's, and had his half-pension, as Master of the Horse, taken away. But I think the lowest depth of Marlborough's fall was when he humbly sent to ask General Webb when he might wait upon him; he who had commanded the stout old General, who had injured him and sneered at him, who had kept him dangling in his ante-chamber, who could not even after his great service condescend to write him a letter in his own hand! The nation was as eager for peace as ever it had been hot for war. The Prince of Savoy came amongst us, had his audience of the Queen, and got his famous Sword of Honour, and strove with all his force to form a Whig party together, to bring over the young Prince of Hanover—to do anything which might prolong the war, and consummate the ruin of the old sovereign whom he hated so implacably. But the nation was tired of the struggle: so completely wearied of it that not even our defeat at Denain could rouse us into any anger, though such an action so lost two years before would have set all England in a fury. 'Twas easy to see that the great Marlborough was not with the army. Eugene was obliged to fall back in a rage, and forego the dazzling revenge of his life. 'Twas in vain the Duke's side asked, "Would we suffer our arms to be insulted? Would we not send back the only champion who could repair our honour?" The nation had had its bellyful of fighting; nor could taunts or outcries goad up our Britons any more.

For a statesman that was always prating of liberty, and had the grandest philosophic maxims in his mouth, it must be owned that Mr. St. John sometimes rather acted like a Turkish than a Greek philosopher, and especially fell foul of one unfortunate set of men, the men of letters, with a tyranny a little extraordinary in a man who professed to respect their calling so much. The literary controversy at this time was very bitter, the Government side was the winning one, the popular one, and I think might have been the merciful one. 'Twas natural that the Opposition should be peevish and cry out: some men did so from their hearts, admiring the Duke of Marlborough's prodigious talents, and deploring the disgrace of the greatest general the world ever knew: 'twas the stomach that caused other patriots to grumble, and such men cried out because they were poor, and paid to do so. Against these my Lord Bolingbroke never showed the slightest mercy, whipping a dozen into prison or into the pillory without the least commiseration.

From having been a man of arms Mr. Esmond had now come to be a man of letters, but on a safer side than that in which the above-cited poor fellows ventured their liberties and ears. There was no danger on ours, which was the winning side; besides, Mr. Esmond pleased himself by thinking that he writ like a gentleman if he did not always succeed as a wit.

Of the famous wits of that age, who have rendered Queen Anne's reign illustrious, and whose works will be in all Englishmen's hands in ages yet to come, Mr. Esmond saw many, but at public places chiefly; never having a great intimacy with any of them, except with honest Dick Steele and Mr. Addison, who parted company with Esmond, however, when that gentleman became a declared Tory, and lived on close terms with the leading persons of that party. Addison kept himself to a few friends, and very rarely opened himself except in their company. A man more upright and conscientious than he it was not possible to find in public life, and one whose conversation was so various, easy, and delightful. Writing now in my mature years, I own that I think Addison's politics were the right, and were my time to come over again, I would be a Whig in England and not a Tory; but with people that take a side in politics, 'tis men rather than principles that commonly bind them. A kindness or a slight puts a man under one flag or the other, and he marches with it to the end of the campaign. Esmond's master in war was injured by Marlborough, and hated him: and the lieutenant fought the quarrels of his leader. Webb coming to London was used as a weapon by Marlborough's enemies (and true steel he was, that honest chief); nor was his aide-de-camp, Mr. Esmond, an unfaithful or unworthy partisan. 'Tis strange here, and on a foreign soil, and in a land that is independent in all but the name (for that the North American colonies shall remain dependants on yonder little island for twenty years more, I never can think), to remember how the nation at home seemed to give itself up to the domination of one or other aristocratic party, and took a Hanoverian king, or a French one, according as either prevailed. And while the Tories, the October Club gentlemen, the High Church parsons that held by the Church of England, were for having a Papist king, for whom many of their Scottish and English leaders, firm churchmen all, laid down their lives with admirable loyalty and devotion; they were governed by men who had notoriously no religion at all, but used it as they would use any opinion for the purpose of forwarding their own ambition. The Whigs, on the other hand, who professed attachment to religion and liberty too, were compelled to send to Holland or Hanover for a monarch around whom they could rally. A strange series of compromises is that English History: compromise of principle, compromise of party, compromise of worship! The lovers of English freedom and independence submitted their religious consciences to an Act of Parliament; could not consolidate their liberty without sending to Zell or the Hague for a king to live under; and could not find amongst the proudest people in the world a man speaking their own language, and understanding their laws, to govern them. The Tory and High Church patriots were ready to die in defence of a Papist family that had sold us to France; the great Whig nobles, the sturdy republican recusants who had cut off Charles Stuart's head for treason, were fain to accept a King whose title came to him through a royal grandmother, whose own royal grandmother's head had fallen under Queen Bess's hatchet. And our proud English nobles sent to a petty German town for a monarch to come and reign in London; and our prelates kissed the ugly hands of his Dutch mistresses, and thought it no dishonour. In England you can but belong to one party or t'other, and you take the house you live in with all its encumbrances, its retainers, its antique discomforts, and ruins even; you patch up, but you never build up anew. Will we of the New World submit much longer, even nominally, to this ancient British superstition? There are signs of the times which make me think that ere long we shall care as little about King George here, and peers temporal and peers spiritual, as we do for King Canute or the Druids.

This chapter began about the wits, my grandson may say, and hath wandered very far from their company. The pleasantest of the wits I knew were the Doctors Garth and Arbuthnot, and Mr. Gay, the author of "Trivia," the most charming kind soul that ever laughed at a joke or cracked a bottle. Mr. Prior I saw, and he was the earthen pot swimming with the pots of brass down the stream, and always and justly frightened lest he should break in the voyage. I met him both at London and Paris, where he was performing piteous congees to the Duke of Shrewsbury, not having courage to support the dignity which his undeniable genius and talent had won him, and writing coaxing letters to Secretary St. John, and thinking about his plate and his place, and what on earth should become of him should his party go out. The famous Mr. Congreve I saw a dozen of times at Button's, a splendid wreck of a man, magnificently attired, and though gouty, and almost blind, bearing a brave face against fortune.

The great Mr. Pope (of whose prodigious genius I have no words to express my admiration) was quite a puny lad at this time, appearing seldom in public places. There were hundreds of men, wits, and pretty fellows frequenting the theatres and coffee-houses of that day—whom "nunc perscribere longum est." Indeed I think the most brilliant of that sort I ever saw was not till fifteen years afterwards, when I paid my last visit in England, and met young Harry Fielding, son of the Fielding that served in Spain and afterwards in Flanders with us, and who for fun and humour seemed to top them all. As for the famous Doctor Swift, I can say of him, "Vidi tantum." He was in London all these years up to the death of the Queen; and in a hundred public places where I saw him, but no more; he never missed Court of a Sunday, where once or twice he was pointed out to your grandfather. He would have sought me out eagerly enough had I been a great man with a title to my name, or a star on my coat. At Court the Doctor had no eyes but for the very greatest. Lord Treasurer and St. John used to call him Jonathan, and they paid him with this cheap coin for the service they took of him. He writ their lampoons, fought their enemies, flogged and bullied in their service, and it must be owned with a consummate skill and fierceness. 'Tis said he hath lost his intellect now, and forgotten his wrongs and his rage against mankind. I have always thought of him and of Marlborough as the two greatest men of that age. I have read his books (who doth not know them?) here in our calm woods, and imagine a giant to myself as I think of him, a lonely fallen Prometheus, groaning as the vulture tears him. Prometheus I saw, but when first I ever had any words with him, the giant stepped out of a sedan chair in the Poultry, whither he had come with a tipsy Irish servant parading before him, who announced him, bawling out his Reverence's name, whilst his master below was as yet haggling with the chairman. I disliked this Mr. Swift, and heard many a story about him, of his conduct to men, and his words to women. He could flatter the great as much as he could bully the weak; and Mr. Esmond, being younger and hotter in that day than now, was determined, should he ever meet this dragon, not to run away from his teeth and his fire.

Men have all sorts of motives which carry them onwards in life, and are driven into acts of desperation, or it may be of distinction, from a hundred different causes. There was one comrade of Esmond's, an honest little Irish lieutenant of Handyside's, who owed so much money to a camp sutler, that he began to make love to the man's daughter, intending to pay his debt that way; and at the battle of Malplaquet, flying away from the debt and lady too, he rushed so desperately on the French lines, that he got his company; and came a captain out of the action, and had to marry the sutler's daughter after all, who brought him his cancelled debt to her father as poor Roger's fortune. To run out of the reach of bill and marriage, he ran on the enemy's pikes; and as these did not kill him he was thrown back upon t'other horn of his dilemma. Our great Duke at the same battle was fighting, not the French, but the Tories in England; and risking his life and the army's, not for his country but for his pay and places; and for fear of his wife at home, that only being in life whom he dreaded. I have asked about men in my own company (new drafts of poor country boys were perpetually coming over to us during the wars, and brought from the ploughshare to the sword), and found that a half of them under the flags were driven thither on account of a woman: one fellow was jilted by his mistress and took the shilling in despair; another jilted the girl, and fled from her and the parish to the tents where the law could not disturb him. Why go on particularising? What can the sons of Adam and Eve expect, but to continue in that course of love and trouble their father and mother set out on? O my grandson! I am drawing nigh to the end of that period of my history, when I was acquainted with the great world of England and Europe; my years are past the Hebrew poet's limit, and I say unto thee, all my troubles and joys too, for that matter, have come from a woman; as thine will when thy destined course begins. 'Twas a woman that made a soldier of me, that set me intriguing afterwards; I believe I would have spun smocks for her had she so bidden me; what strength I had in my head I would have given her; hath not every man in his degree had his Omphale and Delilah? Mine befooled me on the banks of the Thames, and in dear old England; thou mayest find thine own by Rappahannoc.

To please that woman then I tried to distinguish myself as a soldier, and afterwards as a wit and a politician; as to please another I would have put on a black cassock and a pair of bands, and had done so but that a superior fate intervened to defeat that project. And I say, I think the world is like Captain Esmond's company I spoke of anon; and could you see every man's career in life, you would find a woman clogging him; or clinging round his march and stopping him; or cheering him and goading him; or beckoning him out of her chariot, so that he goes up to her, and leaves the race to be run without him; or bringing him the apple, and saying "Eat;" or fetching him the daggers and whispering "Kill! yonder lies Duncan, and a crown, and an opportunity."

Your grandfather fought with more effect as a politician than as a wit; and having private animosities and grievances of his own and his General's against the great Duke in command of the army, and more information on military matters than most writers, who had never seen beyond the fire of a tobacco-pipe at "Wills's," he was enabled to do good service for that cause which he embarked in, and for Mr. St. John and his party. But he disdained the abuse in which some of the Tory writers indulged; for instance, Doctor Swift, who actually chose to doubt the Duke of Marlborough's courage, and was pleased to hint that his Grace's military capacity was doubtful: nor were Esmond's performances worse for the effect they were intended to produce (though no doubt they could not injure the Duke of Marlborough nearly so much in the public eyes as the malignant attacks of Swift did, which were carefully directed so as to blacken and degrade him), because they were writ openly and fairly by Mr. Esmond, who made no disguise of them, who was now out of the army, and who never attacked the prodigious courage and talents, only the selfishness and rapacity, of the chief.

The Colonel then, having writ a paper for one of the Tory journals, called the *Post-Boy* (a letter upon Bouchain, that the town talked about for two whole days, when the appearance of an Italian singer supplied a fresh subject for conversation), and having business at the Exchange, where Mrs. Beatrix wanted a pair of gloves or a fan very likely, Esmond went to correct his paper, and was sitting at the printer's, when the famous Doctor Swift came in, his Irish fellow with him that used to walk before his chair, and bawled out his master's name with great dignity.

Mr. Esmond was waiting for the printer too, whose wife had gone to the tavern to fetch him, and was meantime engaged in drawing a picture of a soldier on horseback for a dirty little pretty boy of the printer's wife, whom she had left behind her.

"I presume you are the editor of the *Post-Boy*, sir?" says the Doctor in a grating voice that had an Irish twang; and he looked at the Colonel from under his two bushy eyebrows with a pair of very clear blue eyes. His complexion was muddy, his figure rather fat, his chin double. He wore a shabby cassock, and a shabby hat over his black wig, and he pulled out a great gold watch, at which he looks very fierce.

"I am but a contributor, Doctor Swift," says Esmond, with the little boy still on his knee. He was sitting with his back in the window, so that the Doctor could not see him.

"Who told you I was Doctor Swift?" says the Doctor, eyeing the other very haughtily.

"Your Reverence's valet bawled out your name," says the Colonel. "I should judge you brought him from Ireland?"

"And pray, sir, what right have you to judge whether my servant came from Ireland or no? I want to speak with your employer, Mr. Leach. I'll thank ye go fetch him."

"Where's your papa, Tommy?" asks the Colonel of the child, a smutty little wretch in a frock.

Instead of answering, the child begins to cry; the Doctor's appearance had no doubt frightened the poor little imp.

"Send that squalling little brat about his business, and do what I bid ye, sir," says the Doctor.

"I must finish the picture first for Tommy," says the Colonel, laughing. "Here, Tommy, will you have your Pandour with whiskers or without?"

"Whisters," says Tommy, quite intent on the picture.

"Who the devil are ye, sir?" cries the Doctor; "are ye a printer's man, or are ye not?" he pronounced it like *naught*.

"Your Reverence needn't raise the devil to ask who I am," says Colonel Esmond. "Did you ever hear of Doctor Faustus, little Tommy? or Friar Bacon, who invented gunpowder, and set the Thames on fire?"

Mr. Swift turned quite red, almost purple. "I did not intend any offence, sir," says he.

"I dare say, sir, you offended without meaning," says the other drily.

"Who are ye, sir? Do you know who I am, sir? You are one of the pack of Grubb Street scribblers that my friend Mr. Secretary hath laid by the heels. How dare ye, sir, speak to me in this tone?" cries the Doctor in a great fume.

"I beg your honour's humble pardon if I have offended your honour," says Esmond, in a tone of great humility. "Rather than be sent to the Compter, or be put in the pillory, there's nothing I wouldn't do. But Mrs. Leach, the printer's lady, told me to mind Tommy whilst she went for her husband to the tavern, and I daren't leave the child lest he should fall into the fire; but if your Reverence will hold him——"

"I take the little beast!" says the Doctor, starting back. "I am engaged to your betters, fellow. Tell Mr. Leach that when he makes an appointment with Doctor Swift he had best keep it, do ye hear? And keep a respectful tongue in your head, sir, when you address a person like me."

"I'm but a poor broken-down soldier," says the Colonel, "and I've seen better days, though I am forced now to turn my hand to writing. We can't help our fate, sir."

"You're the person that Mr. Leach hath spoken to me of, I presume. Have the goodness to speak civilly when you are spoken to—and tell Leach to call at my lodgings in Bury Street, and bring the papers with him to-night at ten o'clock. And the next time you see me, you'll know me, and be civil, Mr. Kemp."

Poor Kemp, who had been a lieutenant at the beginning of the war, and fallen into misfortune, was the writer of the *Post-Boy*, and now took honest Mr. Leach's pay in place of her Majesty's. Esmond had seen this gentleman, and a very ingenious, hard-working, honest fellow he was, toiling to give bread to a great family, and watching up many a long winter night to keep the wolf from his door. And Mr. St. John, who had liberty always on his tongue, had just sent a dozen of the Opposition writers into prison, and one actually into the pillory, for what he called libels, but libels not half so violent as those writ on our side. With regard to this very piece of tyranny, Esmond had remonstrated strongly with the Secretary, who laughed, and said the rascals were served quite right; and told Esmond a joke of Swift's regarding the matter. Nay, more, this Irishman, when St. John was about to pardon a poor wretch condemned to death for rape, absolutely prevented the Secretary from exercising this act of good-nature, and boasted that he had had the man hanged; and great as the Doctor's genius might be, and splendid his ability, Esmond for one would affect no love for him, and never desired to make his acquaintance. The Doctor was at Court every Sunday assiduously enough, a place the Colonel frequented but rarely, though he had a great inducement to go there in the person of a fair maid of honour of her Majesty's; and the airs and patronage Mr. Swift gave himself, forgetting gentlemen of his country whom he knew perfectly, his loud talk at once insolent and servile, nay, perhaps, his very intimacy with Lord Treasurer and the Secretary, who indulged all his freaks and called him Jonathan, you may be sure, were remarked by many a person of whom the proud priest himself took no note, during that time of his vanity and triumph.

'Twas but three days after the 15th of November 1712 (Esmond minds him well of the date), that he went by invitation to dine with his General, the foot of whose table he used to take on these festive occasions, as he had done at many a board, hard and plentiful, during the campaign. This was a great feast, and of the latter sort; the honest old gentleman loved to treat his friends splendidly: his Grace of Ormonde, before he joined his army as Generalissimo; my Lord Viscount Bolingbroke, one of her Majesty's Secretaries of State; my Lord Orkney, that had served with us abroad, being of the party. His Grace of Hamilton, Master of the Ordnance, and in whose honour the feast had been given, upon his approaching departure as Ambassador to Paris, had sent an excuse to General Webb at two o'clock, but an hour before the dinner: nothing but the most immediate business, his Grace said, should have prevented him having the pleasure of drinking a parting glass to the health of General Webb. His absence disappointed Esmond's old chief, who suffered much from his wounds besides; and though the company was grand, it was rather gloomy. St. John came last, and brought a friend with him: "I'm sure," says my General, bowing very politely, "my table hath always a place for Doctor Swift."

Mr. Esmond went up to the Doctor with a bow and a smile:—"I gave Doctor Swift's message," says he, "to the printer: I hope he brought your pamphlet to your lodgings in time." Indeed poor Leach had come to his house very soon after the Doctor left it, being brought away rather tipsy from the tavern by his thrifty wife; and he talked of Cousin Swift in a maudlin way, though of course Mr. Esmond did not allude to this relationship. The Doctor scowled, blushed, and was much confused, and said scarce a word during the whole of dinner. A very little stone will sometimes knock down these Goliaths of wit; and this one was often discomfited when met by a man of any spirit; he took his place sulkily, put water in his wine that the others drank plentifully, and scarce said a word.

The talk was about the affairs of the day, or rather about persons than affairs: my Lady Marlborough's fury, her daughters in old clothes and mob-caps looking out from their windows and seeing the company pass to the Drawing-room; the gentleman-usher's horror when the Prince of Savoy was introduced to her Majesty in a tie-wig, no man out of a full-bottomed periwig ever having kissed the Royal hand before; about the Mohawks and the damage they were doing, rushing through the town, killing and murdering. Some one said the ill-omened face of Mohun had been seen at the theatre the night before, and Macartney and Meredith with him. Meant to be a feast, the meeting, in spite of drink and talk, was as dismal as a funeral. Every topic started subsided into gloom. His Grace of Ormonde went away because the conversation got upon Denain, where we had been defeated in the last campaign. Esmond's General was affected at the allusion to this action too, for his comrade of Wynendael, the Count of Nassau Woudenbourg, had been slain there. Mr. Swift, when Esmond pledged him, said he drank no wine, and took his hat from the peg and went away, beckoning my Lord Bolingbroke to follow him; but the other bade him take his chariot and save his coach-hire—he had to speak with Colonel Esmond; and when the rest of the company withdrew to cards, these two remained behind in the dark.

Bolingbroke always spoke freely when he had drunk freely. His enemies could get any secret out of him in that condition;

women were even employed to ply him, and take his words down. I have heard that my Lord Stair, three years after, when the Secretary fled to France and became the Pretender's Minister, got all the information he wanted by putting female spies over St. John in his cups. He spoke freely now :—"Jonathan knows nothing of this for certain, though he suspects it, and by George, Webb will take an Archbishopric, and Jonathan a—no,—damme—Jonathan will take an Archbishopric from James, I warrant me, gladly enough. Your Duke hath the string of the whole matter in his hand," the Secretary went on. "We have that which will force Marlborough to keep his distance, and he goes out of London in a fortnight. Prior hath his business; he left me this morning, and mark me, Harry, should fate carry off our august, our beloved, our most gouty and plethoric Queen, and Defender of the Faith, la bonne cause triomphera. A la santé de la bonne cause! Everything good comes from France. Wine comes from France; give us another bumper to the bonne cause." We drank it together.

"Will the bonne cause turn Protestant?" asked Mr. Esmond.

"No, hang it," says the other, "he'll defend our Faith as in duty bound, but he'll stick by his own. The Hind and the Panther shall run in the same car, by Jove! Righteousness and peace shall kiss each other: and we'll have Father Massillon to walk down the aisle of St. Paul's, cheek by jowl with Dr. Sacheverel. Give us more wine: here's a health to the bonne cause, kneeling—damme, let's drink it kneeling!" He was quite flushed and wild with wine as he was talking.

"And suppose," says Esmond, who always had this gloomy apprehension, "the bonne cause should give us up to the French, as his father and uncle did before him?"

"Give us up to the French!" starts up Bolingbroke: "is there any English gentleman that fears that? You who have seen Blenheim and Ramillies, afraid of the French! Your ancestors and mine, and brave old Webb's yonder, have met them in a hundred fields, and our children will be ready to do the like. Who's he that wishes for more men from England? My cousin Westmoreland? Give us up to the French, pshaw!"

"His uncle did," says Mr. Esmond.

"And what happened to his grandfather?" broke out St. John, filling out another bumper. "Here's to the greatest monarch England ever saw; here's to the Englishman that made a kingdom of her. Our great King came from Huntingdon, not Hanover; our fathers didn't look for a Dutchman to rule us. Let him come and we'll keep him, and we'll show him Whitehall. If he's a traitor, let us have him here to deal with him; and then there are spirits here as great as any that have gone before. There are men here that can look at danger in the face and not be frightened at it. Traitor! treason! what names are these to scare you and me? Are all Oliver's men dead, or his glorious name forgotten in fifty years? Are there no men equal to him, think you, as good—ay, as good? God save the King! and, if the monarchy fails us, God save the British Republic!"

He filled another great bumper, and tossed it up and drained it wildly, just as the noise of rapid carriage wheels approaching was stopped at our door, and after a hurried knock and a moment's interval, Mr. Swift came into the hall, ran upstairs to the room we were dining in, and entered it with a perturbed face. St. John, excited with drink, was making some wild quotation out of "Macbeth," but Swift stopped him.

"Drink no more, my Lord, for God's sake!" says he. "I come with the most dreadful news."

"Is the Queen dead?" cries out Bolingbroke, seizing on a water-glass.

"No, Duke Hamilton is dead; he was murdered an hour ago by Mohun and Macartney; they had a quarrel this morning; they gave him not so much time as to write a letter. He went for a couple of his friends, and he is dead, and Mohun, too, the bloody villain, who was set on him. They fought in Hyde Park just before sunset; the Duke killed Mohun, and Macartney came up and stabbed him, and the dog is fled. I have your chariot below; send to every part of the country and apprehend that villain; come to the Duke's house and see if any life be left in him."

"O Beatrix, Beatrix," thought Esmond, "and here ends my poor girl's ambition!"

CHAPTER VI

POOR BEATRIX

THERE had been no need to urge upon Esmond the necessity of a separation between him and Beatrix: Fate had done that completely; and I think from the very moment poor Beatrix had accepted the Duke's offer, she began to assume the majestic air of a Duchess, nay, Queen Elect, and to carry herself as one sacred and removed from us common people. Her mother and kinsman both fell into her ways, the latter scornfully perhaps, and uttering his usual gibes at her vanity and his own. There was a certain charm about this girl of which neither Colonel Esmond nor his fond mistress could forego the fascination; in spite of her faults and her pride and wilfulness, they were forced to love her; and, indeed, might be set down as the two chief flatterers of the brilliant creature's court.

Who, in the course of his life, hath not been so bewitched, and worshipped some idol or another? Years after this passion hath been dead and buried, along with a thousand other worldly cares and ambitions, he who felt it can recall it out of its grave, and admire, almost as fondly as he did in his youth, that lovely queenly creature. I invoke that beautiful spirit from the shades and love her still; or rather I should say such a past is always present to a man; such a passion once felt forms a part of his whole being, and cannot be separated from it; it becomes a portion of the man of to-day, just as any great faith or conviction, the discovery of poetry, the awakening of religion, ever afterwards influence him; just as the wound I had at Blenheim, and of which I wear the scar, hath become part of my frame and influenced my whole body, nay, spirit subsequently, though 'twas got and healed forty years ago. Parting and forgetting! What faithful heart can do these? Our great thoughts, our great affections, the Truths of our life, never leave us. Surely, they cannot separate from our consciousness; shall follow it whithersoever that shall go; and are of their nature divine and immortal.

With the horrible news of this catastrophe, which was confirmed by the weeping domestics at the Duke's own door, Esmond rode homewards as quick as his lazy coach would carry him, devising all the time how he should break the intelligence to the person most concerned in it; and if a satire upon human vanity could be needed, that poor soul afforded it in the altered company and occupations in which Esmond found her. For days before, her chariot had been rolling the street from mercer to toyshop—from goldsmith to laceman: her taste was perfect, or at least the fond bridegroom had thought so, and had given her entire authority over all tradesmen, and for all the plate, furniture, and equipages, with which his Grace the Ambassador wished to adorn his splendid mission. She must have her picture by Kneller, a duchess not being complete without a portrait, and a noble one he made, and actually sketched in, on a cushion, a coronet which she was about to wear. She vowed she would wear it at King James the Third's coronation, and never a princess in the land would have become ermine better. Esmond found the ante-chamber crowded with milliners and toyshop women, obsequious goldsmiths with jewels, salvers, and tankards; and mercers' men with hangings, and velvets, and brocades. My Lady Duchess elect was giving audience to one famous silversmith from Exeter Change, who brought with him a great chased salver, of which he was pointing out the beauties as Colonel Esmond entered. "Come," says she, "cousin, and admire the taste of this pretty thing." I think Mars and Venus were lying in the golden bower, that one gilt Cupid carried off the war-god's casque—another his sword—another his great buckler, upon which my Lord Duke Hamilton's arms with ours were to be engraved—and a fourth was kneeling down to the reclining goddess with the ducal coronet in her hands, God help us! The next time Mr. Esmond saw that piece of plate, the arms were changed: the ducal coronet had been replaced by a viscount's: it formed part of the fortune of the thrifty goldsmith's own daughter, when she married my Lord Viscount Squanderfield two years after.

"Isn't this a beautiful piece?" says Beatrix, examining it, and she pointed out the arch graces of the Cupids, and the fine carving of the languid prostrate Mars. Esmond sickened as he thought of the warrior dead in his chamber, his servants and children weeping around him; and of this smiling creature attiring herself, as it were, for that nuptial deathbed. "'Tis a pretty piece of vanity," says he, looking gloomily at the beautiful creature: there were flambeaux in the room lighting up the brilliant mistress of it. She lifted up the great gold salver with her fair arms.

"Vanity!" says she haughtily. "What is vanity in you, sir, is propriety in me. You ask a Jewish price for it, Mr. Graves; but have it I will, if only to spite Mr. Esmond."

"O Beatrix, lay it down!" says Mr. Esmond. "Herodias! you know not what you carry in the charger."

She dropped it with a clang; the eager goldsmith running to seize his fallen ware. The lady's face caught the fright from Esmond's pale countenance, and her eyes shone out like beacons of alarm:—"What is it, Henry?" says she, running to him, and seizing both his hands. "What do you mean by your pale face and gloomy tones?"

"Come away, come away!" says Esmond, leading her: she clung frightened to him, and he supported her upon his heart, bidding the scared goldsmith leave them. The man went into the next apartment, staring with surprise, and hugging his precious charger.

"Oh, my Beatrix, my sister!" says Esmond, still holding in his arms the pallid and affrighted creature, "you have the greatest courage of any woman in the world; prepare to show it now, for you have a dreadful trial to bear."

She sprang away from the friend who would have protected her:—"Hath he left me?" says she. "We had words this morning: he was very gloomy, and I angered him: but he dared not, he dared not!" As she spoke a burning blush flushed over her whole face and bosom. Esmond saw it reflected in the glass by which she stood, with clenched hands, pressing her swelling heart.

"He has left you," says Esmond, wondering that rage rather than sorrow was in her looks.

"And he is alive," cries Beatrix, "and you bring me this commission! He has left me, and you haven't dared to avenge me! You, that pretend to be the champion of our house, have let me suffer this insult! Where is Castlewood? I will go to my brother."

"The Duke is not alive, Beatrix," said Esmond.

She looked at her cousin wildly, and fell back to the wall as though shot in the breast:—"And you come here, and—and—you killed him?"

"No; thank Heaven!" her kinsman said. "The blood of that noble heart doth not stain my sword! In its last hour it was faithful to thee, Beatrix Esmond. Vain and cruel woman! kneel and thank the awful Heaven which awards life and death, and chastises pride, that the noble Hamilton died true to you; at least that 'twas not your quarrel, or your pride, or your wicked vanity, that drove him to his fate. He died by the bloody sword which already had drunk your own father's blood. O woman, O sister! to that sad field where two corpses are lying—for the murderer died too by the hand of the man he slew—can you bring no mourners but your revenge and your vanity? God help and pardon thee, Beatrix, as He brings this awful punishment to your hard and rebellious heart."

Esmond had scarce done speaking, when his mistress came in. The colloquy between him and Beatrix had lasted but a few minutes, during which time Esmond's servant had carried the disastrous news through the household. The army of Vanity Fair, waiting without, gathered up all their fripperies and fled aghast. Tender Lady Castlewood had been in talk above with Dean Atterbury, the pious creature's almoner and director; and the Dean had entered with her as a physician whose place was at a sick-bed. Beatrix's mother looked at Esmond and ran towards her daughter, with a pale face and open heart and hands, all kindness and pity. But Beatrix passed her by, nor would she have any of the medicaments of the spiritual physician. "I am best in my own room and by myself," she said. Her eyes were quite dry; nor did Esmond ever see them otherwise save once, in respect to that grief. She gave him a cold hand as she went out: "Thank you, brother," she said, in a low voice, and with a simplicity more touching than tears; "all you have said is true and kind, and I will go away and ask pardon." The three others remained behind, and talked over the dreadful story. It affected Doctor Atterbury more even than us, as it seemed. The death of Mohun, her husband's murderer, was more awful to my mistress than even the Duke's unhappy end. Esmond gave at length what particulars he knew of their quarrel, and the cause of it. The two noblemen had long been at war with respect to the Lord Gerard's property, whose two daughters my Lord Duke and Mohun had married. They had met by appointment that day at the lawyer's in Lincoln's Inn Fields; had words which, though they appeared very trifling to those who heard them, were not so to men exasperated by long and previous enmity. Mohun asked my Lord Duke where he could see his Grace's friends, and within an hour had sent two of his own to arrange this deadly duel. It was pursued with such fierceness, and sprang from so trifling a cause, that all men agreed at the time that there was a party, of which these three notorious brawlers were but agents, who desired to take Duke Hamilton's life away. They fought three on a side, as in that tragic meeting twelve years back, which hath been recounted already, and in which Mohun performed his second murder. They rushed in, and closed upon each other at once without any feints or crossing of swords even, and stabbed one at the other desperately, each receiving many wounds; and Mohun having his death-wound, and my Lord Duke lying by him, Macartney came up and stabbed his Grace as he lay on the ground, and gave him the blow of which he died. Colonel Macartney denied this, of which the horror and indignation of the whole kingdom would nevertheless have him guilty, and fled the country, whither he never returned.

What was the real cause of the Duke Hamilton's death?—a paltry quarrel that might easily have been made up, and with a ruffian so low, base, profligate, and degraded with former crimes and repeated murders, that a man of such renown and princely rank as my Lord Duke might have disdained to sully his sword with the blood of such a villain. But his spirit was so high that those who wished his death knew that his courage was like his charity, and never turned any man away; and he died by the hands of Mohun, and the other two cut-throats that were set on him. The Queen's Ambassador to Paris died, the loyal and devoted servant of the House of Stuart, and a Royal Prince of Scotland himself, and carrying the confidence, the repentance of Queen Anne along with his own open devotion, and the good-will of millions in the country more, to the Queen's exiled brother and sovereign.

That party to which Lord Mohun belonged had the benefit of his service, and now were well rid of such a ruffian. He, and Meredith, and Macartney, were the Duke of Marlborough's men; and the two colonels had been broke but the year before for drinking perdition to the Tories. His Grace was a Whig now and a Hanoverian, and as eager for war as Prince Eugene himself. I say not that he was privy to Duke Hamilton's death: I say that his party profited by it; and that three desperate and bloody instruments were found to effect that murder.

As Esmond and the Dean walked away from Kensington discoursing of this tragedy, and how fatal it was to the cause which they both had at heart, the street-criers were already out with their broadsides, shouting through the town the full, true, and horrible account of the death of Lord Mohun and Duke Hamilton in a duel. A fellow had got to Kensington and was crying it in the square there at very early morning, when Mr. Esmond happened to pass by. He drove the man from under Beatrix's very window, whereof the casement had been set open. The sun was shining though 'twas November: he had seen the market-carts rolling into London, the guard relieved at the palace, the labourers trudging to their work in the gardens between Kensington and the City—the wandering merchants and hawkers filling the air with their cries. The world was going to its business again, although dukes lay dead and ladies mourned for them; and kings, very likely, lost their chances. So night and day pass away, and to-morrow comes, and our place knows us not. Esmond thought of the courier, now galloping on the North road to inform him, who was Earl of Arran yesterday, that he was Duke of Hamilton to-day, and of a thousand great schemes, hopes, ambitions, that were alive in the gallant heart, beating a few hours since, and now in a little dust quiescent.

CHAPTER VII

I VISIT CASTLEWOOD ONCE MORE

THUS, for a third time, Beatrix's ambitious hopes were circumvented, and she might well believe that a special malignant fate watched and pursued her, tearing her prize out of her hand just as she seemed to grasp it, and leaving her with only rage and grief for her portion. Whatever her feelings might have been of anger or of sorrow (and I fear me that the former emotion was that which most tore her heart), she would take no confidant, as people of softer natures would have done under such a calamity; her mother and her kinsman knew that she would disdain their pity, and that to offer it would be but to infuriate the cruel wound which fortune had inflicted. We knew that her pride was awfully humbled and punished by this sudden and terrible blow; she wanted no teaching of ours to point out the sad moral of her story. Her fond mother could give but her prayers, and her kinsman his faithful friendship and patience to the unhappy, stricken creature; and it was only by hints, and a word or two uttered months afterwards, that Beatrix showed she understood their silent commiseration, and on her part was secretly thankful for their forbearance. The people about the Court said there was that in her manner which frightened away scoffing and condolence: she was above their triumph and their pity, and acted her part in that dreadful tragedy greatly and courageously; so that those who liked her least were yet forced to admire her. We, who watched her after her disaster, could not but respect the indomitable courage and majestic calm with which she bore it. "I would rather see her tears than her pride," her mother said, who was accustomed to bear her sorrows in a very different way, and to receive them as the stroke of God, with an awful submission and meekness. But Beatrix's nature was different to that tender parent's; she seemed to accept her grief, and to defy it; nor would she allow it (I believe not even in private and in her own chamber) to extort from her the confession of even a tear of humiliation or a cry of pain. Friends and children of our race, who come after me, in which way will you bear your trials? I know one that prays God will give you love rather than pride, and that the Eye all-seeing shall find you in the humble place. Not that we should judge proud spirits otherwise than charitably. 'Tis nature hath fashioned some for ambition and dominion, as it hath formed others for obedience and gentle submission. The leopard follows her nature as the lamb does, and acts after leopard law; she can neither help her beauty, nor her courage, nor her cruelty; nor a single spot on her shining coat; nor the conquering spirit which impels her; nor the shot which brings her down.

During that well-founded panic the Whigs had, lest the Queen should forsake their Hanoverian Prince, bound by oaths and treaties as she was to him, and recall her brother, who was allied to her by yet stronger ties of nature and duty,—the Prince of Savoy, and the boldest of that party of the Whigs, were for bringing the young Duke of Cambridge over, in spite of the Queen, and the outcry of her Tory servants, arguing that the Electoral Prince, a Peer and Prince of the Blood-Royal of this Realm too, and in the line of succession to the crown, had a right to sit in the Parliament whereof he was a member, and to dwell in the country which he one day was to govern. Nothing but the strongest ill-will expressed by the Queen, and the people about her, and menaces of the Royal resentment, should this scheme be persisted in, prevented it from being carried into effect.

The boldest on our side were, in like manner, for having our Prince into the country. The undoubted inheritor of the right divine; the feelings of more than half the nation, of almost all the clergy, of the gentry of England and Scotland with him; entirely innocent of the crime for which his father suffered—brave, young, handsome, unfortunate—who in England would dare to molest the Prince should he come among us, and fling himself upon British generosity, hospitality, and honour? An invader with an army of Frenchmen behind him, Englishmen of spirit would resist to the death, and drive back to the shores whence he came; but a Prince, alone, armed with his right only, and relying on the loyalty of his people, was sure, many of his friends argued, of welcome, at least of safety, among us. The hand of his sister the Queen, of the people his subjects, never could be raised to do him a wrong. But the Queen was timid by nature, and the successive Ministers she had, had private causes for their irresolution. The bolder and honester men, who had at heart the illustrious young exile's cause, had no scheme of interest of their own to prevent them from seeing the right done, and, provided only he came as an Englishman, were ready to venture their all to welcome and defend him.

St. John and Harley both had kind words in plenty for the Prince's adherents, and gave him endless promises of future support;

but hints and promises were all they could be got to give; and some of his friends were for measures much bolder, more efficacious, and more open. With a party of these, some of whom are yet alive, and some whose names Mr. Esmond has no right to mention, he found himself engaged the year after that miserable death of Duke Hamilton, which deprived the Prince of his most courageous ally in this country. Dean Atterbury was one of the friends whom Esmond may mention, as the brave bishop is now beyond exile and persecution, and to him, and one or two more, the Colonel opened himself of a scheme of his own, that, backed by a little resolution on the Prince's part, could not fail of bringing about the accomplishment of their dearest wishes.

My young Lord Viscount Castlewood had not come to England to keep his majority, and had now been absent from the country for several years. The year when his sister was to be married and Duke Hamilton died, my Lord was kept at Bruxelles by his wife's lying-in. The gentle Clotilda could not bear her husband out of her sight; perhaps she mistrusted the young scapegrace should he ever get loose from her leading-strings; and she kept him by her side to nurse the baby and administer posset to the gossips. Many a laugh poor Beatrix had had about Frank's uxoriousness: his mother would have gone to Clotilda when her time was coming, but that the mother-in-law was already in possession, and the negotiations for poor Beatrix's marriage were begun. A few months after the horrid catastrophe in Hyde Park, my mistress and her daughter retired to Castlewood, where my Lord, it was expected, would soon join them. But, to say truth, their quiet household was little to his taste; he could be got to come to Walcote but once after his first campaign; and then the young rogue spent more than half his time in London, not appearing at Court or in public under his own name and title, but frequenting plays, bagnios, and the very worst company, under the name of Captain Esmond (whereby his innocent kinsman got more than once into trouble); and so under various pretexts, and in pursuit of all sorts of pleasures, until he plunged into the lawful one of marriage, Frank Castlewood had remained away from this country and was unknown, save amongst the gentlemen of the army, with whom he had served abroad. The fond heart of his mother was pained by this long absence. 'Twas all that Henry Esmond could do to soothe her natural mortification, and find excuses for his kinsman's levity.

In the autumn of the year 1713, Lord Castlewood thought of returning home. His first child had been a daughter; Clotilda was in the way of gratifying his Lordship with a second, and the pious youth thought that, by bringing his wife to his ancestral home, by prayers to St. Philip of Castlewood, and what not, Heaven might be induced to bless him with a son this time, for whose coming the expectant mamma was very anxious.

The long-debated peace had been proclaimed this year at the end of March; and France was open to us. Just as Frank's poor mother had made all things ready for Lord Castlewood's reception, and was eagerly expecting her son, it was by Colonel Esmond's means that the kind lady was disappointed of her longing, and obliged to defer once more the darling hope of her heart.

Esmond took horses to Castlewood. He had not seen its ancient grey towers and well-remembered woods for nearly fourteen years, and since he rode thence with my Lord, to whom his mistress with her young children by her side waved an adieu. What ages seemed to have passed since then, what years of action and passion, of care, love, hope, disaster! The children were grown up now, and had stories of their own. As for Esmond, he felt to be a hundred years old; his dear mistress only seemed unchanged; she looked and welcomed him quite as of old. There was the fountain in the court babbling its familiar music, the old hall and its furniture, the carved chair my late lord used, the very flagon he drank from. Esmond's mistress knew he would like to sleep in the little room he used to occupy; 'twas made ready for him, and wallflowers and sweet herbs set in the adjoining chamber, the chaplain's room.

In tears of not unmanly emotion, with prayers of submission to the awful Dispenser of death and life, of good and evil fortune, Mr. Esmond passed a part of that first night at Castlewood, lying awake for many hours as the clock kept tolling (in tones so well remembered), looking back, as all men will, that revisit their home of childhood, over the great gulf of time, and surveying himself on the distant bank yonder, a sad little melancholy boy with his lord still alive—his dear mistress, a girl yet, her children sporting around her. Years ago, a boy on that very bed, when she had blessed him and called him her knight, he had made a vow to be faithful and never desert her dear service. Had he kept that fond boyish promise? Yes, before Heaven; yes, praise be to God! His life had been hers; his blood, his fortune, his name, his whole heart ever since had been hers and her children's. All night long he was dreaming his boyhood over again, and waking fitfully; he half fancied he heard Father Holt calling to him from the next chamber, and that he was coming in and out from the mysterious window.

Esmond rose up before the dawn, passed into the next room, where the air was heavy with the odour of the wallflowers; looked into the brazier where the papers had been burnt, into the old presses where Holt's books and papers had been kept, and tried the spring and whether the window worked still. The spring had not been touched for years, but yielded at length, and the whole fabric of the window sank down. He lifted it and it relapsed into its frame; no one had ever passed thence since Holt used it sixteen years ago.

Esmond remembered his poor lord saying, on the last day of his life, that Holt used to come in and out of the house like a ghost, and knew that the Father liked these mysteries, and practised such secret disguises, entrances and exits: this was the way the ghost came and went, his pupil had always conjectured. Esmond closed the casement up again as the dawn was rising over Castlewood village; he could hear the clinking at the blacksmith's forge yonder among the trees, across the green, and past the river, on which a mist still lay sleeping.

Next Esmond opened that long cupboard over the woodwork of the mantelpiece, big enough to hold a man, and in which Mr. Holt used to keep sundry secret properties of his. The two swords he remembered so well as a boy lay actually there still, and Esmond took them out and wiped them, with a strange curiosity of emotion. There were a bundle of papers here, too, which no doubt had been left at Holt's last visit to the place, in my Lord Viscount's life, that very day when the priest had been arrested and taken to Hexham Castle. Esmond made free with these papers, and found treasonable matter of King William's reign, the names of Charnock and Perkins, Sir John Fenwick and Sir John Friend, Rookwood and Lodwick, Lords Montgomery and Ailesbury, Clarendon and Yarmouth, that had all been engaged in plots against the usurper; a letter from the Duke of Berwick too, and one from the King at St. Germains, offering to confer upon his trusty and well-beloved Francis, Viscount Castlewood, the titles of Earl and Marquis of Esmond, bestowed by patent royal, and in the fourth year of his reign, upon Thomas, Viscount Castlewood, and the heirs-male of his body, in default of which issue the ranks and dignities were to pass to Francis aforesaid.

This was the paper, whereof my Lord had spoken, which Holt showed him the very day he was arrested, and for an answer to which he would come back in a week's time. I put these papers hastily into the crypt whence I had taken them, being interrupted by a tapping of a light finger at the ring of the chamber-door: 'twas my kind mistress, with her face full of love and welcome. She, too, had passed the night wakefully no doubt: but neither asked the other how the hours had been spent. There are things we divine without speaking, and know though they happen out of our sight. This fond lady hath told me that she knew both days when I was wounded abroad. Who shall say how far sympathy reaches, and how truly love can prophesy? "I looked into your room," was all she said; "the bed was vacant, the little old bed! I knew I should find you here." And tender and blushing faintly, with a benediction in her eyes, the gentle creature kissed him.

They walked out, hand-in-hand, through the old court, and to the terrace-walk, where the grass was glistening with dew, and the birds in the green woods above were singing their delicious choruses under the blushing morning sky. How well all things were remembered! The ancient towers and gables of the Hall darkling against the east, the purple shadows on the green slopes, the quaint devices and carvings of the dial, the forest-crowned heights, the fair yellow plain cheerful with crops and corn, the shining river rolling through it towards the pearly hills beyond; all these were before us, along with a thousand beautiful memories of our youth, beautiful and sad, but as real and vivid in our minds as that fair and always-remembered scene our eyes beheld once more. We forget nothing. The memory sleeps, but wakens again; I often think how it shall be when, after the last sleep of death, the *réveillée* shall arouse us for ever, and the past in one flash of self-consciousness rush back, like the soul revivified.

The house would not be up for some hours yet (it was July, and the dawn was only just awake), and here Esmond opened himself to his mistress of the business he had in hand, and what part Frank was to play in it. He knew he could confide anything to her, and that the fond soul would die rather than reveal it; and bidding her keep the secret from all, he laid it entirely before his mistress (always as staunch a little loyalist as any in the kingdom), and indeed was quite sure that any plan of his was secure of her applause and sympathy. Never was such a glorious scheme to her partial mind, never such a devoted knight to execute it. An hour or two may have passed whilst they were having their colloquy. Beatrix came out to them just as their talk was over; her tall beautiful form robed in sable (which she wore without ostentation ever since last year's catastrophe), sweeping over the green terrace, and casting its shadows before her across the grass.

She made us one of her grand curtseys smiling, and called us "the young people." She was older, paler, and more majestic than in the year before; her mother seemed the younger of the two. She never once spoke of her grief, Lady Castlewood told Esmond, or alluded, save by a quiet word or two, to the death of her hopes.

When Beatrix came back to Castlewood she took to visiting all the cottages and all the sick. She set up a school of children, and taught singing to some of them. We had a pair of beautiful old organs in Castlewood Church, on which she played admirably, so that the music there became to be known in the country for many miles round, and no doubt people came to see the fair organist as well as to hear her. Parson Tusher and his wife were established at the vicarage, but his wife had brought him no children wherewith Tom might meet his enemies at the gate. Honest Tom took care not to have many such, his great shovel-hat was in his hand for everybody. He was profuse of bows and compliments. He behaved to Esmond as if the Colonel had been a Commander-in-Chief; he dined at the Hall that day, being Sunday, and would not partake of pudding except under extreme pressure. He deplored my Lord's perversion, but drank his Lordship's health very devoutly; and an hour before at church sent the Colonel to sleep, with a long, learned, and refreshing sermon.

Esmond's visit home was but for two days; the business he had in hand calling him away and out of the country. Ere he went, he saw Beatrix but once alone, and then she summoned him out of the long tapestry room, where he and his mistress were sitting, quite as in old times, into the adjoining chamber, that had been Viscountess Isabel's sleeping apartment, and where Esmond perfectly well remembered seeing the old lady sitting up in the bed, in her night-rail, that morning when the troop of guard came to fetch her. The most beautiful woman in England lay in that bed now, whereof the great damask hangings were scarce faded since Esmond saw them last.

Here stood Beatrix in her black robes, holding a box in her hand; 'twas that which Esmond had given her before her marriage, stamped with a coronet which the disappointed girl was never to wear; and containing his aunt's legacy of diamonds.

"You had best take these with you, Harry," says she; "I have no need of diamonds any more." There was not the least token of emotion in her quiet low voice. She held out the black shagreen-case with her fair arm, that did not shake in the least. Esmond saw she wore a black velvet bracelet on it, with my Lord Duke's picture in enamel; he had given it her but three days before he fell.

Esmond said the stones were his no longer, and strove to turn off that proffered restoration with a laugh: "Of what good," says he, "are they to me? The diamond loop to his hat did not set off Prince Eugene, and will not make my yellow face look any handsomer."

"You will give them to your wife, cousin," says she. "My cousin, your wife has a lovely complexion and shape."

"Beatrix," Esmond burst out, the old fire flaming out as it would at times, "will you wear those trinkets at your marriage? You whispered once you did not know me: you know me better now: how I sought, what I have sighed for, for ten years, what foregone!"

"A price for your constancy, my Lord!" says she; "such a preux chevalier wants to be paid. Oh fie, cousin!"

"Again," Esmond spoke out, "if I do something you have at heart; something worthy of me and you; something that shall make me a name with which to endow you; will you take it? There was a chance for me once, you said; is it impossible to recall it? Never shake your head, but hear me; say you will hear me a year hence. If I come back to you and bring you fame, will that please you? If I do what you desire most—what he who is dead desired most—will that soften you?"

"What is it, Henry?" says she, her face lighting up; "what mean you?"

"Ask no questions," he said; "wait, and give me but time; if I bring back that you long for, that I have a thousand times heard you pray for, will you have no reward for him who has done you that service? Put away those trinkets, keep them: it shall not be at my marriage, it shall not be at yours; but if man can do it, I swear a day shall come when there shall be a feast in your house, and you shall be proud to wear them. I say no more now; put aside these words, and lock away yonder box until the day when I shall remind you of both. All I pray of you now is, to wait and to remember."

"You are going out of the country?" says Beatrix, in some agitation.

"Yes, to-morrow," says Esmond.

"To Lorraine, cousin?" says Beatrix, laying her hand on his arm; 'twas the hand on which she wore the Duke's bracelet. "Stay, Harry!" continued she, with a tone that had more despondency in it than she was accustomed to show. "Hear a last word. I do love you. I do admire you—who would not, that has known such love as yours has been for us all? But I think I have no heart; at least, I have never seen the man that could touch it; and, had I found him, I would have followed him in rags had he been a private soldier, or to sea, like one of those buccaneers you used to read to us about when we were children. I would do anything for such a man, bear anything for him: but I never found one. You were ever too much of a slave to win my heart; even my Lord Duke could not command it. I had not been happy had I married him. I knew that three months after our engagement—

and was too vain to break it. O Harry! I cried once or twice, not for him, but with tears of rage because I could not be sorry for him. I was frightened to find I was glad of his death; and were I joined to you, I should have the same sense of servitude, the same longing to escape. We should both be unhappy, and you the most, who are as jealous as the Duke was himself. I tried to love him; I tried, indeed I did: affected gladness when he came; submitted to hear when he was by me, and tried the wife's part I thought I was to play for the rest of my days. But half-an-hour of that complaisance wearied me, and what would a lifetime be? My thoughts were away when he was speaking; and I was thinking, Oh that this man would drop my hand, and rise up from before my feet! I knew his great and noble qualities, greater and nobler than mine a thousand times, as yours are, cousin, I tell you, a million and a million times better. But 'twas not for these I took him. I took him to have a great place in the world, and I lost it. I lost it, and do not deplore him—and I often thought, as I listened to his fond vows and ardent words, Oh, if I yield to this man and meet *the other*, I shall hate him and leave him! I am not good, Harry: my mother is gentle and good like an angel. I wonder how she should have had such a child. She is weak, but she would die rather than do a wrong; I am stronger than she, but I would do it out of defiance. I do not care for what the parsons tell me with their droning sermons: I used to see them at Court as mean and as worthless as the meanest woman there. Oh, I am sick and weary of the world! I wait but for one thing, and when 'tis done, I will take Frank's religion and your poor mother's and go into a nunnery, and end like her. Shall I wear the diamonds then?—they say the nuns wear their best trinkets the day they take the veil. I will put them away as you bid me. Farewell, cousin: mamma is pacing the next room, racking her little head to know what we have been saying. She is jealous: all women are. I sometimes think that is the only womanly quality I have."

"Farewell. Farewell, brother." She gave him her cheek as a brotherly privilege. The cheek was as cold as marble.

Esmond's mistress showed no signs of jealousy when he returned to the room where she was. She had schooled herself so as to look quite inscrutably, when she had a mind. Amongst her other feminine qualities she had that of being a perfect dissembler.

He rid away from Castlewood to attempt the task he was bound on, and stand or fall by it; in truth his state of mind was such, that he was eager for some outward excitement to counteract that gnawing malady which he was inwardly enduring.

CHAPTER VIII

I TRAVEL TO FRANCE AND BRING HOME A PORTRAIT OF RIGAUD

MR. ESMOND did not think fit to take leave at Court, or to inform all the world of Pall Mall and the coffee-houses, that he was about to quit England; and chose to depart in the most private manner possible. He procured a pass as for a Frenchman, through Doctor Atterbury, who did that business for him, getting the signature even from Lord Bolingbroke's office, without any personal application to the Secretary. Lockwood, his faithful servant, he took with him to Castlewood, and left behind there: giving out ere he left London that he himself was sick, and gone to Hampshire for country air, and so departed as silently as might be upon his business.

As Frank Castlewood's aid was indispensable for Mr. Esmond's scheme, his first visit was to Bruxelles (passing by way of Antwerp, where the Duke of Marlborough was in exile), and in the first-named place Harry found his dear young Benedict, the married man, who appeared to be rather out of humour with his matrimonial chain, and clogged with the obstinate embraces which Clotilda kept around his neck. Colonel Esmond was not presented to her; but Monsieur Simon was, a gentleman of the Royal Cravat (Esmond bethought him of the regiment of his honest Irishman, whom he had seen that day after Malplaquet, when he first set eyes on the young King); and Monsieur Simon was introduced to the Viscountess Castlewood, *née* Comptesse Wertheim; to the numerous Counts, the Lady Clotilda's tall brothers; to her father the Chamberlain; and to the lady his wife, Frank's mother-in-law, a tall and majestic person of large proportions, such as became the mother of such a company of grenadiers as her warlike sons formed. The whole race were at free quarters in the little castle nigh to Bruxelles which Frank had taken; rode his horses; drank his wine; and lived easily at the poor lad's charges. Mr. Esmond had always maintained a perfect fluency in the French, which was his mother tongue; and if this family (that spoke French with the twang which the Flemings use) discovered any inaccuracy in Mr. Simon's pronunciation, 'twas to be attributed to the latter's long residence in England, where he had married and remained ever since he was taken prisoner at Blenheim. His story was perfectly pat; there were none there to doubt it save honest Frank, and he was charmed with his kinsman's scheme, when he became acquainted with it; and, in truth, always admired Colonel Esmond with an affectionate fidelity, and thought his cousin the wisest and best of all cousins and men. Frank entered heart and soul into the plan, and liked it the better as it was to take him to Paris, out of reach of his brothers, his father, and his mother-in-law, whose attentions rather fatigued him.

Castlewood, I have said, was born in the same year as the Prince of Wales; had not a little of the Prince's air, height, and figure; and, especially since he had seen the Chevalier de St. George on the occasion before-named, took no small pride in his resemblance to a person so illustrious; which likeness he increased by all means in his power, wearing fair brown periwigs, such as the Prince wore, and ribands, and so forth, of the Chevalier's colour.

This resemblance was, in truth, the circumstance on which Mr. Esmond's scheme was founded; and having secured Frank's secrecy and enthusiasm, he left him to continue his journey, and see the other personages on whom its success depended. The place whither Mr. Simon next travelled was Bar, in Lorraine, where that merchant arrived with a consignment of broadcloths, valuable laces from Malines, and letters for his correspondent there.

Would you know how a prince, heroic from misfortunes, and descended from a line of kings, whose race seemed to be doomed like the Atridæ of old—would you know how he was employed, when the envoy who came to him through danger and difficulty beheld him for the first time? The young King, in a flannel jacket, was at tennis with the gentlemen of his suite, crying out after the balls, and swearing like the meanest of his subjects. The next time Mr. Esmond saw him, 'twas when Monsieur Simon took a packet of laces to Miss Oglethorpe: the Prince's antechamber in those days, at which ignoble door men were forced to knock for admission to his Majesty. The admission was given, the envoy found the King and the mistress together: the pair were at cards, and his Majesty was in liquor. He cared more for three honours than three kingdoms; and a half-dozen glasses of ratafia made him forget all his woes and his losses, his father's crown, and his grandfather's head.

Mr. Esmond did not open himself to the Prince then. His Majesty was scarce in a condition to hear him; and he doubted whether a King who drank so much could keep a secret in his fuddled head; or whether a hand that shook so, was strong enough to grasp at a crown. However, at last, and after taking counsel with the Prince's advisers, amongst whom were many gentlemen, honest and faithful, Esmond's plan was laid before the King, and her actual Majesty Queen Oglethorpe, in counsel. The Prince liked the scheme well enough: 'twas easy and daring, and suited to his reckless gaiety and lively youthful spirit. In the morning after he had slept his wine off he was very gay, lively, and agreeable. His manner had an extreme charm of archness, and a kind simplicity; and, to do her justice, her Oglethorpean Majesty was kind, acute, resolute, and of good counsel; she gave the Prince much good advice that he was too weak to follow, and loved him with a fidelity which he returned with an ingratitude quite Royal.

Having his own forebodings regarding his scheme should it ever be fulfilled, and his usual sceptic doubts as to the benefit which might accrue to the country by bringing a tipsy young monarch back to it, Colonel Esmond had his audience of leave, and quiet Monsieur Simon took his departure. At any rate the youth at Bar was as good as the older Pretender at Hanover; if the worst came to the worst, the Englishman could be dealt with as easy as the German. Monsieur Simon trotted on that long journey from Nancy to Paris, and saw that famous town, stealthily and like a spy, as in truth he was; and where, sure, more magnificence and more misery is heaped together, more rags and lace, more filth and gilding, than in any city in this world. Here he was put in communication with the King's best friend, his half-brother, the famous Duke of Berwick; Esmond recognised him as the stranger who had visited Castlewood now near twenty years ago. His Grace opened to him when he found that Mr. Esmond was one of Webb's brave regiment, that had once been his Grace's own. He was the sword and buckler indeed of the Stuart cause; there was no stain on his shield except the bar across it, which Marlborough's sister left him. Had Berwick been his father's heir, James the Third had assuredly sat on the English throne. He could dare, endure, strike, speak, be silent. The fire and genius, perhaps, he had not (that were given to baser men), but except these he had some of the best qualities of a leader. His Grace knew Esmond's father and history; and hinted at the latter in such a way as made the Colonel to think he was aware of the particulars of that story. But Esmond did not choose to enter on it, nor did the Duke press him. Mr. Esmond said, "No doubt he should come by his name if ever greater people came by theirs."

What confirmed Esmond in his notion that the Duke of Berwick knew of his case was, that when the Colonel went to pay his duty at St. Germains, her Majesty once addressed him by the title of Marquis. He took the Queen the dutiful remembrances of her goddaughter, and the lady whom, in the days of her prosperity, her Majesty had befriended. The Queen remembered Rachel Esmond perfectly well, had heard of my Lord Castlewood's conversion, and was much edified by that act of Heaven in his favour. She knew that others of that family had been of the only true Church too: "Your father and your mother, M. le Marquis," her Majesty said (that was the only time she used the phrase). Monsieur Simon bowed very low, and said he had found other parents than his own, who had taught him differently; but these had only one King: on which her Majesty was pleased to give him a medal blessed by the Pope, which had been found very efficacious in cases similar to his own, and to promise she would offer up prayers for his conversion and that of the family: which no doubt this pious lady did, though up to the present moment, and after twenty-seven years, Colonel Esmond is bound to say that neither the medal nor the prayers have had the slightest known effect upon his religious convictions.

As for the splendours of Versailles, Monsieur Simon, the merchant, only beheld them as a humble and distant spectator, seeing the old King but once, when he went to feed his carps: and asking for no presentation at his Majesty's Court.

By this time my Lord Viscount Castlewood was got to Paris, where, as the London prints presently announced, her Ladyship was brought to bed of a son and heir. For a long while afterwards she was in a delicate state of health, and ordered by the physicians not to travel; otherwise 'twas well known that the Viscount Castlewood proposed returning to England, and taking up his residence at his own seat.

Whilst he remained at Paris, my Lord Castlewood had his picture done by the famous French painter, Monsieur Rigaud, a present for his mother in London; and this piece Monsieur Simon took back with him when he returned to that city, which he reached about May, in the year 1714, very soon after which time my Lady Castlewood and her daughter, and their kinsman, Colonel Esmond, who had been at Castlewood all this time, likewise returned to London; her Ladyship occupying her house at Kensington, Mr. Esmond returning to his lodgings at Knightsbridge, nearer the town, and once more making his appearance at all public places, his health greatly improved by his long stay in the country.

The portrait of my Lord, in a handsome gilt frame, was hung up in the place of honour in her Ladyship's drawing-room. His Lordship was represented in his scarlet uniform of Captain of the Guard, with a light brown periwig, a cuirass under his coat, a blue riband, and a fall of Bruxelles lace. Many of her Ladyship's friends admired the piece beyond measure, and flocked to see it; Bishop Atterbury, Mr. Lesly, good old Mr. Collier, and others amongst the clergy, were delighted with the performance, and many among the first quality examined and praised it; only I must own that Doctor Tusher happening to come up to London, and seeing the picture (it was ordinarily covered by a curtain, but on this day Miss Beatrix happened to be looking at it when the Doctor arrived), the Vicar of Castlewood vowed he could not see any resemblance in the piece to his old pupil, except, perhaps, a little about the chin and the periwig; but we all of us convinced him that he had not seen Frank for five years or more; that he knew no more about the Fine Arts than a ploughboy, and that he must be mistaken; and we sent him home assured that the piece was an excellent likeness. As for my Lord Bolingbroke, who honoured her Ladyship with a visit occasionally, when Colonel Esmond showed him the picture he burst out laughing, and asked what devilry he was engaged on? Esmond owned simply that the portrait was not that of Viscount Castlewood; besought the Secretary on his honour to keep the secret; said that the ladies of the house were enthusiastic Jacobites, as was well known; and confessed that the picture was that of the Chevalier St. George.

The truth is, that Mr. Simon, waiting upon Lord Castlewood one day at Monsieur Rigaud's, whilst his Lordship was sitting for his picture, affected to be much struck with a piece representing the Chevalier, whereof the head only was finished, and purchased it of the painter for a hundred crowns. It had been intended, the artist said, for Miss Oglethorpe, the Prince's mistress, but that young lady quitting Paris, had left the work on the artist's hands; and taking this piece home, when my Lord's portrait arrived, Colonel Esmond, alias Monsieur Simon, had copied the uniform and other accessories from my Lord's picture to fill up Rigaud's incomplete canvas: the Colonel all his life having been a practitioner of painting, and especially followed it during his long residence in the cities of Flanders, among the masterpieces of Vandyck and Rubens. My grandson hath the piece, such as it is, in Virginia now.

At the commencement of the month of June, Miss Beatrix Esmond, and my Lady Viscountess, her mother, arrived from Castlewood; the former to resume her services at Court, which had been interrupted by the fatal catastrophe of Duke Hamilton's death. She once more took her place, then, in her Majesty's suite and at the Maids' table, being always a favourite with Mrs. Masham, the Queen's chief woman, partly perhaps on account of their bitterness against the Duchess of Marlborough, whom Miss Beatrix loved no better than her rival did. The gentlemen about the Court, my Lord Bolingbroke amongst others, owned that the young lady had come back handsomer than ever, and that the serious and tragic air which her face now involuntarily wore became her better than her former smiles and archness.

All the old domestics at the little house of Kensington Square were changed; the old steward that had served the family any time these five-and-twenty years, since the birth of the children of the house, was despatched into the kingdom of Ireland to see my Lord's estate there; the housekeeper, who had been my Lady's woman time out of mind, and the attendant of the young children, was sent away grumbling to Walcote, to see to the new painting and preparing of that house, which my Lady Dowager intended to occupy for the future, giving up Castlewood to her daughter-in-law that might be expected daily from France. Another servant the Viscountess had was dismissed too—with a gratuity—on the pretext that her Ladyship's train of domestics must be diminished; so, finally, there was not left in the household a single person who had belonged to it during the time my young Lord Castlewood was yet at home.

For the plan which Colonel Esmond had in view, and the stroke he intended, 'twas necessary that the very smallest number of persons should be put in possession of his secret. It scarce was known, except to three or four out of his family, and it was kept to a wonder.

On the 10th of June 1714, there came by Mr. Prior's messenger from Paris a letter from my Lord Viscount Castlewood to his mother, saying that he had been foolish in regard of money matters, that he was ashamed to own he had lost at play, and by other extravagances; and that, instead of having great entertainments as he had hoped at Castlewood this year, he must live as quiet as he could, and make every effort to be saving. So far every word of poor Frank's letter was true, nor was there a doubt that he and his tall brothers-in-law had spent a great deal more than they ought, and engaged the revenues of the Castlewood property, which the fond mother had husbanded and improved so carefully during the time of her guardianship.

His "Clotilda," Castlewood went on to say, "was still delicate, and the physicians thought her lying-in had best take place at Paris. He should come without her Ladyship, and be at his mother's house about the 17th or 18th day of June, proposing to take horse from Paris immediately, and bringing but a single servant with him; and he requested that the lawyers of Gray's Inn might be invited to meet him with their account, and the land-steward come from Castlewood with his, so that he might settle with them speedily, raise a sum of money whereof he stood in need, and be back to his viscountess by the time of her lying-in." Then his Lordship gave some of the news of the town, sent his remembrance to kinsfolk, and so the letter ended. 'Twas put in the common post, and no doubt the French police and the English there had a copy of it, to which they were exceeding welcome.

Two days after another letter was despatched by the public post of France, in the same open way, and this, after giving news of the fashion at Court there, ended by the following sentences, in which, but for those that had the key, 'twould be difficult for any man to find any secret lurked at all:—

"(The King will take) medicine on Thursday. His Majesty is better than he hath been of late, though incommoded by indigestion from his too great appetite. Madame Maintenon continues well. They have performed a play of Mons. Racine at St. Cyr. The Duke of Shrewsbury and Mr. Prior, our envoy, and all the English nobility here, were present at it. (The Viscount Castlewood's passports) were refused to him, 'twas said; his Lordship being sued by a goldsmith for *Vaisselle plate*, and a pearl necklace supplied to Mademoiselle Meruel of the French Comedy. 'Tis a pity such news should get abroad (and travel to England) about our young nobility here. Mademoiselle Meruel has been sent to the Fort l'Evesque; they say she has ordered not only plate, but furniture, and a chariot and horses (under that lord's name), of which extravagance his unfortunate Viscountess knows nothing.

"(His Majesty will be) eighty-two years of age on his next birthday. The Court prepares to celebrate it with a great feast. Mr. Prior is in a sad way about their refusing at home to send him his plate. All here admired my Lord Viscount's portrait, and said it was a masterpiece of Rigaud. Have you seen it? It is (at the Lady Castlewood's house in Kensington Square). I think no English painter could produce such a piece.

"Our poor friend the Abbé hath been at the Bastile, but is now transported to the Conciergerie (where his friends may visit him. They are to ask for) a remission of his sentence soon. Let us hope the poor rogue will have repented in prison.

"(The Lord Castlewood) has had the affair of the plate made up, and departs for England.

"Is not this a dull letter? I have a cursed headache with drinking with Mat and some more over-night, and tipsy or sober am

"Thine ever ——."

All this letter save some dozen of words which I have put above between brackets, was mere idle talk, though the substance of the letter was as important as any letter well could be. It told those that had the key, that *The King will take the Viscount Castlewood's passports and travel to England under that lord's name. His Majesty will be at the Lady Castlewood's house in Kensington Square, where his friends may visit him. They are to ask for the Lord Castlewood.* This note may have passed under Mr. Prior's eyes, and those of our new allies the French, and taught them nothing; though it explains sufficiently to persons in London what the event was which was about to happen, as 'twill show those who read my memoirs a hundred years hence, what was that errand on which Colonel Esmond of late had been busy. Silently and swiftly to do that about which others were conspiring, and thousands of Jacobites all over the country clumsily caballing; alone to effect that which the leaders here were only talking about; to bring the Prince of Wales into the country openly in the face of all, under Bolingbroke's very eyes, the walls placarded with the proclamation signed with the Secretary's name, and offering five hundred pounds reward for his apprehension: this was a stroke, the playing and winning of which might well give any adventurous spirit pleasure: the loss of the stake might involve a heavy penalty, but all our family were eager to risk that for the glorious chance of winning the game.

Nor should it be called a game, save perhaps with the chief player, who was not more or less sceptical than most public men with whom he had acquaintance in that age. (Is there ever a public man in England that altogether believes in his party? Is there one, however doubtful, that will not fight for it?) Young Frank was ready to fight without much thinking; he was a Jacobite as his father before him was; all the Esmonds were Royalists. Give him but the word, he would cry, "God save King James!" before the palace guard, or at the Maypole in the Strand; and with respect to the women, as is usual with them, 'twas not a question of party but of faith: their belief was a passion; either Esmond's mistress or her daughter would have died for it cheerfully. I have laughed often, talking of King William's reign, and said I thought Lady Castlewood was disappointed the King did not persecute the family more; and those who know the nature of women may fancy for themselves, what needs not here be written down, the rapture with which these neophytes received the mystery when made known to them; the eagerness with which they looked forward to its completion; the reverence which they paid the minister who initiated them into that secret Truth, now known only to a few, but presently to reign over the world. Sure there is no bound to the trustingness of women. Look at Arria worshipping the drunken clodpate of a husband who beats her; look at Cornelia treasuring as a jewel in her maternal heart the oaf her son. I have known a woman preach Jesuit's bark, and afterwards Dr. Berkeley's tar-water, as though to swallow them were a divine decree, and to refuse them no better than blasphemy.

On his return from France Colonel Esmond put himself at the head of this little knot of fond conspirators. No death or torture he knew would frighten them out of their constancy. When he detailed his plan for bringing the King back, his elder mistress thought that that Restoration was to be attributed under Heaven to the Castlewood family and to its chief, and she worshipped and loved Esmond, if that could be, more than ever she had done. She doubted not for one moment of the success of his scheme, to mistrust which would have seemed impious in her eyes. And as for Beatrix, when she became acquainted with the plan, and joined it, as she did with all her heart, she gave Esmond one of her searching bright looks. "Ah, Harry," says she, "why were you not the head of our house? You are the only one fit to raise it; why do you give that silly boy the name and the honour? But 'tis so in the world: those get the prize that don't deserve or care for it. I wish I could give you *your* silly prize, cousin, but I can't; I have tried, and I can't." And she went away, shaking her head mournfully, but always, it seemed to Esmond, that her liking and respect for him was greatly increased, since she knew what capability he had both to act and bear; to do and to forego.

CHAPTER IX

THE ORIGINAL OF THE PORTRAIT COMES TO ENGLAND

'TWAS announced in the family that my Lord Castlewood would arrive, having a confidential French gentleman in his suite, who acted as secretary to his Lordship, and who, being a Papist, and a foreigner of a good family, though now in rather a menial place, would have his meals served in his chamber, and not with the domestics of the house. The Viscountess gave up her bedchamber contiguous to her daughter's, and having a large convenient closet attached to it, in which a bed was put up, ostensibly for Monsieur Baptiste, the Frenchman; though, 'tis needless to say, when the doors of the apartments were locked, and the two guests retired within it, the young Viscount became the servant of the illustrious Prince whom he entertained, and gave up gladly the more convenient and airy chamber and bed to his master. Madam Beatrix also retired to the upper region, her chamber being converted into a sitting-room for my Lord. The better to carry the deceit, Beatrix affected to grumble before the servants, and to be jealous that she was turned out of her chamber to make way for my Lord.

No small preparations were made, you may be sure, and no slight tremor of expectation caused the hearts of the gentle ladies of Castlewood to flutter, before the arrival of the personages who were about to honour their house. The chamber was ornamented with flowers; the bed covered with the very finest of linen; the two ladies insisting on making it themselves, and kneeling down at the bedside and kissing the sheets out of respect for the web that was to hold the sacred person of a King. The toilet was of silver and crystal; there was a copy of "Eikon Basiliké" laid on the writing-table; a portrait of the martyred King hung always over the mantel, having a sword of my poor Lord Castlewood underneath it, and a little picture or emblem which the widow loved always to have before her eyes on waking, and in which the hair of her lord and her two children was worked together. Her books of private devotions, as they were all of the English Church, she carried away with her to the upper apartment, which she destined for herself. The ladies showed Mr. Esmond, when they were completed, the fond preparations they had made. 'Twas then Beatrix knelt down and kissed the linen sheets. As for her mother, Lady Castlewood made a curtsey at the door, as she would have done to the altar on entering a church, and owned that she considered the chamber in a manner sacred.

The company in the servants' hall never for a moment supposed that these preparations were made for any other person than the young Viscount, the lord of the house, whom his fond mother had been for so many years without seeing. Both ladies were perfect housewives, having the greatest skill in the making of confections, scented waters, &c., and keeping a notable superintendence over the kitchen. Calves enough were killed to feed an army of prodigal sons, Esmond thought, and laughed when he came to wait on the ladies, on the day when the guests were to arrive, to find two pairs of the finest and roundest arms to be seen in England (my Lady Castlewood was remarkable for this beauty of her person), covered with flour up above the elbows, and preparing paste, and turning rolling-pins in the housekeeper's closet. The guest would not arrive till supper-time, and my Lord would prefer having that meal in his own chamber. You may be sure the brightest plate of the house was laid out there, and can understand why it was that the ladies insisted that they alone would wait upon the young chief of the family.

Taking horse, Colonel Esmond rode rapidly to Rochester, and there awaited the King in that very town where his father had last set his foot on the English shore. A room had been provided at an inn there for my Lord Castlewood and his servant; and Colonel Esmond timed his ride so well that he had scarce been half-an-hour in the place, and was looking over the balcony into the yard of the inn, when two travellers rode in at the inn gate, and the Colonel running down, the next moment embraced his dear young lord.

My Lord's companion, acting the part of a domestic, dismounted, and was for holding the Viscount's stirrup; but Colonel Esmond, calling to his own man, who was in the court, bade him take the horses and settle with the lad who had ridden the post along with the two travellers, crying out in a cavalier tone in the French language to my Lord's companion, and affecting to grumble that my Lord's fellow was a Frenchman, and did not know the money or habits of the country:—"My man will see to the horses, Baptiste," says Colonel Esmond: "do you understand English?" "Very leetle." "So, follow my Lord and wait upon him at dinner in his own room." The landlord and his people came up presently bearing the dishes; 'twas well they made a noise and stir in the gallery, or they might have found Colonel Esmond on his knee before Lord Castlewood's servant, welcoming his Majesty to his kingdom, and kissing the hand of the King. We told the landlord that the Frenchman would wait on his master; and Esmond's man was ordered to keep sentry in the gallery without the door. The Prince dined with a good appetite, laughing and talking very gaily, and condescendingly bidding his two companions to sit with him at table. He was in better spirits than poor Frank Castlewood, who Esmond thought might be woebegone on account of parting with his divine Clotilda; but the Prince wishing to take a short siesta after dinner, and retiring to an inner chamber where there was a bed, the cause of poor Frank's discomfiture came out; and bursting into tears, with many expressions of fondness, friendship, and humiliation, the faithful lad gave his kinsman to understand that he now knew all the truth, and the sacrifices which Colonel Esmond had made for him.

Seeing no good in acquainting poor Frank with that secret, Mr. Esmond had entreated his mistress also not to reveal it to her son. The Prince had told the poor lad all as they were riding from Dover: "I had as lief he had shot me, cousin," Frank said. "I knew you were the best, and the bravest, and the kindest of all men" (so the enthusiastic young fellow went on); "but I never thought I owed you what I do, and can scarce bear the weight of the obligation."

"I stand in the place of your father," says Mr. Esmond kindly, "and sure a father may dispossess himself in favour of his son. I abdicate the twopenny crown, and invest you with the kingdom of Brentford; don't be a fool and cry; you make a much taller and handsomer viscount than ever I could." But the fond boy, with oaths and protestations, laughter and incoherent outbreaks of passionate emotion, could not be got, for some little time, to put up with Esmond's raillery; wanted to kneel down to him, and kissed his hand; asked him and implored him to order something, to bid Castlewood give his own life or take somebody else's; anything, so that he might show his gratitude for the generosity Esmond showed him.

"The K——, *he* laughed," Frank said, pointing to the door where the sleeper was, and speaking in a low tone. "I don't think he should have laughed as he told me the story. As we rode along from Dover, talking in French, he spoke about you, and your coming to him at Bar; he called you 'le grand sérieux,' Don Bellianis of Greece, and I don't know what names; mimicking your manner" (here Castlewood laughed himself)—"and he did it very well.

He seems to sneer at everything. He is not like a king: somehow, Harry, I fancy you are like a king. He does not seem to think what a stake we are all playing. He would have stopped at Canterbury to run after a barmaid there, had I not implored him to come on. He hath a house at Chaillot, where he used to go and bury himself for weeks away from the Queen, and with all sorts of bad company," says Frank, with a demure look. "You may smile, but I am not the wild fellow I was; no, no, I have been taught better," says Castlewood devoutly, making a sign on his breast.

"Thou art my dear brave boy," said Colonel Esmond, touched at the young fellow's simplicity, "and there will be a noble gentleman at Castlewood so long as my Frank is there."

The impetuous young lad was for going down on his knees again, with another explosion of gratitude, but that we heard the voice from the next chamber of the august sleeper, just waking, calling out, "Eh, La Fleur, un verre d'eau!" His Majesty came out yawning:—"A pest," says he, "upon your English ale, 'tis so strong that, *ma foi*, it hath turned my head."

The effect of the ale was like a spur upon our horses, and we rode very quickly to London, reaching Kensington at nightfall. Mr. Esmond's servant was left behind at Rochester, to take care of the tired horses, whilst we had fresh beasts provided along the road. And galloping by the Prince's side the Colonel explained to the Prince of Wales what his movements had been; who the friends were that knew of the expedition; whom, as Esmond conceived, the Prince should trust; entreating him, above all, to maintain the very closest secrecy until the time should come when his Royal Highness should appear. The town swarmed with friends of the Prince's cause: there were scores of correspondents with St. Germains; Jacobites known and secret; great in station and humble; about the Court and the Queen; in the Parliament, Church, and among the merchants in the City. The Prince had friends numberless in the army, in the Privy Council, and the Officers of State. The great object, as it seemed, to the small band of persons who had concerted that bold stroke, who had brought the Queen's brother into his native country, was, that his visit should remain unknown till the proper time came, when his presence should surprise friends and enemies alike; and the latter should be found so unprepared and disunited, that they should not find time to attack him. We feared more from his friends than from his enemies. The lies and tittle-tattle sent over to St. Germains by the Jacobite agents about London, had done an incalculable mischief to his cause, and woefully misguided him, and it was from these especially, that the persons engaged in the present venture were anxious to defend the chief actor in it.*

The party reached London by nightfall, leaving their horses at the Posting-House over against Westminster, and being ferried over the water, where Lady Esmond's coach was already in waiting. In another hour we were all landed at Kensington, and the mistress of the house had that satisfaction which her heart had yearned after for many years, once more to embrace her son, who, on his side, with all his waywardness, ever retained a most tender affection for his parent.

She did not refrain from this expression of her feeling, though the domestics were by, and my Lord Castlewood's attendant stood in the hall. Esmond had to whisper to him in French to take his hat off. Monsieur Baptiste was constantly neglecting his part with an inconceivable levity: more than once on the ride to London, little observations of the stranger, light remarks, and words betokening the greatest ignorance of the country the Prince came to govern, had hurt the susceptibility of the two gentlemen forming his escort; nor could either help owning in his secret mind that they would have had his behaviour otherwise, and that the laughter and the lightness, not to say licence, which characterised his talk, scarce befitted such a great Prince, and such a solemn occasion. Not but that he could act at proper times with spirit and dignity. He had behaved, as we all knew, in a very courageous manner on the field. Esmond had seen a copy of the letter the Prince had writ with his own hand when urged by his friends in England to abjure his religion, and admired that manly and magnanimous reply by which he refused to yield to the temptation. Monsieur Baptiste took off his hat, blushing at the hint Colonel Esmond ventured to give him, and said, "Tenez, elle est jolie, la petite mère. Foi de Chevalier! elle est charmante; mais l'autre, qui est cette nymphe, cet astre qui brille, cette Diane qui descend sur nous?" And he started back, and pushed forward, as Beatrix was descending the stair. She was in colours for the first time at her own house; she wore the diamonds Esmond gave her; it had been agreed between them, that she should wear these brilliants on the day when the King should enter the house, and a queen she looked, radiant in charms, and magnificent and imperial in beauty.

Castlewood himself was startled by that beauty and splendour;

* The managers were the Bishop, who cannot be hurt by having his name mentioned, a very active and loyal Nonconformist Divine, a lady in the highest favour at Court, with whom Beatrix Esmond had communication, and two noblemen of the greatest rank, and a member of the House of Commons, who was implicated in more transactions than one in behalf of the Stuart family.

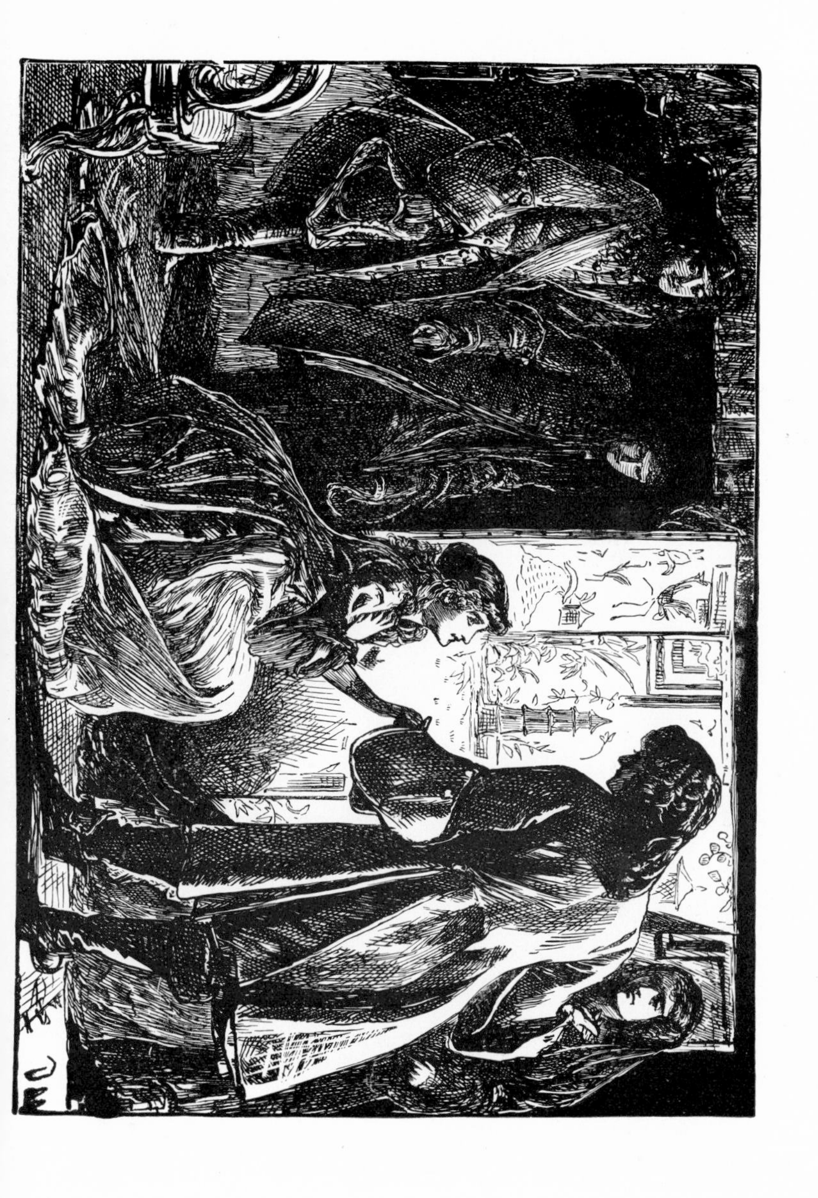

he stepped back and gazed at his sister as though he had not been aware before (nor was he very likely) how perfectly lovely she was, and I thought blushed as he embraced her. The Prince could not keep his eyes off her; he quite forgot his menial part, though he had been schooled to it, and a little light portmanteau prepared expressly that he should carry it. He pressed forward before my Lord Viscount. 'Twas lucky the servants' eyes were busy in other directions, or they must have seen that this was no servant, or at least a very insolent and rude one.

Again Colonel Esmond was obliged to cry out, "Baptiste," in a loud imperious voice, "have a care to the valise!" at which hint the wilful young man ground his teeth together with something very like a curse between them, and then gave a brief look of anything but pleasure to his Mentor. Being reminded, however, he shouldered the little portmanteau, and carried it up the stair, Esmond preceding him, and a servant with lighted tapers. He flung down his burden sulkily in the bedchamber:—"A Prince that will wear a crown must wear a mask," says Mr. Esmond in French.

"Ah peste! I see how it is," says Monsieur Baptiste, continuing the talk in French. "The Great Serious is seriously"—"alarmed for Monsieur Baptiste," broke in the Colonel. Esmond neither liked the tone with which the Prince spoke of the ladies, nor the eyes with which he regarded them.

The bedchamber and the two rooms adjoining it, the closet and the apartment which was to be called my Lord's parlour, were already lighted and awaiting their occupier; and the collation laid for my Lord's supper. Lord Castlewood and his mother and sister came up the stair a minute afterwards, and, so soon as the domestics had quitted the apartment, Castlewood and Esmond uncovered, and the two ladies went down on their knees before the Prince, who graciously gave a hand to each. He looked his part of Prince much more naturally than that of servant, which he had just been trying, and raised them both with a great deal of nobility, as well as kindness in his air. "Madam," says he, "my mother will thank your Ladyship for your hospitality to her son; for you, madam," turning to Beatrix, "I cannot bear to see so much beauty in such a posture. You will betray Monsieur Baptiste if you kneel to him; sure 'tis his place rather to kneel to you."

A light shone out of her eyes; a gleam bright enough to kindle passion in any breast. There were times when this creature was so handsome, that she seemed, as it were, like Venus revealing herself a goddess in a flash of brightness. She appeared so now; radiant, and with eyes bright with a wonderful lustre. A pang, as of rage and jealousy, shot through Esmond's heart, as he caught the look she gave the Prince; and he clenched his hand involuntarily, and looked across to Castlewood, whose eyes answered his alarm-signal, and were also on the alert. The Prince gave his subjects an audience of a few minutes, and then the two ladies and Colonel Esmond quitted the chamber. Lady Castlewood pressed his hand as they descended the stair, and the three went down to the lower rooms, where they waited awhile till the travellers above should be refreshed and ready for their meal.

Esmond looked at Beatrix, blazing with her jewels on her beautiful neck. "I have kept my word," says he. "And I mine," says Beatrix, looking down on the diamonds.

"Were I the Mogul Emperor," says the Colonel, "you should have all that were dug out of Golconda."

"These are a great deal too good for me," says Beatrix, dropping her head on her beautiful breast,—"so are you all, all!" And when she looked up again, as she did in a moment, and after a sigh, her eyes, as they gazed at her cousin, wore that melancholy and inscrutable look which 'twas always impossible to sound.

When the time came for the supper, of which we were advertised by a knocking overhead, Colonel Esmond and the two ladies went to the upper apartment, where the Prince already was, and by his side the young Viscount, of exactly the same age, shape, and with features not dissimilar, though Frank's were the handsomer of the two. The Prince sat down and bade the ladies sit. The gentlemen remained standing: there was, indeed, but one more cover laid at the table:—"Which of you will take it?" says he.

"The head of our house," says Lady Castlewood, taking her son's hand, and looking towards Colonel Esmond with a bow and a great tremor of the voice; "the Marquis of Esmond will have the honour of serving the King."

"I shall have the honour of waiting on his Royal Highness," says Colonel Esmond, filling a cup of wine, and, as the fashion of that day was, he presented it to the King on his knee.

"I drink to my hostess and her family," says the Prince, with no very well-pleased air; but the cloud passed immediately off his face, and he talked to the ladies in a lively, rattling strain, quite undisturbed by poor Mr. Esmond's yellow countenance, that, I dare say, looked very glum.

When the time came to take leave, Esmond marched homewards to his lodgings, and met Mr. Addison on the road that night, walking to a cottage he had at Fulham, the moon shining on his handsome serene face:—"What cheer, brother?" says Addison, laughing: "I thought it was a footpad advancing in the dark, and behold 'tis an old friend. We may shake hands, Colonel, in the dark; 'tis better than fighting by daylight. Why should we quarrel, because I am a Whig and thou art a Tory? Turn thy steps and walk with me to Fulham, where there is a nightingale still singing in the garden, and a cool bottle in a cave I know of; you shall drink to the Pretender if you like, and I will drink my liquor my own way: I have had enough of good liquor?—no, never! There is no such word as enough as a stopper for good wine. Thou wilt not come? Côme any day, come soon. You know I remember *Simois* and the *Sigeia tellus*, and the *prœlia, mixta mero, mixta mero*," he repeated, with ever so slight a touch of *merum* in his voice, and walked back a little way on the road with Esmond, bidding the other remember he was always his friend, and indebted to him for his aid in the "Campaign" poem. And very likely Mr. Under-Secretary would have stepped in and taken t'other bottle at the Colonel's lodging, had the latter invited him, but Esmond's mood was none of the gayest, and he bade his friend an inhospitable good-night at the door.

"I have done the deed," thought he, sleepless, and looking out into the night; "he is here, and I have brought him; he and Beatrix are sleeping under the same roof now. Whom did I mean to serve in bringing him? Was it the Prince? was it Henry Esmond? Had I not best have joined the manly creed of Addison yonder, that scouts the old doctrine of right divine, that boldly declares that Parliament and people consecrate the Sovereign, not bishops, nor genealogies, nor oils, nor coronations." The eager gaze of the young Prince, watching every movement of Beatrix, haunted Esmond and pursued him. The Prince's figure appeared before him in his feverish dreams many times that night. He wished the deed undone for which he had laboured so. He was not the first that has regretted his own act, or brought about his own undoing. Undoing? Should he write that word in his late years? No, on his knees before Heaven, rather be thankful for what then he deemed his misfortune, and which hath caused the whole subsequent happiness of his life.

Esmond's man, honest John Lockwood, had served his master and the family all his life, and the Colonel knew that he could answer for John's fidelity as for his own. John returned with the horses from Rochester betimes the next morning, and the Colonel gave him to understand that on going to Kensington, where he was free of the servants' hall, and indeed courting Miss Beatrix's maid, he was to ask no questions, and betray no surprise, but to vouch stoutly that the young gentleman he should see in a red coat there was my Lord Viscount Castlewood, and that his attendant in grey was Monsieur Baptiste the Frenchman. He was to tell his friends in the kitchen such stories as he remembered of my Lord Viscount's youth at Castlewood; what a wild boy he was; how he used to drill Jack and cane him, before ever he was a soldier; everything, in fine, he knew respecting my Lord Viscount's early days. Jack's ideas of painting had not been much cultivated during his residence in Flanders with his master; and, before my young lord's return, he had been easily got to believe that the picture brought over from Paris, and now hanging in Lady Castlewood's drawing-room, was a perfect likeness of her son, the young lord. And the domestics having all seen the picture many times, and catching but a momentary imperfect glimpse of the two strangers on the night of their arrival, never had a reason to doubt the fidelity of the portrait; and next day, when they saw the original of the piece habited exactly as he was represented in the painting, with the same periwig, ribands, and uniform of the Guard, quite naturally addressed the gentleman as my Lord Castlewood, my Lady Viscountess's son.

The secretary of the night previous was now the Viscount; the Viscount wore the secretary's grey frock; and John Lockwood was instructed to hint to the world below stairs that my Lord being a Papist, and very devout in that religion, his attendant might be no other than his chaplain from Bruxelles; hence, if he took his meals in my Lord's company there was little reason for surprise. Frank was further cautioned to speak English with a foreign accent, which task he performed indifferently well, and this caution was the more necessary because the Prince himself scarce spoke our language like a native of the island: and John Lockwood laughed with the folks below stairs at the manner in which my Lord, after five years abroad, sometimes forget his own tongue and spoke it like a Frenchman. "I warrant," says he, "that with the English beef and beer, his Lordship will soon get back the proper use of his mouth;" and, to do his new lordship justice, he took to beer and beef very kindly.

The Prince drank so much, and was so loud and imprudent in his talk after his drink, that Esmond often trembled for him. His meals were served as much as possible in his own chamber, though frequently he made his appearance in Lady Castlewood's parlour and drawing-room, calling Beatrix "sister," and her Ladyship "mother," or "madam," before the servants. And, choosing to act entirely up to the part of brother and son, the Prince sometimes saluted Mrs. Beatrix and Lady Castlewood with a freedom which his secretary did not like, and which, for his part, set Colonel Esmond tearing with rage.

The guests had not been three days in the house when poor Jack Lockwood came with a rueful countenance to his master, and said: "My Lord—that is, the gentleman—has been tampering with

Mrs. Lucy" (Jack's sweetheart), "and given her guineas and a kiss." I fear that Colonel Esmond's mind was rather relieved than otherwise when he found that the ancillary beauty was the one whom the Prince had selected. His Royal tastes were known to lie that way, and continued so in after life. The heir of one of the greatest names, of the greatest kingdoms, and of the greatest misfortunes in Europe, was often content to lay the dignity of his birth and grief at the wooden shoes of a French chambermaid, and to repent afterwards (for he was very devout) in ashes taken from the dust-pan. 'Tis for mortals such as these that nations suffer, that parties struggle, that warriors fight and bleed. A year afterwards gallant heads were falling, and Nithsdale in escape, and Derwentwater on the scaffold; whilst the heedless ingrate, for whom they risked and lost all, was tippling with his seraglio of mistresses in his *petite maison* of Chaillot.

Blushing to be forced to bear such an errand, Esmond had to go to the Prince and warn him that the girl whom his Highness was bribing was John Lockwood's sweetheart, an honest resolute man, who had served in six campaigns, and feared nothing, and who knew that the person calling himself Lord Castlewood was not his young master: and the Colonel besought the Prince to consider what the effect of a single man's jealousy might be, and to think of other designs he had in hand, more important than the seduction of a waiting-maid, and the humiliation of a brave man.

Ten times, perhaps, in the course of as many days, Mr. Esmond had to warn the royal young adventurer of some imprudence or some freedom. He received these remonstrances very testily, save perhaps in this affair of poor Lockwood's, when he deigned to burst out a-laughing, and said, "What! the *soubrette* has peached to the *amoureux*, and Crispin is angry, and Crispin has served, and Crispin has been a corporal, has he? Tell him we will reward his valour with a pair of colours, and recompense his fidelity."

Colonel Esmond ventured to utter some other words of entreaty, but the Prince, stamping imperiously, cried out, "Assez, milord: je m'ennuye à la prêche; I am not come to London to go to the sermon." And he complained afterwards to Castlewood, that "le petit jaune, le noir Colonel, le Marquis Misanthrope" (by which facetious names his Royal Highness was pleased to designate Colonel Esmond), "fatigued him with his grand airs and virtuous homilies."

The Bishop of Rochester, and other gentlemen engaged in the transaction which had brought the Prince over, waited upon his Royal Highness, constantly asking for my Lord Castlewood on their arrival at Kensington, and being openly conducted to his

Royal Highness in that character, who received them either in my Lady's drawing-room below, or above in his own apartment; and all implored him to quit the house as little as possible, and to wait there till the signal should be given for him to appear. The ladies entertained him at cards, over which amusement he spent many hours in each day and night. He passed many hours more in drinking, during which time he would rattle and talk very agreeably, and especially if the Colonel was absent, whose presence always seemed to frighten him; and the poor "Colonel Noir" took that hint as a command accordingly, and seldom intruded his black face upon the convivial hours of this august young prisoner. Except for those few persons of whom the porter had the list, Lord Castlewood was denied to all friends of the house who waited on his Lordship. The wound he had received had broke out again from his journey on horseback, so the world and the domestics were informed. And Doctor A——,* his physician (I shall not mention his name, but he was physician to the Queen, of the Scots nation, and a man remarkable for his benevolence as well as his wit), gave orders that he should be kept perfectly quiet until the wound should heal. With this gentleman, who was one of the most active and influential of our party, and the others before spoken of, the whole secret lay; and it was kept with so much faithfulness, and the story we told so simple and natural, that there was no likelihood of a discovery except from the imprudence of the Prince himself, and an adventurous levity that we had the greatest difficulty to control. As for Lady Castlewood, although she scarce spoke a word, 'twas easy to gather from her demeanour, and one or two hints she dropped, how deep her mortification was at finding the hero whom she had chosen to worship all her life (and whose restoration had formed almost the most sacred part of her prayers), no more than a man, and not a good one. She thought misfortune might have chastened him; but that instructress had rather rendered him callous than humble. His devotion, which was quite real, kept him from no sin he had a mind to. His talk showed good-humour, gaiety, even wit enough; but there was a levity in his acts and words that he had brought from among those libertine devotees with whom he had been bred, and that shocked the simplicity and purity of the English lady, whose guest he was. Esmond spoke his mind to Beatrix pretty freely about the Prince, getting her brother to put in a word of warning. Beatrix was entirely of their opinion; she thought he was very light, very light and reckless; she could not even see the good looks Colonel Esmond

* There can be very little doubt that the Doctor mentioned by my dear father was the famous Doctor Arbuthnot.—R. E. W.

had spoken of. The Prince had bad teeth, and a decided squint. How could we say he did not squint? His eyes were fine, but there was certainly a cast in them. She rallied him at table with wonderful wit; she spoke of him invariably as of a mere boy; she was more fond of Esmond than ever, praised him to her brother, praised him to the Prince, when his Royal Highness was pleased to sneer at the Colonel, and warmly espoused his cause: "And if your Majesty does not give him the Garter his father had, when the Marquis of Esmond comes to your Majesty's Court, I will hang myself in my own garters, or will cry my eyes out." "Rather than lose those," says the Prince, "he shall be made Archbishop and Colonel of the Guard" (it was Frank Castlewood who told me of this conversation over their supper).

"Yes," cries she, with one of her laughs—I fancy I hear it now. Thirty years afterwards I hear that delightful music. "Yes, he shall be Archbishop of Esmond and Marquis of Canterbury."

"And what will your Ladyship be?" says the Prince; "you have but to choose your place."

"I," says Beatrix, "will be mother of the maids to the Queen of his Majesty King James the Third—Vive le Roy!" and she made him a great curtsey, and drank a part of a glass of wine in his honour.

"The Prince seized hold of the glass and drank the last drop of it," Castlewood said, "and my mother, looking very anxious, rose up and asked leave to retire. But that Trix is my mother's daughter, Harry," Frank continued, "I don't know what a horrid fear I should have of her. I wish—I wish this business were over. You are older than I am, and wiser, and better, and I owe you everything, and would die for you--before George I would; but I wish the end of this were come."

Neither of us very likely passed a tranquil night; horrible doubts and torments racked Esmond's soul; 'twas a scheme of personal ambition, a daring stroke for a selfish end—he knew it. What cared he, in his heart, who was king? Were not his very sympathies and secret convictions on the other side—on the side of People, Parliament, Freedom? And here was he, engaged for a Prince that had scarce heard the word liberty; that priests and women, tyrants by nature, both made a tool of. The misanthrope was in no better humour after hearing that story, and his grim face more black and yellow than ever.

CHAPTER X

WE ENTERTAIN A VERY DISTINGUISHED GUEST AT KENSINGTON

SHOULD any clue be found to the dark intrigues at the latter end of Queen Anne's time, or any historian be inclined to follow it, 'twill be discovered, I have little doubt, that not one of the great personages about the Queen had a defined scheme of policy, independent of that private and selfish interest which each was bent on pursuing: St. John was for St. John, and Harley for Oxford, and Marlborough for John Churchill, always; and according as they could get help from St. Germains or Hanover, they sent over proffers of allegiance to the princes there, or betrayed one to the other: one cause, or one sovereign, was as good as another to them, so that they could hold the best place under him; and, like Lockit and Peachum, the Newgate chiefs in the "Rogue's Opera" Mr. Gay wrote afterwards, had each in his hand documents and proofs of treason which would hang the other, only he did not dare to use the weapon, for fear of that one which his neighbour also carried in his pocket. Think of the great Marlborough, the greatest subject in all the world, a conqueror of princes, that had marched victorious over Germany, Flanders, and France, that had given the law to sovereigns abroad, and been worshipped as a divinity at home, forced to sneak out of England—his credit, honours, places, all taken from him; his friends in the army broke and ruined; and flying before Harley, as abject and powerless as a poor debtor before a bailiff with a writ. A paper, of which Harley got possession, and showing beyond doubt that the Duke was engaged with the Stuart family, was the weapon with which the Treasurer drove Marlborough out of the kingdom. He fled to Antwerp, and began intriguing instantly on the other side, and came back to England, as all know, a Whig and a Hanoverian.

Though the Treasurer turned out of the army and office every man, military or civil, known to be the Duke's friend, and gave the vacant posts among the Tory party; he, too, was playing the double game between Hanover and St. Germains, awaiting the expected catastrophe of the Queen's death to be Master of the

State, and offer it to either family that should bribe him best, or that the nation should declare for. Whichever the King was, Harley's object was to reign over him; and to this end he supplanted the former famous favourite, decried the actions of the war which had made Marlborough's name illustrious, and disdained no more than the great fallen competitor of his, the meanest arts, flatteries, intimidations, that would secure his power. If the greatest satirist the world ever hath seen had writ against Harley, and not for him, what a history had he left behind of the last years of Queen Anne's reign! But Swift, that scorned all mankind, and himself not the least of all, had this merit of a faithful partisan, that he loved those chiefs who treated him well, and stuck by Harley bravely in his fall, as he gallantly had supported him in his better fortune.

Incomparably more brilliant, more splendid, eloquent, accomplished than his rival, the great St. John could be as selfish as Oxford was, and could act the double part as skilfully as ambidextrous Churchill. He whose talk was always of liberty, no more shrank from using persecution and the pillory against his opponents than if he had been at Lisbon and Grand Inquisitor. This lofty patriot was on his knees at Hanover and St. Germains too; notoriously of no religion, he toasted Church and Queen as boldly as the stupid Sacheverel, whom he used and laughed at; and to serve his turn, and to overthrow his enemy, he could intrigue, coax, bully, wheedle, fawn on the Court favourite, and creep up the backstair as silently as Oxford, who supplanted Marlborough, and whom he himself supplanted. The crash of my Lord Oxford happened at this very time whereat my history is now arrived. He was come to the very last days of his power, and the agent whom he employed to overthrow the conqueror of Blenheim, was now engaged to upset the conqueror's conqueror, and hand over the staff of government to Bolingbroke, who had been panting to hold it.

In expectation of the stroke that was now preparing, the Irish regiments in the French service were all brought round about Boulogne in Picardy, to pass over if need were with the Duke of Berwick; the soldiers of France no longer, but subjects of James the Third of England and Ireland King. The fidelity of the great mass of the Scots (though a most active, resolute, and gallant Whig party, admirably and energetically ordered and disciplined, was known to be in Scotland too) was notoriously unshaken in their King. A very great body of Tory clergy, nobility, and gentry, were public partisans of the exiled Prince; and the indifferents might be counted on to cry King George or King James, according as either should prevail. The Queen, especially in her latter days, inclined towards her own family. The Prince was lying actually in London, within a stone's-cast of his sister's palace; the first Minister toppling to his fall, and so tottering that the weakest push of a woman's finger would send him down; and as for Bolingbroke, his successor, we know on whose side his power and his splendid eloquence would be on the day when the Queen should appear openly before her Council and say:—"This, my Lords, is my brother; here is my father's heir, and mine after me."

During the whole of the previous year the Queen had had many and repeated fits of sickness, fever, and lethargy, and her death had been constantly looked for by all her attendants. The Elector of Hanover had wished to send his son, the Duke of Cambridge—to pay his court to his cousin the Queen, the Elector said;—in truth, to be on the spot when death should close her career. Frightened perhaps to have such a *memento mori* under her royal eyes, her Majesty had angrily forbidden the young Prince's coming into England. Either she desired to keep the chances for her brother open yet; or the people about her did not wish to close with the Whig candidate till they could make terms with him. The quarrels of her Ministers before her face at the Council board, the pricks of conscience very likely, the importunities of her Ministers, and constant turmoil and agitation round about her, had weakened and irritated the Princess extremely; her strength was giving way under these continual trials of her temper, and from day to day it was expected she must come to a speedy end of them. Just before Viscount Castlewood and his companion came from France, her Majesty was taken ill. The St. Anthony's fire broke out on the Royal legs; there was no hurry for the presentation of the young lord at Court, or that person who should appear under his name; and my Lord Viscount's wound breaking out opportunely, he was kept conveniently in his chamber until such time as his physician would allow him to bend his knee before the Queen. At the commencement of July that influential lady, with whom it has been mentioned that our party had relations, came frequently to visit her young friend, the Maid of Honour, at Kensington, and my Lord Viscount (the real or supposititious), who was an invalid at Lady Castlewood's house.

On the 27th day of July, the lady in question, who held the most intimate post about the Queen, came in her chair from the Palace hard by, bringing to the little party in Kensington Square intelligence of the very highest importance. The final blow had been struck, and my Lord of Oxford and Mortimer was no longer Treasurer. The staff was as yet given to no successor, though my Lord Bolingbroke would undoubtedly be the man. And now the time was come, the Queen's Abigail said: and now my Lord Castlewood ought to be presented to the Sovereign.

After that scene which Lord Castlewood witnessed and described to his cousin, who passed such a miserable night of mortification and jealousy as he thought over the transaction, no doubt the three persons who were set by nature as protectors over Beatrix came to the same conclusion, that she must be removed from the presence of a man whose desires towards her were expressed only too clearly; and who was no more scrupulous in seeking to gratify them than his father had been before him. I suppose Esmond's mistress, her son, and the Colonel himself, had been all secretly debating this matter in their minds, for when Frank broke out, in his blunt way, with: "I think Beatrix had best be anywhere but here,"—Lady Castlewood said: "I thank you, Frank, I have thought so, too;" and Mr. Esmond, though he only remarked that it was not for him to speak, showed plainly, by the delight on his countenance, how very agreeable that proposal was to him.

"One sees that you think with us, Henry," says the Viscountess, with ever so little of sarcasm in her tone: "Beatrix is best out of this house whilst we have our guest in it, and as soon as this morning's business is done, she ought to quit London."

"What morning's business?" asked Colonel Esmond, not knowing what had been arranged, though in fact the stroke next in importance to that of bringing the Prince, and of having him acknowledged by the Queen, was now being performed at the very moment we three were conversing together.

The Court lady with whom our plan was concerted, and who was a chief agent in it, the Court physician, and the Bishop of Rochester, who were the other two most active participators in our plan, had held many councils in our house at Kensington and elsewhere, as to the means best to be adopted for presenting our young adventurer to his sister the Queen. The simple and easy plan proposed by Colonel Esmond had been agreed to by all parties, which was that on some rather private day, when there were not many persons about the Court, the Prince should appear there as my Lord Castlewood, should be greeted by his sister-in-waiting, and led by that other lady into the closet of the Queen. And according to her Majesty's health or humour, and the circumstances that might arise during the interview, it was to be left to the discretion of those present at it, and to the Prince himself, whether he should declare that it was the Queen's own brother, or the brother of Beatrix Esmond, who kissed her Royal hand. And this plan being determined on, we were all waiting in very much anxiety for the day and signal of execution.

Two mornings after that supper, it being the 27th day of July, the Bishop of Rochester breakfasting with Lady Castlewood and her family, and the meal scarce over, Doctor A.'s coach drove up to our house at Kensington, and the Doctor appeared amongst the party there, enlivening a rather gloomy company; for the mother and daughter had had words in the morning in respect to the transactions of that supper, and other adventures perhaps, and on the day succeeding. Beatrix's haughty spirit brooked remonstrances from no superior, much less from her mother, the gentlest of creatures, whom the girl commanded rather than obeyed. And feeling she was wrong, and that by a thousand coquetries (which she could no more help exercising on every man that came near her, than the sun can help shining on great and small) she had provoked the Prince's dangerous admiration, and allured him to the expression of it, she was only the more wilful and imperious the more she felt her error.

To this party, the Prince being served with chocolate in his bedchamber, where he lay late sleeping away the fumes of his wine, the Doctor came, and by the urgent and startling nature of his news, dissipated instantly that private and minor unpleasantry under which the family of Castlewood was labouring.

He asked for the guest; the guest was above in his own apartment: he bade *Monsieur Baptiste* go up to his master instantly, and requested that *my Lord Viscount Castlewood* would straightway put his uniform on, and come away in the Doctor's coach now at the door.

He then informed Madam Beatrix what her part of the comedy was to be:—"In half-an-hour," says he, "her Majesty and her favourite lady will take the air in the Cedar walk behind the new Banqueting-house. Her Majesty will be drawn in a garden chair, Madam Beatrix Esmond and *her brother*, *my Lord Viscount Castlewood*, will be walking in the private garden (here is Lady Masham's key), and will come unawares upon the Royal party. The man that draws the chair will retire, and leave the Queen, the favourite, and the Maid of Honour and her brother together; Mistress Beatrix will present her brother, and then!—and then, my Lord Bishop will pray for the result of the interview, and his Scots clerk will say Amen! Quick, put on your hood, Madam Beatrix: why doth not his Majesty come down? Such another chance may not present itself for months again."

The Prince was late and lazy, and indeed had all but lost that chance through his indolence. The Queen was actually about to leave the garden just when the party reached it; the Doctor, the Bishop, the Maid of Honour, and her brother, went off together in the physician's coach, and had been gone half-an-hour when Colonel Esmond came to Kensington Square.

The news of this errand, on which Beatrix was gone, of course for a moment put all thoughts of private jealousy out of Colonel Esmond's head. In half-an-hour more the coach returned; the Bishop descended from it first, and gave his arm to Beatrix, who now came out. His Lordship went back into the carriage again, and the Maid of Honour entered the house alone. We were all gazing at her from the upper window, trying to read from her countenance the result of the interview from which she had just come

She came into the drawing-room in a great tremor and very pale; she asked for a glass of water as her mother went to meet her, and after drinking that and putting off her hood, she began to speak:—"We may all hope for the best," says she; "it has cost the Queen a fit. Her Majesty was in her chair in the Cedar walk, accompanied only by Lady ——, when we entered by the private wicket from the west side of the garden, and turned towards her, the Doctor following us. They waited in a side walk hidden by the shrubs, as we advanced towards the chair. My heart throbbed so I scarce could speak; but my Prince whispered, 'Courage, Beatrix,' and marched on with a steady step. His face was a little flushed, but he was not afraid of the danger. He who fought so bravely at Malplaquet fears nothing." Esmond and Castlewood looked at each other at this compliment, neither liking the sound of it.

"The Prince uncovered," Beatrix continued, "and I saw the Queen turning round to Lady Masham, as if asking who these two were. Her Majesty looked very pale and ill, and then flushed up; the favourite made us a signal to advance, and I went up, leading my Prince by the hand, quite close to the chair: 'Your Majesty will give my Lord Viscount your hand to kiss,' says her lady, and the Queen put out her hand, which the Prince kissed, kneeling on his knee, he who should kneel to no mortal man or woman.

"'You have been long from England, my Lord,' says the Queen: 'why were you not here to give a home to your mother and sister?'

"'I am come, madam, to stay now, if the Queen desires me,' says the Prince, with another low bow.

"'You have taken a foreign wife, my Lord, and a foreign religion; was not that of England good enough for you?"

"'In returning to my father's Church,' says the Prince, 'I do not love my mother the less, nor am I the less faithful servant of your Majesty.'

"Here," says Beatrix, "the favourite gave me a little signal with her hand to fall back, which I did, though I died to hear what should pass; and whispered something to the Queen, which made her Majesty start and utter one or two words in a hurried manner, looking towards the Prince, and catching hold with her hand of the arm of her chair. He advanced still nearer towards it; he began to speak very rapidly; I caught the words, 'Father, blessing, forgiveness,'—and then presently the Prince fell on his knees; took from his breast a paper he had there, handed it to the Queen, who, as soon as she saw it, flung up both her arms with a scream, and took away that hand nearest the Prince, and which he endeavoured to kiss. He went on speaking with great animation of gesture, now clasping his hands together on his heart, now opening them as though to say: 'I am here, your brother, in your power.' Lady Masham ran round on the other side of the chair, kneeling too, and speaking with great energy. She clasped the Queen's hand on her side, and picked up the paper her Majesty had let fall. The Prince rose and made a further speech as though he would go; the favourite on the other hand urging her mistress, and then, running back to the Prince, brought him back once more close to the chair. Again he knelt down and took the Queen's hand, which she did not withdraw, kissing it a hundred times; my Lady all the time, with sobs and supplications, speaking over the chair. This while the Queen sat with a stupefied look, crumpling the paper with one hand, as my Prince embraced the other; then of a sudden she uttered several piercing shrieks, and burst into a great fit of hysteric tears and laughter. 'Enough, enough, sir, for this time,' I heard Lady Masham say: and the chairman, who had withdrawn round the Banqueting-room, came back, alarmed by the cries. 'Quick,' says Lady Masham, 'get some help,' and I ran towards the Doctor, who, with the Bishop of Rochester, came up instantly. Lady Masham whispered the Prince he might hope for the very best and to be ready to-morrow; and he hath gone away to the Bishop of Rochester's house to meet several of his friends there. And so the great stroke is struck," says Beatrix, going down on her knees, and clasping her hands. "God save the King! God save the King!"

Beatrix's tale told, and the young lady herself calmed somewhat of her agitation, we asked with regard to the Prince, who was absent with Bishop Atterbury, and were informed that 'twas likely he might remain abroad the whole day. Beatrix's three kinsfolk looked at one another at this intelligence: 'twas clear the same thought was passing through the minds of all.

But who should begin to break the news? Monsieur Baptiste,

that is Frank Castlewood, turned very red, and looked towards Esmond; the Colonel bit his lips, and fairly beat a retreat into the window: it was Lady Castlewood that opened upon Beatrix with the news which we knew would do anything but please her.

"We are glad," says she, taking her daughter's hand, and speaking in a gentle voice, "that the guest is away."

Beatrix drew back in an instant, looking round her at us three, and as if divining a danger. "Why glad?" says she, her breast beginning to heave; "are you so soon tired of him?"

"We think one of us is devilishly too fond of him," cries out Frank Castlewood.

"And which is it—you, my Lord, or is it mamma, who is jealous because he drinks my health? or is it the head of the family" (here she turned with an imperious look towards Colonel Esmond), "who has taken of late to preach the King sermons?"

"We do not say you are too free with his Majesty."

"I thank you, madam," says Beatrix, with a toss of the head and a curtsey.

But her mother continued, with very great calmness and dignity: "At least we have not said so, though we might, were it possible for a mother to say such words to her own daughter, your father's daughter.'

"*Eh? mon père,*" breaks out Beatrix, "was no better than other persons' fathers." And again she looked towards the Colonel.

We all felt a shock as she uttered those two or three French words; her manner was exactly imitated from that of our foreign guest.

"You had not learned to speak French a month ago, Beatrix," says her mother sadly, "nor to speak ill of your father."

Beatrix, no doubt, saw that slip she had made in her flurry, for she blushed crimson: "I have learnt to honour the King," says she, drawing up, "and 'twere as well that others suspected neither his Majesty nor me."

"If you respected your mother a little more," Frank said, "Trix, you would do yourself no hurt."

"I am no child," says she, turning round on him; "we have lived very well these five years without the benefit of your advice or example, and I intend to take neither now. Why does not the head of the house speak?" she went on; "he rules everything here. When his chaplain has done singing the psalms, will his Lordship deliver the sermon? I am tired of the psalms." The Prince had used almost the very same words in regard to Colonel Esmond that the imprudent girl repeated in her wrath.

"You show yourself a very apt scholar, madam," says the

Colonel; and, turning to his mistress, "Did your guest use these words in your Ladyship's hearing, or was it to Beatrix in private that he was pleased to impart his opinion regarding my tiresome sermon?"

"Have you seen him alone?" cries my Lord, starting up with an oath: "by God, have you seen him alone?"

"Were he here, you wouldn't dare so to insult me; no, you would not dare!" cries Frank's sister. "Keep your oaths, my Lord, for your wife; we are not used here to such language. Till you came, there used to be kindness between me and mamma, and I cared for her when you never did, when you were away for years with your horses and your mistress, and your Popish wife."

"By ——," says my Lord, rapping out another oath, "Clotilda is an angel; how dare you say a word against Clotilda?"

Colonel Esmond could not refrain from a smile, to see how easy Frank's attack was drawn off by that feint. "I fancy Clotilda is not the subject in hand," says Mr. Esmond, rather scornfully; "her Ladyship is at Paris, a hundred leagues off, preparing baby-linen. It is about my Lord Castlewood's sister, and not his wife, the question is."

"He is not my Lord Castlewood," says Beatrix, "and he knows he is not; he is Colonel Francis Esmond's son, and no more, and he wears a false title; and he lives on another man's land, and he knows it." Here was another desperate sally of the poor beleaguered garrison, and an *alerte* in another quarter.

"Again, I beg your pardon," says Esmond. "If there are no proofs of my claim, I have no claim. If my father acknowledged no heir, yours was his lawful successor, and my Lord Castlewood hath as good a right to his rank and small estate as any man in England. But that again is not the question, as you know very well; let us bring our talk back to it, as you will have me meddle in it. And I will give you frankly my opinion, that a house where a Prince lies all day, who respects no woman, is no house for a young unmarried lady; that you were better in the country than here; that he is here on a great end, from which no folly should divert him; and that having nobly done your part of this morning, Beatrix, you should retire off the scene a while, and leave it to the other actors of the play."

As the Colonel spoke with a perfect calmness and politeness, such as 'tis to be hoped he hath always shown to women,* his mistress

* My dear father saith quite truly, that his manner towards our sex was uniformly courteous. From my infancy upwards, he treated me with an extreme gentleness, as though I was a little lady. I can scarce remember (though I tried him often) ever hearing a rough word from him, nor was he less grave and kind in his manner to the humblest negresses on his estate. He was familiar with no one except my mother, and it was delightful to witness up to the very last days

stood by him on one side of the table, and Frank Castlewood on the other, hemming in poor Beatrix, that was behind it, and, as it were, surrounding her with our approaches.

Having twice sallied out and been beaten back, she now, as I expected, tried the *ultima ratio* of women, and had recourse to tears. Her beautiful eyes filled with them; I never could bear in her, nor in any woman, that expression of pain:—"I am alone," sobbed she; "you are three against me—my brother, my mother, and you. What have I done, that you should speak and look so unkindly at me? Is it my fault that the Prince should, as you say, admire me? Did I bring him here? Did I do aught but what you bade me, in making him welcome? Did you not tell me that our duty was to die for him? Did you not teach me, mother, night and morning to pray for the King, before even ourselves? What would you have of me, cousin, for you are the chief of the conspiracy against me; I know you are, sir, and that my mother and brother are acting but as you bid them: whither would you have me go?"

"I would but remove from the Prince," says Esmond gravely, "a dangerous temptation. Heaven forbid I should say you would yield: I would only have him free of it. Your honour needs no guardian, please God, but his imprudence doth. He is so far removed from all women by his rank, that his pursuit of them cannot but be unlawful. We would remove the dearest and fairest of our family from the chance of that insult, and that is why we would have you go, dear Beatrix."

"Harry speaks like a book," says Frank, with one of his oaths, "and, by ——, every word he saith is true. You can't help being handsome, Trix; no more can the Prince help following you. My counsel is that you go out of harm's way; for, by the Lord, were the Prince to play any tricks with you, King as he is, or is to be, Harry Esmond and I would have justice of him."

"Are not two such champions enough to guard me?" says Beatrix, something sorrowfully; "sure with you two watching, no evil could happen to me."

"In faith, I think not, Beatrix," says Colonel Esmond; "nor if the Prince knew us would he try."

the confidence between them. He was obeyed eagerly by all under him; and my mother and all her household lived in a constant emulation to please him, and quite a terror lest in any way they should offend him. He was the humblest man, with all this; the least exacting, the most easily contented; and Mr. Benson, our minister at Castlewood, who attended him at the last, ever said: "I know not what Colonel Esmond's doctrine was, but his life and death were those of a devout Christian."—R. E. W.

"But does he know you?" interposed Lady Castlewood, very quiet: "he comes of a country where the pursuit of kings is thought no dishonour to a woman. Let us go, dearest Beatrix! Shall we go to Walcote or to Castlewood? We are best away from the city; and when the Prince is acknowledged, and our champions have restored him, and he hath his own house at St. James's or Windsor, we can come back to ours here. Do you not think so, Harry and Frank?"

Frank and Harry thought with her, you may be sure.

"We will go, then," says Beatrix, turning a little pale; "Lady Masham is to give me warning to-night how her Majesty is, and to-morrow——"

"I think we had best go to-day, my dear," says my Lady Castlewood; "we might have the coach and sleep at Hounslow, and reach home to-morrow. 'Tis twelve o'clock; bid the coach, cousin, be ready at one."

"For shame!" burst out Beatrix, in a passion of tears and mortification. "You disgrace me by your cruel precautions; my own mother is the first to suspect me, and would take me away as my gaoler. I will not go with you, mother; I will go as no one's prisoner. If I wanted to deceive, do you think I could find no means of evading you? My family suspects me. As those mistrust me that ought to love me most, let me leave them; I will go, but I will go alone: to Castlewood, be it. I have been unhappy there and lonely enough; let me go back, but spare me at least the humiliation of setting a watch over my misery, which is a trial I can't bear. Let me go when you will, but alone, or not at all. You three can stay and triumph over my unhappiness, and I will bear it as I have borne it before. Let my gaoler-in-chief go order the coach that is to take me away. I thank you, Henry Esmond, for your share in the conspiracy. All my life long I'll thank you, and remember you, and you, brother, and you, mother, how shall I show my gratitude to you for your careful defence of my honour?"

She swept out of the room with the air of an empress, flinging glances of defiance at us all, and leaving us conquerors of the field, but scared, and almost ashamed of our victory. It did indeed seem hard and cruel that we three should have conspired the banishment and humiliation of that fair creature. We looked at each other in silence; 'twas not the first stroke by many of our actions in that unlucky time, which, being done, we wished undone. We agreed it was best she should go alone, speaking stealthily to one another, and under our breaths, like persons engaged in an act they felt ashamed in doing.

In a half-hour, it might be, after our talk she came back, her countenance wearing the same defiant air which it had borne when she left us. She held a shagreen case in her hand; Esmond knew it as containing his diamonds which he had given to her for her marriage with Duke Hamilton, and which she had worn so splendidly on the inauspicious night of the Prince's arrival. "I have brought back," says she, "to the Marquis of Esmond the present he deigned to make me in days when he trusted me better than now. I will never accept a benefit or a kindness from Henry Esmond more, and I give back these family diamonds, which belonged to one King's mistress, to the gentleman that suspected I would be another. Have you been upon your message of coach-caller, my Lord Marquis? Will you send your valet to see that I do not run away?" We were right, yet, by her manner, she had put us all in the wrong; we were conquerors, yet the honours of the day seemed to be with the poor oppressed girl.

That luckless box containing the stones had first been ornamented with a Baron's coronet, when Beatrix was engaged to the young gentleman from whom she parted, and afterwards the gilt crown of a Duchess figured on the cover, which also poor Beatrix was destined never to wear. Lady Castlewood opened the case mechanically and scarce thinking what she did; and, behold, besides the diamonds, Esmond's present, there lay in the box the enamelled miniature of the late Duke, which Beatrix had laid aside with her mourning when the King came into the house; and which the poor heedless thing very likely had forgotten.

"Do you leave this, too, Beatrix?" says her mother, taking the miniature out, and with a cruelty she did not very often show; but there are some moments when the tenderest women are cruel, and some triumphs which angels can't forego.*

Having delivered this stab, Lady Castlewood was frightened at the effect of her blow. It went to poor Beatrix's heart: she flushed up and passed a handkerchief across her eyes, and kissed the miniature, and put it into her bosom:—"I had forgot it," says she; "my injury made me forget my grief: my mother has recalled both to me. Farewell, mother; I think I never can forgive you; something hath broke between us that no tears nor years can repair. I always said I was alone: you never loved me, never—and were jealous of me from the time I sat on my father's knee.

* This remark shows how unjustly and contemptuously even the best of men will sometimes judge of our sex. Lady Castlewood had no intention of triumphing over her daughter; but from a sense of duty alone pointed out her deplorable wrong.—R. E.

Let me go away, the sooner the better: I can bear to be with you no more."

"Go, child," says her mother, still very stern; "go and bend your proud knees and ask forgiveness; go, pray in solitude for humility and repentance. 'Tis not your reproaches that make me unhappy, 'tis your hard heart, my poor Beatrix: may God soften it, and teach you one day to feel for your mother."

If my mistress was cruel, at least she never could be got to own as much. Her haughtiness quite overtopped Beatrix's; and, if the girl had a proud spirit, I very much fear it came to her by inheritance.

CHAPTER XI

OUR GUEST QUITS US AS NOT BEING HOSPITABLE ENOUGH

BEATRIX'S departure took place within an hour, her maid going with her in the post-chaise, and a man armed on the coach-box to prevent any danger of the road. Esmond and Frank thought of escorting the carriage, but she indignantly refused their company, and another man was sent to follow the coach, and not to leave it till it had passed over Hounslow Heath on the next day. And these two forming the whole of Lady Castlewood's male domestics, Mr. Esmond's faithful John Lockwood came to wait on his mistress during their absence, though he would have preferred to escort Mrs. Lucy, his sweetheart, on her journey into the country.

We had a gloomy and silent meal; it seemed as if a darkness was over the house, since the bright face of Beatrix had been withdrawn from it. In the afternoon came a message from the favourite to relieve us somewhat from this despondency. "The Queen hath been much shaken," the note said; "she is better now, and all things will go well. Let *my Lord Castlewood* be ready against we send for him."

At night there came a second billet: "There hath been a great battle in Council; Lord Treasurer hath broke his staff, and hath fallen never to rise again; no successor is appointed. Lord B—— receives a great Whig company to-night at Golden Square. If he is trimming, others are true; the Queen hath no more fits, but is a-bed now, and more quiet. Be ready against morning, when I still hope all will be well."

The Prince came home shortly after the messenger who bore this billet had left the house. His Royal Highness was so much the better for the Bishop's liquor, that to talk affairs to him now was of little service. He was helped to the Royal bed; he called Castlewood familiarly by his own name; he quite forgot the part upon the acting of which his crown, his safety, depended. 'Twas lucky that my Lady Castlewood's servants were out of the way, and only those heard him who would not betray him. He inquired after the adorable Beatrix, with a Royal hiccup in his voice; he was easily got to bed, and in a minute or two plunged in that deep slumber and forgetfulness with which Bacchus rewards the votaries of that god. We wished Beatrix had been there to see him in his cups. We regretted, perhaps, that she was gone.

One of the party at Kensington Square was fool enough to ride to Hounslow that night, *coram latronibus*, and to the inn which the family used ordinarily in their journeys out of London. Esmond desired my landlord not to acquaint Madam Beatrix with his coming, and had the grim satisfaction of passing by the door of the chamber where she lay with her maid, and of watching her chariot set forth in the early morning. He saw her smile and slip money into the man's hand who was ordered to ride behind the coach as far as Bagshot. The road being open, and the other servant armed, it appeared she dispensed with the escort of a second domestic; and this fellow, bidding his young mistress adieu with many bows, went and took a pot of ale in the kitchen, and returned in company with his brother servant, John Coachman, and his horses, back to London.

They were not a mile out of Hounslow when the two worthies stopped for more drink, and here they were scared by seeing Colonel Esmond gallop by them. The man said in reply to Colonel Esmond's stern question, that his young mistress had sent her duty; only that, no other message: she had had a very good night, and would reach Castlewood by nightfall. The Colonel had no time for further colloquy, and galloped on swiftly to London, having business of great importance there, as my reader very well knoweth. The thought of Beatrix riding away from the danger soothed his mind not a little. His horse was at Kensington Square (honest Dapple knew the way thither well enough) before the tipsy guest of last night was awake and sober.

The account of the previous evening was known all over the town early next day. A violent altercation had taken place before the Queen in the Council Chamber; and all the coffee-houses had their version of the quarrel. The news brought my Lord Bishop early to Kensington Square, where he awaited the waking of his Royal master above stairs, and spoke confidently of having him proclaimed as Prince of Wales and heir to the throne before that day was over. The Bishop had entertained on the previous afternoon certain of the most influential gentlemen of the true British party. His Royal Highness had charmed all, both Scots and English, Papists and Churchmen: "Even Quakers," says he, "were at our meeting; and, if the stranger took a little too much British punch and ale, he will soon grow more accustomed to those liquors; and my Lord Castlewood," says the Bishop with a laugh, "must bear the cruel charge of having been for once in his life a little tipsy. He toasted your lovely sister a dozen times, at which we all laughed," says the Bishop, "admiring so much fraternal affection. —Where is that charming nymph, and why doth she not adorn your Ladyship's tea-table with her bright eyes?"

Her Ladyship said drily, that Beatrix was not at home that morning; my Lord Bishop was too busy with great affairs to trouble himself much about the presence or absence of any lady, however beautiful.

We were yet at table when Dr. A—— came from the Palace with a look of great alarm; the shocks the Queen had had the day before had acted on her severely; he had been sent for, and had ordered her to be blooded. The surgeon of Long Acre had come to cup the Queen, and her Majesty was now more easy and breathed more freely. What made us start at the name of Mr. Aymé?" "Il faut être aimable pour être aimé," says the merry Doctor; Esmond pulled his sleeve, and bade him hush. It was to Aymé's house, after his fatal duel, that my dear Lord Castlewood, Frank's father, had been carried to die.

No second visit could be paid to the Queen on that day at any rate; and when our guest above gave his signal that he was awake, the Doctor, the Bishop, and Colonel Esmond waited upon the Prince's levée, and brought him their news, cheerful or dubious. The Doctor had to go away presently, but promised to keep the Prince constantly acquainted with what was taking place at the Palace hard by. His counsel was, and the Bishop's, that as soon as ever the Queen's malady took a favourable turn, the Prince should be introduced to her bedside; the Council summoned; the guard at Kensington and St. James's, of which two regiments were to be entirely relied on, and one known not to be hostile, would declare for the Prince, as the Queen would before the Lords of her Council, designating him as the heir to her throne.

With locked doors, and Colonel Esmond acting as secretary, the Prince and his Lordship of Rochester passed many hours of this day, composing Proclamations and Addresses to the Country, to the Scots, to the Clergy, to the People of London and England; announcing the arrival of the exile descendant of three Sovereigns, and his acknowledgment by his sister as heir to the throne. Every safeguard for their liberties, the Church and people could ask, was promised to them. The Bishop could answer for the adhesion of very many prelates, who besought of their flocks and brother ecclesiastics to recognise the sacred right of the future Sovereign and to purge the country of the sin of rebellion.

During the composition of these papers more messengers than

one came from the Palace regarding the state of the august patient there lying. At mid-day she was somewhat better; at evening the torpor again seized her and she wandered in her mind. At night Dr. A—— was with us again, with a report rather more favourable; no instant danger at any rate was apprehended. In the course of the last two years her Majesty had had many attacks similar, but more severe.

By this time we had finished a half-dozen of Proclamations (the wording of them so as to offend no parties, and not to give umbrage to Whigs or Dissenters, required very great caution), and the young Prince, who had indeed shown, during a long day's labour, both alacrity at seizing the information given him, and ingenuity and skill in turning the phrases which were to go out signed by his name, here exhibited a good-humour and thoughtfulness that ought to be set down to his credit.

"Were these papers to be mislaid," says he, "or our scheme to come to mishap, my Lord Esmond's writing would bring him to a place where I heartily hope never to see him; and so, by your leave, I will copy the papers myself, though I am not very strong in spelling; and if they are found they will implicate none but the person they most concern;" and so, having carefully copied the Proclamations out, the Prince burned those in Colonel Esmond's handwriting: "And now, and now, gentlemen," says he, "let us go to supper, and drink a glass with the ladies. My Lord Esmond, you will sup with us to-night; you have given us of late too little of your company."

The Prince's meals were commonly served in the chamber which had been Beatrix's bedroom, adjoining that in which he slept. And the dutiful practice of his entertainers was to wait until their Royal guest bade them take their places at table before they sat down to partake of the meal. On this night, as you may suppose, only Frank Castlewood and his mother were in waiting when the supper was announced to receive the Prince; who had passed the whole of the day in his own apartment, with the Bishop as his Minister of State, and Colonel Esmond officiating as Secretary of his Council.

The Prince's countenance wore an expression by no means pleasant, when looking towards the little company assembled, and waiting for him, he did not see Beatrix's bright face there as usual to greet him. He asked Lady Esmond for his fair introducer of yesterday: her Ladyship only cast her eyes down, and said quietly, Beatrix could not be of the supper that night; nor did she show the least sign of confusion, whereas Castlewood turned red, and Esmond was no less embarrassed. I think women have an instinct of dissimulation; they know by nature how to disguise their emotions far better than the most consummate male courtiers can do. Is not the better part of the life of many of them spent in hiding their feelings, in cajoling their tyrants, in masking over with fond smiles and artful gaiety their doubt, or their grief, or their terror?

Our guest swallowed his supper very sulkily; it was not till the second bottle his Highness began to rally. When Lady Castlewood asked leave to depart, he sent a message to Beatrix, hoping she would be present at the next day's dinner, and applied himself to drink, and to talk afterwards, for which there was subject in plenty.

The next day, we heard from our informer at Kensington that the Queen was somewhat better, and had been up for an hour, though she was not well enough yet to receive any visitor.

At dinner a single cover was laid for his Royal Highness; and the two gentlemen alone waited on him. We had had a consultation in the morning with Lady Castlewood, in which it had been determined that, should his Highness ask further questions about Beatrix, he should be answered by the gentlemen of the house.

He was evidently disturbed and uneasy, looking towards the door constantly, as if expecting some one. There came, however, nobody, except honest John Lockwood, when he knocked, with a dish, which those within took from him; so the meals were always arranged, and I believe the council in the kitchen were of opinion that my young lord had brought over a priest, who had converted us all into Papists, and that Papists were like Jews, eating together, and not choosing to take their meals in the sight of Christians.

The Prince tried to cover his displeasure: he was but a clumsy dissembler at that time, and when out of humour could with difficulty keep a serene countenance; and having made some foolish attempts at trivial talk, he came to his point presently, and in as easy a manner as he could, saying to Lord Castlewood, he hoped, he requested, his Lordship's mother and sister would be of the supper that night. As the time hung heavy on him, and he must not go abroad, would not Miss Beatrix hold him company at a game of cards?

At this, looking up at Esmond, and taking the signal from him, Lord Castlewood informed his Royal Highness* that his sister Beatrix was not at Kensington; and that her family had thought it best she should quit the town.

"Not at Kensington!" says he. "Is she ill? she was well yesterday; wherefore should she quit the town? Is it at your orders, my Lord, or Colonel Esmond's, who seems the master of this house?"

* In London we addressed the Prince as Royal Highness invariably; though the women persisted in giving him the title of King.

"Not of this, sir," says Frank very nobly, "only of our house in the country, which he hath given to us. This is my mother's house, and Walcote is my father's, and the Marquis of Esmond knows he hath but to give his word, and I return his to him."

"The Marquis of Esmond!—the Marquis of Esmond," says the Prince, tossing off a glass, "meddles too much with my affairs, and presumes on the service he hath done me. If you want to carry your suit with Beatrix, my Lord, by locking her up in gaol, let me tell you that is not the way to win a woman."

"I was not aware, sir, that I had spoken of my suit to Madam Beatrix to your Royal Highness."

"Bah, bah, monsieur! we need not be a conjurer to see that. It makes itself seen at all moments. You are jealous, my Lord, and the Maid of Honour cannot look at another face without yours beginning to scowl. That which you do is unworthy, monsieur; is inhospitable—is, is lâche, yes, lâche" (he spoke rapidly in French, his rage carrying him away with each phrase): "I come to your house; I risk my life; I pass it in ennui; I repose myself on your fidelity; I have no company but your Lordship's sermons or the conversations of that adorable young lady, and you take her from me, and you, you rest! Merci, monsieur! I shall thank you when I have the means; I shall know to recompense a devotion a little importunate, my Lord—a little importunate. For a month past your airs of protector have annoyed me beyond measure. You deign to offer me the crown, and bid me take it on my knees like King John—eh! I know my history, monsieur, and mock myself of frowning barons. I admire your mistress, and you send her to a Bastile of the Province; I enter your house, and you mistrust me. I will leave it, monsieur; from to-night I will leave it. I have other friends whose loyalty will not be so ready to question mine. If I have garters to give away, 'tis to noblemen who are not so ready to think evil. Bring me a coach and let me quit this place, or let the fair Beatrix return to it. I will not have your hospitality at the expense of the freedom of that fair creature."

This harangue was uttered with rapid gesticulation such as the French use, and in the language of that nation. The Prince striding up and down the room; his face flushed, and his hands trembling with anger. He was very thin and frail from repeated illness and a life of pleasure. Either Castlewood or Esmond could have broke him across their knee, and in half-a-minute's struggle put an end to him; and here he was insulting us both, and scarce deigning to hide from the two, whose honour it most concerned, the passion he felt for the young lady of our family. My Lord Castlewood replied to the Prince's tirade very nobly and simply.

"Sir," says he, "your Royal Highness is pleased to forget that others risk their lives, and for your cause. Very few Englishmen, please God, would dare to lay hands on your sacred person, though none would ever think of respecting ours. Our family's lives are at your service, and everything we have, except our honour."

"Honour! bah, sir, who ever thought of hurting your honour?" says the Prince with a peevish air.

"We implore your Royal Highness never to think of hurting it," says Lord Castlewood with a low bow. The night being warm, the windows were open both towards the Gardens and the Square. Colonel Esmond heard through the closed door the voice of the watchman calling the hour, in the Square on the other side. He opened the door communicating with the Prince's room; Martin, the servant that had rode with Beatrix to Hounslow, was just going out of the chamber as Esmond entered it, and when the fellow was gone, and the watchman again sang his cry of "Past ten o'clock, and a starlight night," Esmond spoke to the Prince in a low voice, and said, "Your Royal Highness hears that man?"

"Après, monsieur?" says the Prince.

"I have but to beckon him from the window, and send him fifty yards, and he returns with a guard of men, and I deliver up to him the body of the person calling himself James the Third, for whose capture Parliament hath offered a reward of £500, as your Royal Highness saw on our ride from Rochester. I have but to say the word, and, by the Heaven that made me, I would say it if I thought the Prince, for his honour's sake, would not desist from insulting ours. But the first gentleman of England knows his duty too well to forget himself with the humblest, or peril his crown for a deed that were shameful if it were done."

"Has your Lordship anything to say," says the Prince, turning to Frank Castlewood, and quite pale with anger; "any threat or any insult, with which you would like to end this agreeable night's entertainment?"

"I follow the head of our house," says Castlewood, bowing gravely. "At what time shall it please the Prince that we should wait upon him in the morning?"

"You will wait on the Bishop of Rochester early, you will bid him bring his coach hither; and prepare an apartment for me in his own house, or in a place of safety. The King will reward you handsomely, never fear, for all you have done in his behalf. I wish you a good night, and shall go to bed, unless it pleases the Marquis of Esmond to call his colleague, the watchman, and that I should pass the night with the Kensington guard. Fare you well; be sure I will remember you. My Lord Castlewood, I can go to bed to-night without need of a chamberlain." And the Prince dismissed us with a grim bow, locking one door as he spoke, that into the supping-room, and the other through which we passed, after us. It led into the small chamber which Frank Castlewood or *Monsieur Baptiste* occupied, and by which Martin entered when Colonel Esmond but now saw him in the chamber.

At an early hour next morning the Bishop arrived, and was closeted for some time with his master in his own apartment, where the Prince laid open to his counsellor the wrongs which, according to his version, he had received from the gentlemen of the Esmond family. The worthy prelate came out from the conference with an air of great satisfaction; he was a man full of resources, and of a most assured fidelity, and possessed of genius, and a hundred good qualities; but captious and of a most jealous temper, that could not help exulting at the downfall of any favourite; and he was pleased in spite of himself to hear that the Esmond Ministry was at an end.

"I have soothed your guest," says he, coming out to the two gentlemen and the widow, who had been made acquainted with somewhat of the dispute of the night before. (By the version we gave her, the Prince was only made to exhibit anger because we doubted of his intentions in respect to Beatrix; and to leave us, because we questioned his honour.) "But I think, all things considered, 'tis as well he should leave this house; and then, my Lady Castlewood," says the Bishop, "my pretty Beatrix may come back to it."

"She is quite as well at home at Castlewood," Esmond's mistress said, "till everything is over."

"You shall have your title, Esmond, that I promise you," says the good Bishop, assuming the airs of a Prime Minister. "The Prince hath expressed himself most nobly in regard of the little difference of last night, and I promise you he hath listened to my sermon, as well as to that of other folks," says the Doctor archly; "he hath every great and generous quality, with perhaps a weakness for the sex which belongs to his family, and hath been known in scores of popular sovereigns from King David downwards."

"My Lord, my Lord!" breaks out Lady Esmond, "the levity with which you speak of such conduct towards our sex shocks me, and what you call weakness I call deplorable sin."

"Sin it is, my dear creature," says the Bishop, with a shrug, taking snuff; "but consider what a sinner King Solomon was, and in spite of a thousand of wives too."

"Enough of this, my Lord," says Lady Castlewood, with a fine blush, and walked out of the room very stately.

The Prince entered it presently with a smile on his face, and if he felt any offence against us on the previous night, at present exhibited none. He offered a hand to each gentleman with great courtesy. "If all your bishops preach so well as Doctor Atterbury," says he, "I don't know, gentlemen, what may happen to me. I spoke very hastily, my lords, last night, and ask pardon of both of you. But I must not stay any longer," says he, "giving umbrage to good friends, or keeping pretty girls away from their homes. My Lord Bishop hath found a safe place for me, hard by at a curate's house, whom the Bishop can trust, and whose wife is so ugly as to be beyond all danger; we will decamp into those new quarters, and I leave you, thanking you for a hundred kindnesses here. Where is my hostess, that I may bid her farewell? to welcome her in a house of my own, soon, I trust, where my friends shall have no cause to quarrel with me."

Lady Castlewood arrived presently, blushing with great grace, and tears filling her eyes as the Prince graciously saluted her. She looked so charming and young, that the Doctor, in his bantering way, could not help speaking of her beauty to the Prince; whose compliment made her blush, and look more charming still.

CHAPTER XII

A GREAT SCHEME, AND WHO BALKED IT

AS characters written with a secret ink come out with the application of fire, and disappear again and leave the paper white, so soon as it is cool; a hundred names of men, high in repute and favouring the Prince's cause, that were writ in our private lists, would have been visible enough on the great roll of the conspiracy, had it ever been laid open under the sun. What crowds would have pressed forward, and subscribed their names and protested their loyalty, when the danger was over! What a number of Whigs, now high in place and creatures of the all-powerful Minister, scorned Mr. Walpole then! If ever a match was gained by the manliness and decision of a few at a moment of danger; if ever one was lost by the treachery and imbecility of those that had the cards in their hands, and might have played them, it was in that momentous game which was enacted in the next three days, and of which the noblest crown in the world was the stake.

From the conduct of my Lord Bolingbroke, those who were interested in the scheme we had in hand saw pretty well that he was not to be trusted. Should the Prince prevail, it was his Lordship's gracious intention to declare for him: should the Hanoverian party bring in their Sovereign, who more ready to go on his knee, and cry "God save King George"? And he betrayed the one Prince and the other; but exactly at the wrong time. When he should have struck for King James, he faltered and coquetted with the Whigs; and having committed himself by the most monstrous professions of devotion, which the Elector rightly scorned, he proved the justice of their contempt for him by flying and taking renegade service with St. Germains, just when he should have kept aloof: and that Court despised him, as the manly and resolute men who established the Elector in England had before done. He signed his own name to every accusation of insincerity his enemies made against him; and the King and the Pretender alike could show proofs of St. John's treachery under his own hand and seal.

Our friends kept a pretty close watch upon his motions, as on those of the brave and hearty Whig party, that made little concealment of theirs. They would have in the Elector, and used every means in their power to effect their end. My Lord Marlborough was now with them. His expulsion from power by the Tories had thrown that great captain at once on the Whig side. We heard he was coming from Antwerp; and, in fact, on the day of the Queen's death, he once more landed on English shore. A great part of the army was always with their illustrious leader; even the Tories in it were indignant at the injustice of the persecution which the Whig officers were made to undergo. The chiefs of these were in London, and at the head of them one of the most intrepid men in the world, the Scots Duke of Argyle, whose conduct on the second day after that to which I have now brought down my history, ended, as such honesty and bravery deserved to end, by establishing the present Royal race on the English throne.

Meanwhile there was no slight difference of opinion amongst the councillors surrounding the Prince, as to the plan his Highness should pursue. His female Minister at Court, fancying she saw some amelioration in the Queen, was for waiting a few days, or hours it might be, until he could be brought to her bedside, and acknowledged as her heir. Mr. Esmond was for having him march thither, escorted by a couple of troops of Horse Guards, and openly presenting himself to the Council. During the whole of the night of the 29th–30th July, the Colonel was engaged with gentlemen of the military profession, whom 'tis needless here to name; suffice it to say that several of them had exceeding high rank in the army, and one of them in especial was a General, who, when he heard the Duke of Marlborough was coming on the other side, waved his crutch over his head with a huzzah, at the idea that he should march out and engage him. Of the three Secretaries of State, we knew that one was devoted to us. The Governor of the Tower was ours; the two companies on duty at Kensington barrack were safe; and we had intelligence, very speedy and accurate, of all that took place at the Palace within.

At noon, on the 30th of July, a message came to the Prince's friends that the Committee of Council was sitting at Kensington Palace, their Graces of Ormonde and Shrewsbury, and Archbishop of Canterbury and the three Secretaries of State, being there assembled. In an hour afterwards, hurried news was brought that the two great Whig Dukes, Argyle and Somerset, had broke into the Council Chamber without a summons, and taken their seat at table. After holding a debate there, the whole party proceeded to the chamber of the Queen, who was lying in great weakness, but still sensible, and the Lords recommended his Grace of Shrewsbury as the fittest person to take the vacant place of Lord Treasurer; her Majesty gave him the staff, as all know. "And now," writ my messenger from Court, "*now or never is the time.*"

Now or never was the time indeed. In spite of the Whig Dukes, our side had still the majority in the Council, and Esmond, to whom the message had been brought (the personage at Court not being aware that the Prince had quitted his lodging in Kensington Square), and Esmond's gallant young aide-de-camp, Frank Castlewood, putting on sword and uniform, took a brief leave of their dear lady, who embraced and blessed them both, and went to her chamber to pray for the issue of the great event which was then pending.

Castlewood sped to the barrack to give warning to the captain of the Guard there; and then went to the "King's Arms" tavern at Kensington, where our friends were assembled, having come by parties of twos and threes, riding or in coaches, and were got together in the upper chamber, fifty-three of them; their servants, who had been instructed to bring arms likewise, being below in the garden of the tavern, where they were served with drink. Out of this garden is a little door that leads into the road of the Palace, and through this it was arranged that masters and servants were to march; when that signal was given, and that Personage appeared, for whom all were waiting. There was in our company the famous officer next in command to the Captain-General of the Forces, his Grace the Duke of Ormonde, who was within at the Council. There were with him two more lieutenant-generals, nine major-generals and brigadiers, seven colonels, eleven Peers of Parliament, and twenty-one members of the House of Commons. The Guard was with us within and without the Palace; the Queen was with us; the Council (save the two Whig Dukes, that must have succumbed); the day was our own, and with a beating heart Esmond walked rapidly to the Mall of Kensington, where he had parted with the Prince on the night before. For three nights the Colonel had not been to bed; the last had been passed summoning the Prince's friends together, of whom the great majority had no sort of inkling of the transaction pending until they were told that he was actually on the spot, and were summoned to strike the blow. The night before and after the altercation with the Prince, my gentleman, having suspicions of his Royal Highness, and fearing lest he should be minded to give us the slip, and fly off after his fugitive beauty, had spent, if the truth must be told, at the "Greyhound" tavern, over against my Lady Castlewood's house in Kensington Square, with an eye on the door, lest the Prince should escape from it. The night before that he had passed in his boots at the "Crown" at Hounslow, where he must watch forsooth all night, in order to get one moment's glimpse of Beatrix in the morning. And fate had decreed that he was to have a fourth night's ride and wakefulness before his business was ended.

He ran to the curate's house in Kensington Mall, and asked for Mr. Bates, the name the Prince went by. The curate's wife said Mr. Bates had gone abroad very early in the morning in his boots, saying he was going to the Bishop of Rochester's house at Chelsey. But the Bishop had been at Kensington himself two hours ago to seek for Mr. Bates, and had returned in his coach to his own house, when he heard that the gentleman was gone thither to seek him.

This absence was most unpropitious, for an hour's delay might cost a kingdom; Esmond had nothing for it but to hasten to the "King's Arms," and tell the gentlemen there assembled that Mr. George (as we called the Prince there) was not at home, but that Esmond would go fetch him; and taking a General's coach that happened to be there, Esmond drove across the country to Chelsey, to the Bishop's house there.

The porter said two gentlemen were with his Lordship, and Esmond ran past this sentry up to the locked door of the Bishop's study, at which he rattled, and was admitted presently. Of the Bishop's guests one was a brother prelate, and the other the Abbé G——.

"Where is Mr. George?" says Mr. Esmond; "now is the time." The Bishop looked scared: "I went to his lodging," he said, "and they told me he was come hither. I returned as quick as coach would carry me; and he hath not been here."

The Colonel burst out with an oath; that was all he could say to their reverences: ran down the stairs again, and bidding the coachman, an old friend and fellow campaigner, drive as if he was charging the French with his master at Wynendael—they were back at Kensington in half-an-hour.

Again Esmond went to the curate's house. Mr. Bates had not returned. The Colonel had to go with this blank errand to the gentlemen at the "King's Arms," that were grown very impatient by this time.

Out of the window of the tavern, and looking over the garden wall, you can see the green before Kensington Palace, the Palace gate (round which the Ministers' coaches were standing), and the barrack building. As we were looking out from this window in gloomy discourse, we heard presently trumpets blowing, and some of us ran to the window of the front-room, looking into the High Street of Kensington, and saw a regiment of horse coming.

"It's Ormonde's Guards," says one.

"No, by God, it's Argyle's old regiment!" says my General, clapping down his crutch.

It was, indeed, Argyle's regiment that was brought from Westminster, and that took the place of the regiment at Kensington on which we could rely.

"O Harry!" says one of the Generals there present, "you were born under an unlucky star; I begin to think that there's no Mr. George, nor Mr. Dragon either. 'Tis not the peerage I care for, for our name is so ancient and famous, that merely to be called Lord Lydiard would do me no good; but 'tis the chance you promised me of fighting Marlborough."

As we were talking, Castlewood entered the room with a disturbed air.

"What news, Frank?" says the Colonel. "Is Mr. George coming at last?"

"Damn him, look here!" says Castlewood, holding out a paper. "I found it in the book—the what you call it, 'Eikum Basilikum,'—that villain Martin put it there—he said his young mistress bade him. It was directed to me, but it was meant for him I know, and I broke the seal and read it."

The whole assembly of officers seemed to swim away before Esmond's eyes as he read the paper; all that was written on it was:—"Beatrix Esmond is sent away to prison, to Castlewood, where she will pray for happier days."

"Can you guess where he is?" says Castlewood.

"Yes," says Colonel Esmond. He knew full well; Frank knew full well: our instinct told whither that traitor had fled.

He had courage to turn to the company and say: "Gentlemen, I fear very much that Mr. George will not be here to-day; something hath happened—and—and—I very much fear some accident may befall him, which must keep him out of the way. Having had your noon's draught, you had best pay the reckoning and go home; there can be no game where there is no one to play it."

Some of the gentlemen went away without a word, others called to pay their duty to her Majesty and ask for her health. The little army disappeared into the darkness out of which it had been called; there had been no writings, no paper to implicate any man. Some few officers and members of Parliament had been invited over night to breakfast at the "King's Arms," at Kensington; and they had called for their bill and gone home.

CHAPTER XIII

AUGUST 1ST, 1714

"DOES my mistress know of this?" Esmond asked of Frank, as they walked along.

"My mother found the letter in the book, on the toilet-table. She had writ it ere she had left home," Frank said. "Mother met her on the stairs, with her hand upon the door, trying to enter, and never left her after that till she went away. He did not think of looking at it there, nor had Martin the chance of telling him. I believe the poor devil meant no harm, though I half killed him; he thought 'twas to Beatrix's brother he was bringing the letter."

Frank never said a word of reproach to me for having brought the villain amongst us. As we knocked at the door I said, "When will the horses be ready?" Frank pointed with his cane, they were turning the street that moment.

We went up and bade adieu to our mistress; she was in a dreadful state of agitation by this time, and that Bishop was with her whose company she was so fond of.

"Did you tell him, my Lord," says Esmond, "that Beatrix was at Castlewood?" The Bishop blushed and stammered: "Well," says he, "I—— "

"You served the villain right," broke out Mr. Esmond, "and he has lost a crown by what you told him."

My mistress turned quite white. "Henry, Henry," says she, "do not kill him!"

"It may not be too late," says Esmond; "he may not have gone to Castlewood; pray God, it is not too late." The Bishop was breaking out with some *banale* phrases about loyalty, and the sacredness of the Sovereign's person; but Esmond sternly bade him hold his tongue, burn all papers, and take care of Lady Castlewood; and in five minutes he and Frank were in the saddle, John Lockwood behind them, riding towards Castlewood at a rapid pace.

We were just got to Alton, when who should meet us but old Lockwood, the porter from Castlewood, John's father, walking by the side of the Hexton flying-coach, who slept the night at

Alton. Lockwood said his young mistress had arrived at home on Wednesday night, and this morning, Friday, had despatched him with a packet for my Lady at Kensington, saying the letter was of great importance.

We took the freedom to break it, while Lockwood stared with wonder, and cried out his "Lord bless me's," and "Who'd a thought it's," at the sight of his young lord, whom he had not seen these seven years.

The packet from Beatrix contained no news of importance at all. It was written in a jocular strain, affecting to make light of her captivity. She asked whether she might have leave to visit Mrs. Tusher, or to walk beyond the court and the garden wall. She gave news of the peacocks, and a fawn she had there. She bade her mother send her certain gowns and smocks by old Lockwood; she sent her duty to a certain Person, if certain other persons permitted her to take such a freedom; how that, as she was not able to play cards with him, she hoped he would read good books, such as Doctor Atterbury's sermons and "Eikon Basiliké:" she was going to read good books; she thought her pretty mamma would like to know she was not crying her eyes out.

"Who is in the house besides you, Lockwood?" says the Colonel.

"There be the laundry-maid, and the kitchen-maid, Madam Beatrix's maid, the man from London, and that be all; and he sleepeth in my lodge away from the maids," says old Lockwood.

Esmond scribbled a line with a pencil on the note, giving it to the old man, and bidding him go on to his lady. We knew why Beatrix had been so dutiful on a sudden, and why she spoke of "Eikon Basiliké." She writ this letter to put the Prince on the scent, and the porter out of the way.

"We have a fine moonlight night for riding on," says Esmond; "Frank, we may reach Castlewood in time yet." All the way along they made inquiries at the post-houses, when a tall young gentleman in a grey suit, with a light brown periwig, just the colour of my Lord's, had been seen to pass. He had set off at six that morning, and we at three in the afternoon. He rode almost as quickly as we had done; he was seven hours ahead of us still when we reached the last stage.

We rode over Castlewood Downs before the breaking of dawn. We passed the very spot where the car was upset fourteen years since, and Mohun lay. The village was not up yet, nor the forge lighted, as we rode through it, passing by the elms, where the rooks were still roosting, and by the church, and over the bridge. We got off our horses at the bridge and walked up to the gate.

"If she is safe," says Frank, trembling, and his honest eyes filling with tears, "a silver statue to Our Lady!" He was going to rattle at the great iron knocker on the oak gate; but Esmond stopped his kinsman's hand. He had his own fears, his own hopes, his own despairs and griefs, too; but he spoke not a word of these to his companion, or showed any signs of emotion.

He went and tapped at the little window at the porter's lodge, gently, but repeatedly, until the man came to the bars.

"Who's there?" says he, looking out. It was the servant from Kensington.

"My Lord Castlewood and Colonel Esmond," we said, from below. "Open the gate and let us in without any noise."

"My Lord Castlewood?" says the other; "my Lord's here, and in bed."

"Open, d—— you," says Castlewood, with a curse.

"I shall open to no one," says the man, shutting the glass window as Frank drew a pistol. He would have fired at the porter, but Esmond again held his hand.

"There are more ways than one," says he, "of entering such a great house as this." Frank grumbled that the west gate was half-a-mile round. "But I know of a way that's not a hundred yards off," says Mr Esmond; and leading his kinsman close along the wall, and by the shrubs which had now grown thick on what had been an old moat about the house, they came to the buttress, at the side of which the little window was, which was Father Holt's private door. Esmond climbed up to this easily, broke a pane that had been mended, and touched the spring inside, and the two gentlemen passed in that way, treading as lightly as they could; and so going through the passage into the court, over which the dawn was now reddening, and where the fountain plashed in the silence.

They sped instantly to the porter's lodge, where the fellow had not fastened his door that led into the court; and pistol in hand came upon the terrified wretch, and bade him be silent. Then they asked him (Esmond's head reeled, and he almost fell as he spoke) when Lord Castlewood had arrived? He said on the previous evening, about eight of the clock.—"And what then?"—His Lordship supped with his sister.—"Did the man wait?"—Yes, he and my Lady's maid both waited: the other servants made the supper; and there was no wine, and they could give his Lordship but milk, at which he grumbled; and—and Madam Beatrix kept Miss Lucy always in the room with her. And there being a bed across the court in the Chaplain's room, she had arranged my Lord was to sleep there. Madam Beatrix had come downstairs laughing with the maids, and had locked herself in, and my Lord had stood for a while talking to her through the door, and she laughing at him. And then he paced the court awhile, and she came again to the upper window; and my Lord implored her to come down and walk in the room; but she would not, and laughed at him again, and shut the window; and so my Lord, uttering what seemed curses, but in a foreign language, went to the Chaplain's room to bed.

"Was this all?"—"All," the man swore upon his honour; all, as he hoped to be saved.—"Stop, there was one thing more. My Lord, on arriving, and once or twice during supper, did kiss his sister, as was natural, and she kissed him." At this Esmond ground his teeth with rage, and well-nigh throttled the amazed miscreant who was speaking, whereas Castlewood, seizing hold of his cousin's hand, burst into a great fit of laughter.

"If it amuses thee," says Esmond in French, "that your sister should be exchanging of kisses with a stranger, I fear poor Beatrix will give thee plenty of sport."—Esmond darkly thought, how Hamilton, Ashburnham, had before been masters of those roses that the young Prince's lips were now feeding on. He sickened at that notion. Her cheek was desecrated, her beauty tarnished; shame and honour stood between it and him. The love was dead within him; had she a crown to bring him with her love, he felt that both would degrade him.

But this wrath against Beatrix did not lessen the angry feelings of the Colonel against the man who had been the occasion if not the cause of the evil. Frank sat down on a stone bench in the courtyard, and fairly fell asleep, while Esmond paced up and down the court, debating what should ensue. What mattered how much or how little had passed between the Prince and the poor faithless girl? They were arrived in time perhaps to rescue her person, but not her mind: had she not instigated the young Prince to come to her, suborned servants, dismissed others, so that she might communicate with him? The treacherous heart within her had surrendered, though the place was safe; and it was to win this that he had given a life's struggle and devotion; this, that she was ready to give away for the bribe of a coronet or a wink of the Prince's eye.

When he had thought his thoughts out he shook up poor Frank from his sleep, who rose yawning, and said he had been dreaming of Clotilda. "You must back me," says Esmond, "in what I am going to do. I have been thinking that yonder scoundrel may have been instructed to tell that story, and that the whole of it may be a lie; if it be, we shall find it out from the gentleman who is asleep yonder. See if the door leading to my Lady's rooms" (so we called the rooms at the north-west angle of the house), "see if the door is barred as he saith." We tried; it was indeed as the lacquey had said, closed within.

"It may have been opened and shut afterwards," says poor Esmond; "the foundress of our family let our ancestor in in that way."

"What will you do, Harry, if—if what that fellow saith should turn out untrue?" The young man looked scared and frightened into his kinsman's face; I dare say it wore no very pleasant expression.

"Let us first go see whether the two stories agree," says Esmond; and went in at the passage and opened the door into what had been his own chamber now for well-nigh five-and-twenty years. A candle was still burning, and the Prince asleep dressed on the bed—Esmond did not care for making a noise. The Prince started up in his bed, seeing two men in his chamber: "Qui est là?" says he, and took a pistol from under his pillow.

"It is the Marquis of Esmond," says the Colonel, "come to welcome his Majesty to his house of Castlewood, and to report of what hath happened in London. Pursuant to the King's orders, I passed the night before last, after leaving his Majesty, in waiting upon the friends of the King. It is a pity that his Majesty's desire to see the country and to visit our poor house should have caused the King to quit London without notice yesterday, when the opportunity happened which in all human probability may not occur again; and had the King not chosen to ride to Castlewood, the Prince of Wales might have slept at St. James's."

"'Sdeath! gentlemen," says the Prince, starting off his bed, whereon he was lying in his clothes, "the Doctor was with me yesterday morning, and after watching by my sister all night, told me I might not hope to see the Queen."

"It would have been otherwise," says Esmond with another bow; "as, by this time, the Queen may be dead in spite of the Doctor. The Council was met, a new Treasurer was appointed, the troops were devoted to the King's cause; and fifty loyal gentlemen of the greatest names of this kingdom were assembled to accompany the Prince of Wales, who might have been the acknowledged heir of the throne, or the possessor of it by this time, had your Majesty not chosen to take the air. We were ready: there was only one person that failed us, your Majesty's gracious——"

"Morbleu, monsieur, you give me too much Majesty," said the Prince, who had now risen up and seemed to be looking to one of us to help him to his coat. But neither stirred.

"We shall take care," says Esmond, "not much oftener to offend in that particular."

"What mean you, my Lord?" says the Prince, and muttered something about a *guet-à-pens*, which Esmond caught up.

"The snare, sir," said he, "was not of our laying; it is not we that invited you. We came to avenge, and not to compass, the dishonour of our family."

"Dishonour! Morbleu, there has been no dishonour," says the Prince, turning scarlet, "only a little harmless playing."

"That was meant to end seriously."

"I swear," the Prince broke out impetuously, "upon the honour of a gentleman, my lords——"

"That we arrived in time. No wrong hath been done, Frank," says Colonel Esmond, turning round to young Castlewood, who stood at the door as the talk was going on. "See! here is a paper whereon his Majesty hath deigned to commence some verses in honour, or dishonour, of Beatrix. Here is 'Madame' and 'Flamme,' 'Cruelle' and 'Rebelle,' and 'Amour' and 'Jour,' in the Royal writing and spelling. Had the Gracious lover been happy, he had not passed his time in sighing." In fact, and actually as he was speaking, Esmond cast his eyes down towards the table, and saw a paper on which my young Prince had been scrawling a madrigal, that was to finish his charmer on the morrow.

"Sir," says the Prince, burning with rage (he had assumed his Royal coat unassisted by this time), "did I come here to receive insults?"

"To confer them, may it please your Majesty," says the Colonel, with a very low bow, "and the gentlemen of our family are come to thank you."

"*Malédiction!*" says the young man, tears starting into his eyes with helpless rage and mortification. "What will you with me, gentlemen?"

"If your Majesty will please to enter the next apartment," says Esmond, preserving his grave tone, "I have some papers there which I would gladly submit to you, and by your permission I will lead the way;" and, taking the taper up, and backing before the Prince with very great ceremony, Mr. Esmond passed into the little Chaplain's room, through which we had just entered into the house. "Please to set a chair for his Majesty, Frank," says the Colonel to his companion, who wondered almost as much at this scene, and was as much puzzled by it, as the other actor in it. Then going to the crypt over the mantelpiece, the Colonel opened it, and drew thence the papers which so long had lain there.

"Here, may it please your Majesty," says he, "is the Patent of Marquis sent over by your Royal Father at St. Germains to Viscount Castlewood, my father: here is the witnessed certificate of my father's marriage to my mother, and of my birth and christening; I was christened of that religion of which your sainted sire gave all through life so shining an example. These are my titles, dear Frank, and this what I do with them: here go Baptism and Marriage, and here the Marquisate and the August Sign-Manual, with which your predecessor was pleased to honour our race." And as Esmond spoke he set the papers burning in the brazier. "You will please, sir, to remember," he continued, "that our family hath ruined itself by fidelity to yours: that my grandfather spent his estate, and gave his blood and his son to die for your service; that my dear lord's grandfather (for lord you are now, Frank, by right and title too) died for the same cause; that my poor kinswoman, my father's second wife, after giving away her honour to your wicked perjured race, sent all her wealth to the King; and got in return that precious title that lies in ashes, and this inestimable yard of blue riband. I lay this at your feet and stamp upon it: I draw this sword, and break it and deny you; and, had you completed the wrong you designed us, by Heaven I would have driven it through your heart, and no more pardoned you than your father pardoned Monmouth. Frank will do the same, won't you, cousin?"

Frank, who had been looking on with a stupid air at the papers as they flamed in the old brazier, took out his sword and broke it, holding his head down:—"I go with my cousin," says he, giving Esmond a grasp of the hand. Marquis or not, by ——, I stand by him any day. I beg your Majesty's pardon for swearing; that is—that is—I'm for the Elector of Hanover. It's all your Majesty's own fault. The Queen's dead most likely by this time. And you might have been King if you hadn't come dangling after Trix."

"Thus to lose a crown," says the young Prince, starting up, and speaking French in his eager way; "to lose the loveliest woman in the world; to lose the loyalty of such hearts as yours, is not this, my lords, enough of humiliation?—Marquis, if I go on my knees will you pardon me?—No, I can't do that, but I can offer you reparation, that of honour, that of gentlemen. Favour me by crossing the sword with mine: yours is broke—see, yonder in the armoire are two;" and the Prince took them out as eager as a boy, and held them towards Esmond:—"Ah! you will? Merci, monsieur, merci!"

Extremely touched by this immense mark of condescension and repentance for wrong done, Colonel Esmond bowed down so low as almost to kiss the gracious young hand that conferred on him such an honour, and took his guard in silence. The swords were no sooner met, than Castlewood knocked up Esmond's with the blade of his own, which he had broke off short at the shell; and the Colonel falling back a step dropped his point with another very low bow, and declared himself perfectly satisfied.

"Eh bien, Vicomte!" says the young Prince, who was a boy, and a French boy, "il ne nous reste qu'une chose à faire:" he placed his sword upon the table, and the fingers of his two hands upon his breast:—"We have one more thing to do," says he; "you do not divine it?" He stretched out his arms:—"*Embrassons nous!*"

The talk was scarce over when Beatrix entered the room:—What came she to seek there? She started and turned pale at the sight of her brother and kinsman, drawn swords, broken sword-blades, and papers yet smouldering in the brazier.

"Charming Beatrix," says the Prince, with a blush which became him very well, "these lords have come a-horseback from London, where my sister lies in a despaired state, and where her successor makes himself desired. Pardon me for my escapade of last evening. I had been so long a prisoner, that I seized the occasion of a promenade on horseback, and my horse naturally bore me towards you. I found you a queen in your little court, where you deigned to entertain me. Present my homages to your maids of honour. I sighed as you slept, under the window of your chamber, and then retired to seek rest in my own. It was there that these gentlemen agreeably roused me. Yes, milords, for that is a happy day that makes a Prince acquainted, at whatever cost to his vanity, with such a noble heart as that of the Marquis of Esmond. Mademoiselle, may we take your coach to town? I saw it in the hangar, and this poor Marquis must be dropping with sleep."

"Will it please the King to breakfast before he goes?" was all Beatrix could say. The roses had shuddered out of her cheeks; her eyes were glaring; she looked quite old. She came up to Esmond and hissed out a word or two:—"If I did not love you before, cousin," says she, "think how I love you now." If words could stab, no doubt she would have killed Esmond; she looked at him as if she could.

But her keen words gave no wound to Mr. Esmond; his heart was too hard. As he looked at her, he wondered that he could ever have loved her. His love of ten years was over; it fell down dead on the spot, at the Kensington tavern, where Frank brought him the note out of "Eikon Basiliké." The Prince blushed and bowed low, as she gazed at him, and quitted the chamber. I have never seen her from that day.

Horses were fetched and put to the chariot presently. My

THE LAST OF BEATRIX.

Lord rode outside, and as for Esmond he was so tired that he was no sooner in the carriage than he fell asleep, and never woke till night, as the coach came into Alton.

As we drove to the "Bell Inn" comes a mitred coach with our old friend Lockwood beside the coachman. My Lady Castlewood and the Bishop were inside; she gave a little scream when she saw us. The two coaches entered the inn almost together; the landlord and people coming out with lights to welcome the visitors.

We in our coach sprang out of it, as soon as ever we saw the dear lady, and above all, the Doctor in his cassock. What was the news? Was there yet time? Was the Queen alive? These questions were put hurriedly, as Boniface stood waiting before his noble guests to bow them up the stair.

"Is she safe?" was what Lady Castlewood whispered in a flutter to Esmond.

"All's well, thank God," says he, as the fond lady took his hand and kissed it, and called him her preserver and her dear. *She* wasn't thinking of Queens and crowns.

The Bishop's news was reassuring; at least all was not lost; the Queen yet breathed, or was alive when they left London, six hours since. ("It was Lady Castlewood who insisted on coming," the Doctor said.) Argyle had marched up regiments from Portsmouth, and sent abroad for more; the Whigs were on the alert, a pest on them (I am not sure but the Bishop swore as he spoke), and so too were our people. And all might be saved, if only the Prince could be at London in time. We called for horses, instantly to return to London. We never went up poor crestfallen Boniface's stairs, but into our coaches again. The Prince and his Prime Minister in one, Esmond in the other, with only his dear mistress as a companion.

Castlewood galloped forwards on horseback to gather the Prince's friends and warn them of his coming. We travelled through the night—Esmond discoursing to his mistress of the events of the last twenty-four hours: of Castlewood's ride and his; of the Prince's generous behaviour and their reconciliation. The night seemed short enough; and the starlit hours passed away serenely in that fond company.

So we came along the road; the Bishop's coach heading ours; and, with some delays in procuring horses, we got to Hammersmith about four o'clock on Sunday morning, the first of August, and half-an-hour after, it being then bright day, we rode by my Lady Warwick's house, and so down the street of Kensington.

Early as the hour was, there was a bustle in the street, and many people moving to and fro. Round the gate leading to the Palace, where the guard is, there was especially a great crowd. And the coach ahead of us stopped, and the Bishop's man got down to know what the concourse meant.

There presently came from out of the gate—Horse Guards with their trumpets, and a company of heralds with their tabards. The trumpets blew, and the herald-at-arms came forward and proclaimed GEORGE, by the Grace of God, of Great Britain, France, and Ireland, King, Defender of the Faith. And the people shouted, God save the King!

Among the crowd shouting and waving their hats, I caught sight of one sad face, which I had known all my life, and seen under many disguises. It was no other than poor Mr. Holt's, who had slipped over to England to witness the triumph of the good cause; and now beheld its enemies victorious, amidst the acclamations of the English people. The poor fellow had forgot to huzzah or to take his hat off, until his neighbours in the crowd remarked his want of loyalty, and cursed him for a Jesuit in disguise, when he ruefully uncovered and began to cheer. Sure he was the most unlucky of men: he never played a game but he lost it; or engaged in a conspiracy but 'twas certain to end in defeat. I saw him in Flanders after this, whence he went to Rome to the headquarters of his Order; and actually reappeared among us in America, very old, and busy, and hopeful. I am not sure that he did not assume the hatchet and moccasins there; and, attired in a blanket and war-paint, skulk about a missionary amongst the Indians. He lies buried in our neighbouring province of Maryland now, with a cross over him, and a mound of earth above him; under which that unquiet spirit is for ever at peace.

With the sound of King George's trumpets, all the vain hopes of the weak and foolish young Pretender were blown away; and with that music, too, I may say, the drama of my own life was ended. That happiness, which hath subsequently crowned it, cannot be written in words; 'tis of its nature sacred and secret, and not to be spoken of, though the heart be ever so full of thankfulness, save to Heaven and the One Ear alone—to one fond being, the truest and tenderest and purest wife ever man was blessed with. As I think of the immense happiness which was in store for me, and of the depth and intensity of that love which, for so many years, hath blessed me, I own to a transport of wonder and gratitude for such a boon—nay, am thankful to have been endowed with a heart capable of feeling and knowing the immense beauty and value of the gift which God hath bestowed upon me. Sure, love *vincit omnia;* is immeasurably above all ambition, more precious than wealth, more noble than name. He knows not life who knows not that: he hath not felt the highest faculty of the soul who hath not enjoyed it. In the name of my wife I write the completion of hope, and the summit of happiness. To have such a love is the one blessing, in comparison of which all earthly joy is of no value; and to think of her, is to praise God.

It was at Bruxelles, whither we retreated after the failure of our plot—our Whig friends advising us to keep out of the way—that the great joy of my life was bestowed upon me, and that my dear mistress became my wife. We had been so accustomed to an extreme intimacy and confidence, and had lived so long and tenderly together, that we might have gone on to the end without thinking of a closer tie; but circumstances brought about that event which so prodigiously multiplied my happiness and hers (for which I humbly thank Heaven), although a calamity befell us, which, I blush to think, hath occurred more than once in our house. I know not what infatuation of ambition urged the beautiful and wayward woman, whose name hath occupied so many of these pages, and who was served by me with ten years of such constant fidelity and passion; but ever after that day at Castlewood, when we rescued her, she persisted in holding all her family as her enemies, and left us, and escaped to France, to what a fate I disdain to tell. Nor was her son's house a home for my dear mistress; my poor Frank was weak, as perhaps all our race hath been, and led by women. Those around him were imperious, and in a terror of his mother's influence over him, lest he should recant, and deny the creed which he had adopted by their persuasion. The difference of their religion separated the son and the mother: my dearest mistress felt that she was severed from her children and alone in the world—alone but for one constant servant on whose fidelity, praised be Heaven, she could count. 'Twas after a scene of ignoble quarrel on the part of Frank's wife and mother (for the poor lad had been made to marry the whole of that German family with whom he had connected himself), that I found my mistress one day in tears, and then besought her to confide herself to the care and devotion of one who, by God's help, would never forsake her. And then the tender matron, as beautiful in her autumn, and as pure as virgins in their spring, with blushes of love and "eyes of meek surrender," yielded to my respectful importunity, and consented to share my home. Let the last words I write thank her, and bless her who hath blessed it.

By the kindness of Mr. Addison, all danger of prosecution, and every obstacle against our return to England, was removed; and my son Frank's gallantry in Scotland made his peace with the King's Government. But we two cared no longer to live in England: and Frank formally and joyfully yielded over to us the possession of that estate which we now occupy, far away from Europe and its troubles, on the beautiful banks of the Potomac, where we have built a new Castlewood, and think with grateful hearts of our old home. In our Transatlantic country we have a season, the calmest and most delightful of the year, which we call the Indian summer: I often say the autumn of our life resembles that happy and serene weather, and am thankful for its rest and its sweet sunshine. Heaven hath blessed us with a child, which each parent loves for her resemblance to the other. Our diamonds are turned into ploughs and axes for our plantations; and into negroes, the happiest and merriest, I think, in all this country: and the only jewel by which my wife sets any store, and from which she hath never parted, is that gold button she took from my arm on the day when she visited me in prison, and which she wore ever after, as she told me, on the tenderest heart in the world.

THE LECTURES

THE ENGLISH HUMOURISTS
OF THE
EIGHTEENTH CENTURY

THE ENGLISH HUMOURISTS

OF THE

EIGHTEENTH CENTURY*

SWIFT

IN treating of the English Humourists of the past age, it is of the men and of their lives, rather than of their books, that I ask permission to speak to you; and in doing so, you are aware that I cannot hope to entertain you with a merely humourous or facetious story. Harlequin without his mask is known to present a very sober countenance, and was himself, the story goes, the melancholy patient whom the doctor advised to go and see Harlequin †—a man full of cares and perplexities like the rest of us, whose Self must always be serious to him, under whatever mask or disguise or uniform he presents it to the public. And as all of you here must needs be grave when you think of your own past and present, you will not look to find, in the histories of those whose lives and feelings I am going to try and describe to you, a story that is otherwise than serious, and often very sad. If Humour only meant laughter, you would scarcely feel more interest about humourous writers than about the private life of poor Harlequin just mentioned, who possesses in common with these the power of making you laugh. But the men regarding whose lives and stories your kind presence here shows that you have curiosity and sympathy, appeal to a great number of our other faculties, besides our mere sense of ridicule. The humourous writer professes to awaken and direct your love,

* The notes to these lectures were chiefly written by James Hannay. A few corrections and additions, chiefly due to later investigations, are now inserted; for which the publishers have to thank Mr. Austin Dobson, Mr. Sidney Lee, and Mr. L. Stephen.

† The anecdote is frequently told of our performer John Rich (1682?–1761), who first introduced pantomimes, and himself acted Harlequin.

your pity, your kindness—your scorn for untruth, pretension, imposture—your tenderness for the weak, the poor, the oppressed, the unhappy. To the best of his means and ability he comments on all the ordinary actions and passions of life almost. He takes upon himself to be the week-day preacher, so to speak. Accordingly, as he finds, and speaks, and feels the truth best, we regard him, esteem him—sometimes love him. And, as his business is to mark other people's lives and peculiarities, we moralise upon *his* life when he has gone—and yesterday's preacher becomes the text for to-day's sermon.

Of English parents, and of a good English family of clergymen,* Swift was born in Dublin in 1667, seven months after the death of his father, who had come to practise there as a lawyer. The boy went to school at Kilkenny, and afterwards to Trinity College, Dublin, where he got a degree with difficulty, and was wild, and witty, and poor. In 1688, by the recommendation of his mother, Swift was received into the family of Sir William Temple, who had known Mrs. Swift in Ireland. He left his patron in 1694, and the next year took orders in Dublin. But he threw up the small Irish preferment which he got and returned to Temple, in whose family he remained until Sir William's death in 1699. His hopes of advancement in England failing, Swift returned to Ireland, and took the living of Laracor. Hither he invited Esther Johnson,† Temple's

* He was from a younger branch of the Swifts of Yorkshire. His grandfather, the Reverend Thomas Swift, vicar of Goodrich, in Herefordshire, suffered for his loyalty in Charles I.'s time. That gentleman married Elizabeth Dryden, a member of the family of the poet. Sir Walter Scott gives, with his characteristic minuteness in such points, the exact relationship between these famous men. Swift was "the son of Dryden's second cousin." Swift, too, was the enemy of Dryden's reputation. Witness the "Battle of the Books":—"The difference was greatest among the horse," says he of the moderns, "where every private trooper pretended to the command, from Tasso and Milton to Dryden and Withers." And in *Poetry, a Rhapsody*, he advises the poetaster to—

> "Read all the Prefaces of Dryden,
> For these our critics much confide in,
> Though merely writ, at first for filling,
> To raise the volume's price a shilling."

"Cousin Swift, you will never be a poet," was the phrase of Dryden to his kinsman, which remained alive in a memory tenacious of such matters.

† "Miss Hetty" she was called in the family—where her face, and her dress, and Sir William's treatment of her, all made the real fact about her birth plain enough. Sir William left her a thousand pounds. [The statement that Esther Johnson was Temple's natural daughter, was first made by a writer in the *Gentleman's Magazine* for 1757, who also asserted that Swift was Temple's natural son; and that a discovery of their relationship was the secret of Swift's melancholy. The statement about Swift is inconsistent with known dates. The story about Esther may be true, but it depends mainly upon late and anonymous evidence.]

natural daughter, with whom he had contracted a tender iendship while they were both dependants of Temple's. And with an occasional visit to England, Swift now passed nine years at home.

In 1710 he came to England, and, with a brief visit to Ireland, during which he took possession of his deanery of Saint Patrick, he now passed four years in England, taking the most distinguished part in the political transactions which terminated with the death of Queen Anne. After her death, his party disgraced, and his hopes of ambition over, Swift returned to Dublin, where he remained twelve years. In this time he wrote the famous "Drapier's Letters" and "Gulliver's Travels." He married * Esther Johnson (Stella), and buried Esther Vanhomrigh (Vanessa), who had followed him to Ireland from London, where she had contracted a violent passion for him. In 1726 and 1727 Swift was in England, which he quitted for the last time on hearing of his wife's illness. Stella died in January 1728, and Swift not until 1745, having passed the last five of the seventy-eight years of his life with an impaired intellect, and keepers to watch him.†

You know, of course, that Swift has had many biographers; his life has been told by the kindest and most good-natured of men, Scott, who admires but can't bring himself to love him; and by stout old Johnson,‡ who, forced to admit him into the company of

* The marriage is accepted by Swift's last biographer, Sir H. Craik. It was disbelieved by Forster, and cannot be regarded as certain.

† Sometimes, during his mental affliction, he continued walking about the house for many consecutive hours; sometimes he remained in a kind of torpor. At times he would seem to struggle to bring into distinct consciousness, and shape into expression the intellect that lay smothering under gloomy obstruction in him. A pier-glass falling by accident, nearly fell on him. He said he wished it had! He once repeated slowly several times, "I am what I am." The last thing he wrote was an epigram on the building of a magazine for arms and stores, which was pointed out to him as he went abroad during his mental disease:—

"Behold a proof of Irish sense:
Here Irish wit is seen:
When nothing's left that's worth defence,
They build a magazine!"

‡ Besides these famous books of Scott's and Johnson's, there is a copious "Life" by Thomas Sheridan (Doctor Johnson's "Sherry"), father of Richard Brinsley, and son of that good-natured, clever Irish Doctor Thomas Sheridan, Swift's intimate, who lost his chaplaincy by so unluckily choosing for a text on the King's birthday, "Sufficient for the day is the evil thereof!" Not to mention less important works, there is also the *Remarks on the Life and Writings of Doctor Jonathan Swift*, by that polite and dignified writer, the Earl of Orrery. His Lordship is said to have striven for literary renown, chiefly that he might make up for the slight passed on him by his father, who

poets, receives the famous Irishman, and takes off his hat to him with a bow of surly recognition, scans him from head to foot, and passes over to the other side of the street. Doctor (afterwards Sir W. R.) Wilde of Dublin,* who has written a most interesting volume on the closing years of Swift's life, calls Johnson "the most malignant of his biographers:" it is not easy for an English critic to please Irishmen—perhaps to try and please them. And yet Johnson truly admires Swift: Johnson does not quarrel with Swift's change of politics, or doubt his sincerity of religion: about the famous Stella and Vanessa controversy the Doctor does not bear very hardly on Swift. But he could not give the Dean that honest hand of his; the stout old man puts it into his breast, and moves off from him.†

Would we have liked to live with him? That is a question which, in dealing with these people's works, and thinking of their lives and peculiarities, every reader of biographies must put to himself. Would you have liked to be a friend of the great Dean? I should like to have been Shakspeare's shoeblack—just to have lived in his house, just to have worshipped him—to have run on his errands, and seen that sweet serene face. I should like, as a young man, to have lived on Fielding's staircase in the Temple, and after helping him up to bed perhaps, and opening his door with his latchkey, to have shaken hands with him in the morning, and heard him talk and crack jokes over his breakfast and his mug of small beer. Who would not give something to pass a night at the club with Johnson, and Goldsmith, and James Boswell, Esquire,

left his library away from him. It is to be feared that the ink he used to wash out that stain only made it look bigger. He had, however, known Swift, and corresponded with people who knew him. His work (which appeared in 1751) provoked a good deal of controversy, calling out, among other *brochures*, the interesting *Observations on Lord Orrery's Remarks*, &c., of Doctor Delany.

* Wilde's book was written on the occasion of the remains of Swift and Stella being brought to the light of day—a thing which happened in 1835, when certain works going on in Saint Patrick's Cathedral, Dublin, afforded an opportunity of their being examined. One hears with surprise of these skulls "going the rounds" of houses, and being made the objects of *dilettante* curiosity. The larynx of Swift was actually carried off! Phrenologists had a low opinion of his intellect from the observations they took.

Wilde traces the symptoms of ill-health in Swift, as detailed in his writings from time to time. He observes, likewise, that the skull gave evidence of "diseased action" of the brain during life—such as would be produced by an increasing tendency to "cerebral congestion." [In 1882 Dr Bucknell wrote an interesting article to show that Swift's disease was 'labyrinthine vertigo,' an affection of the ear, which would account for some of the symptoms.]

† "He [Doctor Johnson] seemed to me to have an unaccountable prejudice against Swift; for I once took the liberty to ask him if Swift had personally offended him, and he told me he had not."—BOSWELL'S *Tour to the Hebrides.*

of Auchinleck? The charm of Addison's companionship and conversation has passed to us by fond tradition—but Swift? If you had been his inferior in parts (and that, with a great respect for all persons present, I fear is only very likely), his equal in mere social station, he would have bullied, scorned, and insulted you; if, undeterred by his great reputation, you had met him like a man, he would have quailed before you,* and not had the pluck to reply, and gone home, and years after written a foul epigram about you—watched for you in a sewer, and come out to assail you with a coward's blow and a dirty bludgeon. If you had been a lord with a blue riband, who flattered his vanity, or could help his ambition, he would have been the most delightful company in the world. He would have been so manly, so sarcastic, so bright, odd, and original, that you might think he had no object in view but the indulgence of his humour, and that he was the most reckless simple creature in the world. How he would have torn your enemies to pieces for you! and made fun of the Opposition! His servility was so boisterous that it looked like independence; † he would have done your errands, but with the air of patronising you; and after fighting your battles, masked, in the street or the press, would have kept on his hat before your wife and daughters in the drawing-room,

* Few men, to be sure, dared this experiment, but yet their success was encouraging. One gentleman made a point of asking the Dean whether his uncle Godwin had not given him his education. Swift, who hated *that* subject cordially, and, indeed, cared little for his kindred, said sternly, "Yes; he gave me the education of a dog." "Then, sir,' cried the other, striking his fist on the table, "you have not the gratitude of a dog!"

Other occasions there were when a bold face gave the Dean pause, even after his Irish almost-royal position was established. But he brought himself into greater danger on a certain occasion, and the amusing circumstances may be once more repeated here. He had unsparingly lashed the notable Dublin lawyer, Mr. Serjeant Bettesworth—

"Thus at the bar, the booby Bettesworth,
Though half-a-crown o'erpays his sweat's worth,
Who knows in law nor text nor margent,
Calls Singleton his brother-serjeant!"

The Serjeant, it is said, swore to have his life. He presented himself at the deanery. The Dean asked his name. "Sir, I am Serjeant Bett-es-worth."

"*In what regiment, pray?*" asked Swift.

A guard of volunteers formed themselves to defend the Dean at this time.

† "But, my Hamilton, I will never hide the freedom of my sentiments from you. I am much inclined to believe that the temper of my friend Swift might occasion his English friends to wish him happily and properly promoted at a distance. His spirit, for I would give it the softest name, was ever untractable. The motions of his genius were often irregular. He assumed more the air of a patron than of a friend. He affected rather to dictate than advise."—*Orrery.*

content to take that sort of pay for his tremendous services as a bravo.*

He says as much himself in one of his letters to Bolingbroke:—"All my endeavours to distinguish myself were only for want of a great title and fortune, that I might be used like a lord by those who have an opinion of my parts; whether right or wrong is no great matter. And so the reputation of wit and great learning does the office of a blue riband or a coach-and-six." †

Could there be a greater candour? It is an outlaw, who says, "These are my brains; with these I'll win titles and compete with fortune. These are my bullets; these I'll turn into gold;" and he hears the sound of coaches and six, takes the road like Macheath, and makes society stand and deliver. They are all on their knees before him. Down go my Lord Bishop's apron, and his Grace's blue riband, and my Lady's brocade petticoat in the mud. He eases the one of a living, the other of a patent place, the third of a little snug post about the Court, and gives them over to followers of his own. The great prize has not come yet. The coach with the mitre and crozier in it, which he intends to have for *his* share, has been delayed on the way from Saint James's; and he waits and waits

* ". . . An anecdote, which, though only told by Mrs. Pilkington, is well attested, bears, that the last time he was in London he went to dine with the Earl of Burlington, who was but newly married. The Earl, it is supposed, being willing to have a little diversion, did not introduce him to his lady, nor mention his name. After dinner said the Dean, 'Lady Burlington, I hear you can sing; sing me a song.' The lady looked on this unceremonious manner of asking a favour with distaste, and positively refused. He said, 'She should sing, or he would make her. Why, madam, I suppose you take me for one of your poor English hedge-parsons; sing when I bid you.' As the Earl did nothing but laugh at this freedom, the lady was so vexed that she burst into tears and retired. His first compliment to her when he saw her again was, 'Pray, madam, are you as proud and ill-natured now as when I saw you last?' To which she answered with great good-humour, 'No, Mr. Dean; I'll sing for you if you please.' From which time he conceived a great esteem for her."—SCOTT'S *Life*. ". . . He had not the least tincture of vanity in his conversation. He was, perhaps, as he said himself, too proud to be vain. When he was polite, it was in a manner entirely his own. In his friendships he was constant and undisguised. He was the same in his enmities."—*Orrery*.

† "I make no figure but at Court, where I affect to turn from a lord to the meanest of my acquaintances."—*Journal to Stella*.

"I am plagued with bad authors, verse and prose, who send me their books and poems, the vilest I ever saw; but I have given their names to my man, never to let them see me."—*Journal to Stella*.

The following curious paragraph illustrates the life of a courtier:—

"Did I ever tell you that the Lord Treasurer hears ill with the left ear, just as I do? . . . I dare not tell him that I am so, *for fear he should think that I counterfeited to make my court!*"—*Journal to Stella*.

until nightfall, when his runners come and tell him that the coach has taken a different road, and escaped him. So he fires his pistols into the air with a curse, and rides away into his own country.*

Swift's seems to me to be as good a name to point a moral or adorn a tale of ambition as any hero's that ever lived and failed. But we must remember that the morality was lax—that other gentlemen besides himself took the road in his day—that public society was in a strange disordered condition, and the State was ravaged by other condottieri. The Boyne was being fought and won, and lost—the bells rung in William's victory, in the very same tone with which they would have pealed for James's. Men were loose upon politics, and had to shift for themselves. They, as well as old beliefs and institutions, had lost their moorings and gone adrift in the storm. As in the South Sea Bubble, almost everybody gambled; as in the Railway mania — not many centuries ago — almost every one took his unlucky share: a man of that time, of the vast talents and ambition of Swift, could scarce do otherwise than grasp at his prize, and make his spring at his opportunity.

* The war of pamphlets was carried on fiercely on one side and the other: and the Whig attacks made the Ministry Swift served very sore. Bolingbroke laid hold of several of the Opposition pamphleteers, and bewails their "factitiousness" in the following letter:—

Bolingbroke to the Earl of Strafford.

"WHITEHALL: *July 23rd*, 1712.

"IT is a melancholy consideration that the laws of our country are too weak to punish effectually those factitious scribblers, who presume to blacken the brightest characters, and to give even scurrilous language to those who are in the first degrees of honour. This, my Lord, among others, is a symptom of the decayed condition of our Government, and serves to show how fatally we mistake licentiousness for liberty. All I could do was to take up Hart, the printer, to send him to Newgate, and to bind him over upon bail to be prosecuted; this I have done; and if I can arrive at legal proof against the author, Ridpath, he shall have the same treatment."

Swift was not behind his illustrious friend in this virtuous indignation. In the history of the last four years of the Queen, the Dean speaks in the most edifying manner of the licentiousness of the press and the abusive language of the other party:—

"It must be acknowledged that the bad practices of printers have been such as to deserve the severest animadversion from the public. . . . The adverse party, full of rage and leisure since their fall, and unanimous in their cause, employ a set of writers by subscription, who are well versed in all the topics of defamation, and have a style and genius levelled to the generality of their readers. . . . However, the mischiefs of the press were too exorbitant to be cured by such a remedy as a tax upon small papers, and a Bill for a much more effectual regulation of it was brought into the House of Commons, but so late in the

His bitterness, his scorn, his rage, his subsequent misanthropy are ascribed by some panegyrists to a deliberate conviction of mankind's unworthiness, and a desire to amend them by castigation. His youth was bitter, as that of a great genius bound down by ignoble ties, and powerless in a mean dependence; his age was bitter,* like that of a great genius, that had fought the battle and nearly won it, and lost it, and thought of it afterwards, writhing in a lonely exile. A man may attribute to the gods, if he likes, what is caused by his own fury, or disappointment, or self-will. What public man—what statesman projecting a *coup*—what king determined on an invasion of his neighbour—what satirist meditating an onslaught on society or an individual, can't give a pretext for his move? There was a French General the other day who proposed to march into this country and put it to sack and pillage, in revenge for humanity outraged by our conduct at Copenhagen: there is always

session that there was no time to pass it, for there always appeared an unwillingness to cramp overmuch the liberty of the press."

But to a clause in the proposed Bill, that the names of authors should be set to every printed book, pamphlet, or paper, his Reverence objects altogether; for, says he, "besides the objection to this clause from the practice of pious men, who, in publishing excellent writings for the service of religion, have chosen, *out of an humble Christian spirit, to conceal their names*, it is certain that all persons of true genius or knowledge have an invincible modesty and suspicion of themselves upon first sending their thoughts into the world."

This "invincible modesty" was no doubt the sole reason which induced the Dean to keep the secret of the "Drapier's Letters" and a hundred humble Christian works of which he was the author. As for the Opposition, the Doctor was for dealing severely with them. He writes to Stella:—

Journal. Letter XIX.

"LONDON: *March 25th*, 1710–11.

". . . We have let Guiscard be buried at last, after showing him pickled in a trough this fortnight for twopence a piece; and the fellow that showed would point to his body and say, 'See, gentlemen, this is the wound that was given him by his Grace the Duke of Ormond;' and 'This is the wound,' &c.; and then the show was over, and another set of rabble came in. 'Tis hard that our laws would not suffer us to hang his body in chains, because he was not tried; and in the eye of the law every man is innocent till then. . . ."

Journal. Letter XXVII.

"LONDON: *July 25th*, 1711.

"I was this afternoon with Mr. Secretary at his office, and helped to hinder a man of his pardon, who was condemned for a rape. The Under-Secretary was willing to save him; but I told the Secretary he could not pardon him without a favourable report from the Judge; besides, he was a fiddler, and consequently a rogue, and deserved hanging for something else, and so he shall swing."

* It was his constant practice to keep his birthday as a day of mourning.

some excuse for men of the aggressive turn. They are of their nature warlike, predatory, eager for fight, plunder, dominion.*

As fierce a beak and talon as ever struck—as strong a wing as ever beat, belonged to Swift. I am glad, for one, that fate wrested the prey out of his claws, and cut his wings and chained him. One can gaze, and not without awe and pity, at the lonely eagle chained behind the bars.

That Swift was born at No. 7 Hoey's Court, Dublin, on the 30th November 1667, is a certain fact, of which nobody will deny the sister island the honour and glory; but, it seems to me, he was no more an Irishman than a man born of English parents at Calcutta is a Hindoo.† Goldsmith was an Irishman, and always an Irishman: Steele was an Irishman, and always an Irishman: Swift's heart was English and in England, his habits English, his logic

* "These devils of Grub Street rogues, that write the *Flying Post* and *Medley* in one paper, will not be quiet. They are always mauling Lord Treasurer, Lord Bolingbroke, and me. We have the dog under prosecution, but Bolingbroke is not active enough; but I hope to swinge him. He is a Scotch rogue, one Ridpath. They get out upon bail, and write on. We take them again, and get fresh bail; so it goes round."—*Journal to Stella.*

† Swift was by no means inclined to forget such considerations; and his English birth makes its mark, strikingly enough, every now and then in his writings. Thus in a letter to Pope (SCOTT'S *Swift*, vol. xix. p. 97), he says:—

"We have had your volume of letters. . . . Some of those who highly value you, and a few who knew you personally, are grieved to find you make no distinction between the English gentry of this kingdom, and the savage old Irish (who are only the vulgar, and some gentlemen who live in the Irish parts of the kingdom); but the English colonies, who are three parts in four, are much more civilised than many counties in England, and speak better English, and are much better bred."

And again, in the fourth Drapier's Letter, we have the following:—

"A short paper, printed at Bristol, and reprinted here, reports Mr. Wood to say 'that he wonders at the impudence and insolence of the Irish in refusing his coin.' When, by the way, it is the true English people of Ireland who refuse it, although we take it for granted that the Irish will do so too whenever they are asked."—SCOTT'S *Swift*, vol. vi. p. 453.

He goes further, in a good-humoured satirical paper, *On Barbarous Denominations in Ireland*, where (after abusing, as he was wont, the Scotch cadence, as well as expression) he advances to the "*Irish Brogue*," and speaking of the "censure" which it brings down, says:—

"And what is yet worse, it is too well known that the bad consequence of this opinion affects those among us who are not the least liable to such reproaches farther than the misfortune of being born in Ireland, although of English parents, and whose education has been chiefly in that kingdom."—*Ibid.* vol. vii. p. 149.

But, indeed, if we are to make *anything* of Race at all, we must call that man an Englishman whose father comes from an old Yorkshire family, and his mother from an old Leicestershire one!

eminently English; his statement is elaborately simple; he shuns tropes and metaphors, and uses his ideas and words with a wise thrift and economy, as he used his money: with which he could be generous and splendid upon great occasions, but which he husbanded when there was no need to spend it. He never indulges in needless extravagance of rhetoric, lavish epithets, profuse imagery. He lays his opinion before you with a grave simplicity and a perfect neatness.* Dreading ridicule too, as a man of his humour—above all, an Englishman of his humour—certainly would, he is afraid to use the poetical power which he really possessed; one often fancies in reading him that he dares not be eloquent when he might; that he does not speak above his voice, as it were, and the tone of society.

His initiation into politics, his knowledge of business, his knowledge of polite life, his acquaintance with literature even, which he could not have pursued very sedulously during that reckless career at Dublin, Swift got under the roof of Sir William Temple. He was fond of telling in after life what quantities of books he devoured there, and how King William taught him to cut asparagus in the Dutch fashion. It was at Shene and at Moor Park, with a salary of twenty pounds and a dinner at the upper servants' table, that this great and lonely Swift passed a ten years' apprenticeship—wore a cassock that was only not a livery—bent down a knee as proud as Lucifer's to supplicate my Lady's good graces, or run on his honour's errands.† It was here, as he was writing at Temple's table, or following his patron's walk, that he saw and heard the men who had governed the great world—measured himself with them, looking up from his silent corner, gauged their brains, weighed their wits, turned them, and tried them, and marked them. Ah!

* "The style of his conversation was very much of a piece with that of his writings, concise and clear and strong. Being one day at a Sheriff's feast, who amongst other toasts called out to him, 'Mr. Dean, The Trade of Ireland!' he answered quick: 'Sir, I drink no memories!' . . .

"Happening to be in company with a petulant young man who prided himself on saying pert things . . . and who cried out—'You must know, Mr. Dean, that I set up for a wit!' 'Do you so?' says the Dean. 'Take my advice, and sit down again!'

"At another time, being in company, where a lady whisking her long train [long trains were then in fashion] swept down a fine fiddle and broke it; Swift cried out—

'Mantua væ miseræ nimium vicina Cremonæ!'"

—DR. DELANY: *Observations upon Lord Orrery's "Remarks, &c. on Swift."* London, 1754.

† "Don't you remember how I used to be in pain when Sir William Temple would look cold and out of humour for three or four days, and I used to suspect

what platitudes he must have heard! what feeble jokes! what pompous commonplaces! what small men they must have seemed under those enormous periwigs, to the swarthy, uncouth, silent Irish secretary. I wonder whether it ever struck Temple, that that Irishman was his master? I suppose that dismal conviction did not present itself under the ambrosial wig, or Temple could never have lived with Swift. Swift sickened, rebelled, left the service—ate humble pie and came back again; and so for ten years went on, gathering learning, swallowing scorn, and submitting with a stealthy rage to his fortune.

Temple's style is the perfection of practised and easy good breeding. If he does not penetrate very deeply into a subject, he professes a very gentlemanly acquaintance with it; if he makes rather a parade of Latin, it was the custom of his day, as it was the custom for a gentleman to envelop his head in a periwig and his hands in lace ruffles. If he wears buckles and square-toed shoes, he steps in them with a consummate grace, and you never hear their creak, or find them treading upon any lady's train or any rival's heels in the Court crowd. When that grows too hot or too agitated for him, he politely leaves it. He retires to his retreat of Shene or Moor Park; and lets the King's party and the Prince of Orange's party battle it out among themselves. He reveres the Sovereign (and no man perhaps ever testified to his loyalty by so elegant a bow); he admires the Prince of Orange; but there is one person whose ease and comfort he loves more than all the princes in Christendom, and that valuable member of society is himself, Gulielmus Temple, Baronettus. One sees him in his retreat: between his study-chair and his tulip-beds,* clipping his

a hundred reasons? I have plucked up my spirits since then, faith; he spoiled a fine gentleman."—*Journal to Stella.*

[It should be added that this statement about the twenty pounds a year, and the upper servants' table, came from a hostile story told long afterwards by a nephew of Temple to Richardson the novelist. It is probably true enough of Swift's first stay as a raw lad in the family; but Temple came to value Swift's services much more highly, and induced him to return from Ireland by promises of preferment. Temple's death prevented their fulfilment, but it is clear that he had come to treat Swift with great respect.]

* ". . . The Epicureans were more intelligible in their notion, and fortunate in their expression, when they placed a man's happiness in the tranquillity of his mind and indolence of body; for while we are composed of both, I doubt both must have a share in the good or ill we feel. As men of several languages say the same things in very different words, so in several ages, countries, constitutions of laws and religion, the same thing seems to be meant by very different expressions: what is called by the Stoics apathy, or dispassion; by the sceptics, indisturbance; by the Molinists, quietism; by common men, peace of conscience—seems all to mean but great tranquillity of mind. . . . For this

apricots and pruning his essays,—the statesman, the ambassador no more; but the philosopher, the Epicurean, the fine gentleman and courtier at Saint James's as at Shene; where, in place of kings and fair ladies, he pays his court to the Ciceronian majesty; or walks a minuet with the Epic Muse; or dallies by the south wall with the ruddy nymph of gardens.

Temple seems to have received and exacted a prodigious deal of veneration from his household, and to have been coaxed, and warmed, and cuddled by the people round about him, as delicately as any of the plants which he loved. When he fell ill in 1693, the household was aghast at his indisposition; mild Dorothea his wife, the best companion of the best of men—

> "Mild Dorothea, peaceful, wise, and great,
> Trembling beheld the doubtful hand of fate."

As for Dorinda, his sister,—

> "Those who would grief describe, might come and trace
> Its watery footsteps in Dorinda's face.
> To see her weep, joy every face forsook,
> And grief flung sables on each menial look.
> The humble tribe mourned for the quickening soul,
> That furnished spirit and motion through the whole."

Isn't that line in which grief is described as putting the menials into a mourning livery, a fine image? One of the menials wrote it,

reason Epicurus passed his life wholly in his garden; there he studied, there he exercised, there he taught his philosophy; and, indeed, no other sort of abode seems to contribute so much to both the tranquillity of mind and indolence of body, which he made his chief ends. The sweetness of the air, the pleasantness of smell, the verdure of plants, the cleanness and lightness of food, the exercise of working or walking; but, above all, the exemption from cares and solicitude, seem equally to favour and improve both contemplation and health, the enjoyment of sense and imagination, and thereby the quiet and ease both of the body and mind. . . . Where Paradise was, has been much debated, and little agreed; but what sort of place is meant by it may perhaps easier be conjectured. It seems to have been a Persian word, since Xenophon and other Greek authors mention it as what was much in use and delight among the kings of those Eastern countries. Strabo describing Jericho: 'Ibi est palmetum, cui immixtæ sunt etiam aliæ stirpes hortenses, locus ferax palmis abundans, spatio stadiorum centum, totus irriguus: ibi est Regis Balsami paradisus.'"—*Essay on Gardens.*

In the same famous essay Temple speaks of a friend, whose conduct and prudence he characteristically admires:—

". . . I thought it very prudent in a gentleman of my friends in Staffordshire, who is a great lover of his garden, to pretend no higher, though his soil be good enough, than to the perfection of plums; and in these (by bestowing south walls upon them) he has very well succeeded, which he could never have done in attempts upon peaches and grapes; and *a good plum is certainly better than an ill peach.*"

who did not like that Temple livery nor those twenty-pound wages. Cannot one fancy the uncouth young servitor, with downcast eyes, books and papers in hand, following at his honour's heels in the garden walk; or taking his honour's orders as he stands by the great chair, where Sir William has the gout, and his feet all blistered with moxa? When Sir William has the gout or scolds it must be hard work at the second table;* the Irish secretary owned as much afterwards; and when he came to dinner, how he must have lashed and growled and torn the household with his gibes and scorn! What would the steward say about the pride of them Irish schollards—and this one had got no great credit even at his Irish college, if the truth were known—and what a contempt his Excellency's own gentleman must have had for Parson Teague from Dublin! (The valets and chaplains were always at war. It is hard to say which Swift thought the more contemptible.) And what must have been the sadness, the sadness and terror, of the

* Swift's Thoughts on Hanging.

(*Directions to Servants.*)

"To grow old in the office of a footman is the highest of all indignities; therefore, when you find years coming on without hopes of a place at Court, a command in the army, a succession to the stewardship, an employment in the revenue (which two last you cannot obtain without reading and writing), or running away with your master's niece or daughter, I directly advise you to go upon the road, which is the only post of honour left you: there you will meet many of your old comrades, and live a short life and a merry one, and make a figure at your exit, wherein I will give you some instructions.

"The last advice I give you relates to your behaviour when you are going to be hanged: which, either for robbing your master, for housebreaking, or going upon the highway, or in a drunken quarrel by killing the first man you meet, may very probably be your lot, and is owing to one of these three qualities: either a love of good-fellowship, a generosity of mind, or too much vivacity of spirits. Your good behaviour on this article will concern your whole community: deny the fact with all solemnity of imprecations: a hundred of your brethren, if they can be admitted, will attend about the bar, and be ready upon demand to give you a character before the court; let nothing prevail on you to confess, but the promise of a pardon for discovering your comrades: but I suppose all this to be in vain; for if you escape now, your fate will be the same another day. Get a speech to be written by the best author of Newgate: some of your kind wenches will provide you with a holland shirt and white cap, crowned with a crimson or black ribbon: take leave cheerfully of all your friends in Newgate: mount the cart with courage: fall on your knees; lift up your eyes; hold a book in your hands, although you cannot read a word; deny the fact at the gallows; kiss and forgive the hangman, and so farewell: you shall be buried in pomp at the charge of the fraternity: the surgeon shall not touch a limb of you; and your frame shall continue until a successor of equal renown succeeds in your place. . . ."

housekeeper's little daughter with the curling black ringlets and the sweet smiling face, when the secretary who teaches her to read and write, and whom she loves and reverences above all things—above mother, above mild Dorothea, above that tremendous Sir William in his square toes and periwig,—when *Mr. Swift* comes down from his master with rage in his heart, and has not a kind word even for little Hester Johnson?

Perhaps, for the Irish secretary, his Excellency's condescension was even more cruel than his frowns. Sir William *would* perpetually quote Latin and the ancient classics *à propos* of his gardens and his Dutch statues, and *plates-bandes*, and talk about Epicurus and Diogenes Laertius, Julius Cæsar, Semiramis, and the gardens of the Hesperides, Mæcenas, Strabo describing Jericho, and the Assyrian kings. *À propos* of beans, he would mention Pythagoras's precept to abstain from beans, and that this precept probably meant that wise men should abstain from public affairs. *He* is a placid Epicurean; *he* is a Pythagorean philosopher; *he* is a wise man—that is the deduction. Does not Swift think so? One can imagine the downcast eyes lifted up for a moment, and the flash of scorn which they emit. Swift's eyes were as azure as the heavens; Pope says nobly (as everything Pope said and thought of his friend was good and noble), "His eyes are as azure as the heavens, and have a charming archness in them." And one person in that household, that pompous, stately, kindly Moor Park, saw heaven nowhere else.

But the Temple amenities and solemnities did not agree with Swift. He was half-killed with a surfeit of Shene pippins; and in a garden-seat which he devised for himself at Moor Park, and where he devoured greedily the stock of books within his reach, he caught a vertigo and deafness which punished and tormented him through life. He could not bear the place or the servitude. Even in that poem of courtly condolence, from which we have quoted a few lines of mock melancholy, he breaks out of the funereal procession with a mad shriek, as it were, and rushes away crying his own grief, cursing his own fate, foreboding madness, and forsaken by fortune, and even hope.

I don't know anything more melancholy than the letter to Temple, in which, after having broke from his bondage, the poor wretch crouches piteously towards his cage again, and deprecates his master's anger. He asks for testimonials for orders

"The particulars required of me are what relate to morals and learning; and the reasons of quitting your honour's family—that is, whether the last was occasioned by any ill action. They are left entirely to your honour's mercy, though in the first I think I cannot reproach myself for anything further than for *infirmities*. This is all I dare at present beg from your honour, under circumstances of life not worth your regard: what is left me to wish (next to the health and prosperity of your honour and family) is that Heaven would one day allow me the opportunity of leaving my acknowledgments at your feet. I beg my most humble duty and service be presented to my ladies, your honour's lady and sister."

Can prostration fall deeper? could a slave bow lower?*

Twenty years afterwards Bishop Kennet, describing the same man, says:—

"Dr. Swift came into the coffee-house and had a bow from everybody but me. When I came to the antechamber [at Court] to wait before prayers, Dr. Swift was the principal man of talk and business. He was soliciting the Earl of Arran to speak to his

* "He continued in Sir William Temple's house till the death of that great man."—*Anecdotes of the Family of Swift*, by the Dean.

"It has since pleased God to take this good and great person to himself."—*Preface to Temple's Works.*

On all *public* occasions, Swift speaks of Sir William in the same tone. [The letter given above was written 6th October 1694, and is humiliating enough. Swift's relation to Temple changed, as already said. The passages, however, which follow, no doubt show a strong sense of "indignities" at one time or other.] But the reader will better understand how acutely he remembered the indignities he suffered in his household, from the subjoined extracts from the *Journal to Stella*:—

"I called at Mr. Secretary the other day, to see what the d—— ailed him on Sunday: I made him a very proper speech; told him I observed he was much out of temper, that I did not expect he would tell me the cause, but would be glad to see he was in better; and one thing I warned him of—never to appear cold to me, for I would not be treated like a schoolboy; that I had felt too much of that in my life already" (*meaning Sir William Temple*), &c. &c.—*Journal to Stella.*

"I am thinking what a veneration we used to have for Sir William Temple because he might have been Secretary of State at fifty; and here is a young fellow hardly thirty in that employment."—*Ibid.*

"The Secretary is as easy with me as Mr. Addison was. I have often thought what a splutter Sir William Temple makes about being Secretary of State."—*Ibid.*

"Lord Treasurer has had an ugly fit of the rheumatism, but is now quite well. I was playing at *one-and-thirty* with him and his family the other night. He gave us all twelvepence apiece to begin with; it put me in mind of Sir William Temple."—*Ibid.*

"I thought I saw Jack Temple [*nephew to Sir William*] and his wife pass by me to-day in their coach; but I took no notice of them. I am glad I have wholly shaken off that family."—*S. to S., Sept.* 1710.

brother, the Duke of Ormond, to get a place for a clergyman. He was promising Mr. Thorold to undertake, with my Lord Treasurer, that he should obtain a salary of £200 per annum as member of the English Church at Rotterdam. He stopped F. Gwynne, Esquire, going into the Queen with the red bag, and told him aloud, he had something to say to him from my Lord Treasurer. He took out his gold watch, and telling the time of day, complained that it was very late. A gentleman said he was too fast. 'How can I help it,' says the Doctor, 'if the courtiers give me a watch that won't go right?' Then he instructed a young nobleman, that the best poet in England was Mr. Pope (a papist), who had begun a translation of Homer into English, for which he would have them all subscribe: 'For,' says he, 'he shall not begin to print till I have a thousand guineas for him.' * Lord Treasurer, after leaving the Queen, came through the room, beckoning Doctor Swift to follow him—both went off just before prayers." †

There's a little malice in the Bishop's "just before prayers."

This picture of the great Dean seems a true one, and is harsh, though not altogether unpleasant. He was doing good, and to deserving men, too, in the midst of these intrigues and triumphs. His journals and a thousand anecdotes of him relate his kind acts and rough manners. His hand was constantly stretched out to relieve an honest man—he was cautious about his money, but ready. If you were in a strait, would you like such a benefactor? I think I would rather have had a potato and a friendly word from Goldsmith than have been beholden to the Dean for a guinea and a dinner.‡ He insulted a man as he served him, made women

* "Swift must be allowed," says Doctor Johnson, "for a time, to have dictated the political opinions of the English nation."

A conversation on the Dean's pamphlets excited one of the Doctor's liveliest sallies. "One, in particular, praised his *Conduct of the Allies*.—JOHNSON: 'Sir, his *Conduct of the Allies* is a performance of very little ability. . . . Why, sir, Tom Davies might have written the *Conduct of the Allies!*'"—BOSWELL'S *Life of Johnson*.

† The passage as quoted in the text is slightly abbreviated. It may be observed that Swift fulfilled his promises of support to the "clergyman," Dr. Fiddes, author of a good life of Wolsey, and was very useful to Pope. Many other instances could be given of the "kind acts" mentioned in the next paragraph.

‡ "Whenever he fell into the company of any person for the first time, it was his custom to try their tempers and disposition by some abrupt question that bore the appearance of rudeness. If this were well taken, and answered with good-humour, he afterwards made amends by his civilities. But if he saw any marks of resentment, from alarmed pride, vanity, or conceit, he dropped all further intercourse with the party. This will be illustrated by an anecdote of

DEAN SWIFT AT COURT.

cry, guests look foolish, bullied unlucky friends, and flung his benefactions into poor men's faces. No; the Dean was no Irishman —no Irishman ever gave but with a kind word and a kind heart.

It is told, as if it were to Swift's credit, that the Dean of Saint Patrick's performed his family devotions every morning regularly, but with such secrecy that the guests in his house were never in the least aware of the ceremony. There was no need surely why a Church dignitary should assemble his family privily in a crypt, and as if he was afraid of heathen persecution. But I think the world was right, and the bishops who advised Queen Anne when they counselled her not to appoint the author of the "Tale of a Tub" to a bishopric, gave perfectly good advice. The man who wrote the arguments and illustrations in that wild book, could not but be aware what must be the sequel of the propositions which he laid down. The boon companion of Pope and Bolingbroke, who chose these as the friends of his life, and the recipients of his confidence and affection, must have heard many an argument, and joined in many a conversation over Pope's port, or St. John's burgundy, which would not bear to be repeated at other men's boards.

I know of few things more conclusive as to the sincerity of Swift's religion than his advice to poor John Gay to turn clergyman, and look out for a seat on the Bench. Gay, the author of the "Beggar's Opera"—Gay, the wildest of the wits about town—it was this man that Jonathan Swift advised to take orders—to invest in a cassock and bands—just as he advised him to husband his shillings and put his thousand pounds out at interest. The Queen, and the bishops, and the world, were right in mistrusting the religion of that man.*

that sort related by Mrs. Pilkington. After supper, the Dean, having decanted a bottle of wine, poured what remained into a glass, and seeing it was muddy, presented it to Mr. Pilkington to drink it. 'For,' said he, 'I always keep some poor parson to drink the foul wine for me.' Mr. Pilkington, entering into his humour, thanked him, and told him 'he did not know the difference, but was glad to get a glass at any rate.' 'Why, then,' said the Dean, 'you shan't, for I'll drink it myself. Why, —— take you, you are wiser than a paltry curate whom I asked to dine with me a few days ago; for upon my making the same speech to him, he said he did not understand such usage, and so walked off without his dinner. By the same token, I told the gentleman who recommended him to me that the fellow was a blockhead, and I had done with him.'" —SHERIDAN's *Life of Swift.*

* *From the Archbishop of Cashell.*

"CASHELL: *May 31st*, 1735.

"DEAR SIR,—I have been so unfortunate in all my contests of late, that I am resolved to have no more, especially where I am likely to be overmatched; and as I have some reason to hope what is past will be forgotten, I confess I

I am not here, of course, to speak of any man's religious views, except in so far as they influence his literary character, his life, his humour. The most notorious sinners of all those fellow-mortals whom it is our business to discuss—Harry Fielding and Dick Steele—were especially loud, and I believe really fervent in their expressions of belief; they belaboured freethinkers, and stoned imaginary atheists on all sorts of occasions, going out of their way to bawl their own creed, and persecute their neighbour's, and if they sinned and stumbled, as they constantly did with debt, with drink, with all sorts of bad behaviour, they got upon their knees and cried

did endeavour in my last to put the best colour I could think of upon a very bad cause. My friends judge right of my idleness; but, in reality, it has hitherto proceeded from a hurry and confusion, arising from a thousand unlucky unforeseen accidents rather than mere sloth. I have but one troublesome affair now upon my hands, which, by the help of the prime serjeant, I hope soon to get rid of; and then you shall see me a true Irish bishop. Sir James Ware has made a very useful collection of the memorable actions of my predecessors. He tells me, they were born in such a town of England or Ireland; were consecrated such a year; and if not translated, were buried in the Cathedral Church, either on the north or south side. Whence I conclude that a good bishop has nothing more to do than to eat, drink, grow fat, rich, and die; which laudable example I propose for the remainder of my life to follow; for to tell you the truth, I have for these four or five years past met with so much treachery, baseness, and ingratitude among mankind, that I can hardly think it incumbent on any man to endeavour to do good to so perverse a generation.

"I am truly concerned at the account you give me of your health. Without doubt a southern ramble will prove the best remedy you can take to recover your flesh; and I do not know, except in one stage, where you can choose a road so suited to your circumstances, as from Dublin hither. You have to Kilkenny a turnpike and good inns, at every ten or twelve miles' end. From Kilkenny hither is twenty long miles, bad road, and no inns at all: but I have an expedient for you. At the foot of a very high hill, just midway, there lives in a neat thatched cabin a parson, who is not poor; his wife is allowed to be the best little woman in the world. Her chickens are the fattest, and her ale the best in all the country. Besides, the parson has a little cellar of his own, of which he keeps the key, where he always has a hogshead of the best wine that can be got, in bottles well corked, upon their side; and he cleans, and pulls out the cork better, I think, than Robin. Here I design to meet you with a coach; if you be tired, you shall stay all night; if not, after dinner, we will set out about four, and be at Cashell by nine; and by going through fields and bye-ways, which the parson will show us, we shall escape all the rocky and stony roads that lie between this place and that, which are certainly very bad. I hope you will be so kind as to let me know a post or two before you set out, the very day you will be at Kilkenny, that I may have all things prepared for you. It may be, if you ask him, Cope will come: he will do nothing for me. Therefore, depending upon your positive promise, I shall add no more arguments to persuade you, and am, with the greatest truth, your most faithful and obedient servant,

"THEO. CASHELL."

"Peccavi" with a most sonorous orthodoxy. Yes; poor Harry Fielding and poor Dick Steele were trusty and undoubting Church of England men; they abhorred Popery, Atheism, and wooden shoes and idolatries in general; and hiccupped Church and State with fervour.

But Swift? *His* mind had had a different schooling, and possessed a very different logical power. *He* was not bred up in a tipsy guardroom, and did not learn to reason in a Covent Garden tavern. He could conduct an argument from beginning to end. He could see forward with a fatal clearness. In his old age, looking at the "Tale of a Tub," when he said, "Good God, what a genius I had when I wrote that book!" I think he was admiring, not the genius, but the consequences to which the genius had brought him—a vast genius, a magnificent genius, a genius wonderfully bright, and dazzling, and strong,—to seize, to know, to see, to flash upon falsehood and scorch it into perdition, to penetrate into the hidden motives, and expose the black thoughts of men,—an awful, an evil spirit.

Ah man! you, educated in Epicurean Temple's library, you whose friends were Pope and St. John—what made you to swear to fatal vows, and bind yourself to a life-long hypocrisy before the Heaven which you adored with such real wonder, humility, and reverence? For Swift's was a reverent, was a pious spirit—for Swift could love and could pray. Through the storms and tempests of his furious mind, the stars of religion and love break out in the blue, shining serenely, though hidden by the driving clouds and the maddened hurricane of his life.

It is my belief that he suffered frightfully from the consciousness of his own scepticism, and that he had bent his pride so far down as to put his apostasy out to hire.* The paper left behind him, called "Thoughts on Religion," is merely a set of excuses for not professing disbelief. He says of his sermons that he preached pamphlets: they have scarce a Christian characteristic; they might be preached from the steps of a synagogue, or the floor of a mosque, or the box of a coffee-house almost. There is little or no cant—he is too great and too proud for that; and, in so far as the badness of his sermons goes, he is honest. But having put that cassock on, it poisoned him; he was strangled in his bands. He goes through life, tearing, like a man possessed with a devil. Like Abudah in the Arabian story, he is always looking out for the Fury, and knows that the night will come and the inevitable hag with it.

* "Mr. Swift lived with him [Sir William Temple] some time, but resolving to settle himself in some way of living, was inclined to take orders. However, although his fortune was very small, he had a scruple of entering into the Church merely for support."—*Anecdotes of the Family of Swift*, by the Dean.

What a night, my God, it was! what a lonely rage and long agony—what a vulture that tore the heart of that giant! * It is awful to think of the great sufferings of this great man. Through life he always seems alone, somehow. Goethe was so. I can't fancy Shakspeare otherwise. The giants must live apart. The kings can have no company. But this man suffered so; and deserved so to suffer. One hardly reads anywhere of such a pain.

The "sæva indignatio" of which he spoke as lacerating his heart, and which he dares to inscribe on his tombstone—as if the wretch who lay under that stone waiting God's judgment had a right to be angry—breaks out from him in a thousand pages of his writing, and tears and rends him. Against men in office, he having been overthrown; against men in England, he having lost his chance of preferment there, the furious exile never fails to rage and curse. Is it fair to call the famous "Drapier's Letters" patriotism? They are masterpieces of dreadful humour and invective: they are reasoned logically enough too, but the proposition is as monstrous and fabulous as the Lilliputian island. It is not that the grievance is so great, but there is his enemy—the assault is wonderful for its activity and terrible rage. It is Samson, with a bone in his hand, rushing on his enemies and felling them: one admires not the cause so much as the strength, the anger, the fury of the champion. As is the case with madmen, certain subjects provoke him, and awaken his fits of wrath. Marriage is one of these; in a hundred passages in his writings he rages against it; rages against children; an object of constant satire, even more contemptible in his eyes than a lord's chaplain, is a poor curate with a large family. The idea of this luckless paternity never fails to bring down from him gibes and foul language. Could Dick Steele, or Goldsmith, or Fielding, in his most reckless moment of satire, have written anything like the Dean's famous "Modest Proposal" for eating children? Not one of these but melts at the thoughts of childhood, fondles and caresses it. Mr. Dean has no such softness, and enters the nursery with the tread and gaiety of an ogre.† "I have been assured," says he in the "Modest

* "Dr. Swift had a natural severity of face, which even his smiles could scarce soften, or his utmost gaiety render placid and serene; but when that sternness of visage was increased by rage, it is scarce possible to imagine looks or features that carried in them more terror and austerity."—*Orrery.*

† "LONDON: *April 10th*, 1713.

"Lady Masham's eldest boy is very ill: I doubt he will not live; and she stays at Kensington to nurse him, which vexes us all. She is so excessively fond, it makes me mad. She should never leave the Queen, but leave everything, to stick to what is so much the interest of the public, as well as her own. . ."—*Journal.*

Proposal," "by a very knowing American of my acquaintance in London, that a young healthy child, well nursed, is, at a year old, a most delicious, nourishing, and wholesome food, whether stewed, roasted, baked, or boiled; and I make no doubt it will equally serve in a *ragoût*." And taking up this pretty joke, as his way is, he argues it with perfect gravity and logic. He turns and twists this subject in a score of different ways; he hashes it; and he serves it up cold; and he garnishes it; and relishes it always. He describes the little animal as "dropped from its dam," advising that the mother should let it suck plentifully in the last month, so as to render it plump and fat for a good table! "A child," says his Reverence, "will make two dishes at an entertainment for friends; and when the family dines alone, the fore or hind quarter will make a reasonable dish," and so on; and the subject being so delightful that he can't leave it, he proceeds to recommend, in place of venison for squires' tables, "the bodies of young lads and maidens not exceeding fourteen or under twelve." Amiable humourist! laughing castigator of morals! There was a process well known and practised in the Dean's gay days; when a lout entered the coffee-house, the wags proceeded to what they called "roasting" him. This is roasting a subject with a vengeance. The Dean had a native genius for it. As the "Almanach des Gourmands" says, "On naît rôtisseur."

And it was not merely by the sarcastic method that Swift exposed the unreasonableness of loving and having children. In "Gulliver," the folly of love and marriage is urged by graver arguments and advice. In the famous Lilliputian kingdom, Swift speaks with approval of the practice of instantly removing children from their parents and educating them by the State; and amongst his favourite horses, a pair of foals are stated to be the very utmost a well-regulated equine couple would permit themselves. In fact, our great satirist was of opinion that conjugal love was unadvisable, and illustrated the theory by his own practice and example—God help him!—which made him about the most wretched being in God's world.*

The grave and logical conduct of an absurd proposition, as exemplified in the cannibal proposal just mentioned, is our author's constant method through all his works of humour. Given a country of people six inches or sixty feet high, and by the mere process of the logic, a thousand wonderful absurdities are evolved, at so many stages of the calculation. Turning to the First Minister who waited behind him with a white staff near as tall as the mainmast of the

* "My health is somewhat mended, but at best I have an ill head and an aching heart."—*In May* 1719.

Royal Sovereign, the King of Brobdingnag observes how contemptible a thing human grandeur is, as represented by such a contemptible little creature as Gulliver. "The Emperor of Lilliput's features are strong and masculine" (what a surprising humour there is in this description!)—"The Emperor's features," Gulliver says, "are strong and masculine, with an Austrian lip, an arched nose, his complexion olive, his countenance erect, his body and limbs well proportioned, and his deportment majestic. He is taller *by the breadth of my nail* than any of his Court, which alone is enough to strike an awe into beholders."

What a surprising humour there is in these descriptions! How noble the satire is here! how just and honest! How perfect the image! Mr. Macaulay has quoted the charming lines of the poet where the king of the pigmies is measured by the same standard. We have all read in Milton of the spear that was like "the mast of some great ammiral"; but these images are surely likely to come to the comic poet originally. The subject is before him. He is turning it in a thousand ways. He is full of it. The figure suggests itself naturally to him, and comes out of his subject, as in that wonderful passage, when Gulliver's box having been dropped by the eagle into the sea, and Gulliver having been received into the ship's cabin, he calls upon the crew to bring the box into the cabin, and put it on the table, the cabin being only a quarter the size of the box. It is the *veracity* of the blunder which is so admirable. Had a man come from such a country as Brobdingnag, he would have blundered so.

But the best stroke of humour, if there be a best in that abounding book, is that where Gulliver, in the unpronounceable country, describes his parting from his master the horse.*

* Perhaps the most melancholy satire in the whole of the dreadful book is the description of the very old people in the "Voyage to Laputa." At Lugnag, Gulliver hears of some persons who never die, called the Struldbrugs, and expressing a wish to become acquainted with men who must have so much learning and experience, his colloquist describes the Struldbrugs to him.

"He said: They commonly acted like mortals, till about thirty years old, after which, by degrees, they grew melancholy and dejected, increasing in both till they came to fourscore. This he learned from their own confession: for otherwise there not being above two or three of that species born in an age, they were too few to form a general observation by. When they came to fourscore years, which is reckoned the extremity of living in this country, they had not only all the follies and infirmities of other old men, but many more, which arose from the dreadful prospect of never dying. They were not only opinionative, peevish, covetous, morose, vain, talkative, but incapable of friendship, and dead to all natural affection, which never descended below their grandchildren. Envy and impotent desires are their prevailing passions. But those objects against which their envy seems principally directed, are the vices of the younger sort and the deaths of the old. By reflecting on the

"I took," he says, "a second leave of my master, but as I was going to prostrate myself to kiss his hoof, he did me the honour to raise it gently to my mouth. I am not ignorant how much I have been censured for mentioning this last particular. Detractors are pleased to think it improbable that so illustrious a person should descend to give so great a mark of distinction to a creature so inferior as I. Neither have I forgotten how apt some travellers are to boast of extraordinary favours they have received. But if these censurers were better acquainted with the noble and courteous disposition of the Houyhnhnms they would soon change their opinion."

The surprise here, the audacity of circumstantial evidence, the astounding gravity of the speaker, who is not ignorant how much he has been censured, the nature of the favour conferred, and the respectful exultation at the receipt of it, are surely complete: it is truth topsy-turvy, entirely logical and absurd.

As for the humour and conduct of this famous fable, I suppose

former, they find themselves cut off from all possibility of pleasure; and whenever they see a funeral, they lament, and repine that others are gone to a harbour of rest, to which they themselves never can hope to arrive. They have no remembrance of anything but what they learned and observed in their youth and middle age, and even that is very imperfect. And for the truth or particulars of any fact, it is safer to depend on common tradition than upon their best recollections. The least miserable among them appear to be those who turn to dotage, and entirely lose their memories; these meet with more pity and assistance, because they want many bad qualities which abound in others.

"If a Struldbrug happen to marry one of his own kind, the marriage is dissolved of course, by the courtesy of the kingdom, as soon as the younger of the two comes to be fourscore. For the law thinks it a reasonable indulgence that those who are condemned, without any fault of their own, to a perpetual continuance in the world, should not have their misery doubled by the load of a wife.

"As soon as they have completed the term of eighty years, they are looked on as dead in law; their heirs immediately succeed to their estates, only a small pittance is reserved for their support; and the poor ones are maintained at the public charge. After that period they are held incapable of any employment of trust or profit, they cannot purchase lands or take leases, neither are they allowed to be witnesses in any cause, either civil or criminal, not even for the decision of meers and bounds.

"At ninety they lose their teeth and hair; they have at that age no distinction of taste, but eat and drink whatever they can get without relish or appetite. The diseases they were subject to still continue, without increasing or diminishing. In talking, they forget the common appellation of things, and the names of persons, even of those who are their nearest friends and relations. For the same reason, they can never amuse themselves with reading, because their memory will not serve to carry them from the begin-

there is no person who reads but must admire; as for the moral, I think it horrible, shameful, unmanly, blasphemous; and giant and great as this Dean is, I say we should hoot him. Some of this audience mayn't have read the last part of Gulliver, and to such I would recall the advice of the venerable Mr. Punch to persons about to marry, and say "Don't." When Gulliver first lands among the Yahoos, the naked howling wretches clamber up trees and assault him, and he describes himself as "almost stifled with the filth which fell about him." The reader of the fourth part of "Gulliver's Travels" is like the hero himself in this instance. It is Yahoo language: a monster gibbering shrieks, and gnashing imprecations against mankind—tearing down all shreds of modesty, past all sense of manliness and shame; filthy in word, filthy in thought, furious, raging, obscene.

And dreadful it is to think that Swift knew the tendency of his creed—the fatal rocks towards which his logic desperately drifted. That last part of "Gulliver" is only a consequence of what has

ning of a sentence to the end; and by this defect they are deprived of the only entertainment whereof they might otherwise be capable.

"The language of this country being always upon the flux, the Struldbrugs of one age do not understand those of another; neither are they able, after two hundred years, to hold any conversation (further than by a few general words) with their neighbours, the mortals; and thus they lie under the disadvantage of living like foreigners in their own country.

"This was the account given me of the Struldbrugs, as near as I can remember. I afterwards saw five or six of different ages, the youngest not above two hundred years old, who were brought to me at several times by some of my friends; but although they were told 'that I was a great traveller, and had seen all the world,' they had not the least curiosity to ask me a question; only desired I would give them slumskudask, or a token of remembrance: which is a modest way of begging, to avoid the law, that strictly forbids it, because they are provided for by the public, although indeed with a very scanty allowance.

"They are despised and hated by all sorts of people; w en one of them is born, it is reckoned ominous, and their birth is recorded very particularly; so that you may know their age by consulting the register, which, however, has not been kept above a thousand years past, or at least has been destroyed by time or public disturbances. But the usual way of computing how old they are, is by asking them what kings or great persons they can remember, and then consulting history; for infallibly the last prince in their mind did not begin his reign after they were fourscore years old.

"They were the most mortifying sight I ever beheld, and the women more horrible than the men; besides the usual deformities in extreme old age, they acquired an additional ghastliness, in proportion to their number of years, which is not to be described; and among half-a-dozen, I soon distinguished which was the eldest, although there was not above a century or two between them."—*Gulliver's Travels.*

gone before; and the worthlessness of all mankind, the pettiness, cruelty, pride, imbecility, the general vanity, the foolish pretension, the mock greatness, the pompous dulness, the mean aims, the base successes—all these were present to him; it was with the din of these curses of the world, blasphemies against Heaven, shrieking in his ears, that he began to write his dreadful allegory—of which the meaning is that man is utterly wicked, desperate, and imbecile, and his passions are so monstrous, and his boasted powers so mean, that he is and deserves to be the slave of brutes, and ignorance is better than his vaunted reason. What had this man done? what secret remorse was rankling at his heart? what fever was boiling in him, that he should see all the world bloodshot? We view the world with our own eyes, each of us; and we make from within us the world we see. A weary heart gets no gladness out of sunshine; a selfish man is sceptical about friendship, as a man with no ear doesn't care for music. A frightful self-consciousness it must have been, which looked on mankind so darkly through those keen eyes of Swift.

A remarkable story is told by Scott, of Delany, who interrupted Archbishop King and Swift in a conversation which left the prelate in tears, and from which Swift rushed away with marks of strong terror and agitation in his countenance, upon which the Archbishop said to Delany, "You have just met the most unhappy man on earth; but on the subject of his wretchedness you must never ask a question." *

The most unhappy man on earth;—*Miserrimus*—what a character of him! And at this time all the great wits of England had been at his feet. All Ireland had shouted after him, and worshipped him as a liberator, a saviour, the greatest Irish patriot and citizen. Dean Drapier Bickerstaff Gulliver—the most famous statesmen and the greatest poets of his day had applauded him and done him homage; and at this time, writing over to Bolingbroke from Ireland, he says, "It is time for me to have done with the world, and so I would if I could get into a better before I was called into the best, *and not die here in a rage, like a poisoned rat in a hole.*"

We have spoken about the men, and Swift's behaviour to them; and now it behoves us not to forget that there are certain other persons in the creation who had rather intimate relations with the great Dean.† Two women whom he loved and injured are known

* This remarkable story came to Scott from an unnamed friend of Delany's widow. It has been supposed to confirm the conjecture about his natural relationship to Stella; but, even if correctly reported, is open to any number of interpretations.

† The name of Varina has been thrown into the shade by those of the famous Stella and Vanessa; but she had a story of her own to tell about

by every reader of books so familiarly that if we had seen them, or if they had been relatives of our own, we scarcely could have known them better. Who hasn't in his mind an image of Stella? Who does not love her? Fair and tender creature: pure and affectionate heart! Boots it to you, now that you have been at rest for a hundred and twenty years, not divided in death from the cold heart which caused yours, whilst it beat, such faithful pangs of love and grief—boots it to you now, that the whole world loves and deplores you? Scarce any man, I believe, ever thought of that grave, that did not cast a flower of pity on it, and write over it a sweet epitaph. Gentle lady, so lovely, so loving, so unhappy! you have had countless champions; millions of manly hearts mourning for you. From generation to generation we take up the fond tradition of your beauty, we watch and follow your tragedy, your bright morning love and purity, your constancy, your grief, your sweet martyrdom. We know your legend by heart. You are one of the saints of English story.

And if Stella's love and innocence are charming to contemplate, I will say that, in spite of ill-usage, in spite of drawbacks, in spite of mysterious separation and union, of hope delayed and sickened heart—in the teeth of Vanessa, and that little episodical aberration which plunged Swift into such woeful pitfalls and quagmires of amorous perplexity—in spite of the verdicts of most women, I believe, who, as far as my experience and conversation go, generally take Vanessa's part in the controversy—in spite of the tears which Swift caused Stella to shed, and the rocks and barriers which fate and temper interposed, and which prevented the pure course of that true love from running smoothly—the brightest part of Swift's

the blue eyes of young Jonathan. One may say that the book of Swift's Life opens at places kept by these blighted flowers! Varina must have a paragraph.

She was a Miss Jane Waryng, sister to a college chum of his. In 1696, when Swift was nineteen years old, we find him writing a love-letter to her, beginning, "Impatience is the most inseparable quality of a lover." But absence made a great difference in his feelings; so, four years afterwards, the tone is changed. He writes again, a very curious letter, offering to marry her, and putting the offer in such a way that nobody could possibly accept it.

After dwelling on his poverty, &c., he says, conditionally, "I shall be blessed to have you in my arms, without regarding whether your person be beautiful, or your fortune large. Cleanliness in the first, and competency in the second, is all I ask for!"

The editors do not tell us what became of Varina in life. One would be glad to know that she met with some worthy partner, and lived long enough to see her little boys laughing over Lilliput, without any *arrière pensée* of a sad character about the great Dean!

story, the pure star in that dark and tempestuous life of Swift's, is his love for Hester Johnson. It has been my business, professionally of course, to go through a deal of sentimental reading in my time, and to acquaint myself with love-making, as it has been described in various languages, and at various ages of the world; and I know of nothing more manly, more tender, more exquisitely touching, than some of these brief notes, written in what Swift calls "his little language" in his journal to Stella.* He writes to her night and morning often. He never sends away a letter to her but he begins a new one on the same day. He can't bear to let go her kind little hand, as it were. He knows that she is thinking of him, and longing for him far away in Dublin yonder. He takes her letters from under his pillow and talks to them, familiarly, paternally, with fond epithets and pretty caresses—as he would to the sweet and artless creature who loved him. "Stay," he writes one morning—it is the 14th of December 1710—"Stay, I will answer some of your letter this morning in bed. Let me see. Come and appear, little letter! Here I am, says he, and what say you to Stella this morning fresh and fasting? And can Stella read this writing without hurting her dear eyes?" he goes on, after more kind prattle and fond whispering. The dear eyes shine clearly upon him then—the good angel of his life is with him and blessing him. Ah, it was a hard fate that wrung from them so many tears, and stabbed pitilessly that pure and tender bosom. A hard fate: but would she have changed it? I have heard a woman say that she would have taken Swift's cruelty to have had his tenderness. He had a sort of worship for her whilst he wounded her. He speaks of her after she is gone; of her wit, of her kindness, of her grace, of her beauty, with a simple love and reverence that are indescribably touching; in contemplation of her goodness his hard heart melts into pathos; his cold rhyme kindles and glows into poetry, and he falls down on his knees, so to speak, before the angel whose life he had embittered, confesses his own wretched-

* A sentimental Champollion might find a good deal of matter for his art, in expounding the symbols of the "Little Language." Usually, Stella is "M.D.," but sometimes her companion, Mrs. Dingley, is included in it. Swift is "Presto"; also P.D.F.R. We have "Good-night, M.D.; Night, M.D.; Little M.D.; Stellakins; Pretty Stella; Dear, roguish, impudent, pretty M.D.' Every now and then he breaks into rhyme, as—

> "I wish you both a merry new year,
> Roast-beef, mince-pies, and good strong beer,
> And me a share of your good cheer,
> That I was there, as you were here,
> And you are a little saucy dear."

ness and unworthiness, and adores her with cries of remorse and love :—

> "When on my sickly couch I lay,
> Impatient both of night and day,
> And groaning in unmanly strains,
> Called every power to ease my pains,
> Then Stella ran to my relief,
> With cheerful face and inward grief,
> And though by Heaven's severe decree
> She suffers hourly more than me,
> No cruel master could require
> From slaves employed for daily hire,
> What Stella, by her friendship warmed,
> With vigour and delight performed.
> Now, with a soft and silent tread,
> Unheard she moves about my bed:
> My sinking spirits now supplies
> With cordials in her hands and eyes.
> Best pattern of true friends ! beware
> You pay too dearly for your care
> If, while your tenderness secures
> My life, it must endanger yours:
> For such a fool was never found
> Who pulled a palace to the ground,
> Only to have the ruins made
> Materials for a house decayed."

One little triumph Stella had in her life—one dear little piece of injustice was performed in her favour, for which I confess, for my part, I can't help thanking fate and the Dean. *That other person* was sacrificed to her—that—that young woman, who lived five doors from Doctor Swift's lodgings in Bury Street, and who flattered him, and made love to him in such an outrageous manner —Vanessa was thrown over.

Swift did not keep Stella's letters to him in reply to those he wrote to her.* He kept Bolingbroke's, and Pope's, and Harley's,

* The following passages are from a paper begun by Swift on the evening of the day of her death, Jan. 28, 1727–28 :—

"She was sickly from her childhood, until about the age of fifteen; but then she grew into perfect health, and was looked upon as one of the most beautiful, graceful, and agreeable young women in London—only a little too fat. Her hair was blacker than a raven, and every feature of her face in perfection.

". . . Properly speaking"—he goes on, with a calmness which, under the circumstances, is terrible—"she has been dying six months! . . .

"Never was any of her sex born with better gifts of the mind, or who more improved them by reading and conversation. . . . All of us who had the happiness of her friendship agreed unanimously, that in an afternoon's or evening's

and Peterborough's: but Stella "very carefully," the Lives say, kept Swift's. Of course: that is the way of the world: and so we cannot tell what her style was, or of what sort were the little letters which the Doctor placed there at night, and bade to appear from under his pillow of a morning. But in Letter IV. of that famous collection he describes his lodging in Bury Street, where he has the first-floor, a dining-room and bed-chamber, at eight shillings a week; and in Letter VI. he says "he has visited a lady just come to town," whose name somehow is not mentioned; and in Letter VIII. he enters a query of Stella's—"What do you mean 'that boards near me, that I dine with now and then'? What the deuce! You know whom I have dined with every day since I left you, better than I do." Of course she does. Of course Swift has not the slightest idea of what she means. But in a few letters more it turns out that the Doctor has been to dine "gravely" with a Mrs. Vanhomrigh: then that he has been to "his neighbour": then that he has been unwell, and means to dine for the whole week with his neighbour! Stella was quite right in her previsions. She saw from the very first hint what was going to happen; and scented Vanessa in the air.* The rival is at the Dean's feet.

conversation she never failed before we parted of delivering the best thing that was said in the company. Some of us have written down several of her sayings, or what the French call *bons mots*, wherein she excelled beyond belief."

The specimens on record, however, in the Dean's paper, called "Bon Mots de Stella," scarcely bear out this last part of the panegyric. But the following prove her wit:—

"A gentleman who had been very silly and pert in her company, at last began to grieve at remembering the loss of a child lately dead. A bishop sitting by comforted him—that he should be easy, because 'the child was gone to heaven.' 'No, my Lord,' said she; 'that is it which most grieves him, because he is sure never to see his child there.'

"When she was extremely ill, her physician said, 'Madam, you are near the bottom of the hill, but we will endeavour to get you up again.' She answered, 'Doctor, I fear I shall be out of breath before I get up to the top.'

"A very dirty clergyman of her acquaintance, who affected smartness and repartees, was asked by some of the company how his nails came to be so dirty. He was at a loss; but she solved the difficulty by saying, 'The Doctor's nails grew dirty by scratching himself.'

"A Quaker apothecary sent her a vial, corked; it had a broad brim, and a label of paper about its neck. 'What is that?'—said she—'my apothecary's son!' The ridiculous resemblance, and the suddenness of the question, set us all a-laughing."—*Swift's Works*, Scott's ed. vol. ix. 295-96.

* "I am so hot and lazy after my morning's walk, that I loitered at Mrs. Vanhomrigh's, where my best gown and periwig was, and *out of mere listlessness dine there very often*; so I did to-day."—*Journal to Stella.*

Mrs. Vanhomrigh, "Vanessa's" mother, was the widow of a Dutch merchant

The pupil and teacher are reading together, and drinking tea together, and going to prayers together, and learning Latin together, and conjugating *amo, amas, amavi* together. The "little language" is over for poor Stella. By the rule of grammar and the course of conjugation, doesn't *amavi* come after *amo* and *amas?*

The loves of Cadenus and Vanessa * you may peruse in Cadenus's own poem on the subject, and in poor Vanessa's vehement expostulatory verses and letters to him; she adores him, implores him, admires him, thinks him something god-like, and only prays to be admitted to lie at his feet.† As they are bringing him home from church, those divine feet of Doctor Swift's are found pretty often in Vanessa's parlour. He likes to be admired and adored. He finds Miss Vanhomrigh to be a woman of great taste and spirit, and beauty and wit, and a fortune too. He sees her every day; he does not tell Stella about the business; until the impetuous Vanessa becomes too fond of him, until the Doctor is quite frightened by the young woman's ardour, and confounded by her warmth. He wanted to marry neither of them

who held lucrative appointments in King William's time. The family settled in London in 1709, and had a house in Bury Street, St. James's—a street made notable by such residents as Swift and Steele; and, in our own time, Moore and Crabbe.

* "Vanessa was excessively vain. The character given of her by Cadenus is fine painting, but in general fictitious. She was fond of dress; impatient to be admired; very romantic in her turn of mind; superior, in her own opinion, to all her sex; full of pertness, gaiety, and pride; not without some agreeable accomplishments, but far from being either beautiful or genteel; . . . happy in the thoughts of being reported Swift's concubine, but still aiming and intending to be his wife."—*Lord Orrery.*

† "You bid me be easy, and you would see me as often as you could. You had better have said, as often as you can get the better of your inclinations so much; or as often as you remember there was such a one in the world. If you continue to treat me as you do, you will not be made uneasy by me long. It is impossible to describe what I have suffered since I saw you last: I am sure I could have borne the rack much better than those killing words of yours. Sometimes I have resolved to die without seeing you more; but those resolves, to your misfortune, did not last long; for there is something in human nature that prompts one so to find relief in this world I must give way to it, and beg you would see me, and speak kindly to me; for I am sure you'd not condemn any one to suffer what I have done, could you but know it. The reason I write to you is, because I cannot tell it to you should I see you; for when I begin to complain, then you are angry, and there is something in your looks so awful that it strikes me dumb. Oh! that you may have but so much regard for me left that this complaint may touch your soul with pity. I say as little as ever I can; did you but know what I thought, I am sure it would move you to forgive me; and believe I cannot help telling you this and live."—*Vanessa.* (M. 1714.)

—that I believe was the truth; but if he had not married Stella, Vanessa would have had him in spite of himself. When he went back to Ireland, his Ariadne, not content to remain in her isle, pursued the fugitive Dean. In vain he protested, he vowed, he soothed, and bullied; the news of the Dean's marriage with Stella at last came to her, and it killed her—she died of that passion.*

And when she died, and Stella heard that Swift had written beautifully regarding her, "That doesn't surprise me," said Mrs. Stella, "for we all know the Dean could write beautifully about a broomstick." A woman—a true woman! Would you have had one of them forgive the other?

In a note in his biography, Scott says that his friend Doctor Tuke, of Dublin, has a lock of Stella's hair, enclosed in a paper by Swift, on which are written in the Dean's hand, the words: "*Only a woman's hair.*" An instance, says Scott, of the Dean's desire to veil his feelings under the mask of cynical indifference.

See the various notions of critics! Do those words indicate

* "If we consider Swift's behaviour, so far only as it relates to women, we shall find that he looked upon them rather as busts than as whole figures."—*Orrery.*

"You would have smiled to have found his house a constant seraglio of very virtuous women, who attended him from morning till night."—*Orrery.*

A correspondent of Sir Walter Scott's furnished him with the materials on which to found the following interesting passage about Vanessa—after she had retired to cherish her passion in retreat:—

"Marley Abbey, near Celbridge, where Miss Vanhomrigh resided, is built much in the form of a real cloister, especially in its external appearance. An aged man (upwards of ninety, by his own account) showed the grounds to my correspondent. He was the son of Mrs. Vanhomrigh's gardener, and used to work with his father in the garden when a boy. He remembered the unfortunate Vanessa well; and his account of her corresponded with the usual description of her person, especially as to her *embonpoint.* He said she went seldom abroad, and saw little company: her constant amusement was reading, or walking in the garden. . . . She avoided company, and was always melancholy, save when Dean Swift was there, and then she seemed happy. The garden was to an uncommon degree crowded with laurels. The old man said that when Miss Vanhomrigh expected the Dean she always planted with her own hand a laurel or two against his arrival. He showed her favourite seat, still called 'Vanessa's bower.' Three or four trees and some laurels indicate the spot. . . . There were two seats and a rude table within the bower, the opening of which commanded a view of the Liffey. . . . In this sequestered spot, according to the old gardener's account, the Dean and Vanessa used often to sit, with books and writing-materials on the table before them."—SCOTT'S *Swift*, vol. i. pp. 246–7.

". . . But Miss Vanhomrigh, irritated at the situation in which she found herself, determined on bringing to a crisis those expectations of a union with the

indifference or an attempt to hide feeling? Did you ever hear or read four words more pathetic? Only a woman's hair; only love, only fidelity, only purity, innocence, beauty; only the tenderest heart in the world stricken and wounded, and passed away now out of reach of pangs of hope deferred, love insulted, and pitiless desertion:—only that lock of hair left; and memory and remorse, for the guilty lonely wretch, shuddering over the grave of his victim.*

And yet to have had so much love, he must have given some. Treasures of wit and wisdom, and tenderness, too, must that man have had locked up in the caverns of his gloomy heart, and shown fitfully to one or two whom he took in there. But it was not good to visit that place. People did not remain there long, and suffered

object of her affections—to the hope of which she had clung amid every vicissitude of his conduct towards her. The most probable bar was his undefined connection with Mrs. Johnson, which, as it must have been perfectly known to her, had, doubtless, long excited her secret jealousy, although only a single hint to that purpose is to be found in their correspondence, and that so early as 1713, when she writes to him—then in Ireland—'If you are very happy, it is ill-natured of you not to tell me so, *except 'tis what is inconsistent with mine.*' Her silence and patience under this state of uncertainty for no less than eight years, must have been partly owing to her awe for Swift, and partly, perhaps, to the weak state of her rival's health, which, from year to year, seemed to announce speedy dissolution. At length, however, Vanessa's impatience prevailed, and she ventured on the decisive step of writing to Mrs. Johnson herself, requesting to know the nature of that connection. Stella, in reply, informed her of her marriage with the Dean; and full of the highest resentment against Swift for having given another female such a right in him as Miss Vanhomrigh's inquiries implied, she sent to him her rival's letter of interrogation, and without seeing him, or awaiting his reply, retired to the house of Mr. Ford, near Dublin. Every reader knows the consequence. Swift, in one of those paroxysms of fury to which he was liable, both from temper and disease, rode instantly to Marley Abbey. As he entered the apartment, the sternness of his countenance, which was peculiarly formed to express the fiercer passions, struck the unfortunate Vanessa with such terror that she could scarce ask whether he would not sit down. He answered by flinging a letter on the table, and, instantly leaving the house, mounted his horse, and returned to Dublin. When Vanessa opened the packet, she only found her own letter to Stella. It was her death-warrant. She sunk at once under the disappointment of the delayed yet cherished hopes which had so long sickened her heart, and beneath the unrestrained wrath of him for whose sake she had indulged them. How long she survived this last interview is uncertain, but the time does not seem to have exceeded a few weeks."—*Scott.*

* Thackeray wrote to Hayward, who had said something of this lecture when originally delivered, and had apparently misunderstood this passage, that the phrase quoted seemed to him to be "the most affecting words I ever heard, indicating the truest love, passion, and remorse."—*Hayward Correspondence*, i. 119.

for having been there.* He shrank away from all affection sooner or later. Stella and Vanessa both died near him, and away from him. He had not heart enough to see them die. He broke from his fastest friend, Sheridan; he slunk away from his fondest admirer, Pope. His laugh jars on one's ear after seven score years. He was always alone—alone and gnashing in the darkness, except when Stella's sweet smile came and shone upon him. When that went, silence and utter night closed over him. An immense genius: an awful downfall and ruin. So great a man he seems to me, that thinking of him is like thinking of an empire falling. We have other great names to mention—none I think, however, so great or so gloomy.

* "M. Swift est Rabelais dans son bon sens, et vivant en bonne compagnie. Il n'a pas, à la vérité, la gaîté du premier, mais il a toute la finesse, la raison, le choix, le bon goût qui manquent à notre curé de Meudon. Ses vers sont d'un goût singulier, et presque inimitable; la bonne plaisanterie est son partage en vers et en prose; mais pour le bien entendre il faut faire un petit voyage dans son pays."—VOLTAIRE: *Lettres sur les Anglais.* Lettre XX.

CONGREVE AND ADDISON

A GREAT number of years ago, before the passing of the Reform Bill, there existed at Cambridge a certain debating club, called the "Union"; and I remember that there was a tradition amongst the undergraduates who frequented that renowned school of oratory, that the great leaders of the Opposition and Government had their eyes upon the University Debating Club, and that if a man distinguished himself there he ran some chance of being returned to Parliament as a great nobleman's nominee. So Jones of John's, or Thomson of Trinity, would rise in their might, and draping themselves in their gowns, rally round the monarchy, or hurl defiance at priests and kings, with the majesty of Pitt or the fire of Mirabeau, fancying all the while that the great nobleman's emissary was listening to the debate from the back benches, where he was sitting with the family seat in his pocket. Indeed, the legend said that one or two young Cambridge men, orators of the "Union," were actually caught up thence, and carried down to Cornwall or Old Sarum, and so into Parliament. And many a young fellow deserted the jogtrot University curriculum, to hang on in the dust behind the fervid wheels of the parliamentary chariot.

Where, I have often wondered, were the sons of Peers and Members of Parliament in Anne's and George's time? Were they all in the army, or hunting in the country, or boxing the watch? How was it that the young gentlemen from the University got such a prodigious number of places? A lad composed a neat copy of verses at Christchurch or Trinity, in which the death of a great personage was bemoaned, the French King assailed, the Dutch or Prince Eugene complimented, or the reverse; and the party in power was presently to provide for the young poet; and a commissionership, or a post in the Stamps, or the secretaryship of an Embassy, or a clerkship in the Treasury, came into the bard's possession. A wonderful fruit-bearing rod was that of Busby's. What have men of letters got in *our* time? Think, not only of Swift, a king fit to rule in any time or empire—but Addison,

Steele, Prior, Tickell, Congreve, John Gay, John Dennis, and many others, who got public employment, and pretty little pickings out of the public purse.* The wits of whose names we shall treat in this lecture and two following, all (save one) touched the King's coin, and had, at some period of their lives, a happy quarter-day coming round for them.

They all began at school or college in the regular way, producing panegyrics upon public characters, what were called odes upon public events, battles, sieges, Court marriages and deaths, in which the gods of Olympus and the tragic muse were fatigued with invocations, according to the fashion of the time in France and in England. "Aid us, Mars, Bacchus, Apollo," cried Addison, or Congreve, singing of William or Marlborough. "Accourez, chastes nymphes du Permesse," says Boileau, celebrating the Grand Monarch. "Des sons que ma lyre enfante ces arbres sont réjouis; marquez-en bien la cadence; et vous, vents, faites silence! je vais parler de Louis!" Schoolboys' themes and foundation exercises are the only relics left now of this scholastic fashion. The Olympians are left quite undisturbed in their mountain. What man of note, what contributor to the poetry of a country newspaper, would now think of writing a congratulatory ode on the birth of the heir to a dukedom, or the marriage of a nobleman? In the past century the young gentlemen of the Universities all exercised themselves at these queer compositions; and some got fame, and some gained

* The following is a *conspectus* of them :—

ADDISON.—Commissioner of Appeals; Under-Secretary of State; Secretary to the Lord Lieutenant of Ireland; Keeper of the Records in Ireland; Lord of Trade; and one of the Principal Secretaries of State, successively.

STEELE.—Commissioner of the Stamp Office; Surveyor of the Royal Stables at Hampton Court; and Governor of the Royal Company of Comedians; Commissioner of "Forfeited Estates in Scotland."

PRIOR.—Secretary to the Embassy at the Hague; Gentleman of the Bed-chamber to King William; Secretary to the Embassy in France; Under-Secretary of State; Ambassador to France.

TICKELL.—Under-Secretary of State; Secretary to the Lords Justices of Ireland.

CONGREVE.—Commissioner for licensing Hackney-Coaches; Commissioner for Wine Licences; place in the Pipe Office; post in the Custom House; Secretary of Jamaica.

GAY.—Secretary to the Earl of Clarendon (when Ambassador to Hanover).

JOHN DENNIS.—A place in the Custom House.

"En Angleterre . . . les lettres sont plus en honneur qu'ici."—**VOLTAIRE**: *Lettres sur les Anglais.* Lettre XX.

patrons and places for life, and many more took nothing by these efforts of what they were pleased to call their muses.

William Congreve's * Pindaric Odes are still to be found in "Johnson's Poets," that now unfrequented poets'-corner, in which so many forgotten bigwigs have a niche; but though he was also voted to be one of the greatest tragic poets of any day, it was Congreve's wit and humour which first recommended him to courtly fortune. And it is recorded that his first play, the "Old Bachelor," brought our author to the notice of that great patron of English muses, Charles Montague, Lord Halifax—who, being desirous to place so eminent a wit in a state of ease and tranquillity, instantly made him one of the Commissioners for licensing hackney-coaches, bestowed on him soon after a place in the Pipe Office, and likewise a post in the Custom House of the value of £600.†

A commissionership of hackney-coaches—a post in the Custom House—a place in the Pipe Office, and all for writing a comedy! Doesn't it sound like a fable, that place in the Pipe Office? ‡ "Ah, l'heureux temps que celui de ces fables!" Men of letters there still be: but I doubt whether any Pipe Offices are left. The public has smoked them long ago.

Words, like men, pass current for a while with the public, and, being known everywhere abroad, at length take their places in society; so even the most secluded and refined ladies here present will have heard the phrase from their sons or brothers at school, and will permit me to call William Congreve, Esquire, the most eminent literary "swell" of his age. In my copy of "Johnson's

* He was the son of Colonel William Congreve, and grandson of Richard Congreve, Esquire, of Congreve and Stretton in Staffordshire—a very ancient family.

† The *Old Bachelor* was produced January 1693. Congreve was made Commissioner of Hackney-Coaches in 1695.

‡ "PIPE.—*Pipa*, in law, is a roll in the Exchequer, called also the *great roll*.

"*Pipe Office* is an office in which a person called the *Clerk of the Pipe* makes out leases of Crown lands, by warrant from the Lord Treasurer, or Commissioners of the Treasury, or Chancellor of the Exchequer.

"Clerk of the Pipe makes up all accounts of sheriffs, &c."—REES: *Cyclopæd.* Art. PIPE.

"*Pipe Office.*—Spelman thinks so called, because the papers were kept in a large *pipe* or cask.

"'These be at last brought into that office of her Majesty's Exchequer, which we, by a metaphor, do call the *pipe* . . . because the whole receipt is finally conveyed into it by means of divers small *pipes* or quills.'—BACON: *The Office of Alienations*."

[We are indebted to Richardson's *Dictionary* for this fragment of erudition. But a modern man of letters can know little on these points—by experience.]

Lives" Congreve's wig is the tallest, and put on with the jauntiest air of all the laurelled worthies. "I am the great Mr. Congreve," he seems to say, looking out from his voluminous curls. People called him the great Mr. Congreve.* From the beginning of his career until the end everybody admired him. Having got his education in Ireland, at the same school and college with Swift, he came to live in the Middle Temple, London, where he luckily bestowed no attention to the law; but splendidly frequented the coffee-houses and theatres, and appeared in the side-box, the tavern, the Piazza, and the Mall, brilliant, beautiful, and victorious from the first. Everybody acknowledged the young chieftain. The great Mr. Dryden † declared that he was equal to Shakspeare, and bequeathed to him his own undisputed poetical crown, and writes of him: "Mr. Congreve has done me the favour to review the 'Æneis' and compare my version with the original. I shall

* "It has been observed that no change of Ministers affected him in the least; nor was he ever removed from any post that was given to him, except to a better. His place in the Custom House, and his office of Secretary in Jamaica, are said to have brought him in upwards of twelve hundred a year."—*Biog. Brit.* Art. CONGREVE.

† Dryden addressed his "twelfth epistle" to "My dear friend, Mr. Congreve," on his comedy called the *Double Dealer*, in which he says:—

> "Great Jonson did by strength of judgment please;
> Yet, doubling Fletcher's force, he wants his ease.
> In differing talents both adorned their age:
> One for the study, t'other for the stage.
> But both to Congreve justly shall submit,
> One match'd in judgment, both o'ermatched in wit.
> In him all beauties of this age we see," &c. &c.

The *Double Dealer*, however, was not so palpable a hit as the *Old Bachelor*, but, at first, met with opposition. The critics having fallen foul of it, our "Swell" applied the scourge to that presumptuous body, in the "Epistle Dedicatory" to the "Right Honourable Charles Montague."

"I was conscious," said he, "where a true critic might have put me upon my defence. I was prepared for the attack . . . but I have not heard anything said sufficient to provoke an answer."

He goes on—

"But there is one thing at which I am more concerned than all the false criticisms that are made upon me; and that is, some of the ladies are offended. I am heartily sorry for it; for I declare, I would rather disoblige all the critics in the world than one of the fair sex. They are concerned that I have represented some women vicious and affected. How can I help it? It is the business of a comic poet to paint the vices and follies of human kind. . . . I should be very glad of an opportunity to make my compliments to those ladies who are offended. But they can no more expect it in a comedy, than *to be tickled by a surgeon when he is letting their blood.*"

never be ashamed to own that this excellent young man has showed me many faults which I have endeavoured to correct."

The "excellent young man" was but three or four and twenty when the great Dryden thus spoke of him: the greatest literary chief in England, the veteran field-marshal of letters, himself the marked man of all Europe, and the centre of a school of wits who daily gathered round his chair and tobacco-pipe at Will's. Pope dedicated his "Iliad" to him;* Swift, Addison, Steele, all acknowledge Congreve's rank, and lavish compliments upon him. Voltaire went to wait upon him as on one of the Representatives of Literature; and the man who scarce praises any other living person—who flung abuse at Pope, and Swift, and Steele, and Addison—the Grub Street Timon, old John Dennis,† was hat in hand to Mr. Congreve; and said that when he retired from the stage, Comedy went with him.

Nor was he less victorious elsewhere. He was admired in the drawing-rooms as well as the coffee-houses; as much beloved in the side-box as on the stage. He loved, and conquered, and jilted the beautiful Bracegirdle,‡ the heroine of all his plays, the favourite of all the town of her day; and the Duchess of Marlborough, Marlborough's daughter, had such an admiration of him, that when he died she had an ivory figure made to imitate him,§ and a large wax doll with gouty feet to be dressed just as the great Congreve's gouty

* "Instead of endeavouring to raise a vain monument to myself, let me leave behind me a memorial of my friendship with one of the most valuable men as well as finest writers of my age and country—one who has tried, and knows by his own experience, how hard an undertaking it is to do justice to Homer—and one who, I am sure, seriously rejoices with me at the period of my labours. To him, therefore, having brought this long work to a conclusion, I desire to dedicate it, and to have the honour and satisfaction of placing together in this manner the names of Mr. Congreve and of—A. POPE."—*Postscript to Translation of the Iliad of Homer*, March 25, 1720.

† "When asked why he listened to the praises of Dennis, he said he had much rather be flattered than abused. Swift had a particular friendship for our author, and generously took him under his protection in his high authoritative manner."—THOS. DAVIES: *Dramatic Miscellanies.*

‡ "Congreve was very intimate for years with Mrs. Bracegirdle, and lived in the same street, his house very near hers, until his acquaintance with the young Duchess of Marlborough. He then quitted that house. The Duchess showed me a diamond necklace (which Lady Di used afterwards to wear) that cost seven thousand pounds, and was purchased with the money Congreve left her. How much better would it have been to have given it to poor Mrs. Bracegirdle."—Dr. YOUNG. *Spence's Anecdotes.*

§ "A glass was put in the hand of the statue, which was supposed to bow to her Grace and to nod in approbation of what she spoke to it."—THOS. DAVIES: *Dramatic Miscellanies.*

feet were dressed in his great lifetime. He saved some money by his Pipe office, and his Custom House office, and his Hackney-Coach office, and nobly left it, not to Bracegirdle,* who wanted it, but to the Duchess of Marlborough, who didn't.†

How can I introduce to you that merry and shameless Comic Muse who won him such a reputation? Nell Gwynn's servant fought the other footman for having called his mistress a bad name; and in like manner, and with pretty little epithets, Jeremy Collier attacked that godless reckless Jezebel, the English comedy of his time, and called her what Nell Gwynn's man's fellow-servants called Nell Gwynn's man's mistress. The servants of the theatre, Dryden, Congreve,‡ and others, defended themselves with the same success, and for the same cause which set Nell's lacquey fighting. She was a disreputable, daring, laughing, painted French baggage, that Comic Muse. She came over from the Continent with Charles (who chose many more of his female friends there) at the Restoration—a wild dishevelled Laïs, with eyes bright with wit and wine—a saucy Court-favourite that sat at the King's knees, and laughed in his face, and when she showed her bold cheeks at her chariot-window, had some of the noblest and most famous people of the land bowing round her wheel. She was kind and popular enough, that daring Comedy, that audacious poor Nell: she was gay and

* The sum Congreve left Mrs. Bracegirdle was £200, as is said in the *Dramatic Miscellanies* of Tom Davies; where are some particulars about this charming actress and beautiful woman.

She had a "lively aspect," says Tom, on the authority of Cibber, and "such a glow of health and cheerfulness in her countenance, as inspired everybody with desire." "Scarce an audience saw her that were not half of them her lovers."

Congreve and Rowe courted her in the persons of their lovers. "In Tamerlane, Rowe courted her Selima, in the person of Axalla . . . ; Congreve insinuated his addresses in his Valentine to her Angelica, in *Love for Love;* in his Osmyn to her Almena, in the *Mourning Bride;* and, lastly, in his Mirabel to her Millamant, in the *Way of the World.* Mirabel, the fine gentleman of the play, is, I believe, not very distant from the real character of Congreve."—*Dramatic Miscellanies*, vol. iii. 1784.

She retired from the stage when Mrs. Oldfield began to be the public favourite. She died in 1748, in the eighty-fifth year of her age.

† Johnson calls his legacy the "accumulation of attentive parsimony, which," he continues, "though to her (the Duchess) superfluous and useless, might have given great assistance to the ancient family from which he descended, at that time, by the imprudence of his relation, reduced to difficulties and distress."—*Lives of the Poets.*

‡ He replied to Collier, in the pamphlet called *Amendments of Mr. Collier's False and Imperfect Citations*, &c. A specimen or two are subjoined:—

"The greater part of these examples which he has produced are only

generous, kind, frank, as such people can afford to be: and the men who lived with her and laughed with her, took her pay and drank her wine, turned out when the Puritans hooted her, to fight and defend her. But the jade was indefensible, and it is pretty certain her servants knew it.

There is life and death going on in everything: truth and lies always at battle. Pleasure is always warring against self-restraint. Doubt is always crying Psha! and sneering. A man in life, a humourist, in writing about life, sways over to one principle or the other, and laughs with the reverence for right and the love of truth in his heart, or laughs at these from the other side. Didn't I tell you that dancing was a serious business to Harlequin? I have read two or three of Congreve's plays over before speaking of him; and my feelings were rather like those, which I dare say most of us here have had, at Pompeii, looking at Sallust's house and the relics of an orgy; a dried wine-jar or two, a charred supper-table, the breast of a dancing-girl pressed against the ashes, the laughing skull of a jester: a perfect stillness round about, as the cicerone twangs his moral, and the blue sky shines calmly over the ruin. The Congreve Muse is dead, and her song choked in Time's ashes. We gaze at the skeleton, and wonder at the life which once revelled in its mad veins. We take the skull up, and muse over the frolic and daring, the wit, scorn, passion, hope, desire, with which that empty bowl once fermented. We think of the glances that allured, the tears that melted, of the bright eyes that shone in those vacant sockets; and of lips whispering love, and cheeks dimpling with smiles, that once covered yon ghastly yellow framework. They used to call those teeth pearls once. See, there's the cup she drank from, the gold-chain she wore on her neck, the vase which held the rouge for her cheeks, her looking-glass, and the harp she used to dance to. Instead of a feast we find a gravestone, and in place of a mistress, a few bones!

demonstrations of his own impurity: they only savour of his utterance, and were sweet enough till tainted by his breath.

"Where the expression is unblameable in its own pure and genuine signification, he enters into it, himself, like the evil spirit; he possesses the innocent phrase, and makes it bellow forth his own blasphemies.

"If I do not return him civilities in calling him names, it is because I am not very well versed in his nomenclatures. . . . I will only call him Mr. Collier, and that I will call him as often as I think he shall deserve it.

"The corruption of a rotten divine is the generation of a sour critic."

"Congreve," says Doctor Johnson, "a very young man, elated with success, and impatient of censure, assumed an air of confidence and security. . . . The dispute was protracted through ten years; but at last comedy grew more modest, and Collier lived to see the reward of his labours in the reformation of the theatre."—*Life of Congreve.*

Reading in these plays now, is like shutting your ears and looking at people dancing. What does it mean? the measures, the grimaces, the bowing, shuffling, and retreating, the *cavalier seul* advancing upon those ladies—those ladies and men twirling round at the end in a mad galop, after which everybody bows and the quaint rite is celebrated. Without the music we can't understand that comic dance of the last century—its strange gravity and gaiety, its decorum or its indecorum. It has a jargon of its own quite unlike life; a sort of moral of its own quite unlike life too. I'm afraid it's a Heathen mystery, symbolising a Pagan doctrine; protesting—as the Pompeians very likely were, assembled at their theatre and laughing at their games; as Sallust and his friends, and their mistresses protested, crowned with flowers, with cups in their hands—against the new, hard, ascetic, pleasure-hating doctrine whose gaunt disciples, lately passed over from the Asian shores of the Mediterranean, were for breaking the fair images of Venus and flinging the altars of Bacchus down.

I fancy poor Congreve's theatre is a temple of Pagan delights, and mysteries not permitted except among heathens. I fear the theatre carries down that ancient tradition and worship, as masons have carried their secret signs and rites from temple to temple. When the libertine hero carries off the beauty in the play, and the dotard is laughed to scorn for having the young wife: in the ballad, when the poet bids his mistress to gather roses while she may, and warns her that old Time is still a-flying: in the ballet, when honest Corydon courts Phillis under the treillage of the pasteboard cottage, and leers at her over the head of grandpapa in red stockings, who is opportunely asleep; and when seduced by the invitations of the rosy youth she comes forward to the footlights, and they perform on each other's tiptoes that *pas* which you all know, and which is only interrupted by old grandpapa awaking from his doze at the pasteboard châlet (whither he returns to take another nap in case the young people get an encore): when Harlequin, splendid in youth, strength, and agility, arrayed in gold and a thousand colours, springs over the heads of countless perils, leaps down the throat of bewildered giants, and, dauntless and splendid, dances danger down: when Mr. Punch, that godless old rebel, breaks every law and laughs at it with odious triumph, outwits his lawyer, bullies the beadle, knocks his wife about the head, and hangs the hangman,—don't you see in the comedy, in the song, in the dance, in the ragged little Punch's puppet-show—the Pagan protest? Doesn't it seem as if Life puts in its plea and sings its comment? Look how the lovers walk and hold each other's hands and whisper! Sings the chorus—"There is nothing like love, there is nothing like youth, there is nothing like beauty of your springtime. Look! how old age tries to meddle with merry sport! Beat him with his own crutch, the wrinkled old dotard! There is nothing like youth, there is nothing like beauty, there is nothing like strength. Strength and valour win beauty and youth. Be brave and conquer. Be young and happy. Enjoy, enjoy, enjoy! Would you know the *Segreto per esser felice?* Here it is, in a smiling mistress and a cup of Falernian." As the boy tosses the cup and sings his song—hark! what is that chaunt coming nearer and nearer? What is that dirge which *will* disturb us? The lights of the festival burn dim—the cheeks turn pale—the voice quavers—and the cup drops on the floor. Who's there? Death and Fate are at the gate, and they *will* come in.

Congreve's comic feast flares with lights, and round the table, emptying their flaming bowls of drink, and exchanging the wildest jests and ribaldry, sit men and women, waited on by rascally valets and attendants as dissolute as their mistresses—perhaps the very worst company in the world. There doesn't seem to be a pretence of morals. At the head of the table sits Mirabel or Belmour (dressed in the French fashion and waited on by English imitators of Scapin and Frontin). Their calling is to be irresistible, and to conquer everywhere. Like the heroes of the chivalry story, whose long-winded loves and combats they were sending out of fashion, they are always splendid and triumphant—overcome all dangers, vanquish all enemies, and win the beauty at the end. Fathers, husbands, usurers, are the foes these champions contend with. They are merciless in old age, invariably, and an old man plays the part in the dramas which the wicked enchanter or the great blundering giant performs in the chivalry tales, who threatens and grumbles and resists—a huge stupid obstacle always overcome by the knight. It is an old man with a money-box: Sir Belmour his son or nephew spends his money and laughs at him. It is an old man with a young wife whom he locks up: Sir Mirabel robs him of his wife, trips up his gouty old heels and leaves the old hunks. The old fool, what business has he to hoard his money, or to lock up blushing eighteen? Money is for youth, love is for youth, away with the old people. When Millamant is sixty, having of course divorced the first Lady Millamant, and married his friend Doricourt's granddaughter out of the nursery—it will be his turn; and young Belmour will make a fool of him. All this pretty morality you have in the comedies of William Congreve, Esquire. They are full of wit. Such manners as he observes, he observes with great humour; but ah! it's a weary feast, that banquet of wit where no love is. It palls very soon; sad indigestions follow it and lonely blank headaches in the morning.

I can't pretend to quote scenes from the splendid Congreve's plays *—which are undeniably bright, witty, and daring—any more than I could ask you to hear the dialogue of a witty bargeman and a brilliant fishwoman exchanging compliments at Billingsgate; but some of his verses—they were amongst the most famous lyrics of

* The scene of Valentine's pretended madness in *Love for Love* is a splendid specimen of Congreve's daring manner:—

"*Scandal.* And have you given your master a hint of their plot upon him?

"*Jeremy.* Yes, sir; he says he'll favour it, and mistake her for *Angelica.*

"*Scandal.* It may make us sport.

"*Foresight.* Mercy on us!

"*Valentine.* Husht—interrupt me not—I'll whisper predictions to thee, and thou shalt prophesie;—I am truth, and can teach thy tongue a new trick, —I have told thee what's passed—now I'll tell what's to come:—Dost thou know what will happen to-morrow? Answer me not—for I will tell thee. To-morrow knaves will thrive thro' craft, and fools thro' fortune: and honesty will go as it did, frost-nipt in a summer suit. Ask me questions concerning to-morrow.

"*Scandal.* Ask him, *Mr. Foresight.*

"*Foresight.* Pray what will be done at Court?

"*Valentine. Scandal* will tell you;—I am truth, I never come there.

"*Foresight.* In the city?

"*Valentine.* Oh, prayers will be said in empty churches at the usual hours. Yet you will see such zealous faces behind counters as if religion were to be sold in every shop. Oh, things will go methodically in the city, the clocks will strike twelve at noon, and the horn'd herd buzz in the Exchange at two. Husbands and wives will drive distinct trades, and care and pleasure separately occupy the family. Coffee-houses will be full of smoke and stratagem. And the cropt 'prentice that sweeps his master's shop in the morning, may, ten to one, dirty his sheets before night. But there are two things, that you will see very strange; which are, wanton wives with their legs at liberty, and tame cuckolds with chains about their necks. But hold, I must examine you before I go further; you look suspiciously. Are you a husband?

"*Foresight.* I am married.

"*Valentine.* Poor creature! Is your wife of Covent-garden *Parish?*

"*Foresight.* No; St. Martin's-in-the-Fields.

"*Valentine.* Alas, poor man! his eyes are sunk, and his hands shrivelled; his legs dwindled, and his back bow'd. Pray, pray for a metamorphosis—change thy shape, and shake off age; get thee *Medea's* kettle and be boiled anew; come forth with lab'ring callous hands, and chine of steel, and *Atlas'* shoulders. Let Taliacotius trim the calves of twenty chairmen, and make thee pedestals to stand erect upon, and look matrimony in the face. Ha, ha, ha! That a man should have a stomach to a wedding supper, when the pidgeons ought rather to be laid to his feet! Ha, ha, ha!

"*Foresight.* His frenzy is very high now, *Mr. Scandal.*

"*Scandal.* I believe it is a spring-tide.

"*Foresight.* Very likely—truly; you understand these matters. *Mr.*

the time, and pronounced equal to Horace by his contemporaries—may give an idea of his power, of his grace, of his daring manner, his magnificence in compliment, and his polished sarcasm. He

Scandal, I shall be very glad to confer with you about these things he has uttered. His sayings are very mysterious and hieroglyphical.

"*Valentine*. Oh! why would *Angelica* be absent from my eyes so long?

"*Jeremy*. She's here, sir.

"*Mrs Foresight*. Now, sister!

"*Mrs. Frail*. O Lord! what must I say?

"*Scandal*. Humour him, madam, by all means.

"*Valentine*. Where is she? Oh! I see her: she comes, like Riches, Health, and Liberty at once, to a despairing, starving, and abandoned wretch. Oh—welcome, welcome!

"*Mrs. Frail*. How d'ye, sir? Can I serve you?

"*Valentine*. Hark'ee—I have a secret to tell you. *Endymion* and the moon shall meet us on *Mount Latmos*, and we'll be married in the dead of night. But say not a word. *Hymen* shall put his torch into a dark lanthorn, that it may be secret; and Juno shall give her peacock poppy-water, that he may fold his ogling tail; and Argus's hundred eyes be shut—ha! Nobody shall know, but *Jeremy*.

"*Mrs Frail*. No, no; we'll keep it secret; it shall be done presently.

"*Valentine*. The sooner the better. *Jeremy*, come hither—closer—that none may overhear us. *Jeremy*, I can tell you news: *Angelica* is turned nun, and I am turning friar, and yet we'll marry one another in spite of the Pope. Get me a cowl and beads, that I may play my part; for she'll meet me two hours hence in black and white, and a long veil to cover the project, and we won't see one another's faces 'till we have done something to be ashamed of, and then we'll blush once for all. . . .

"*Enter* TATTLE.

"*Tattle*. Do you know me, *Valentine?*

"*Valentine*. You!—who are you? No, I hope not.

"*Tattle*. I am *Jack Tattle*, your friend.

"*Valentine*. My friend! What to do? I am no married man, and thou canst not lye with my wife; I am very poor, and thou canst not borrow money of me. Then, what employment have I for a friend?

"*Tattle*. Hah! A good open speaker, and not to be trusted with a secret.

"*Angelica*. Do you know me, *Valentine?*

"*Valentine*. Oh, very well.

"*Angelica*. Who am I?

Valentine. You're a woman, one to whom Heaven gave beauty when it grafted roses on a brier. You are the reflection of Heaven in a pond; and he that leaps at you is sunk. You are all white—a sheet of spotless paper—when you first are born; but you are to be scrawled and blotted by every goose's quill. I know you; for I loved a woman, and loved her so long that I found out a strange thing: I found out what a woman was good for.

"*Tattle*. Ay! pr'ythee, what's that?

"*Valentine*. Why, to keep a secret.

"*Tattle*. O Lord!

"*Valentine*. Oh, exceeding good to keep a secret; for, though she should tell, yet she is not to be believed.

writes as if he was so accustomed to conquer, that he has a poor opinion of his victims. Nothing's new except their faces, says he: "every woman is the same." He says this in his first comedy,

"*Tattle.* Hah! Good again, faith.

"*Valentine.* I would have musick. Sing me the song that I like."—CONGREVE: *Love for Love.*

There is a *Mrs. Nickleby*, of the year 1700, in Congreve's comedy of *The Double Dealer*, in whose character the author introduces some wonderful traits of roguish satire. She is practised on by the gallants of the play, and no more knows how to resist them than any of the ladies above quoted could resist Congreve.

"*Lady Plyant.* Oh! reflect upon the horror of your conduct! Offering to pervert me" [the joke is that the gentleman is pressing the lady for her daughter's hand, not for her own]—"perverting me from the road of virtue, in which I have trod thus long, and never made one trip—not one *faux pas.* Oh, consider it: what would you have to answer for, if you should provoke me to frailty! Alas! humanity is feeble, Heaven knows! Very feeble, and unable to support itself.

"*Mellefont.* Where am I? Is it day? and am I awake? Madam——

"*Lady Plyant.* O Lord, ask me the question! I swear I'll deny it—therefore don't ask me; nay, you shan't ask me, I swear I'll deny it. O Gemini, you have brought all the blood into my face; I warrant I am as red as a turkey-cock. O fie, cousin Mellefont!

"*Mellefont.* Nay, madam, hear me; I mean——

"*Lady Plyant.* Hear you? No, no; I'll deny you first, and hear you afterwards. For one does not know how one's mind may change upon hearing—hearing is one of the senses and all the senses are fallible. I won't trust my honour, I assure you; my honour is infallible and uncomatable.

"*Mellefont.* For Heaven's sake, madam——

"*Lady Plyant.* Oh, name it no more. Bless me, how can you talk of Heaven, and have so much wickedness in your heart? May be, you don't think it a sin. They say some of you gentlemen don't think it a sin; but still, my honour, if it were no sin—— But, then, to marry my daughter for the convenience of frequent opportunities—I'll never consent to that: as sure as can be, I'll break the match.

"*Mellefont.* Death and amazement! Madam, upon my knees——

"*Lady Plyant.* Nay, nay, rise up! come, you shall see my good-nature. I know love is powerful, and nobody can help his passion. 'Tis not your fault; nor I swear, it is not mine. How can I help it, if I have charms? And how can you help it, if you are made a captive? I swear it is pity it should be a fault; but, my honour. Well, but your honour, too—but the sin! Well, but the necessity. O Lord, here's somebody coming. I dare not stay. Well, you must consider of your crime: and strive as much as can be against it—strive, be sure; but don't be melancholick—don't despair; but never think that I'll grant you anything. O Lord, no; but be sure you lay aside all thoughts of the marriage, for though I know you don't love Cynthia, only as a blind to your passion for me—yet it will make me jealous. O Lord, what did I say? Jealous! No, no, I can't be jealous; for I must not love you. Therefore don't hope; but don't despair neither. Oh, they're coming; I *must* fly."—*The Double Dealer*, act ii. sc. v. page 156.

which he wrote languidly * in illness, when he was an "excellent young man." Richelieu at eighty could have hardly said a more excellent thing.

When he advances to make one of his conquests, it is with a splendid gallantry, in full uniform and with the fiddles playing, like Grammont's French dandies attacking the breach of Lerida.

"Cease, cease to ask her name," he writes of a young lady at the Wells of Tunbridge, whom he salutes with a magnificent compliment—

"Cease, cease to ask her name,
The crowned Muse's noblest theme,
Whose glory by immortal fame
Shall only sounded be.
But if you long to know,
Then look round yonder dazzling row:
Who most does like an angel show,
You may be sure 'tis she."

Here are lines about another beauty, who perhaps was not so well pleased at the poet's manner of celebrating her—

"When Lesbia first I saw, so heavenly fair,
With eyes so bright and with that awful air,
I thought my heart which durst so high aspire
As bold as his who snatched celestial fire.

But soon as e'er the beauteous idiot spoke,
Forth from her coral lips such folly broke:
Like balm the trickling nonsense heal'd my wound,
And what her eyes enthralled, her tongue unbound."

Amoret is a cleverer woman than the lovely Lesbia, but the poet does not seem to respect one much more than the other; and describes both with exquisite satirical humour—

"Fair Amoret is gone astray:
Pursue and seek her, every lover.
I'll tell the signs by which you may
The wandering shepherdess discover.

Coquet and coy at once her air,
Both studied, though both seem neglected;
Careless she is with artful care,
Affecting to seem unaffected.

---

* "There seems to be a strange affectation in authors of appearing to have done everything by chance. The *Old Bachelor* was written for amusement in the languor of convalescence. Yet it is apparently composed with great elaborateness of dialogue and incessant ambition of wit."—JOHNSON: *Lives of the Poets.*

With skill her eyes dart every glance,
Yet change so soon you'd ne'er suspect them;
For she'd persuade they wound by chance,
Though certain aim and art direct them.

She likes herself, yet others hates,
For that which in herself she prizes;
And, while she laughs at them, forgets
She is the thing that she despises."

What could Amoret have done to bring down such shafts of ridicule upon her? Could she have resisted the irresistible Mr. Congreve? Could anybody? Could Sabina, when she woke and heard such a bard singing under her window? "See," he writes—

"See! see, she wakes—Sabina wakes!
And now the sun begins to rise.
Less glorious is the morn, that breaks
From his bright beams, than her fair eyes.
With light united, day they give;
But different fates ere night fulfil:
How many by his warmth will live!
How many will her coldness kill!"

Are you melted? Don't you think him a divine man? If not touched by the brilliant Sabina, hear the devout Selinda:—

"Pious Selinda goes to prayers,
If I but ask the favour;
And yet the tender fool's in tears,
When she believes I'll leave her:
Would I were free from this restraint,
Or else had hopes to win her:
Would she could make of me a saint,
Or I of her a sinner!"

What a conquering air there is about these! What an irresistible Mr. Congreve it is! Sinner! of course he will be a sinner, the delightful rascal! Win her! of course he will win her, the victorious rogue! He knows he will: he must—with such a grace, with such a fashion, with such a splendid embroidered suit. You see him with red-heeled shoes deliciously turned out, passing a fair jewelled hand through his dishevelled periwig, and delivering a killing ogle along with his scented billet. And Sabina? What a comparison that is between the nymph and the sun! The sun gives Sabina the *pas*, and does not venture to rise before her ladyship: the morn's *bright beams* are less glorious than her *fair eyes*; but before night everybody will be frozen by her glances: everybody but one lucky rogue who shall be nameless. Louis Quatorze in all his glory is hardly more splendid than our Phœbus Apollo of the Mall and Spring Gardens.*

When Voltaire came to visit the great Congreve, the latter rather affected to despise his literary reputation, and in this perhaps the great Congreve was not far wrong.† A touch of Steele's tenderness is worth all his finery; a flash of Swift's lightning, a beam of Addison's pure sunshine, and his tawdry playhouse taper is invisible. But the ladies loved him, and he was undoubtedly a pretty fellow.‡

We have seen in Swift a humourous philosopher, whose truth frightens one, and whose laughter makes one melancholy. We have had in Congreve a humourous observer of another school, to whom

* "Among those by whom it ('Will's') was frequented, Southerne and Congreve were principally distinguished by Dryden's friendship. . . . But Congreve seems to have gained yet farther than Southerne upon Dryden's friendship. He was introduced to him by his first play, the celebrated *Old Bachelor*, being put into the poet's hands to be revised. Dryden, after making a few alterations to fit it for the stage, returned it to the author with the high and just commendation, that it was the best first play he had ever seen."—SCOTT'S *Dryden*, vol. i. p. 370.

† It was in Surrey Street, Strand (where he afterwards died), that Voltaire visited him, in the decline of his life.

The anecdote relating to his saying that he wished "to be visited on no other footing than as a gentleman who led a life of plainness and simplicity," is common to all writers on the subject of Congreve, and appears in the English version of Voltaire's *Letters concerning the English Nation*, published in London, 1733, as also in Goldsmith's *Memoir of Voltaire*. But it is worthy of remark, that it does not appear in the text of the same Letters in the edition of Voltaire's *Œuvres Complètes* in the "Panthéon Littéraire." Vol. v. of his works. (Paris, 1837.)

"Celui de tous les Anglais qui a porté le plus loin la gloire du théâtre comique est feu M. Congreve. Il n'a fait que peu de pièces, mais toutes sont excellentes dans leur genre. . . . Vous y voyez partout le langage des honnêtes gens avec des actions de fripon; ce qui prouve qu'il connaissait bien son monde, et qu'il vivait dans ce qu'on appelle la bonne compagnie."—VOLTAIRE: *Lettres sur les Anglais*. Lettre XIX.

‡ On the death of Queen Mary he published a Pastoral—*The Mourning Muse of Alexis*. Alexis and Menalcas sing alternately in the orthodox way. The Queen is called PASTORA.

"I mourn PASTORA dead, let Albion mourn,
And sable clouds her chalky cliffs adorn,"

says Alexis. Among other phenomena, we learn that—

"With their sharp nails themselves the Satyrs wound,
And tug their shaggy beards, and bite with grief the ground"—

(a degree of sensibility not always found in the Satyrs of that period). . . . It continues—

the world seems to have no morals at all, and whose ghastly doctrine seems to be that we should eat, drink, and be merry when

"Lord of these woods and wide extended plains,
Stretch'd on the ground and close to earth his face
Scalding with tears the already faded grass.

. . . .

To dust must all that Heavenly beauty come?
And must Pastora moulder in the tomb?
Ah Death! more fierce and unrelenting far
Than wildest wolves or savage tigers are!
With lambs and sheep their hungers are appeased,
But ravenous Death the shepherdess has seized."

This statement that a wolf eats but a sheep, whilst Death eats a shepherdess—that figure of the "Great Shepherd" lying speechless on his stomach, in a state of despair which neither winds nor floods nor air can exhibit—are to be remembered in poetry surely; and this style was admired in its time by the admirers of the great Congreve!

In the *Tears of Amaryllis for Amyntas* (the young Lord Blandford, the great Duke of Marlborough's only son), Amaryllis represents Sarah Duchess!

The tigers and wolves, nature and motion, rivers and echoes, come into work here again. At the sight of her grief—

"Tigers and wolves their wonted rage forego,
And dumb distress and new compassion show,
Nature herself attentive silence kept,
And motion seemed suspended while she wept!"

And Pope dedicated the *Iliad* to the author of these lines—and Dryden wrote to him in his great hand:—

"Time, place, and action may with pains be wrought,
But Genius must be born and never can be taught.
This is your portion, this your native store;
Heaven, that but once was prodigal before,
To SHAKSPEARE gave as much, she could not give him more.
Maintain your Post: that's all the fame you need,
For 'tis impossible you should proceed;
Already I am worn with cares and age,
And just abandoning th' ungrateful stage:
Unprofitably kept at Heaven's expence,
I live a Rent-charge upon Providence:
But you, whom every Muse and Grace adorn,
Whom I foresee to better fortune born,
Be kind to my remains, and oh! defend
Against your Judgment your departed Friend!
Let not the insulting Foe my Fame pursue;
But shade those Lawrels which descend to You:
And take for Tribute what these Lines express;
You merit more, nor could my Love do less."

This is a very different manner of welcome to that of our own day. In Shadwell, Higgons, Congreve, and the comic authors of their time, when gentlemen

we can, and go to the deuce (if there be a deuce) when the time comes. We come now to a humour that flows from quite a different heart and spirit—a wit that makes us laugh and leaves us good and happy; to one of the kindest benefactors that society has ever had; and I believe you have divined already that I am about to mention Addison's honoured name.

From reading over his writings, and the biographies which we have of him, amongst which the famous article in the *Edinburgh Review* * may be cited as a magnificent statue of the great writer and moralist of the last age, raised by the love and the marvellous skill and genius of one of the most illustrious artists of our own: looking at that calm fair face, and clear countenance—those chiselled features pure and cold, I can't but fancy that this great man—in this respect, like him of whom we spoke in the last lecture—was also one of the lonely ones of the world. Such men have very few equals, and they don't herd with those. It is in the nature of such lords of intellect to be solitary—they are in the world, but not of it; and our minor struggles, brawls, successes, pass under them.

Kind, just, serene, impartial, his fortitude not tried beyond easy endurance, his affections not much used, for his books were his family, and his society was in public; admirably wiser, wittier, calmer, and more instructed than almost every man with whom he met, how could Addison suffer, desire, admire, feel much? I may

meet they fall into each other's arms, with "Jack, Jack, I must buss thee;" or, "Fore George, Harry, I must kiss thee, lad." And in a similar manner the poets saluted their brethren. Literary gentleman do not kiss now; I wonder if they love each other better?

Steele calls Congreve "Great Sir" and "Great Author"; says "Well-dressed barbarians knew his awful name," and addresses him as if he were a prince; and speaks of *Pastora* as one of the most famous tragic compositions.

* "To Addison himself we are bound by a sentiment as much like affection as any sentiment can be which is inspired by one who has been sleeping a hundred and twenty years in Westminster Abbey. . . . After full inquiry and impartial reflection we have long been convinced that he deserved as much love and esteem as can justly be claimed by any of our infirm and erring race." —*Macaulay*.

"Many who praise virtue do no more than praise it. Yet it is reasonable to believe that Addison's profession and practice were at no great variance; since, amidst that storm of faction in which most of his life was passed, though his station made him conspicuous, and his activity made him formidable, the character given him by his friends was never contradicted by his enemies. Of those with whom interest or opinion united him, he had not only the esteem but the kindness; and of others, whom the violence of opposition drove against him, though he might lose the love, he retained the reverence."—*Johnson*.

expect a child to admire me for being taller or writing more cleverly than she; but how can I ask my superior to say that I am a wonder when he knows better than I? In Addison's days you could scarcely show him a literary performance, a sermon, or a poem, or a piece of literary criticism, but he felt he could do better. His justice must have made him indifferent. He didn't praise, because he measured his compeers by a higher standard than common people have.* How was he who was so tall to look up to any but the loftiest genius? He must have stooped to put himself on a level with most men. By that profusion of graciousness and smiles with which Goethe or Scott, for instance, greeted almost every literary beginner, every small literary adventurer who came to his court and went away charmed from the great king's audience, and cuddling to his heart the compliment which his literary majesty had paid him—each of the two good-natured potentates of letters brought their star and riband into discredit. Everybody had his majesty's orders. Everybody had his majesty's cheap portrait, on a box surrounded by diamonds worth twopence apiece. A very great and just and wise man ought not to praise indiscriminately, but give his idea of the truth. Addison praises the ingenious Mr. Pinkethman: Addison praises the ingenious Mr. Doggett, the actor, whose benefit is coming off that night: Addison praises Don Saltero: Addison praises Milton with all his heart, bends his knee and frankly pays homage to that imperial genius.† But between those degrees of his men his praise is very scanty. I don't think the great Mr. Addison liked young Mr. Pope, the Papist, much; I don't think he abused him. But when Mr. Addison's men abused

* "Addison was perfect good company with intimates, and had something more charming in his conversation than I ever knew in any other man; but with any mixture of strangers, and sometimes only with one, he seemed to preserve his dignity much, with a stiff sort of silence."—POPE. *Spence's Anecdotes.*

† "Milton's chief talent, and indeed his distinguishing excellence, lies in the sublimity of his thoughts. There are others of the moderns, who rival him in every other part of poetry; but in the greatness of his sentiments he triumphs over all the poets, both modern and ancient, Homer only excepted. It is impossible for the imagination of man to distend itself with greater ideas than those which he has laid together in his first, second, and sixth books." —*Spectator*, No. 279.

"If I were to name a poet that is a perfect master in all these arts of working on the imagination, I think Milton may pass for one."—*Ibid.* No. 417.

These famous papers appeared in each Saturday's *Spectator*, from January 19th to May 3rd, 1712. Besides his services to Milton, we may place those he did to Sacred Music.

Mr. Pope, I don't think Addison took his pipe out of his mouth to contradict them.*

Addison's father was a clergyman of good repute in Wiltshire, and rose in the Church.† His famous son never lost his clerical training and scholastic gravity, and was called "a parson in a tye-wig"‡ in London afterwards at a time when tie-wigs were only worn by the laity, and the fathers of theology did not think it decent to appear except in a full bottom. Having been at school at Salisbury, and the Charterhouse, in 1687, when he was fifteen years old, he went to Queen's College, Oxford, where he speedily began to distinguish himself by the making of Latin verses. The beautiful and fanciful poem of "The Pigmies and the Cranes," is still read by lovers of that sort of exercise; and verses are extant in honour of King William, by which it appears that it was the loyal youth's custom to toast that sovereign in bumpers of purple Lyæus: many more works are in the Collection, including one on the Peace of Ryswick, in 1697, which was so good that Montague got him a pension of £300 a year, on which Addison set out on his travels.

During his ten years at Oxford, Addison had deeply imbued himself with the Latin poetical literature, and had these poets at

* "Addison was very kind to me at first, but my bitter enemy afterwards." —POPE. *Spence's Anecdotes.*

"'Leave him as soon as you can,' said Addison to me, speaking of Pope; 'he will certainly play you some devilish trick else: he has an appetite to satire.'"—LADY WORTLEY MONTAGU. *Spence's Anecdotes.*

† Lancelot Addison, his father, was the son of another Lancelot Addison, a clergyman in Westmoreland. He became Dean of Lichfield and Archdeacon of Coventry.

‡ "The remark of Mandeville, who, when he had passed an evening in his company, declared that he was 'a parson in a tye-wig,' can detract little from his character. He was always reserved to strangers, and was not incited to uncommon freedom by a character like that of Mandeville."—JOHNSON: *Lives of the Poets.* (Mandeville was the author of the famous *Fable of the Bees.*)

"Old Jacob Tonson did not like Mr. Addison: he had a quarrel with him, and, after his quitting the secretaryship, used frequently to say of him—'One day or other you'll see that man a bishop—I'm sure he looks that way; and indeed I ever thought him a priest in his heart.'"—POPE. *Spence's Anecdotes.*

"Mr. Addison stayed above a year at Blois. He would rise as early as between two and three in the height of summer, and lie abed till between eleven and twelve in the depth of winter. He was untalkative whilst here, and often thoughtful: sometimes so lost in thought, that I have come into his room and stayed five minutes there before he has known anything of it. He had his masters generally at supper with him; kept very little company besides; and had no amour that I know of; and I think I should have known it if he had had any."—ABBÉ PHILIPPEAUX OF BLOIS. *Spence's Anecdotes.*

his fingers' ends when he travelled in Italy.* His patron went out of office, and his pension was unpaid: and hearing that this great scholar, now eminent and known to the literati of Europe (the great Boileau,† upon perusal of Mr. Addison's elegant hexameters, was first made aware that England was not altogether a barbarous nation)—hearing that the celebrated Mr. Addison, of Oxford, proposed to travel as governor to a young gentleman on the grand tour, the great Duke of Somerset proposed to Mr. Addison to accompany his son, Lord Hertford.

Mr. Addison was delighted to be of use to his Grace, and his Lordship his Grace's son, and expressed himself ready to set forth.

His Grace the Duke of Somerset now announced to one of the most famous scholars of Oxford and Europe that it was his gracious intention to allow my Lord Hertford's tutor one hundred guineas per annum. Mr. Addison wrote back that his services were his Grace's, but he by no means found his account in the recompense for them. The negotiation was broken off. They parted with a profusion of *congées* on one side and the other.‡

Addison remained abroad for some time, living in the best society of Europe. How could he do otherwise? He must have been one of the finest gentlemen the world ever saw: at all moments of life serene and courteous, cheerful and calm.§ He could scarcely ever have had a degrading thought. He might have omitted a virtue or two, or many, but could not have committed many faults for which he need blush or turn pale. When warmed into confidence, his conversation appears to have been so delightful that the greatest wits sat rapt and charmed to listen to him. No man bore poverty and narrow fortune with a more lofty cheerfulness. His letters to his friends at this period of his life, when he had lost his Government pension and given up his college chances,

* "His knowledge of the Latin poets, from Lucretius and Catullus down to Claudian and Prudentius, was singularly exact and profound."—*Macaulay*.

† "Our country owes it to him, that the famous Monsieur Boileau first conceived an opinion of the English genius for poetry, by perusing the present he made him of the *Musæ Anglicanæ*." TICKELL: *Preface to Addison's Works*.

‡ This proposal was made to Addison when he was in Holland on the return from his travels. He was recommended to the Duke by the bookseller, Tonson, for whom he had undertaken a translation of Herodotus. He had as yet published nothing separately, though he was well known in Oxford, and to some of the Whig nobility.

§ "It was my fate to be much with the wits; my father was acquainted with all of them. *Addison was the best company in the world.* I never knew anybody that had so much wit as Congreve."—LADY WORTLEY MONTAGU. *Spence's Anecdotes*.

are full of courage and a gay confidence and philosophy: and they are none the worse in my eyes, and I hope not in those of his last and greatest biographer (though Mr. Macaulay is bound to own and lament a certain weakness for wine, which the great and good Joseph Addison notoriously possessed, in common with countless gentlemen of his time), because some of the letters are written when his honest hand was shaking a little in the morning after libations to purple Lyæus over-night. He was fond of drinking the healths of his friends: he writes to Wyche,* of Hamburg, gratefully remembering Wyche's "hoc." "I have been drinking your health to-day with Sir Richard Shirley," he writes to Bathurst. "I have lately had the honour to meet my Lord Effingham at Amsterdam, where we have drunk Mr. Wood's health a hundred times in excellent champagne," he writes again. Swift † describes him over his cups, when Joseph yielded to a temptation which Jonathan resisted. Joseph was of a cold nature, and needed perhaps the fire of wine to warm his blood. If he was a parson, he wore a tie-wig, recollect. A better and more Christian man scarcely ever breathed than Joseph Addison. If he had not that little weakness for wine—why, we

* *Mr. Addison to Mr. Wyche.*

"DEAR SIR,—My hand at present begins to grow steady enough for a letter, so the properest use I can put it to is to thank ye honest gentleman that set it a shaking. I have had this morning a desperate design in my head to attack you in verse, which I should certainly have done could I have found out a rhyme to rummer. But though you have escaped for ye present, you are not yet out of danger, if I can a little recover my talent at crambo. I am sure, in whatever way I write to you, it will be impossible for me to express ye deep sense I have of ye many favours you have lately shown me. I shall only tell you that Hambourg has been the pleasantest stage I have met with in my travails. If any of my friends wonder at me for living so long in that place, I dare say it will be thought a very good excuse when I tell him Mr. Wyche was there. As your company made our stay at Hambourg agreeable, your wine has given us all ye satisfaction that we have found in our journey through Westphalia. If drinking your health will do you any good, you may expect to be as long-lived as Methuselah, or, to use a more familiar instance, as ye oldest hoc in ye cellar. I hope ye two pair of legs that was left a swelling behind us are by this time come to their shapes again. I can't forbear troubling you with my hearty respects to ye owners of them, and desiring you to believe me always,

"Dear Sir,

"Yours," &c.

"To Mr. Wyche, His Majesty's Resident at
"Hambourg, May 1703."

—*From the Life of Addison, by* Miss AIKIN. Vol. i. p. 146.

† It is pleasing to remember that the relation between Swift and Addison was, on the whole, satisfactory from first to last. The value of Swift's testi-

could scarcely have found a fault with him, and could not have liked him as we do.*

At thirty-three years of age, this most distinguished wit, scholar, and gentleman was without a profession and an income. His book of "Travels" had failed: his "Dialogues on Medals" † had had no particular success: his Latin verses, even though reported the best since Virgil, or Statius at any rate, had not brought him a Government place, and Addison was living up three shabby pair of stairs in the Haymarket (in a poverty over which old Samuel Johnson rather chuckles), when in these shabby rooms an emissary from Government and Fortune came and found him.‡ A poem was wanted about the Duke of Marlborough's victory of Blenheim. Would Mr. Addison write one? Mr. Boyle, afterwards Lord

mony, when nothing personal inflamed his vision or warped his judgment, can be doubted by nobody.

"*Sept.* 10, 1710.—I sat till ten in the evening with Addison and Steele.

"11.—Mr. Addison and I dined together at his lodgings, and I sat with him part of this evening.

"18.—To-day I dined with Mr. Stratford at Mr. Addison's retirement near Chelsea. . . . I will get what good offices I can from Mr. Addison.

"27.—To-day all our company dined at Will Frankland's, with Steele and Addison, too.

"29.—I dined with Mr. Addison," &c.—*Journal to Stella.*

Addison inscribed a presentation copy of his Travels "To Dr. Jonathan Swift, the most agreeable companion, the truest friend, and the greatest genius of his age."—(SCOTT. From the information of Mr. Theophilus Swift.)

"Mr. Addison, who goes over first secretary, is a most excellent person; and being my most intimate friend, I shall use all my credit to set him right in his notions of persons and things."—*Letters.*

"I examine my heart, and can find no other reason why I write to you now, besides that great love and esteem I have always had for you. I have nothing to ask you either for my friend or for myself."—SWIFT to ADDISON (1717). SCOTT'S *Swift.* Vol. xix. p. 274.

Political differences only dulled for a while their friendly communications. Time renewed them: and Tickell enjoyed Swift's friendship as a legacy from the man with whose memory his is so honourably connected.

* "Addison usually studied all the morning; then met his party at Button's; dined there, and stayed five or six hours, and sometimes far into the night. I was of the company for about a year, but found it too much for me: it hurt my health, and so I quitted it."—POPE. *Spence's Anecdotes.*

† The *Dialogues on Medals* only appeared posthumously. The *Travels* appeared in 1705, *i.e.* after the *Campaign.* It is announced in the *Diverting Post* of December 2–9, 1704, that Mr. Addison's "long-expected poem" on the Campaign is to be published "next week."

‡ "When he returned to England (in 1702), with a meanness of appearance which gave testimony of the difficulties to which he had been reduced, he found his old patrons out of power, and was, therefore, for a time, at full leisure for the cultivation of his mind."—JOHNSON: *Lives of the Poets.*

Carleton, took back the reply to the Lord Treasurer Godolphin, that Mr. Addison would. When the poem had reached a certain stage, it was carried to Godolphin; and the last lines which he read were these:—

"But, O my Muse! what numbers wilt thou find
To sing the furious troops in battle join'd?
Methinks I hear the drum's tumultuous sound
The victor's shouts and dying groans confound;
The dreadful burst of cannon rend the skies,
And all the thunder of the battle rise.
'Twas then great Marlborough's mighty soul was proved,
That, in the shock of charging hosts unmoved,
Amidst confusion, horror, and despair,
Examined all the dreadful scenes of war:
In peaceful thought the field of death surveyed,
To fainting squadrons sent the timely aid,
Inspired repulsed battalions to engage,
And taught the doubtful battle where to rage.
So when an angel, by divine command,
With rising tempests shakes a guilty land
(Such as of late o'er pale Britannia passed),
Calm and serene he drives the furious blast;
And, pleased the Almighty's orders to perform,
Rides in the whirlwind and directs the storm."

Addison left off at a good moment. That simile was pronounced to be of the greatest ever produced in poetry. That angel, that good angel, flew off with Mr. Addison, and landed him in the place of Commissioner of Appeals—vice Mr. Locke providentially promoted. In the following year Mr. Addison went to Hanover with Lord Halifax, and the year after was made Under-Secretary of State. O angel visits! you come "few and far between" to literary gentlemen's lodgings! Your wings seldom quiver at second-floor windows now! *

* [The famous story in the text, which has been generally accepted, is probably inaccurate. It was first told in 1732 by Addison's cousin, Eustace Budgell, then ruined and half sane, who was trying to puff himself by professing familiar knowledge of his eminent relation. The circumstantiality of the story is suspicious; Godolphin was the last man to give preferment to a poet in the way described, and Addison was not in the position implied. He had strong claims upon Halifax, his original patron. When Halifax lost office, Addison's pension had ceased. Halifax was now being courted by Godolphin, and could make an effective application on behalf of his client. This and not the simile of the angel, was probably at the bottom of Addison's preferment. It has lately appeared, from the publication of Hearne's diaries by the Oxford Historical Society, that, in December 1705, it was reported that Addison was to marry the Countess of Warwick. The marriage was delayed for eleven years; but it is clear that Addison had powerful friends at this time.]

You laugh? You think it is in the power of few writers nowadays to call up such an angel? Well, perhaps not; but permit us to comfort ourselves by pointing out that there are in the poem of the "Campaign" some as bad lines as heart can desire; and to hint that Mr. Addison did very wisely in not going further with my Lord Godolphin than that angelical simile. Do allow me, just for a little harmless mischief, to read you some of the lines which follow. Here is the interview between the Duke and the King of the Romans after the battle:—

> "Austria's young monarch, whose imperial sway
> Sceptres and thrones are destined to obey,
> Whose boasted ancestry so high extends
> That in the Pagan Gods his lineage ends,
> Comes from afar, in gratitude to own
> The great supporter of his father's throne.
> What tides of glory to his bosom ran
> Clasped in th' embraces of the godlike man!
> How were his eyes with pleasing wonder fixt,
> To see such fire with so much sweetness mixt!
> Such easy greatness, such a graceful port,
> So turned and finished for the camp or court!"

How many fourth-form boys at Mr. Addison's school of Charterhouse could write as well as that now? The "Campaign" has blunders, triumphant as it was; and weak points like all campaigns.*

In the year 1713 "Cato" came out. Swift has left a description of the first night of the performance. All the laurels of Europe were scarcely sufficient for the author of this prodigious poem.†

* "Mr. Addison wrote very fluently; but he was sometimes very slow and scrupulous in correcting. He would show his verses to several friends; and would alter almost everything that any of them hinted at as wrong. He seemed to be too diffident of himself; and too much concerned about his character as a poet; or (as he worded it) too solicitous for that kind of praise which, God knows, is but a very little matter after all!"—POPE. *Spence's Anecdotes.*

† "As to poetical affairs," says Pope in 1713, "I am content at present to be a bare looker-on. . . . Cato was not so much the wonder of Rome in his days, as he is of Britain in ours; and though all the foolish industry possible has been used to make it thought a party play, yet what the author once said of another may the most properly in the world be applied to him on this occasion:—

> "'Envy itself is dumb—in wonder lost;
> And factions strive who shall applaud him most.'

"The numerous and violent claps of the Whig party on the one side of the theatre were echoed back by the Tories on the other; while the author sweated behind the scenes with concern to find their applause proceeding more from the

Laudations of Whig and Tory chiefs, popular ovations, complimentary garlands from literary men, translations in all languages, delight and homage from all—save from John Dennis in a minority of one. Mr. Addison was called the "great Mr. Addison" after this. The Coffee-house Senate saluted him Divus: it was heresy to question that decree.

Meanwhile he was writing political papers and advancing in the political profession. He went Secretary to Ireland. He was appointed Secretary of State in 1717. And letters of his are extant, bearing date some year or two before, and written to young Lord Warwick, in which he addresses him as "my dearest Lord," and asks affectionately about his studies, and writes very prettily about nightingales and birds'-nests, which he has found at Fulham for his Lordship. Those nightingales were intended to warble in the ear of Lord Warwick's mamma. Addison married her Ladyship in 1716; and died at Holland House three years after that splendid but dismal union.*

hand than the head. . . . I believe you have heard that, after all the applauses of the opposite faction, my Lord Bolingbroke sent for Booth, who played Cato, into the box, and presented him with fifty guineas in acknowledgment (as he expressed it) for defending the cause of liberty so well against a perpetual dictator."—POPE'S *Letters to* SIR W. TRUMBULL.

Cato ran for thirty-five nights without interruption. Pope wrote the Prologue, and Garth the Epilogue.

It is worth noticing how many things in *Cato* keep their ground as habitual quotations; *e.g.*—

"... big with the fate
Of Cato and of Rome."

"'Tis not in mortals to command success;
But we'll do more, Sempronius, we'll deserve it."

"Blesses his stars, and thinks it luxury."

"I think the Romans call it Stoicism."

"My voice is still for war."

"When vice prevails, and impious men bear sway,
The post of honour is a private station."

Not to mention—

"The woman who deliberates is lost."

And the eternal—

"Plato, thou reasonest well,"

which avenges, perhaps, on the public their neglect of the play!

* "The lady was persuaded to marry him on terms much like those on which a Turkish princess is espoused—to whom the Sultan is reported to pronounce, 'Daughter, I give thee this man for thy slave.' The marriage, if

But it is not for his reputation as the great author of "Cato" and the "Campaign," or for his merits as Secretary of State, or for his rank and high distinction as my Lady Warwick's husband, or for his eminence as an Examiner of political questions on the Whig side, or a Guardian of British liberties, that we admire Joseph Addison. It is as a Tatler of small talk and a Spectator of mankind, that we cherish and love him, and owe as much pleasure to him as to any human being that ever wrote. He came in that artificial age, and began to speak with his noble, natural voice. He came, the gentle satirist who hit no unfair blow; the kind judge who castigated only in smiling. While Swift went about, hanging and ruthless—a literary Jeffreys—in Addison's kind court only minor cases were tried; only peccadilloes and small sins against society: only a dangerous libertinism in tuckers and

uncontradicted report can be credited, made no addition to his happiness; it neither found them, nor made them, equal. . . . Rowe's ballad of 'The Despairing Shepherd' is said to have been written, either before or after marriage, upon this memorable pair."—*Dr. Johnson.*

"I received the news of Mr. Addison's being declared Secretary of State with the less surprise, in that I knew that post was almost offered to him before. At that time he declined it, and I really believe that he would have done well to have declined it now. Such a post as that, and such a wife as the Countess, do not seem to be, in prudence, eligible for a man that is asthmatic, and we may see the day when he will be heartily glad to resign them both." —LADY WORTLEY MONTAGU to POPE: *Works, Lord Wharncliffe's edit.*, vol. ii. p. 111.

The issue of this marriage was a daughter, Charlotte Addison, who inherited, on her mother's death, the estate of Bilton, near Rugby, which her father had purchased. She was of weak intellect, and died, unmarried, at an advanced age.

Rowe appears to have been faithful to Addison during his courtship, for his Collection contains "Stanzas to Lady Warwick, on Mr. Addison's going to Ireland," in which her Ladyship is called "Chloe," and Joseph Addison "Lycidas"; besides the ballad mentioned by the Doctor, and which is entitled "Colin's Complaint." But not even the interest attached to the name of Addison could induce the reader to peruse this composition, though one stanza may serve as a specimen:—

"What though I have skill to complain—
Though the Muses my temples have crowned;
What though, when they hear my soft strain,
The virgins sit weeping around.

Ah, Colin! thy hopes are in vain;
Thy pipe and thy laurel resign;
Thy false one inclines to a swain
Whose music is sweeter than thine."

hoops; * or a nuisance in the abuse of beaux' canes and snuff-boxes. It may be a lady is tried for breaking the peace of our sovereign lady Queen Anne, and ogling too dangerously from the side-box; or a Templar for beating the watch, or breaking Priscian's head; or a citizen's wife for caring too much for the puppet-show, and too little for her husband and children: every one of the little sinners brought before him is amusing, and he dismisses each with the pleasantest penalties and the most charming words of admonition.

Addison wrote his papers as gaily as if he was going out for a holiday. When Steele's *Tatler* first began his prattle, Addison,

* One of the most humourous of these is the paper on Hoops, which, the *Spectator* tells us, particularly pleased his friend SIR ROGER:—

"Mr. SPECTATOR,—You have diverted the town almost a whole month at the expense of the country; it is now high time that you should give the country their revenge. Since your withdrawing from this place, the fair sex are run into great extravagances. Their petticoats, which began to heave and swell before you left us, are now blown up into a most enormous concave, and rise every day more and more; in short, sir, since our women know themselves to be out of the eye of the SPECTATOR, they will be kept within no compass. You praised them a little too soon, for the modesty of their head-dresses; for as the humour of a sick person is often driven out of one limb into another, their superfluity of ornaments, instead of being entirely banished, seems only fallen from their heads upon their lower parts. What they have lost in height they make up in breadth, and, contrary to all rules of architecture, widen the foundations at the same time that they shorten the superstructure.

"The women give out, in defence of these wide bottoms, that they are airy and very proper for the season; but this I look upon to be only a pretence and a piece of art, for it is well known we have not had a more moderate summer these many years, so that it is certain the heat they complain of cannot be in the weather; besides, I would fain ask these tender-constituted ladies, why they should require more cooling than their mothers before them?

"I find several speculative persons are of opinion that our sex has of late years been very saucy, and that the hoop-petticoat is made use of to keep us at a distance. It is most certain that a woman's honour cannot be better entrenched than after this manner, in circle within circle, amidst such a variety of outworks of lines and circumvallation. A female who is thus invested in whalebone is sufficiently secured against the approaches of an ill-bred fellow, who might as well think of Sir George Etherege's way of making love in a tub as in the midst of so many hoops.

"Among these various conjectures, there are men of superstitious tempers who look upon the hoop-petticoat as a kind of prodigy. Some will have it that it portends the downfall of the *French* king, and observe, that the farthingale appeared in *England* a little before the ruin of the *Spanish* monarchy. Others are of opinion that it foretells battle and bloodshed, and believe it of the same prognostication as the tail of a blazing star. For my part, I am apt to think it is a sign that multitudes are coming into the world rather than going out of it," &c. &c.—*Spectator*, No. 127.

then in Ireland, caught at his friend's notion, poured in paper after paper, and contributed the stores of his mind, the sweet fruits of his reading, the delightful gleanings of his daily observation, with a wonderful profusion, and as it seemed an almost endless fecundity. He was six-and-thirty years old: full and ripe. He had not worked crop after crop from his brain, manuring hastily, sub-soiling indifferently, cutting and sowing and cutting again, like other luckless cultivators of letters. He had not done much as yet: a few Latin poems—graceful prolusions; a polite book of travels; a dissertation on medals, not very deep; four acts of a tragedy, a great classical exercise; and the "Campaign," a large prize poem that won an enormous prize. But with his friend's discovery of the "Tatler," Addison's calling was found, and the most delightful talker in the world began to speak. He does not go very deep: let gentlemen of a profound genius, critics accustomed to the plunge of the bathos, console themselves by thinking that he *couldn't* go very deep. There are no traces of suffering in his writing. He was so good, so honest, so healthy, so cheerfully selfish, if I must use the word. There is no deep sentiment. I doubt, until after his marriage, perhaps, whether he ever lost his night's rest or his day's tranquillity about any woman in his life; * whereas poor Dick Steele had capacity enough to melt, and to languish, and to sigh, and to cry his honest old eyes out, for a dozen. His writings do not show insight into or reverence for the love of women, which I take to be, one the consequence of the other. He walks about the world watching their pretty humours, fashions, follies, flirtations, rivalries: and noting them with the most charming archness. He sees them in public, in the theatre, or the assembly, or the puppet-show; or at the toy-shop higgling for gloves and lace; or at the auction, battling together over a blue porcelain dragon, or a darling monster in Japan; or at church, eyeing the width of their rival's hoops, or the breadth of their laces, as they sweep down the aisles. Or he looks out of his window at the "Garter" in Saint James's Street, at Ardelia's coach, as she blazes to the drawing-room with her coronet and six footmen; and remembering that her father was a Turkey merchant in the City, calculates how many sponges went to purchase her earring, and how many drums of figs to build her coach-box; or he demurely watches behind a tree in Spring Garden as Saccharissa (whom he knows under her mask) trips out of her chair to the alley where Sir Fopling is waiting. He sees only the

* "Mr. Addison has not had one epithalamium that I can hear of, and must even be reduced, like a poorer and a better poet, Spenser, to make his own."—POPE'S *Letters*.

public life of women. Addison was one of the most resolute club men of his day. He passed many hours daily in those haunts. Besides drinking—which, alas! is past praying for—you must know it, he owned, too, ladies, that he indulged in that odious practice of smoking. Poor fellow! He was a man's man, remember. The only woman he *did* know, he didn't write about. I take it there would not have been much humour in that story.

He likes to go and sit in the smoking-room at the "Grecian," or the "Devil"; to pace 'Change and the Mall *—to mingle in

* "I have observed that a reader seldom peruses a book with pleasure till he knows whether the writer of it be a black or a fair man, of a mild or a choleric disposition, married or a bachelor; with other particulars of a like nature, that conduce very much to the right understanding of an author. To gratify this curiosity, which is so natural to a reader, I design this paper and my next as prefatory discourses to my following writings; and shall give some account in them of the persons that are engaged in this work. As the chief trouble of compiling, digesting, and correcting will fall to my share, I must do myself the justice to open the work with my own history. . . . There runs a story in the family, that when my mother was gone with child of me about three months, she dreamt that she was brought to bed of a judge. Whether this might proceed from a lawsuit which was then depending in the family, or my father's being a justice of the peace, I cannot determine; for I am not so vain as to think it presaged any dignity that I should arrive at in my future life, though that was the interpretation which the neighbourhood put upon it. The gravity of my behaviour at my very first appearance in the world, and all the time that I sucked, seemed to favour my mother's dream; for, as she has often told me, I threw away my rattle before I was two months old, and would not make use of my coral till they had taken away the bells from it.

"As for the rest of my infancy, there being nothing in it remarkable, I shall pass it over in silence. I find that during my nonage I had the reputation of a very sullen youth, but was always the favourite of my schoolmaster, who used to say that *my parts were solid and would wear well.* I had not been long at the University before I distinguished myself by a most profound silence; for during the space of eight years, excepting in the public exercises of the college, I scarce uttered the quantity of a hundred words; and, indeed, I do not remember that I ever spoke three sentences together in my whole life. . . .

"I have passed my latter years in this city, where I am frequently seen in most public places, though there are not more than half-a-dozen of my select friends that know me. . . . There is no place of general resort wherein I do not often make my appearance; sometimes I am seen thrusting my head into a round of politicians at 'Will's,' and listening with great attention to the narratives that are made in these little circular audiences. Sometimes I smoke a pipe at 'Child's,' and whilst I seem attentive to nothing but the *Postman*, overhear the conversation of every table in the room. I appear on Tuesday night at 'St. James's Coffee-house'; and sometimes join the little committee of politics in the inner room, as one who comes to hear and improve. My face is likewise very well known at the 'Grecian,' the 'Cocoa-tree,' and in the theatres both of Drury Lane and the Haymarket. I have been taken for

ADDISON AT "CHILD'S."

that great club of the world—sitting alone in it somehow: having good-will and kindness for every single man and woman in it—having need of some habit and custom binding him to some few; never doing any man a wrong (unless it be a wrong to hint a little doubt about a man's parts, and to damn him with faint praise); and so he looks on the world and plays with the ceaseless humours of all of us—laughs the kindest laugh—points our neighbour's foible or eccentricity out to us with the most good-natured smiling confidence; and then, turning over his shoulder, whispers *our* foibles to our neighbour. What would Sir Roger de Coverley be without his follies and his charming little brain-cracks? * If the good knight did not call out to the people sleeping in church, and say "Amen" with such a delightful pomposity; if he did not make a speech in the assize-court *à propos de bottes*, and merely to show his dignity to Mr. Spectator: † if he did not mistake Madam Doll

a merchant upon the Exchange for above these two years; and sometimes pass for a Jew in the assembly of stock-jobbers at 'Jonathan's.' In short, wherever I see a cluster of people, I mix with them, though I never open my lips but in my own club.

"Thus I live in the world rather as a '*Spectator*,' of mankind than as one of the species; by which means I have made myself a speculative statesman, soldier, merchant, and artizan, without ever meddling in any practical part in life. I am very well versed in the theory of a husband or a father, and can discern the errors in the economy, business, and diversions of others, better than those who are engaged in them—as standers-by discover blots which are apt to escape those who are in the game. . . . In short, I have acted, in all the parts of my life, as a looker-on, which is the character I intend to preserve in this paper."—*Spectator*, No. 1.

* "So effectually, indeed, did he retort on vice the mockery which had recently been directed against virtue, that, since his time, the open violation of decency has always been considered, amongst us, the sure mark of a fool."—*Macaulay*.

† "The Court was sat before Sir Roger came; but, notwithstanding all the justices had taken their places upon the bench, they made room for the old knight at the head of them; who for his reputation in the country took occasion to whisper in the judge's ear that *he was glad his Lordship had met with so much good weather in his circuit*. I was listening to the proceedings of the Court with much attention, and infinitely pleased with that great appearance and solemnity which so properly accompanies such a public administration of our laws; when, after about an hour's sitting, I observed, to my great surprise, in the midst of a trial, that my friend Sir Roger was getting up to speak. I was in some pain for him, till I found he had acquitted himself of two or three sentences, with a look of much business and great intrepidity.

"Upon his first rising, the Court was hushed, and a general whisper ran among the country people that Sir Roger *was up*. The speech he made was so little to the purpose, that I shall not trouble my readers with an account of it, and I believe was not so much designed by the knight himself to inform the Court as to give him a figure in my eyes, and to keep up his credit in the country."—*Spectator*, No. 122.

Tearsheet for a lady of quality in Temple Garden: if he were wiser than he is: if he had not his humour to salt his life, and were but a mere English gentleman and game-preserver—of what worth were he to us? We love him for his vanities as much as his virtues. What is ridiculous is delightful in him; we are so fond of him because we laugh at him so. And out of that laughter, and out of that sweet weakness, and out of those harmless eccentricities and follies, and out of that touched brain, and out of that honest manhood and simplicity—we get a result of happiness, goodness, tenderness, pity, piety; such as, if my audience will think their reading and hearing over, doctors and divines but seldom have the fortune to inspire. And why not? Is the glory of Heaven to be sung only by gentlemen in black coats? Must the truth be only expounded in gown and surplice, and out of those two vestments can nobody preach it? Commend me to this dear preacher without orders—this parson in the tie-wig. When this man looks from the world, whose weaknesses he describes so benevolently, up to the Heaven which shines over us all, I can hardly fancy a human face lighted up with a more serene rapture: a human intellect thrilling with a purer love and adoration than Joseph Addison's. Listen to him: from your childhood you have known the verses: but who can hear their sacred music without love and awe?—

"Soon as the evening shades prevail,
The moon takes up the wondrous tale,
And nightly to the listening earth
Repeats the story of her birth;
Whilst all the stars that round her burn,
And all the planets in their turn,
Confirm the tidings as they roll,
And spread the truth from pole to pole.
What though, in solemn silence, all
Move round the dark terrestrial ball;
What though no real voice nor sound
Amid their radiant orbs be found;
In reason's ear they all rejoice,
And utter forth a glorious voice,
For ever singing as they shine,
The hand that made us is divine."

It seems to me those verses shine like the stars. They shine out of a great deep calm. When he turns to Heaven, a Sabbath comes over that man's mind: and his face lights up from it with a glory of thanks and prayer. His sense of religion stirs through his whole being. In the fields, in the town: looking at the birds in the trees: at the children in the streets: in the morning or in the moonlight: over his books in his own room: in a happy party at a country merry-making or a town assembly, good-will and peace to God's creatures, and love and awe of Him who made them, fill his pure heart and shine from his kind face. If Swift's life was the most wretched, I think Addison's was one of the most enviable. A life prosperous and beautiful—a calm death—an immense fame and affection afterwards for his happy and spotless name *

* "Garth sent to Addison (of whom he had a very high opinion) on his death-bed, to ask him whether the Christian religion was true."—DR. YOUNG. *Spence's Anecdotes.*

"I have always preferred cheerfulness to mirth. The latter I consider as an act, the former as an habit of the mind. Mirth is short and transient, cheerfulness fixed and permanent. Those are often raised into the greatest transports of mirth who are subject to the greatest depression of melancholy: on the contrary, cheerfulness, though it does not give the mind such an exquisite gladness, prevents us from falling into any depths of sorrow. Mirth is like a flash of lightning that breaks through a gloom of clouds, and glitters for a moment; cheerfulness keeps up a kind of daylight in the mind, and fills it with a steady and perpetual serenity."—ADDISON: *Spectator*, No. 381.

STEELE

WHAT do we look for in studying the history of a past age? Is it to learn the political transactions and characters of the leading public men? is it to make ourselves acquainted with the life and being of the time? If we set out with the former grave purpose, where is the truth, and who believes that he has it entire? What character of what great man is known to you? You can but make guesses as to character more or less happy. In common life don't you often judge and misjudge a man's whole conduct, setting out from a wrong impression? The tone of a voice, a word said in joke, or a trifle in behaviour—the cut of his hair or the tie of his neckcloth may disfigure him in your eyes, or poison your good opinion; or at the end of years of intimacy it may be your closest friend says something, reveals something which had previously been a secret, which alters all your views about him, and shows that he has been acting on quite a different motive to that which you fancied you knew. And if it is so with those you know, how much more with those you don't know? Say, for example, that I want to understand the character of the Duke of Marlborough. I read Swift's history of the times in which he took a part; the shrewdest of observers and initiated, one would think, into the politics of the age—he hints to me that Marlborough was a coward, and even of doubtful military capacity: he speaks of Walpole as a contemptible boor, and scarcely mentions, except to flout it, the great intrigue of the Queen's latter days, which was to have ended in bringing back the Pretender. Again, I read Marlborough's Life by a copious archdeacon, who has the command of immense papers, of sonorous language, of what is called the best information; and I get little or no insight into this secret motive which, I believe, influenced the whole of Marlborough's career, which caused his turnings and windings, his opportune fidelity and treason, stopped his army almost at Paris gate, and landed him finally on the Hanoverian side—the winning side: I get, I say, no truth, or only a portion of it, in the narrative of either writer, and believe that Coxe's portrait, or Swift's portrait, is quite unlike the real Churchill. I take this as a single instance, prepared to be as sceptical about any other, and say to the Muse of History, "O venerable daughter of Mnemosyne, I doubt every single statement you ever made since your ladyship was a Muse! For all your grave airs and high pretensions, you are not a whit more trustworthy than some of your lighter sisters on whom your partisans look down. You bid me listen to a general's oration to his soldiers: Nonsense! He no more made it than Turpin made his dying speech at Newgate. You pronounce a panegyric on a hero: I doubt it, and say you flatter outrageously. You utter the condemnation of a loose character: I doubt it, and think you are prejudiced and take the side of the Dons. You offer me an autobiography: I doubt all autobiographies I ever read; except those, perhaps, of Mr. Robinson Crusoe, Mariner, and writers of his class. *These* have no object in setting themselves right with the public or their own consciences; these have no motive for concealment or half-truths; these call for no more confidence than I can cheerfully give, and do not force me to tax my credulity or to fortify it by evidence. I take up a volume of Doctor Smollett, or a volume of the *Spectator*, and say the fiction carries a greater amount of truth in solution than the volume which purports to be all true. Out of the fictitious book I get the expression of the life of the time; of the manners, of the movement, the dress, the pleasures, the laughter, the ridicules of society—the old times live again, and I travel in the old country of England. Can the heaviest historian do more for me?"

As we read in these delightful volumes of the *Tatler* and *Spectator* the past age returns, the England of our ancestors is revivified. The Maypole rises in the Strand again in London; the churches are thronged with daily worshippers; the beaux are gathering in the coffee-houses; the gentry are going to the Drawing-room; the ladies are thronging to the toy-shops: the chairmen are jostling in the streets; the footmen are running with links before the chariots, or fighting round the theatre doors. In the country I see the young Squire riding to Eton with his servants behind him, and Will Wimble, the friend of the family, to see him safe. To make that journey from the Squire's and back, Will is a week on horseback. The coach takes five days between London and Bath. The judges and the bar ride the circuit. If my Lady comes to town in her post-chariot, her people carry pistols to fire a salute on Captain Macheath if he should appear, and her couriers ride ahead to prepare apartments for her at the great caravanserais on the road; Boniface receives her under the creaking sign of the "Bell" or the "Ram," and he and his chamberlains bow her up the great stair to the state apartments, whilst her carriage rumbles into the courtyard, where the "Exeter Fly" is housed that performs the journey in eight days, God willing, having achieved its daily flight of twenty miles, and landed its passengers for supper and sleep. The curate is taking his pipe in the kitchen, where the Captain's man — having hung up his master's half-pike — is at his bacon and eggs, bragging of Ramillies and Malplaquet to the townsfolk, who have their club in the chimney-corner. The Captain is ogling the chambermaid in the wooden gallery, or bribing her to know who is the pretty young mistress that has come in the coach. The pack-horses are in the great stable, and the drivers and ostlers carousing in the tap. And in Mrs. Landlady's bar, over a glass of strong waters, sits a gentleman of military appearance, who travels with pistols, as all the rest of the world does, and has a rattling grey mare in the stables which will be saddled and away with its owner half-an-hour before the "Fly" sets out on its last day's flight. And some five miles on the road, as the "Exeter Fly" comes jingling and creaking onwards, it will suddenly be brought to a halt by a gentleman on a grey mare, with a black vizard on his face, who thrusts a long pistol into the coach window, and bids the company to hand out their purses. . . . It must have been no small pleasure even to sit in the great kitchen in those days, and see the tide of humankind pass by. We arrive at places now, but we travel no more. Addison talks jocularly of a difference of manner and costume being quite perceivable at Staines, where there passed a young fellow "with a very tolerable periwig," though, to be sure, his hat was out of fashion, and had a Ramillies cock. I would have liked to travel in those days (being of that class of travellers who are proverbially pretty easy *coram latronibus*) and have seen my friend with the grey mare and the black vizard. Alas! there always came a day in the life of that warrior when it was the fashion to accompany him as he passed—without his black mask, and with a nosegay in his hand, accompanied by halberdiers and attended by the sheriff,—in a carriage without springs, and a clergyman jolting beside him, to a spot close by Cumberland Gate and the Marble Arch, where a stone still records that here Tyburn turnpike stood. What a change in a century; in a few years! Within a few yards of that gate the fields began: the fields of his exploits, behind the hedges of which he lurked and robbed. A great and wealthy city has grown over those meadows. Were a man brought to die there now, the windows would be closed and the inhabitants keep their houses in sickening horror. A hundred years back, people crowded to see that last act of a highwayman's life, and make jokes on it.

Swift laughed at him, grimly advising him to provide a Holland shirt and white cap crowned with a crimson or black riband for his exit, to mount the cart cheerfully—shake hands with the hangman, and so—farewell. Gay wrote the most delightful ballads, and made merry over the same hero. Contrast these with the writings of our present humourists! Compare those morals and ours—those manners and ours!

We can't tell—you would not bear to be told—the whole truth regarding those men and manners. You could no more suffer in a British drawing-room, under the reign of Queen Victoria, a fine gentleman or fine lady of Queen Anne's time, or hear what they heard and said, than you would receive an ancient Briton. It is as one reads about savages, that one contemplates the wild ways, the barbarous feasts, the terrific pastimes, of the men of pleasure of that age. We have our fine gentlemen, and our "fast men"; permit me to give you an idea of one particularly fast nobleman of Queen Anne's days, whose biography has been preserved to us by the law reporters.

In 1691, when Steele was a boy at school, my Lord Mohun was tried by his peers for the murder of William Mountford, comedian. In "Howell's State Trials," the reader will find not only an edifying account of this exceedingly fast nobleman, but of the times and manners of those days. My Lord's friend, a Captain Hill, smitten with the charms of the beautiful Mrs. Bracegirdle, and anxious to marry her at all hazards, determined to carry her off, and for this purpose hired a hackney-coach with six horses, and a half-dozen of soldiers to aid him in the storm. The coach with a pair of horses (the four leaders being in waiting elsewhere) took its station opposite my Lord Craven's house in Drury Lane, by which door Mrs. Bracegirdle was to pass on her way from the theatre. As she passed in company of her mamma and a friend, Mr. Page, the Captain seized her by the hand, the soldiers hustled Mr. Page and attacked him sword in hand, and Captain Hill and his noble friend endeavoured to force Madam Bracegirdle into the coach. Mr. Page called for help: the population of Drury Lane rose: it was impossible to effect the capture; and bidding the soldiers go about their business, and the coach to drive off, Hill let go of his prey sulkily, and waited for other opportunities of revenge. The man of whom he was most jealous was Will Mountford, the comedian; Will removed, he thought Mrs. Bracegirdle might be his: and accordingly the Captain and his Lordship lay that night in wait for Will, and as he was coming out of a house in Norfolk Street, while Mohun engaged him in talk, Hill, in the words of the Attorney-General, made a pass and ran him clean through the body.

Sixty-one of my Lord's peers finding him not guilty of murder, while but fourteen found him guilty, this very fast nobleman was discharged: and made his appearance seven years after in another trial for murder—when he, my Lord Warwick, and three gentlemen of the military profession, were concerned in the fight which ended in the death of Captain Coote.

This jolly company were drinking together in "Lockit's" at Charing Cross, when angry words arose between Captain Coote and Captain French; whom my Lord Mohun and my Lord the Earl of Warwick * and Holland endeavoured to pacify. My Lord Warwick was a dear friend of Captain Coote, lent him £100 to buy his commission in the Guards; once when the Captain was arrested for £13 by his tailor, my Lord lent him five guineas, often paid his reckoning for him, and showed him other offices of friendship. On this evening the disputants, French and Coote, being separated whilst they were upstairs, unluckily stopped to drink ale again at the bar of "Lockit's." The row began afresh—Coote lunged at French over the bar, and at last all six called for chairs, and went to Leicester Fields, where they fell to. Their Lordships engaged on the side of Captain Coote. My Lord of Warwick was severely wounded in the hand, Mr. French also was stabbed, but honest Captain Coote got a couple of wounds—one especially, "a wound in the left side just under the short ribs, and piercing through the diaphragma," which did for Captain Coote. Hence the trials of my Lords Warwick and Mohun: hence the assemblage of peers, the report of the transaction in which these defunct fast men still live for the observation of the curious. My Lord of Warwick is brought to the bar by the Deputy-Governor of the Tower of London, having the axe carried before him by the gentleman gaoler, who stood with it at the bar at the right hand of the prisoner, turning the edge from him; the prisoner, at his

* The husband of the Lady Warwick who married Addison, and the father of the young Earl, who was brought to his stepfather's bed to see "how a Christian could die." He was amongst the wildest of the nobility of that day; and in the curious collection of Chap-Books at the British Museum, I have seen more than one anecdote of the freaks of the gay lord. He was popular in London, as such daring spirits have been in our time. The anecdotists speak very kindly of his practical jokes. Mohun was scarcely out of prison for his second homicide, when he went on Lord Macclesfield's embassy to the Elector of Hanover when Queen Anne sent the Garter to his Highness. The chronicler of the expedition speaks of his Lordship as an amiable young man, who had been in bad company, but was quite repentant and reformed. He and Macartney afterwards murdered the Duke of Hamilton between them, in which act Lord Mohun died. This amiable Baron's name was Charles, and not Henry, as a recent novelist has christened him (in *Esmond*).

approach, making three bows, one to his Grace the Lord High Steward, the other to the peers on each hand; and his Grace and the peers return the salute. And besides these great personages, august in periwigs, and nodding to the right and left, a host of the small come up out of the past and pass before us—the jolly captains brawling in the tavern, and laughing and cursing over their cups—the drawer that serves, the bar-girl that waits, the bailiff on the prowl, the chairmen trudging through the black lampless streets, and smoking their pipes by the railings, whilst swords are clashing in the garden within. "Help there! a gentleman is hurt!" The chairmen put up their pipes, and help the gentleman over the railings, and carry him, ghastly and bleeding, to the Bagnio in Long Acre, where they knock up the surgeon—a pretty tall gentleman: but that wound under the short ribs has done for him. Surgeon, lords, captains, bailiffs, chairmen, and gentleman gaoler with your axe, where be you now? The gentleman axeman's head is off his own shoulders; the lords and judges can wag theirs no longer; the bailiff's writs have ceased to run: the honest chairmen's pipes are put out, and with their brawny calves they have walked away into Hades—all is irrecoverably done for as Will Mountford or Captain Coote. The subject of our night's lecture saw all these people—rode in Captain Coote's company of the Guards very probably—wrote and sighed for Bracegirdle, went home tipsy in many a chair, after many a bottle, in many a tavern—fled from many a bailiff.

In 1709, when the publication of the *Tatler* began, our great-great-grandfathers must have seized upon that new and delightful paper with much such eagerness as lovers of light literature in a later day exhibited when the Waverley novels appeared, upon which the public rushed, forsaking that feeble entertainment of which the Miss Porters, the Anne of Swanseas, and worthy Mrs. Radcliffe herself, with her dreary castles and exploded old ghosts, had had pretty much the monopoly. I have looked over many of the comic books with which our ancestors amused themselves, from the novels of Swift's coadjutrix, Mrs. Manley, the delectable author of the "New Atlantis," to the facetious productions of Tom Durfey, and Tom Brown, and Ned Ward, writer of the "London Spy" and several other volumes of ribaldry. The slang of the taverns and ordinaries, the wit of the bagnios, form the strongest part of the farrago of which these libels are composed. In the excellent newspaper collection at the British Museum, you may see, besides, the *Craftsman** and *Postboy* specimens—and queer specimens they are—of the higher literature of Queen Anne's time. Here is an

* The *Craftsman* did not appear till 1726.

abstract from a notable journal bearing date Wednesday, October 13th, 1708, and entitled *The British Apollo; or, curious amusements for the ingenious, by a society of gentlemen.* The *British Apollo* invited and professed to answer questions upon all subjects of wit, morality, science, and even religion; and two out of its four pages are filled with queries and replies much like some of the oracular penny prints of the present time.

One of the first querists, referring to the passage that a bishop should be the husband of one wife, argues that polygamy is justifiable in the laity. The society of gentlemen conducting the *British Apollo* are posed by this casuist, and promise to give him an answer. Celinda then wishes to know from "the gentleman," concerning the souls of the dead, whether they shall have the satisfaction to know those whom they most valued in this transitory life. The gentlemen of the *Apollo* give but poor comfort to poor Celinda. They are inclined to think not; for, say they, since every inhabitant of those regions will be infinitely dearer than here are our nearest relatives—what have we to do with a partial friendship in that happy place? Poor Celinda! it may have been a child or a lover whom she had lost, and was pining after, when the oracle of *British Apollo* gave her this dismal answer. She has solved the question for herself by this time, and knows quite as well as the society of gentlemen.

From theology we come to physics, and Q. asks, "Why does hot water freeze sooner than cold?" *Apollo* replies, "Hot water cannot be said to freeze sooner than cold; but water once heated and cold may be subject to freeze by the evaporation of the spirituous parts of the water, which renders it less able to withstand the power of frosty weather."

The next query is rather a delicate one. "You, Mr. Apollo, who are said to be the God of Wisdom, pray give us the reason why kissing is so much in fashion: what benefit one receives by it, and who was the inventor, and you will oblige Corinna." To this queer demand the lips of Phœbus, smiling, answer: "Pretty innocent Corinna! *Apollo* owns that he was a little surprised by your kissing question, particularly at that part of it where you desire to know the benefit you receive by it. Ah! madam, had you a lover, you would not come to *Apollo* for a solution; since there is no dispute but the kisses of mutual lovers give infinite satisfaction. As to its invention, 'tis certain nature was its author, and it began with the first courtship."

After a column more of questions, follow nearly two pages of poems, signed by Philander, Armenia, and the like, and chiefly on the tender passion; and the paper winds up with a letter from

Leghorn, an account of the Duke of Marlborough and Prince Eugene before Lille, and proposals for publishing two sheets on the present state of Æthiopia, by Mr. Hill: all of which is printed for the authors by J. Mayo, at the Printing Press against Water Lane in Fleet Street. What a change it must have been—how *Apollo's* oracles must have been struck dumb—when the *Tatler* appeared, and scholars, gentlemen, men of the world, men of genius, began to speak!

Shortly before the Boyne was fought, and young Swift had begun to make acquaintance with English Court manners and English servitude, in Sir William Temple's family, another Irish youth was brought to learn his humanities at the old school of Charterhouse, near Smithfield; to which foundation he had been appointed by James, Duke of Ormond, a governor of the House, and a patron of the lad's family. The boy was an orphan, and described, twenty years after, with a sweet pathos and simplicity, some of the earliest recollections of a life which was destined to be chequered by a strange variety of good and evil fortune.

I am afraid no good report could be given by his masters and ushers of that thick-set, square-faced, black-eyed, soft-hearted little Irish boy. He was very idle. He was whipped deservedly a great number of times. Though he had very good parts of his own, he got other boys to do his lessons for him, and only took just as much trouble as should enable him to scuffle through his exercises, and by good fortune escape the flogging-block. One hundred and fifty years after, I have myself inspected, but only as an amateur, that instrument of righteous torture still existing, and in occasional use, in a secluded private apartment of the old Charterhouse School; and have no doubt it is the very counterpart, if not the ancient and interesting machine itself, at which poor Dick Steele submitted himself to the tormentors.

Besides being very kind, lazy, and good-natured, this boy went invariably into debt with the tart-woman; ran out of bounds, and entered into pecuniary, or rather promissory engagements with the neighbouring lollipop vendors and piemen—exhibited an early fondness and capacity for drinking mum and sack, and borrowed from all his comrades who had money to lend. I have no sort of authority for the statements here made of Steele's early life; but if the child is father of the man, the father of young Steele of Merton, who left Oxford without taking a degree, and entered the Life Guards—the father of Captain Steele of Lucas's Fusiliers, who got his company through the patronage of my Lord Cutts—the father of Mr. Steele the Commissioner of Stamps, the editor of the *Gazette*, the *Tatler*, and *Spectator*, the expelled Member of

Parliament, and the author of the "Tender Husband" and the "Conscious Lovers"; if man and boy resembled each other, Dick Steele the schoolboy must have been one of the most generous, good-for-nothing, amiable little creatures that ever conjugated the verb *tupto*, I beat, *tuptomai*, I am whipped, in any school in Great Britain.

Almost every gentleman who does me the honour to hear me will remember that the very greatest character which he has seen in the course of his life, and the person to whom he has looked up with the greatest wonder and reverence, was the head boy at his school. The schoolmaster himself hardly inspires such an awe. The head boy construes as well as the schoomaster himself. When he begins to speak the hall is hushed, and every little boy listens. He writes off copies of Latin verses as melodiously as Virgil. He is good-natured, and, his own masterpieces achieved, pours out other copies of verses for other boys with an astonishing ease and fluency; the idle ones only trembling lest they should be discovered on giving in their exercises and whipped because their poems were too good. I have seen great men in my time, but never such a great one as that head boy of my childhood: we all thought he must be Prime Minister, and I was disappointed on meeting him in after life to find he was no more than six feet high.

Dick Steele, the Charterhouse gownboy, contracted such an admiration in the years of his childhood, and retained it faithfully through his life. Through the school and through the world, whithersoever his strange fortune led this erring, wayward, affectionate creature, Joseph Addison was always his head boy. Addison, wrote his exercises. Addison did his best themes. He ran on Addison's messages; fagged for him and blacked his shoes: to be in Joe's company was Dick's greatest pleasure; and he took a sermon or a caning from his monitor with the most boundless reverence, acquiescence, and affection.*

Steele found Addison a stately College Don at Oxford, and himself did not make much figure at this place. He wrote a comedy, which, by the advice of a friend, the humble fellow burned there; and some verses, which I dare say are as sublime as other gentlemen's compositions at that age; but being smitten with a sudden love

* "Steele had the greatest veneration for Addison, and used to show it, in all companies, in a particular manner. Addison, now and then, used to play a little upon him; but he always took it well."—POPE. *Spence's Anecdotes.*

"Sir Richard Steele was the best-natured creature in the world: even in his worst state of health, he seemed to desire nothing but to please and be pleased."—DR. YOUNG. *Spence's Anecdotes.*

Steele, it may be noted, was a few weeks older than Addison. He was born in March, Addison on 1st May, 1672.

for military glory, he threw up the cap and gown for the saddle and bridle, and rode privately in the Horse Guards, in the Duke of Ormond's troop—the second—and, probably, with the rest of the gentlemen of his troop, "all mounted on black horses with white feathers in their hats, and scarlet coats richly laced," marched by King William, in Hyde Park, in November 1699,* and a great show of the nobility, besides twenty thousand people, and above a thousand coaches. "The Guards had just got their new clothes," the *London Post* said: "they are extraordinary grand, and thought to be the finest body of horse in the world." But Steele could hardly have seen any actual service. He who wrote about himself, his mother, his wife, his loves, his debts, his friends, and the wine he drank, would have told us of his battles if he had seen any. His old patron, Ormond, probably got him his cornetcy in the Guards, from which he was promoted to be a captain in Lucas's Fusiliers, getting his company through the patronage of Lord Cutts, whose secretary he was, and to whom he dedicated his work called the "Christian Hero." As for Dick, whilst writing this ardent devotional work, he was deep in debt, in drink, and in all the follies of the town; it is related that all the officers of Lucas's, and the gentlemen of the Guards, laughed at Dick.† And in truth

* Steele appears to have been a trooper in the Life Guards; but in 1699 he had received from Lord Cutts an ensigncy in the Coldstream Guards. In 1702 he became captain in Lucas's regiment, which, however, was not called "Fusiliers."—See AITKEN'S *Life of Steele.*

† "The gaiety of his dramatic tone may be seen in this little scene between two brilliant sisters, from his comedy *The Funeral, or Grief à la Mode.* Dick wrote this, he said, from "a necessity of enlivening his character," which, it semed, the *Christian Hero* had a tendency to make too decorous, grave, and respectable in the eyes of readers of that pious piece.

[*Scene draws and discovers* LADY CHARLOTTE, *reading at a table*,—LADY HARRIET, *playing at a glass, to and fro, and viewing herself.*]

"*L. Ha.* Nay, good sister, you may as well talk to me [*looking at herself as she speaks*] as sit staring at a book which I know you can't attend.—Good Dr. Lucas may have writ there what he pleases, but there's no putting Francis, Lord Hardy, now Earl of Brumpton, out of your head, or making him absent from your eyes. Do but look on me, now, and deny it if you can.

"*L. Ch.* You are the maddest girl [*smiling*].

"*L. Ha.* Look ye, I knew you could not say it and forbear laughing. [*Looking over Charlotte.*]—Oh! I see his name as plain as you do—F-r-a-n, Fran, —c-i-s, cis, Francis, 'tis in every line of the book.

L. Ch. [*rising*]. It's in vain, I see, to mind anything in such impertinent company—but, granting 'twere as you say, as to my Lord Hardy—'tis more excusable to admire another than oneself.

"*L. Ha.* No, I think not,—yes, I grant you, than really to be vain of one's person, but I don't admire myself,—Pish! I don't believe my eyes to have that

a theologian in liquor is not a respectable object, and a hermit, though he may be out at elbows, must not be in debt to the tailor. Steele says of himself that he was always sinning and repenting. He beat his breast and cried most piteously when he *did* repent: but as soon as crying had made him thirsty, he fell to sinning again. In that charming paper in the *Tatler*, in which he records his father's death, his mother's griefs, his own most solemn and tender emotions, he says he is interrupted by the arrival of a hamper of wine, "the same as is to be sold at Garraway's next week"; upon the receipt of which he sends for three friends, and they fall to instantly, "drinking two bottles apiece, with great benefit to themselves, and not separating till two o'clock in the morning."

His life was so. Jack the drawer was always interrupting it,

softness. [*Looking in the glass.*] They a'n't so piercing: no, 'tis only stuff, the men will be talking.—Some people are such admirers of teeth—Lord, what signifies teeth! [*Showing her teeth.*] A very black-a-moor has as white a set of teeth as I.—No, sister, I don't admire myself, but I've a spirit of contradiction in me: I don't know I'm in love with myself, only to rival the men.

"*L. Ch.* Ay, but Mr. Campley will gain ground ev'n of that rival of his, your dear self.

"*L. Ha.* Oh, what have I done to you, that you should name that insolent intruder? A confident, opinionative fop. No, indeed, if I am, as a poetical lover of mine sighed and sung of both sexes,

'The public envy and the public care,

I shan't be so easily catched—I thank him—I want but to be sure I should heartily torment him by banishing him, and then consider whether he should depart this life or not.

"*L. Ch.* Indeed, sister, to be serious with you, this vanity in your humour does not at all become you.

"*L. Ha.* Vanity! All the matter is, we gay people are more sincere than you wise folks: all your life's an art.—Speak your soul.—Look you there.—[*Hauling her to the glass.*] Are you not struck with a secret pleasure when you view that bloom in your look, that harmony in your shape, that promptitude in your mien?

"*L. Ch.* Well, simpleton, if I am at first so simple as to be a little taken with myself, I know it a fault, and take pains to correct it.

"*L. Ha.* Pshaw! Pshaw! Talk this musty tale to old Mrs. Fardingale, 'tis too soon for me to think at that rate.

"*L. Ch.* They that think it too soon to understand themselves will very soon find it too late.—But tell me honestly, don't you like Campley?

"*L. Ha.* The fellow is not to be abhorred, if the forward thing did not think of getting me so easily.—Oh, I hate a heart I can't break when I please.—What makes the value of dear china, but that 'tis so brittle?—were it not for that, you might as well have stone mugs in your closet."—*The Funeral*, Oct. 2nd.

"We knew the obligations the stage had to his writings [Steele's]; there being scarcely a comedian of merit in our whole company whom his *Tatlers* had not made better by his recommendation of them."—*Cibber.*

bringing him a bottle from the "Rose," or inviting him over to a bout there with Sir Plume and Mr. Diver; and Dick wiped his eyes, which were whimpering over his papers, took down his laced hat, put on his sword and wig, kissed his wife and children, told them a lie about pressing business, and went off to the "Rose" to the jolly fellows.

While Mr. Addison was abroad, and after he came home in rather a dismal way to wait upon Providence in his shabby lodging in the Haymarket, young Captain Steele was cutting a much smarter figure than that of his classical friend of Charterhouse Cloister and Maudlin Walk. Could not some painter give an interview between the gallant Captain of Lucas's, with his hat cocked, and his lace, and his face too, a trifle tarnished with drink, and that poet, that philosopher, pale, proud, and poor, his friend and monitor of school-days, of all days? How Dick must have bragged about his chances and his hopes, and the fine company he kept, and the charms of the reigning toasts and popular actresses, and the number of bottles that he and my Lord and some other pretty fellows had cracked over-night at the "Devil," or the "Garter"! Cannot one fancy Joseph Addison's calm smile and cold grey eyes following Dick for an instant, as he struts down the Mall to dine with the Guard at Saint James's, before he turns, with his sober pace and threadbare suit, to walk back to his lodgings up the two pair of stairs? Steele's name was down for promotion, Dick always said himself, in the glorious, pious, and immortal William's last table-book. Jonathan Swift's name had been written there by the same hand too.

Our worthy friend, the author of the "Christian Hero," continued to make no small figure about town by the use of his wits.* He was appointed Gazetteer: he wrote, in 1703, "The Tender Husband," his second play, in which there is some delightful farcical writing, and of which he fondly owned in after life, and when Addison was no more, that there were "many applauded strokes" from Addison's beloved hand.† Is it not a pleasant partnership

* "There is not now in his sight that excellent man, whom Heaven made his friend and superior, to be at a certain place in pain for what he should say or do. I will go on in his further encouragement. The best woman that ever man had cannot now lament and pine at his neglect of himself."—STEELE [of himself]: *The Theatre.* No. 12, Feb. 1719-20.

† *The Funeral* supplies an admirable stroke of humour,—one which Sydney Smith has used as an illustration of the faculty in his lectures.

The undertaker is talking to his *employés* about their duty.

"*Sable.* Ha, you!—A little more upon the dismal [*forming their countenances*]; this fellow has a good mortal look,—place him near the corpse: that wainscot-face must be o'top of the stairs; that fellow's almost in a fright (that

to remember? Can't one fancy Steele full of spirits and youth, leaving his gay company to go to Addison's lodging, where his friend sits in the shabby sitting-room, quite serene, and cheerful, and poor? In 1704, Steele came on the town with another comedy, and behold it was so moral and religious, as poor Dick insisted,—so dull the town thought,—that the "Lying Lover" was damned.*

Addison's hour of success now came, and he was able to help our friend the "Christian Hero" in such a way, that, if there had been any chance of keeping that poor tipsy champion upon his legs, his fortune was safe, and his competence assured. Steele procured the place of Commissioner of Stamps: he wrote so richly, so gracefully often, so kindly always, with such a pleasant wit and easy frankness, with such a gush of good spirits and good humour, that his early papers may be compared to Addison's own, and are to be read, by a male reader at least, with quite an equal pleasure.†

looks as if he were full of some strange misery) at the end of the hall. So—But I'll fix you all myself. Let's have no laughing now on any provocation. Look yonder—that hale, well-looking puppy! You ungrateful scoundrel, did not I pity you, take you out of a great man's service, and show you the pleasure of receiving wages? *Did not I give you ten, then fifteen, and twenty shillings a week to be sorrowful?—and the more I give you I think the gladder you are!*"

* There is some confusion here as to dates. Steele's first play, the *Funeral* was brought out in December 1701; his second, the *Lying Lover* in December 1703; and his third the *Tender Husband* in April 1705.

† "From my own Apartment: *Nov.* 16.

"There are several persons who have many pleasures and entertainments in their possession, which they do not enjoy; it is, therefore, a kind and good office to acquaint them with their own happiness, and turn their attention to such instances of their good fortune as they are apt to overlook. Persons in the married state often want such a monitor; and pine away their days by looking upon the same condition in anguish and murmuring, which carries with it, in the opinion of others, a complication of all the pleasures of life, and a retreat from its inquietudes.

"I am led into this thought by a visit I made to an old friend who was formerly my schoolfellow. He came to town last week, with his family, for the winter; and yesterday morning sent me word his wife expected me to dinner. I am, as it were, at home at that house, and every member of it knows me for their well-wisher. I cannot, indeed, express the pleasure it is to be met by the children with so much joy as I am when I go thither. The boys and girls strive who shall come first, when they think it is I that am knocking at the door; and that child which loses the race to me runs back again to tell the father it is Mr. Bickerstaff. This day I was led in by a pretty girl that we all thought must have forgot me; for the family has been out of town these two years. Her knowing me again was a mighty subject with us, and took up our discourse at the first entrance; after which, they began to rally me upon a thousand little stories they heard in the country,

CAPTAIN STEELE.

After the *Tatler* in 1711, the famous *Spectator* made its appearance, and this was followed at various intervals, by many periodicals under the same editor—the *Guardian*—the *Englishman*—the *Lover*, whose love was rather insipid—the *Reader*, of whom the public saw no more after his second appearance—the *Theatre*, under the pseudonym of Sir John Edgar, which Steele wrote while Governor of the Royal Company of Comedians, to which post, and

about my marriage to one of my neighbours' daughters; upon which, the gentleman, my friend, said, 'Nay; if Mr. Bickerstaff marries a child of any of his old companions, I hope mine shall have the preference: there is Mrs. Mary is now sixteen, and would make him as fine a widow as the best of them. But I know him too well; he is so enamoured with the very memory of those who flourished in our youth, that he will not so much as look upon the modern beauties. I remember, old gentleman, how often you went home in a day to refresh your countenance and dress when Teraminta reigned in your heart. As we came up in the coach, I repeated to my wife some of your verses on her.' With such reflections on little passages which happened long ago, we passed our time during a cheerful and elegant meal. After dinner his lady left the room, as did also the children. As soon as we were alone, he took me by the hand: 'Well, my good friend,' says he, 'I am heartily glad to see thee; I was afraid you would never have seen all the company that dined with you to-day again. Do not you think the good woman of the house a little altered since you followed her from the playhouse to find out who she was for me?' I perceived a tear fall down his cheek as he spoke, which moved me not a little. But, to turn the discourse, I said, 'She is not, indeed, that creature she was when she returned me the letter I carried from you, and told me, "She hoped, as I was a gentleman, I would be employed no more to trouble her, who had never offended me; but would be so much the gentleman's friend as to dissuade him from a pursuit which he could never succeed in." You may remember I thought her in earnest, and you were forced to employ your cousin Will, who made his sister get acquainted with her for you. You cannot expect her to be for ever fifteen.' 'Fifteen!' replied my good friend. 'Ah! you little understand—you, that have lived a bachelor—how great, how exquisite a pleasure there is in being really beloved! It is impossible that the most beauteous face in nature should raise in me such pleasing ideas as when I look upon that excellent woman. That fading in her countenance is chiefly caused by her watching with me in my fever. This was followed by a fit of sickness, which had like to have carried me off last winter. I tell you, sincerely, I have so many obligations to her that I cannot, with any sort of moderation, think of her present state of health. But, as to what you say of fifteen, she gives me every day pleasure beyond what I ever knew in the possession of her beauty when I was in the vigour of youth. Every moment of her life brings me fresh instances of her complacency to my inclinations, and her prudence in regard to my fortune. Her face is to me much more beautiful than when I first saw it; there is no decay in any feature which I cannot trace from the very instant it was occasioned by some anxious concern for my welfare and interests. Thus, at the same time, methinks, the love I conceived towards her for what she was, is heightened by my gratitude for what she is. The love of a wife is as much above the idle passion commonly called by that name, as the loud laughter of

to that of Surveyor of the Royal Stables at Hampton Court, and to the Commission of the Peace for Middlesex, and to the honour of knighthood, Steele had been preferred soon after the accession of George I.; whose cause honest Dick had nobly fought, through disgrace, and danger, against the most formidable enemies, against traitors and bullies, against Bolingbroke and Swift in the last reign. With the arrival of the King, that splendid conspiracy broke up;

buffoons is inferior to the elegant mirth of gentlemen. Oh! she is an inestimable jewel! In her examination of her household affairs, she shows a certain fearfulness to find a fault, which makes her servants obey her like children; and the meanest we have has an ingenuous shame for an offence not always to be seen in children in other families. I speak freely to you, my old friend; ever since her sickness, things that gave me the quickest joy before turn now to a certain anxiety. As the children play in the next room, I know the poor things by their steps, and am considering what they must do should they lose their mother in their tender years. The pleasure I used to take in telling my boy stories of battles, and asking my girl questions about the disposal of her baby, and the gossiping of it, is turned into inward reflection and melancholy.'

"He would have gone on in this tender way, when the good lady entered, and, with an inexpressible sweetness in her countenance, told us, 'she had been searching her closet for something very good to treat such an old friend as I was.' Her husband's eyes sparkled with pleasure at the cheerfulness of her countenance; and I saw all his fears vanish in an instant. The lady observing something in our looks which showed we had been more serious than ordinary, and seeing her husband receive her with great concern under a forced cheerfulness, immediately guessed at what we had been talking of; and applying herself to me, said, with a smile, 'Mr. Bickerstaff, do not believe a word of what he tells you; I shall still live to have you for my second, as I have often promised you, unless he takes more care of himself than he has done since his coming to town. You must know he tells me, that he finds London is a much more healthy place than the country; for he sees several of his old acquaintances and schoolfellows are here—*young fellows with fair, full-bottomed periwigs.* I could scarce keep him this morning from going out *open-breasted.*' My friend, who is always extremely delighted with her agreeable humour, made her sit down with us. She did it with that easiness which is peculiar to women of sense; and to keep up the good humour she had brought in with her, turned her raillery upon me. 'Mr. Bickerstaff, you remember you followed me one night from the playhouse; suppose you should carry me thither to-morrow night, and lead me in the front box.' This put us into a long field of discourse about the beauties who were the mothers to the present, and shined in the boxes twenty years ago. I told her 'I was glad she had transferred so many of her charms, and I did not question but her eldest daughter was within half-a-year of being a toast.'

"We were pleasing ourselves with this fantastical preferment of the young lady, when, on a sudden, we were alarmed with the noise of a drum, and immediately entered my little godson to give me a point of war. His mother, between laughing and chiding, would have put him out of the room; but I would not part with him so. I found, upon conversation with him, though he was a little noisy in his mirth, that the child had excellent parts, and was a

and a golden opportunity came to Dick Steele, whose hand, alas, was too careless to gripe it.*

Steele married twice; and outlived his places, his schemes, his wife, his income, his health, and almost everything but his kind heart. That ceased to trouble him in 1729, when he died, worn out and almost forgotten by his contemporaries, in Wales, where he had the remnant of a property.

Posterity has been kinder to this amiable creature; all women especially are bound to be grateful to Steele, as he was the first of our writers who really seemed to admire and respect them. Congreve the Great, who alludes to the low estimation in which women were held in Elizabeth's time, as a reason why the women of Shakspeare make so small a figure in the poet's dialogues, though he can himself pay splendid compliments to women, yet looks on them as mere instruments of gallantry, and destined, like the most consummate fortifications, to fall, after a certain time, before the arts and bravery of the besieger, man. There is a letter of Swift's entitled "Advice to a very Young Married Lady," which shows the Dean's opinion of the female society of his day, and that if he despised man he utterly scorned women too. No lady of our time

great master of all the learning on the other side of eight years old. I perceived him a very great historian in *Æsop's Fables;* but he frankly declared to me his mind, 'that he did not delight in that learning, because he did not believe they were true;' for which reason I found he had very much turned his studies, for about a twelvemonth past, into the lives of Don Bellianis of Greece, Guy of Warwick, 'the Seven Champions,' and other historians of that age. I could not but observe the satisfaction the father took in the forwardness of his son, and that these diversions might turn to some profit. I found the boy had made remarks which might be of service to him during the course of his whole life. He would tell you the mismanagement of John Hickerthrift, find fault with the passionate temper in Bevis of Southampton, and loved Saint George for being the champion of England; and by this means had his thoughts insensibly moulded into the notions of discretion, virtue, and honour. I was extolling his accomplishments, when his mother told me 'that the little girl who led me in this morning was, in her way, a better scholar than he. Betty,' said she, 'deals chiefly in fairies and sprights; and sometimes in a winter night will terrify the maids with her accounts, until they are afraid to go up to bed.'

"I sat with them until it was very late, sometimes in merry sometimes in serious discourse, with this particular pleasure, which gives the only true relish to all conversation, a sense that every one of us liked each other. I went home, considering the different conditions of a married life and that of a bachelor; and I must confess it struck me with a secret concern to reflect, that whenever I go off I shall leave no traces behind me. In this pensive mood I return to my family; that is to say, to my maid, my dog, my cat, who only can be the better or worse for what happens to me."—*The Tatler.*

* He took what he could get, though it was not much.

could be treated by any man, were he ever so much a wit or Dean, in such a tone of insolent patronage and vulgar protection. In this performance, Swift hardly takes pains to hide his opinion that a woman is a fool: tells her to read books, as if reading was a novel accomplishment; and informs her that "not one gentleman's daughter in a thousand has been brought to read or understand her own natural tongue." Addison laughs at women equally; but, with the gentleness and politeness of his nature, smiles at them and watches them, as if they were harmless, half-witted, amusing, pretty creatures, only made to be men's playthings. It was Steele who first began to pay a manly homage to their goodness and understanding, as well as to their tenderness and beauty.* In his comedies the heroes do not rant and rave about the divine beauties of Gloriana or Statira, as the characters were made to do in the chivalry romances and the high-flown dramas just going out of vogue; but Steele admires women's virtue, acknowledges their sense, and adores their purity and beauty, with an ardour and strength which should win the good-will of all women to their hearty and respectful champion. It is this ardour, this respect, this manliness, which makes his comedies so pleasant and their heroes such fine gentlemen. He paid the finest compliment to a woman that perhaps ever was offered. Of one woman, whom Congreve had also admired and celebrated, Steele says, that "to have loved her was a liberal education." "How often," he says, dedicating a volume to his wife, "how often has your tenderness removed pain from my sick head, how often anguish from my afflicted heart! If there are such beings as guardian angels, they are thus employed. I cannot believe one of them to be more good in inclination, or more charming in form than my wife." His breast seems to warm and his eyes to kindle when he meets with a good and beautiful woman, and it is with his heart as well as with his hat that he salutes her. About children, and all that relates to home, he is not less tender, and more than once speaks in apology of what he calls his softness. He would have been

* "As to the pursuits after affection and esteem, the fair sex are happy in this particular, that with them the one is much more nearly related to the other than in men. The love of a woman is inseparable from some esteem of her; and as she is naturally the object of affection, the woman who has your esteem has also some degree of your love. A man that dotes on a woman for her beauty, will whisper his friend, 'That creature has a great deal of wit when you are well acquainted with her.' And if you examine the bottom of your esteem for a woman, you will find you have a greater opinion of her beauty than anybody else. As to us men, I design to pass most of my time with the facetious Harry Bickerstaff; but William Bickerstaff, the most prudent man of our family, shall be my executor."—*Tatler*, No. 206.

nothing without that delightful weakness. It is that which gives his works their worth and his style its charm. It, like his life, is full of faults and careless blunders; and redeemed, like that, by his sweet and compassionate nature

We possess of poor Steele's wild and chequered life some of the most curious memoranda that ever were left of a man's biography.* Most men's letters, from Cicero down to Walpole,

* The Correspondence of Steele passed after his death into the possession of his daughter Elizabeth, by his second wife, Miss Scurlock, of Carmarthenshire. She married the Hon. John, afterwards third Lord Trevor. At her death, part of the letters passed to Mr. Thomas, a grandson of a natural daughter of Steele's; and part to Lady Trevor's next of kin, Mr. Scurlock. They were published by the learned Nichols—from whose later edition of them, in 1809, our specimens are quoted.

Here we have him, in his courtship—which was not a very long one:—

To Mrs. Scurlock.

"*Aug.* 30, 1707.

"MADAM,—I beg pardon that my paper is not finer, but I am forced to write from a coffee-house, where I am attending about business. There is a dirty crowd of busy faces all around me, talking of money; while all my ambition, all my wealth, is love! Love which animates my heart, sweetens my humour, enlarges my soul, and affects every action of my life. It is to my lovely charmer I owe, that many noble ideas are continually affixed to my words and actions; it is the natural effect of that generous passion to create in the admirer some similitude of the object admired. Thus, my dear, am I every day to improve from so sweet a companion. Look up, my fair one, to that Heaven which made thee such; and join with me to implore its influence on our tender innocent hours, and beseech the Author of love to bless the rites He has ordained —and mingle with our happiness a just sense of our transient condition, and a resignation to His will, which only can regulate our minds to a steady endeavour to please Him and each other.

"I am for ever your faithful servant,

"RICH. STEELE."

Some few hours afterwards, apparently, Mistress Scurlock received the next one—obviously written later in the day!—

"*Saturday Night* (*Aug.* 30, 1707).

"DEAR LOVELY MRS. SCURLOCK,—I have been in very good company, where your health, under the character of *the woman I love best*, has been often drunk; so that I may say that I am dead drunk for your sake, which is more than *I die for you.* RICH. STEELE."

To Mrs. Scurlock.

"*Sept.* 1, 1707

"MADAM,—It is the hardest thing in the world to be in love, and yet attend business. As for me, all who speak to me find me out, and I must lock myself up, or other people will do it for me.

"A gentleman asked me this morning, 'What news from Lisbon?' and I answered, 'She is exquisitely handsome.' Another desired to know 'when I had last been at Hampton Court?' I replied, 'It will be on Tuesday come

or down to the great men of our own time, if you will, are doctored compositions, and written with an eye suspicious towards posterity. That dedication of Steele's to his wife is an artificial performance, possibly; at least, it is written with that degree of artifice which an orator uses in arranging a statement for the House, or a poet employs in preparing a sentiment in verse or for the stage. But there are some four hundred letters of Dick Steele's to his wife, which that thrifty woman preserved accurately, and which could have been written but for her and her alone. They contain details

se'nnight.' Pr'ythee allow me at least to kiss your hand before that day, that my mind may be in some composure. O Love!

"'A thousand torments dwell about thee,
Yet who could live, to live without thee?'

"Methinks I could write a volume to you; but all the language on earth would fail in saying how much, and with what disinterested passion,

"I am ever yours,
"RICH. STEELE."

Two days after this, he is found expounding his circumstances and prospects to the young lady's mamma. He dates from "Lord Sunderland's office, Whitehall;" and states his clear income at £1025 per annum. "I promise myself," says he, "the pleasure of an industrious and virtuous life, in studying to do things agreeable to you."

They were married, according to the most probable conjectures, about the 7th Sept. There are traces of a tiff about the middle of the next month; she being prudish and fidgety, as he was impassioned and reckless. General progress, however, may be seen from the following notes. The "house in Bury Street, Saint James's," was now taken.

To Mrs. Steele.

"*Oct.* 16, 1707.

"DEAREST BEING ON EARTH,—Pardon me if you do not see me till eleven o'clock, having met a schoolfellow from India, by whom I am to be informed on things this night which expressly concern your obedient husband,

"RICH. STEELE."

To Mrs. Steele.

"*Eight o'clock, Fountain Tavern:*
"*Oct.* 22, 1707.

"MY DEAR,—I beg of you not to be uneasy; for I have done a great deal of business to-day very successfully, and wait an hour or two about my *Gazette.*"

"*Dec.* 22, 1707.

"MY DEAR, DEAR WIFE,—I write to let you know I do not come home to dinner, being obliged to attend some business abroad, of which I shall give you an account (when I see you in the evening), as becomes your dutiful and obedient husband."

"DEVIL TAVERN, TEMPLE BAR:
"*Jan.* 3, 1707–8.

"DEAR PRUE,—I have partly succeeded in my business to-day, and

of the business, pleasures, quarrels, reconciliations of the pair; they have all the genuineness of conversation; they are as artless as a child's prattle, and as confidential as a curtain-lecture. Some are written from the printing-office, where he is waiting for the proof-sheets of his *Gazette*, or his *Tatler;* some are written from the tavern, whence he promises to come to his wife "within a pint of wine," and where he has given a rendezvous to a friend or a money-lender: some are composed in a high state of vinous excitement, when his head is flustered with burgundy, and his heart

inclose two guineas as earnest of more. Dear Prue, I cannot come home to dinner. I languish for your welfare, and will never be a moment careless more.

"Your faithful husband," &c.

"*Jan.* 14, 1707–8.

"DEAR WIFE,—Mr. Edgecombe, Ned Ask, and Mr. Lumley have desired me to sit an hour with them at the 'George' in Pall Mall, for which I desire your patience till twelve o'clock, and that you will go to bed," &c.

"GRAY'S INN: *Feb.* 3, 1708.

"DEAR PRUE,—If the man who has my shoemaker's bill calls, let him be answered that I shall call on him as I come home. I stay here in order to get Jonson to discount a bill for me, and shall dine with him for that end. He is expected at home every minute. Your most humble, obedient servant," &c.

"TENNIS-COURT COFFEE-HOUSE: *May* 5, 1708.

"DEAR WIFE,—I hope I have done this day what will be pleasing to you; in the meantime shall lie this night at a baker's, one Leg, over against the 'Devil Tavern,' at Charing Cross. I shall be able to confront the fools who wish me uneasy, and shall have the satisfaction to see thee cheerful and at ease.

"If the printer's boy be at home, send him hither; and let Mrs. Todd send by the boy my night-gown, slippers, and clean linen. You shall hear from me early in the morning," &c.

Dozens of similar letters follow, with occasional guineas, little parcels of tea, or walnuts, &c. In 1709 the *Tatler* made its appearance. The following curious note dates April 7th, 1710:—

"I enclose to you ['Dear Prue'] a receipt for the saucepan and spoon, and a note of £23 of Lewis's, which will make up the £50 I promised for your ensuing occasion.

"I know no happiness in this life in any degree comparable to the pleasure I have in your person and society. I only beg of you to add to your other charms a fearfulness to see a man that loves you in pain and uneasiness, to make me as happy as it is possible to be in this life. Rising a little in a morning, and being disposed to a cheerfulness . . . would not be amiss."

In another, he is found excusing his coming home, being "invited to supper to Mr. Boyle's." "Dear Prue," he says on this occasion, "do not send after me, for I shall be ridiculous."

abounds with amorous warmth for his darling Prue: some are under the influence of the dismal headache and repentance next morning: some, alas, are from the lock-up house, where the lawyers have impounded him, and where he is waiting for bail. You trace many years of the poor fellow's career in these letters. In September 1707, from which day she began to save the letters, he married the beautiful Mistress Scurlock. You have his passionate protestations to the lady; his respectful proposals to her mamma; his private prayer to Heaven when the union so ardently desired was completed; his fond professions of contrition and promises of amendment, when, immediately after his marriage, there began to be just cause for the one and need for the other.

Captain Steele took a house for his lady upon their marriage, "the third door from Germain Street, left hand of Berry Street," and the next year he presented his wife with a country house at Hampton. It appears she had a chariot and pair, and sometimes four horses: he himself enjoyed a little horse for his own riding. He paid, or promised to pay, his barber fifty pounds a year, and always went abroad in a laced coat and a large black buckled periwig, that must have cost somebody fifty guineas. He was rather a well-to-do gentleman, Captain Steele, with the proceeds of his estates in Barbadoes (left to him by his first wife), his income as a writer of the *Gazette*, and his office of gentleman waiter to his Royal Highness Prince George. His second wife brought him a fortune too. But it is melancholy to relate, that with these houses and chariots and horses and income, the Captain was constantly in want of money, for which his beloved bride was asking as constantly. In the course of a few pages we begin to find the shoemaker calling for money, and some directions from the Captain, who has not thirty pounds to spare. He sends his wife, "the beautifullest object in the world," as he calls her, and evidently in reply to applications of her own, which have gone the way of all waste paper, and lighted Dick's pipes, which were smoked a hundred and forty years ago—he sends his wife now a guinea, then a half-guinea, then a couple of guineas, then half a pound of tea; and again no money and no tea at all, but a promise that his darling Prue shall have some in a day or two: or a request, perhaps, that she will send over his night-gown and shaving-plate to the temporary lodging where the nomadic Captain is lying, hidden from the bailiffs. Oh that a Christian hero and late Captain in Lucas's should be afraid of a dirty sheriff's officer! That the pink and pride of chivalry should turn pale before a writ! It stands to record in poor Dick's own handwriting—the queer collection is preserved at the British Museum to this present day—that the rent of the nuptial house in Jermyn Street, sacred to unutterable tenderness and Prue, and three doors from Bury Street, was not paid until after the landlord had put in an execution on Captain Steele's furniture. Addison sold the house and furniture at Hampton, and, after deducting the sum which his incorrigible friend was indebted to him, handed over the residue of the proceeds of the sale to poor Dick, who wasn't in the least angry at Addison's summary proceeding, and I dare say was very glad of any sale or execution, the result of which was to give him a little ready money. Having a small house in Jermyn Street for which he couldn't pay, and a country house at Hampton on which he had borrowed money, nothing must content Captain Dick but the taking, in 1712, a much finer, larger, and grander house in Bloomsbury Square: where his unhappy landlord got no better satisfaction than his friend in Saint James's, and where it is recorded that Dick giving a grand entertainment, had a half-dozen queer-looking fellows in livery to wait upon his noble guests, and confessed that his servants were bailiffs to a man. "I fared like a distressed prince," the kindly prodigal writes, generously complimenting Addison for his assistance in the *Tatler*,—"I fared like a distressed prince, who calls in a powerful neighbour to his aid. I was undone by my auxiliary; when I had once called him in, I could not subsist without dependence on him." Poor needy Prince of Bloomsbury! think of him in his palace with his allies from Chancery Lane ominously guarding him.

All sorts of stories are told indicative of his recklessness and his good-humour. One narrated by Doctor Hoadly is exceedingly characteristic; it shows the life of the time; and our poor friend very weak, but very kind both in and out of his cups.

"My father," says Doctor John Hoadly, the Bishop's son, "when Bishop of Bangor, was, by invitation, present at one of the Whig meetings, held at the 'Trumpet,' in Shire Lane, when Sir Richard, in his zeal, rather exposed himself, having the double duty of the day upon him, as well to celebrate the immortal memory of King William, it being the 4th November, as to drink his friend Addison up to conversation pitch, whose phlegmatic constitution was hardly warmed for society by that time. Steele was not fit for it. Two remarkable circumstances happened. John Sly, the hatter of facetious memory, was in the house; and John, pretty mellow, took it into his head to come into the company on his knees, with a tankard of ale in his hand to drink off to the *immortal memory*, and to return in the same manner. Steele, sitting next my father, whispered him—*Do laugh. It is humanity to laugh.* Sir Richard, in the evening, being too much in the same condition, was put into a chair, and sent home. Nothing would serve him but being carried to the Bishop of Bangor's, late as it was. However, the chairman carried him home, and got him upstairs, when his great complaisance would wait on them downstairs, which he did, and then was got quietly to bed." *

There is another amusing story which, I believe, that renowned collector, Mr. Joseph Miller, or his successors, have incorporated into their work. Sir Richard Steele, at a time when he was much occupied with theatrical affairs, built himself a pretty private theatre, and before it was opened to his friends and guests, was anxious to try whether the hall was well adapted for hearing. Accordingly he placed himself in the most remote part of the gallery, and begged the carpenter who had built the house to speak up from the stage. The man at first said that he was unaccustomed to public speaking, and did not know what to say to his honour; but the good-natured knight called out to him to say whatever was uppermost; and, after a moment, the carpenter began, in a voice perfectly audible: "Sir Richard Steele!" he said, "for three months past me and my men has been a working in this theatre, and we've never seen the colour of your honour's money: we will be very much obliged if you'll pay it directly, for until you do we won't drive in another nail." Sir Richard said that his friend's elocution was perfect, but that he didn't like his subject much.

The great charm of Steele's writing is its naturalness. He wrote so quickly and carelessly that he was forced to make the reader his confidant, and had not the time to deceive him. He had a small share of book-learning, but a vast acquaintance with the world. He had known men and taverns. He had lived with gownsmen, with troopers, with gentlemen ushers of the Court, with men and women of fashion; with authors and wits, with the inmates of the spunging-houses, and with the frequenters of all the clubs and coffee-houses in the town. He was liked in all company because he liked it; and you like to see his enjoyment as you like to see the glee of a boxful of children at the pantomime. He was not of those lonely ones of the earth whose greatness obliged them to be solitary; on the contrary, he admired, I think, more than any man who ever wrote; and full of hearty applause and sympathy, wins upon you by calling you to share his delight and good-humour. His laugh rings through the whole house. He

* Of this famous Bishop, Steele wrote—

"Virtue with so much ease on Bangor sits,
All faults he pardons, though he none commits."

This couplet was sent to Hoadly next day in an apologetic letter.

must have been invaluable at a tragedy, and have cried as much as the most tender young lady in the boxes. He has a relish for beauty and goodness wherever he meets it. He admired Shakspeare affectionately, and more than any man of his time: and according to his generous expansive nature, called upon all his company to like what he liked himself. He did not damn with faint praise: he was in the world and of it; and his enjoyment of life presents the strangest contrast to Swift's savage indignation and Addison's lonely serenity.* Permit me to read to you a

* Here we have some of his later letters:—

To Lady Steele.

"HAMPTON COURT: *March* 16, 1716–17.

"DEAR PRUE,—If you have written anything to me which I should have received last night, I beg your pardon that I cannot answer till the next post. . . . Your son at the present writing is mighty well employed in tumbling on the floor of the room, and sweeping the sand with a feather. He grows a most delightful child, and very full of play and spirit. He is also a very great scholar: he can read his primer; and I have brought down my Virgil. He makes most shrewd remarks about the pictures. We are very intimate friends and playfellows. He begins to be very ragged; and I hope I shall be pardoned if I equip him with new clothes and frocks, or what Mrs. Evans and I shall think for his service."

To Lady Steele.

[Undated.]

"You tell me you want a little flattery from me. I assure you I know no one who deserves so much commendation as yourself, and to whom saying the best things would be so little like flattery. The thing speaks for itself, considering you as a very handsome woman that loves retirement—one who does not want wit, and yet is extremely sincere; and so I could go through all the vices which attend the good qualities of other people, of which you are exempt. But, indeed, though you have every perfection, you have an extravagant fault, which almost frustrates the good in you to me; and that is, that you do not love to dress, to appear, to shine out, even at my request, and to make me proud of you, or rather to indulge the pride I have that you are mine. . . .

"Your most affectionate obsequious husband,

"RICHARD STEELE.

"A quarter of Molly's schooling is paid. The children are perfectly well."

To Lady Steele.

"*March* 26, 1717.

"MY DEAREST PRUE,—I have received yours, wherein you give me the sensible affliction of telling me enow of the continual pain in your head. . . . When I lay in your place, and on your pillow, I assure you I fell into tears last night, to think that my charming little insolent might be then awake and in pain; and took it to be a sin to go to sleep.

"For this tender passion towards you, I must be contented that your *Prueship* will condescend to call yourself my well-wisher. . . ."

At the time when the above later letters were written, Lady Steele was in Wales, looking after her estate there. Steele, about this time, was much

passage from each writer, curiously indicative of his peculiar humour: the subject is the same, and the mood the very gravest. We have said that upon all the actions of man, the most trifling and the most solemn, the humourist takes upon himself to comment. All readers of our old masters know the terrible lines of Swift, in which he hints at his philosophy and describes the end of mankind * :—

"Amazed, confused, its fate unknown,
The world stood trembling at Jove's throne;
While each pale sinner hung his head,
Jove, nodding, shook the heavens and said:
'Offending race of human kind,
By nature, reason, learning, blind;
You who through frailty stepped aside,
And you who never err'd through pride;
You who in different sects were shamm'd,
And come to see each other damn'd;
(So some folk told you, but they knew
No more of Jove's designs than you;)
The world's mad business now is o'er,
And I resent your freaks no more;
I to such blockheads set my wit,
I damn such fools—go, go, you're bit!'"

Addison speaking on the very same theme, but with how different a voice, says, in his famous paper on Westminster Abbey (*Spectator*, No. 26):—

"For my own part, though I am always serious, I do not know what it is to be melancholy, and can therefore take a view of nature in her deep and solemn scenes, with the same pleasure as in her most gay and delightful ones. When I look upon the tombs of the great, every emotion of envy dies within me; when I read the epitaphs of the beautiful, every inordinate desire goes out; when I meet with the grief of parents on a tombstone, my heart melts with compassion; when I see the tomb of the parents themselves, I consider the vanity of grieving for those we must quickly follow."

(I have owned that I do not think Addison's heart melted very much, or that he indulged very inordinately in the "vanity of grieving.")

occupied with a project for conveying fish alive, by which, as he constantly assures his wife, he firmly believed he should make his fortune. It did not succeed, however.

Lady Steele died in December of the succeeding year. She lies buried in Westminster Abbey.

* Lord Chesterfield sends these verses to Voltaire in a characteristic letter.

"When," he goes on, "when I see kings lying by those who deposed them: when I consider rival wits placed side by side, or the holy men that divided the world with their contests and disputes—I reflect with sorrow and astonishment on the little competitions, factions, and debates of mankind. And, when I read the several dates on the tombs of some that died yesterday, and some six hundred years ago, I consider that great day when we shall all of us be contemporaries, and make our appearance together."

Our third humourist comes to speak on the same subject. You will have observed in the previous extracts the characteristic humour of each writer—the subject and the contrast—the fact of Death, and the play of individual thought by which each comments on it, and now hear the third writer—death, sorrow, and the grave, being for the moment also his theme.

"The first sense of sorrow I ever knew," Steele says in the *Tatler*, "was upon the death of my father, at which time I was not quite five years of age: but was rather amazed at what all the house meant, than possessed of a real understanding why nobody would play with us. I remember I went into the room where his body lay, and my mother sate weeping alone by it. I had my battledore in my hand, and fell a beating the coffin and calling papa; for, I know not how, I had some idea that he was locked up there. My mother caught me in her arms, and, transported beyond all patience of the silent grief she was before in, she almost smothered me in her embraces, and told me in a flood of tears, 'Papa could not hear me, and would play with me no more: for they were going to put him under ground, whence he would never come to us again.' She was a very beautiful woman, of a noble spirit, and there was a dignity in her grief, amidst all the wildness of her transport, which methought struck me with an instinct of sorrow that, before I was sensible what it was to grieve, seized my very soul, and has made pity the weakness of my heart ever since."

Can there be three more characteristic moods of minds and men? "Fools, do you know anything of this mystery?" says Swift, stamping on a grave, and carrying his scorn for mankind actually beyond it. "Miserable purblind wretches, how dare you to pretend to comprehend the Inscrutable, and how can your dim eyes pierce the unfathomable depths of yonder boundless heaven?" Addison, in a much kinder language and gentler voice, utters much the same sentiment: and speaks of the rivalry of wits, and the contests of holy men, with the same sceptic placidity. "Look what a little vain dust we are," he says, smiling over the tombstones; and catching, as is his wont, quite a divine effulgence as he looks heavenward, he speaks, in words of inspiration almost, of "the Great Day, when we shall all of us be contemporaries, and make our appearance together."

The third, whose theme is Death, too, and who will speak his word of moral as Heaven teaches him, leads you up to his father's coffin, and shows you his beautiful mother weeping, and himself an unconscious little boy wondering at her side. His own natural tears flow as he takes your hand and confidingly asks your sympathy. "See how good and innocent and beautiful women are," he says; "how tender little children! Let us love these and one another, brother—God knows we have need of love and pardon." So it is each looks with his own eyes, speaks with his own voice, and prays his own prayer.

When Steele asks your sympathy for the actors in that charming scene of Love and Grief and Death, who can refuse it? One yields to it as to the frank advance of a child, or to the appeal of a woman. A man is seldom more manly than when he is what you call unmanned—the source of his emotion is championship, pity, and courage; the instinctive desire to cherish those who are innocent and unhappy, and defend those who are tender and weak. If Steele is not our friend he is nothing. He is by no means the most brilliant of wits nor the deepest of thinkers: but he is our friend: we love him, as children love with an A, because he is amiable. Who likes a man best because he is the cleverest or the wisest of mankind; or a woman because she is the most virtuous, or talks French or plays the piano better than the rest of her sex? I own to liking Dick Steele the man, and Dick Steele the author, much better than much better men and much better authors.

The misfortune regarding Steele is, that most part of the company here present must take his amiability upon hearsay, and certainly can't make his intimate acquaintance. Not that Steele was worse than his time; on the contrary, a far better, truer, and higher-hearted man than most who lived in it. But things were done in that society, and names were named, which would make you shudder now. What would be the sensation of a polite youth of the present day, if at a ball he saw the young object of his affections taking a box out of her pocket and a pinch of snuff: or if at dinner, by the charmer's side, she deliberately put her knife into her mouth? If she cut her mother's throat with it, mamma would scarcely be more shocked. I allude to these peculiarities of bygone times as an excuse for my favourite Steele, who was not worse, and often much more delicate than his neighbours.

There exists a curious document * descriptive of the manners of the last age, which describes most minutely the amusements and occupations of persons of fashion in London at the time of which we are speaking; the time of Swift, and Addison, and Steele.

When Lord Sparkish, Tom Neverout, and Colonel Alwit, the immortal personages of Swift's polite conversation, came to breakfast with my Lady Smart, at eleven o'clock in the morning, my Lord Smart was absent at the levée. His Lordship was at home to dinner at three o'clock to receive his guests; and we may sit down to this meal, like the Barmecide's, and see the fops of the last century before us. Seven of them sat down at dinner, and were joined by a country baronet who told them they kept Court hours. These persons of fashion began their dinner with a sirloin of beef, fish, a shoulder of veal, and a tongue. My Lady Smart carved the sirloin, my Lady Answerall helped the fish, and the gallant Colonel cut the shoulder of veal. All made a considerable inroad on the sirloin and the shoulder of veal with the exception of Sir John, who had no appetite, having already partaken of a beefsteak and two mugs of ale, besides a tankard of March beer as soon as he got out of bed. They drank claret, which the master of the house said should always be drunk after fish; and my Lord Smart particularly recommended some excellent cider to my Lord Sparkish, which occasioned some brilliant remarks from that nobleman. When the host called for wine, he nodded to one or other of his guests, and said, "Tom Neverout, my service to you."

After the first course came almond-pudding, fritters, which the Colonel took with his hands out of the dish, in order to help the brilliant Miss Notable; chickens, black puddings, and soup; and Lady Smart, the elegant mistress of the mansion, finding a skewer in a dish, placed it in her plate with directions that it should be carried down to the cook and dressed for the cook's own dinner. Wine and small beer were drunk during the second course; and when the Colonel called for beer, he called the butler Friend, and asked whether the beer was good. Various jocular remarks passed from the gentlefolk to the servants; at breakfast several persons had a word and a joke for Mrs. Betty, my Lady's maid, who warmed the cream and had charge of the canister (the tea cost thirty shillings a pound in those days). When my Lady Sparkish sent her footman out to my Lady Match to come at six o'clock and play at quadrille, her Ladyship warned the man to follow his nose, and if he fell by the way not to stay to get up again. And when the gentlemen asked the hall-porter if his lady was at home, that functionary

* Swift's Polite Conversation."

replied, with manly waggishness, "She was at home just now, but she's not gone out yet."

After the puddings, sweet and black, the fritters and soup, came the third course, of which the chief dish was a hot venison pasty, which was put before Lord Smart, and carved by that nobleman. Besides the pasty, there was a hare, a rabbit, some pigeons, partridges, a goose, and a ham. Beer and wine were freely imbibed during this course, the gentlemen always pledging somebody with every glass which they drank; and by this time the conversation between Tom Neverout and Miss Notable had grown so brisk and lively, that the Derbyshire baronet began to think the young gentlewoman was Tom's sweetheart: on which Miss remarked, that she loved Tom "like pie." After the goose, some of the gentlewomen took a dram of brandy, "which was very good for the wholesomes," Sir John said: and now having had a tolerably substantial dinner, honest Lord Smart bade the butler bring up the great tankard full of October to Sir John. The great tankard was passed from hand to hand and mouth to mouth, but when pressed by the noble host upon the gallant Tom Neverout, he said, "No, faith, my Lord; I like your wine, and won't put a churl upon a gentleman. Your honour's claret is good enough for me." And so, the dinner over, the host said, "Hang saving, bring us up a ha'porth of cheese."

The cloth was now taken away, and a bottle of burgundy was set down, of which the ladies were invited to partake before they went to their tea. When they withdrew, the gentlemen promised to join them in an hour: fresh bottles were brought; the "dead men," meaning the empty bottles, removed; and "D'you hear, John! bring clean glasses," my Lord Smart said. On which the gallant Colonel Alwit said, "I'll keep my glass; for wine is the best liquor to wash glasses in."

After an hour the gentlemen joined the ladies, and then they all sat and played quadrille until three o'clock in the morning, when the chairs and the flambeaux came, and this noble company went to bed.

Such were manners six or seven score years ago. I draw no inference from this queer picture—let all moralists here present deduce their own. Fancy the moral condition of that society in which a lady of fashion joked with a footman, and carved a sirloin. and provided besides a great shoulder of veal, a goose, hare, rabbit, chickens, partridges, black puddings, and a ham for a dinner for eight Christians. What—what could have been the condition of that polite world in which people openly ate goose after almond-pudding, and took their soup in the middle of dinner? Fancy a

Colonel in the Guards putting his hand into a dish of *beignets d'abricot* and helping his neighbour, a young lady *du monde!* Fancy a noble lord calling out to the servants, before the ladies at his table, "Hang expense, bring us a ha'porth of cheese!" Such were the ladies of Saint James's—such were the frequenters of "White's Chocolate House," when Swift used to visit it, and Steele described it as the centre of pleasure, gallantry, and entertainment, a hundred and forty years ago!

Dennis, who ran amuck at the literary society of his day, falls foul of poor Steele, and thus depicts him:—

"Sir John Edgar, of the county of —— in Ireland, is of a middle stature, broad shoulders, thick legs, a shape like the picture of somebody over a farmer's chimney—a short chin, a short nose, a short forehead, a broad flat face, and a dusky countenance. Yet with such a face and such a shape, he discovered at sixty that he took himself for a beauty, and appeared to be more mortified at being told that he was ugly, than he was by any reflection made upon his honour or understanding.

"He is a gentleman born, witness himself, of very honourable family; certainly of a very ancient one, for his ancestors flourished in Tipperary long before the English ever set foot in Ireland. He has testimony of this more authentic than the Heralds' Office, or any human testimony. For God has marked him more abundantly than he did Cain, and stamped his native country on his face, his understanding, his writings, his actions, his passions, and, above all, his vanity. The Hibernian brogue is still upon all these, though long habit and length of days have worn it off his tongue." *

* Steele replied to Dennis in an "Answer to a Whimsical Pamphlet, called the Character of Sir John Edgar." What Steele had to say against the cross-grained old Critic discovers a great deal of humour:—

"Thou never didst let the sun into thy garret, for fear he should bring a bailiff along with him. . . .

"Your years are about sixty-five, an ugly vinegar face, that if you had any command you would be obeyed out of fear, from your ill-nature pictured there; not from any other motive. Your height is about some five feet five inches. You see I can give your exact measure as well as if I had taken your dimension with a good cudgel, which I promise you to do as soon as ever I have the good fortune to meet you. . . .

"Your doughty paunch stands before you like a firkin of butter, and your duck legs seem to be cast for carrying burdens.

"Thy works are libels upon others, and satires upon thyself; and while they bark at men of sense, call him fool and knave that wrote them. Thou hast a great antipathy to thy own species; and hatest the sight of a fool but in thy glass."

Steele had been kind to Dennis, and once got arrested on account of a

Although this portrait is the work of a man who was neither the friend of Steele nor of any other man alive, yet there is a dreadful resemblance to the original in the savage and exaggerated traits of the caricature, and everybody who knows him must recognise Dick Steele. Dick set about almost all the undertakings of his life with inadequate means, and, as he took and furnished a house with the most generous intentions towards his friends, the most tender gallantry towards his wife, and with this only drawback, that he had not wherewithal to pay the rent when quarter-day came,—so, in his life he proposed to himself the most magnificent schemes of virtue, forbearance, public and private good, and the advancement of his own and the national religion; but when he had to pay for these articles—so difficult to purchase and so costly to maintain—poor Dick's money was not forthcoming: and when Virtue called with her little bill, Dick made a shuffling excuse that he could not see her that morning, having a headache from being tipsy over-night; or when stern Duty rapped at the door with his account, Dick was absent and not ready to pay. He was shirking at the tavern; or had some particular business (of somebody's else) at the ordinary; or he was in hiding, or worse than in hiding, in the lock-up house. What a situation for a man! —for a philanthropist—for a lover of right and truth—for a magnificent designer and schemer! Not to dare to look in the face the Religion which he adored and which he had offended: to have to shirk down back lanes and alleys, so as to avoid the friend whom he loved and who had trusted him; to have the house which he had intended for his wife, whom he loved passionately, and for her Ladyship's company which he wished to entertain splendidly, in the possession of a bailiff's man; with a crowd of little creditors, —grocers, butchers, and small-coal men—lingering round the door with their bills and jeering at him. Alas for poor Dick Steele!

pecuniary service which he did him. When John heard of the fact—"'Sdeath!" cries John; "why did not he keep out of the way as I did?"

The "Answer" concludes by mentioning that Cibber had offered Ten Pounds for the discovery of the authorship of Dennis's pamphlet; on which, says Steele, —"I am only sorry he has offered so much, because the *twentieth part* would have overvalued his whole carcase. But I know the fellow that he keeps to give answers to his creditors will betray him; for he gave me his word to bring officers on the top of the house that should make a hole through the ceiling of his garret, and so bring him to the punishment he deserves. Some people think this expedient out of the way, and that he would make his escape upon hearing the least noise. I say so too; but it takes him up half-an-hour every night to fortify himself with his old hair trunk, two or three joint-stools, and some other lumber, which he ties together with cords so fast that it takes him up the same time in the morning to release himself."

For nobody else, of course. There is no man or woman in *our* time who makes fine projects and gives them up from idleness or want of means. When duty calls upon *us*, we no doubt are always at home and ready to pay that grim tax-gatherer. When *we* are stricken with remorse and promise reform, we keep our promise, and are never angry, or idle, or extravagant any more. There are no chambers in *our* hearts, destined for family friends and affections, and now occupied by some Sin's emissary and bailiff in possession. There are no little sins, shabby peccadilloes, importunate remembrances, or disappointed holders of our promises to reform, hovering at our steps, or knocking at our door! Of course not. We are living in the nineteenth century; and poor Dick Steele stumbled and got up again, and got into jail and out again, and sinned and repented, and loved and suffered, and lived and died, scores of years ago. Peace be with him! Let us think gently of one who was so gentle: let us speak kindly of one whose own breast exuberated with human kindness.

PRIOR, GAY, AND POPE

MATTHEW PRIOR was one of those famous and lucky wits of the auspicious reign of Queen Anne, whose name it behoves us not to pass over. Mat was a world-philosopher of no small genius, good-nature, and acumen.* He loved, he drank, he sang. He describes himself, in one of his lyrics, "in a little Dutch chaise on a Saturday night; on his left hand his Horace, and a friend on his right," going out of town from the Hague to pass that

* Gay calls him—"Dear Prior . . . beloved by every muse."—*Mr. Pope's Welcome from Greece.*

Swift and Prior were very intimate, and he is frequently mentioned in the "Journal to Stella." "Mr. Prior," says Swift, "walks to make himself fat, and I to keep myself down. . . . We often walk round the park together."

In Swift's works there is a curious tract called *Remarks on the Characters of the Court of Queen Anne* [Scott's edition, vol. xii.]. The "Remarks" are not by the Dean; but at the end of each is an addition in italics from his hand, and these are always characteristic. Thus, to the Duke of Marlborough, he adds, "*Detestably covetous*," &c. Prior is thus noticed—

"*Matthew Prior, Esquire, Commissioner of Trade.*

"On the Queen's accession to the throne, he was continued in his office; is very well at Court with the ministry, and is an entire creature of my Lord Jersey's, whom he supports by his advice; is one of the best poets in England, but very facetious in conversation. A thin hollow-looked man, turned of forty years old. *This is near the truth.*"

"Yet counting as far as to fifty his years,
His virtues and vices were as other men's are.
High hopes he conceived and he smothered great fears,
In a life party-coloured—half pleasure, half care.

Not to business a drudge, nor to faction a slave,
He strove to make interest and freedom agree;
In public employments industrious and grave,
And alone with his friends, Lord, how merry was he!

Now in equipage stately, now humble on foot,
Both fortunes he tried, but to neither would trust;
And whirled in the round as the wheel turned about,
He found riches had wings, and knew man was but dust."

—PRIOR'S *Poems.* [*For my own monument.*]

evening and the ensuing Sunday boozing at a Spielhaus with his companions, perhaps bobbing for perch in a Dutch canal, and noting down, in a strain and with a grace not unworthy of his Epicurean master, the charms of his idleness, his retreat, and his Batavian Chloe. A vintner's son * in Whitehall, and a distinguished pupil of Busby of the Rod, Prior attracted some notice by writing verses at Saint John's College, Cambridge, and, coming up to town, aided Montague † in an attack on the noble old English lion John Dryden; in ridicule of whose work, "The Hind and the Panther," he brought out that remarkable and famous burlesque, "The Town and Country Mouse." Aren't you all acquainted with it? Have you not all got it by heart? What! have you never heard of it? See what fame is made of! The wonderful part of the satire was, that, as a natural consequence of "The Town and Country Mouse," Matthew Prior was made Secretary of Embassy at the Hague! I believe it is dancing, rather than singing, which distinguishes the young English diplomatists of the present day; and have seen them in various parts perform that part of their duty very finely. In Prior's time it appears a different accomplishment led to preferment.‡ Could you write a copy of Alcaics? that was the question. Could you turn out a neat epigram or two? Could you compose "The Town and Country Mouse"? It is manifest that, by the possession of this faculty, the most difficult treaties, the laws of foreign nations, and the interests of our own, are easily understood. Prior rose in the diplomatic service, and said good things that proved his sense and his spirit. When the apartments at Versailles were shown to him, with the victories of Louis XIV. painted on the walls, and Prior was asked whether the palace of the King of England had any such decorations, "The monuments of my master's actions," Mat said, of William, whom he cordially revered, "are to be seen everywhere except in his own house." Bravo, Mat! Prior rose to be full ambassador at Paris,§ where he somehow was cheated out of his

* [He was a joiner's son. His uncle was a vintner, and kept the Rhenish Wine House in Channel (now Cannon) Row, Westminster.]

† "They joined to produce a parody, entitled *The Town and Country Mouse*, part of which Mr. Bayes is supposed to gratify his old friends, Smart and Johnson, by repeating to them. The piece is therefore founded upon the twice-told jest of the 'Rehearsal.' . . . There is nothing new or original in the idea. . . . In this piece, Prior, though the younger man, seems to have had by far the largest share."—SCOTT's *Dryden*, vol. i. p. 330.

‡ [It is doubtful, however, whether Prior's appointment had much to do with his literary reputation.]

§ "He was to have been in the same commission with the Duke of Shrewsbury, but that that nobleman," says Johnson, "refused to be associated with one so meanly born. Prior therefore continued to act without a title till the ambassadorial plate; and in an heroic poem, addressed by him to her late lamented Majesty, Queen Anne, Mat makes some magnificent allusions to these dishes and spoons, of which Fate had deprived him. All that he wants, he says, is her Majesty's picture; without that he can't be happy.

> "Thee, gracious Anne, thee present I adore:
> Thee, Queen of Peace, if Time and Fate have power
> Higher to raise the glories of thy reign,
> In words sublimer and a nobler strain
> May future bards the mighty theme rehearse.
> Here, Stator Jove, and Phœbus, king of verse,
> The votive tablet I suspend."

With that word the poem stops abruptly. The votive tablet is suspended for ever, like Mahomet's coffin. News came that the Queen was dead. Stator Jove, and Phœbus, king of verse, were left there, hovering to this day, over the votive tablet. The picture was never got, any more than the spoons and dishes: the inspiration ceased, the verses were not wanted—the ambassador wasn't wanted. Poor Mat was recalled from his embassy, suffered disgrace along with his patrons, lived under a sort of cloud ever after, and disappeared in Essex. When deprived of all his pensions and emoluments, the hearty and generous Oxford pensioned him.* They played for gallant stakes—the bold men of those days—and lived and gave splendidly.

Johnson quotes from Spence a legend, that Prior, after spending an evening with Harley, St. John, Pope, and Swift, would go off and smoke a pipe with a couple of friends of his, a soldier and his wife, in Long Acre. Those who have not read his late Excellency's poems should be warned that they smack not a little of the conversation of his Long Acre friends. Johnson speaks slightingly of his lyrics; but with due deference to the great Samuel, Prior's seem to me amongst the easiest, the richest, the most charmingly humourous

Duke's return next year to England, and then he assumed the style and dignity of ambassador."

He had been thinking of slights of this sort when he wrote his Epitaph:—

> "Nobles and heralds, by your leave,
> Here lies what once was Matthew Prior,
> The son of Adam and of Eve:
> Can Bourbon or Nassau claim higher?"

But, in this case, the old prejudice got the better of the old joke.

* [Prior's poems published (in folio) by subscription brought him £4000. Lord Harley (not his father, the Earl of Oxford) added £4000 to this for the purchase of an estate (Down Hall) in Essex.]

of English lyrical poems.* Horace is always in his mind; and his song, and his philosophy, his good sense, his happy easy turns and melody, his loves and his Epicureanism bear a great resemblance to that most delightful and accomplished master. In reading his works one is struck with their modern air, as well as by their happy similarity to the songs of the charming owner of the Sabine farm. In his verses addressed to Halifax, he says, writing of that endless theme to poets, the vanity of human wishes—

"So whilst in fevered dreams we sink,
And waking, taste what we desire,
The real draught but feeds the fire,
The dream is better than the drink.

Our hopes like towering falcons aim
At objects in an airy height:
To stand aloof and view the flight,
Is all the pleasure of the game."

Would not you fancy that a poet of our own days † was sing-

His epigrams have the genuine sparkle:—

The Remedy worse than the Disease.

"I sent for Radcliff; was so ill,
That other doctors gave me over:
He felt my pulse, prescribed his pill,
And I was likely to recover.

But when the wit began to wheeze,
And wine had warmed the politician,
Cured yesterday of my disease,
I died last night of my physician."

"Yes, every poet is a fool;
By demonstration Ned can show it;
Happy could Ned's inverted rule
Prove every fool to be a poet."

"On his deathbed poor Lubin lies,
His spouse is in despair;
With frequent sobs and mutual cries
They both express their care.

'A different cause,' says Parson Sly,
'The same effect may give;
Poor Lubin fears that he shall die,
His wife that he may live.'"

† [Thackeray, however, has ingeniously transposed the order of these verses, which, in the original, are not in the metre made familiar by a poet of our own days].

ing? and in the verses of Chloe weeping and reproaching him for his inconstancy, where he says—

"The God of us versemen, you know, child, the Sun,
How, after his journeys, he sets up his rest.
If at morning o'er earth 'tis his fancy to run,
At night he declines on his Thetis's breast.

So, when I am wearied with wandering all day,
To thee, my delight, in the evening I come:
No matter what beauties I saw in my way,
They were but my visits, but thou art my home!

Then finish, dear Chloe, this pastoral war,
And let us like Horace and Lydia agree:
For thou art a girl as much brighter than her,
As he was a poet sublimer than me."

If Prior read Horace, did not Thomas Moore study Prior? Love and pleasure find singers in all days. Roses are always blowing and fading—to-day as in that pretty time when Prior sang of them, and of Chloe lamenting their decay—

"She sighed, she smiled, and to the flowers
Pointing, the lovely moralist said:
See, friend, in some few fleeting hours,
See yonder what a change is made!

Ah me! the blooming pride of May
And that of Beauty are but one:
At morn both flourish, bright and gay,
Both fade at evening, pale and gone.

At dawn poor Stella danced and sung,
The amorous youth around her bowed:
At night her fatal knell was rung;
I saw, and kissed her in her shroud.

Such as she is who died to-day,
Such I, alas, may be to-morrow:
Go, Damon, bid thy Muse display
The justice of thy Chloe's sorrow."

Damon's knell was rung in 1721. May his turf lie lightly on him! "Deus sit propitius huic potatori," as Walter de Mapes sang.* Perhaps Samuel Johnson, who spoke slightingly of Prior's

* *Prior to Sir Thomas Hanmer.*

"*Aug.* 4, 1709.

"DEAR SIR,—Friendship may live, I grant you, without being fed and cherished by correspondence; but with that additional benefit I am of opinion it will look more cheerful and thrive better: for in this case, as in love, though a man is sure of his own constancy, yet his happiness depends a good deal upon the sentiments of another, and while you and Chloe are alive, 'tis not

verses, enjoyed them more than he was willing to own. The old moralist had studied them as well as Mr. Thomas Moore, and defended them and showed that he remembered them very well

enough that I love you both, except I am sure you both love me again; and as one of her scrawls fortifies my mind more against affliction than all Epictetus, with Simplicius's comments into the bargain, so your single letter gave me more real pleasure than all the works of Plato. . . . I must return my answer to your very kind question concerning my health. The Bath waters have done a good deal towards the recovery of it, and the great specific, *Cape caballum*, will, I think, confirm it. Upon this head I must tell you that my mare Betty grows blind, and may one day, by breaking my neck, perfect my cure: if at Rixham fair any pretty nagg that is between thirteen and fourteen hands presented himself, and you would be pleased to purchase him for me, one of your servants might ride him to Euston, and I might receive him there. This, sir, is just as such a thing happens. If you hear, too, of a Welch widow, with a good jointure, that has her *goings* and is not very skittish, pray be pleased to cast your eye on her for me too. You see, sir, the great trust I repose in your skill and honour, when I dare put two such commissions in your hand. . . ."—*The Hanmer Correspondence*, p. 120.

From Mr. Prior.

"PARIS: *1st–12th May, 1714.*

"MY DEAR LORD AND FRIEND,—Matthew never had so great occasion to write a word to Henry as now: it is noised here that I am soon to return. The question that I wish I could answer to the many that ask, and to our friend Colbert de Torcy (to whom I made your compliments in the manner you commanded) is, what is done for me; and to what I am recalled? It may look like a bagatelle, what is to become of a philosopher like me? but it is not such: what is to become of a person who had the honour to be chosen, and sent hither as intrusted, in the midst of a war, with what the Queen designed should make the peace; returning with the Lord Bolingbroke, one of the greatest men in England, and one of the finest heads in Europe (as they say here, if true or not, *n'importe*); having been left by him in the greatest character (that of her Majesty's Plenipotentiary), exercising that power conjointly with the Duke of Shrewsbury, and solely after his departure; having here received more distinguished honour than any Minister, except an Ambassador, ever did, and some which were never given to any but who had that character; having had all the success that could be expected; having (God be thanked!) spared no pains, at a time when at home the peace is voted safe and honourable—at a time when the Earl of Oxford is Lord Treasurer and Lord Bolingbroke First Secretary of State? This unfortunate person, I say, neglected, forgot, unnamed to anything that may speak the Queen satisfied with his services, or his friends concerned as to his fortune.

"Mr. de Torcy put me quite out of countenance, the other day, by a pity that wounded me deeper than ever did the cruelty of the late Lord Godolphin. He said he would write to Robin and Harry about me. God forbid, my Lord, that I should need any foreign intercession, or owe the least to any Frenchman living, besides the decency of behaviour and the returns of common civility: some say I am to go to Baden, others that I am to be added to the Commissioners for settling the commerce. In all cases I am ready, but in the meantime, *dic aliquid de tribus capellis*. Neither of these two are, I presume,

too, on an occasion when their morality was called in question by that noted puritan, James Boswell, Esquire, of Auchinleck.*

In the great society of the wits, John Gay deserved to be a favourite, and to have a good place.† In his set all were fond of him.

honours or rewards, neither of them (let me say to my dear Lord Bolingbroke, and let him not be angry with me) are what Drift may aspire to, and what Mr. Whitworth, who was his fellow-clerk, has or may possess. I am far from desiring to lessen the great merit of the gentleman I named, for I heartily esteem and love him; but in this trade of ours, my Lord, in which you are the general, as in that of the soldiery, there is a certain right acquired by time and long service. You would do anything for your Queen's service, but you would not be contented to descend, and be degraded to a charge, no way proportioned to that of Secretary of State, any more than Mr. Ross, though he would charge a party with a halbard in his hand, would be content all his life after to be Serjeant. Was my Lord Dartmouth, from Secretary, returned again to be Commissioner of Trade, or from Secretary of War, would Frank Gwyn think himself kindly used to be returned again to be Commissioner? In short, my Lord, you have put me above myself, and if I am to return to myself, I shall return to something very discontented and uneasy. I am sure, my Lord, you will make the best use you can of this hint for my good. If I am to have anything, it will certainly be for her Majesty s service, and the credit of my friends in the Ministry, that it be done before I am recalled from home, lest the world may think either that I have merited to be disgraced, or that ye dare not stand by me. If nothing is to be done, *fiat voluntas Dei.* I have writ to Lord Treasurer upon this subject, and having implored your kind intercession, I promise you it is the last remonstrance of this kind that I will ever make, Adieu, my Lord, all honour, health, and pleasure to you.

"Yours ever, MATT.

"*P.S.*—Lady Jersey is just gone from me. We drank your healths together in usquebaugh after our tea: we are the greatest friends alive. Once more adieu. There is no such thing as the 'Book of Travels' you mentioned; if there be, let friend Tilson send us more particular account of them, for neither I nor Jacob Tonson can find them. Pray send Barton back to me, I hope with some comfortable tidings."—*Bolingbroke's Letters.*

* "I asked whether Prior's poems were to be printed entire; Johnson said they were. I mentioned Lord Hales's censure of Prior in his preface to a collection of sacred poems, by various hands, published by him at Edinburgh a great many years ago, where he mentions 'these impure tales, which will be the eternal opprobrium of their ingenious author.' JOHNSON: 'Sir, Lord Hales has forgot. There is nothing in Prior that will excite to lewdness. If Lord Hales thinks there is, he must be more combustible than other people.' I instanced the tale of 'Paulo Purganti and his wife.' JOHNSON: 'Sir, there is nothing there but that his wife wanted to be kissed, when poor Paulo was out of pocket. No, sir, Prior is a lady's book. No lady is ashamed to have it standing in her library."—BOSWELL'S *Life of Johnson.*

† Gay was of an old Devonshire family, but his pecuniary prospects not being great, was placed in his youth in the house of a silk-mercer in London. He was born in 1688—Pope's year [It has been lately shown that Gay was born in 1685], and in 1712 the Duchess of Monmouth made him her secretary. Next

His success offended nobody. He missed a fortune once or twice. He was talked of for Court favour, and hoped to win it; but the Court favour jilted him. Craggs gave him some South Sea stock; and at one time Gay had very nearly made his fortune. But Fortune shook her swift wings and jilted him too: and so his friends, instead of being angry with him, and jealous of him, were kind and fond of honest Gay. In the portraits of the literary worthies of the early part of the last century, Gay's face is the pleasantest perhaps of all. It appears adorned with neither periwig nor nightcap (the full dress and *néglige* of learning, without which the painters of those days scarcely ever portrayed wits), and he laughs at you over his shoulder with an honest boyish glee—an artless sweet humour. He was so kind, so gentle, so jocular, so delightfully brisk at times, so dismally woebegone at others, such a natural good creature, that the Giants loved him. The great Swift was gentle and sportive with him,* as the enormous Brobdingnag maids of honour were with little Gulliver. He could frisk and fondle round Pope,† and sport, and bark, and caper, without

year he published his *Rural Sports*, which he dedicated to Pope, and so made an acquaintance which became a memorable friendship.

"Gay," says Pope, "was quite a natural man,—wholly without art or design, and spoke just what he thought and as he thought it. He dangled for twenty years about a Court, and at last was offered to be made usher to the young princesses. Secretary Craggs made Gay a present of stock in the South Sea year; and he was once worth £20,000, but lost it all again. He got about £400 by the first 'Beggar's Opera,' and £1100 or £1200 by the second. He was negligent and a bad manager. Latterly, the Duke of Queensberry took his money into his keeping, and let him only have what was necessary out of it, and, as he lived with them, he could not have occasion for much. He died worth upwards of £3000."—POPE. *Spence's Anecdotes.*

* "Mr. Gay is, in all regards, as honest and sincere a man as ever I knew." —SWIFT, *To Lady Betty Germaine*, Jan. 1733.

† "Of manners gentle, of affections mild;
In wit a man; simplicity, a child;
With native humour temp'ring virtuous rage,
Form'd to delight at once and lash the age;
Above temptation in a low estate,
And uncorrupted e'en among the great:
A safe companion, and an easy friend,
Unblamed through life, lamented in thy end.
These are thy honours; not that here thy bust
Is mixed with heroes, or with kings thy dust;
But that the worthy and the good shall say,
Striking their pensive bosoms, '*Here* lies Gay.'"
—POPE'S *Epitaph on Gay*.

"A hare who in a civil way,
Complied with everything, like Gay."
—*Fables*, "*The Hare and many Friends.*"

offending the most thin-skinned of poets and men; and when he was jilted in that little Court affair of which we have spoken, his warm-hearted patrons the Duke and Duchess of Queensberry * (the "Kitty, beautiful and young," of Prior) pleaded his cause with indignation, and quitted the Court in a huff, carrying off with them into their retirement their kind gentle *protégé*. With these kind lordly folks, a real Duke and Duchess, as delightful as those who harboured Don Quixote, and loved that dear old Sancho, Gay

* "I can give you no account of Gay," says Pope curiously, "since he was raffled for, and won back by his Duchess."—*Works, Roscoe's ed.*, vol. ix. p. 392.

Here is the letter Pope wrote to him when the death of Queen Anne brought back Lord Clarendon from Hanover, and lost him the Secretaryship of that nobleman, of which he had had but a short tenure.

Gay's Court prospects were never happy from this time.—His dedication of the *Shepherd's Week* to Bolingbroke, Swift used to call the "original sin" which had hurt him with the house of Hanover:—

"*Sept.* 23, 1714.

"DEAR MR. GAY,—Welcome to your native soil! welcome to your friends! thrice welcome to me! whether returned in glory, blest with Court interest, the love and familiarity of the great, and filled with agreeable hopes; or melancholy with dejection, contemplative of the changes of fortune, and doubtful for the future; whether returned a triumphant Whig, or a desponding Tory, equally all hail! equally beloved and welcome to me! If happy, I am to partake in your elevation; if unhappy, you have still a warm corner in my heart, and a retreat at Binfield in the worst of times at your service. If you are a Tory, or thought so by any man, I know it can proceed from nothing but your gratitude to a few people who endeavoured to serve you, and whose politics were never your concern. If you are a Whig, as I rather hope, and as I think your principles and mine (as brother poets) had ever a bias to the side of liberty, I know you will be an honest man and an inoffensive one. Upon the whole, I know you are incapable of being so much of either party as to be good for nothing. Therefore, once more, whatever you are or in whatever state you are, all hail!

"One or two of your own friends complained they had heard nothing from you since the Queen's death; I told them no man living loved Mr. Gay better than I, yet I had not once written to him in all his voyage. This I thought a convincing proof how truly one may be a friend to another without telling him so every month. But they had reasons, too, themselves to allege in your excuse, as men who really value one another will never want such as make their friends and themselves easy. The late universal concern in public affairs threw us all into a hurry of spirits: even I, who am more a philosopher than to expect anything from any reign, was borne away with the current, and full of the expectation of the successor. During your journeys, I knew not whither to aim a letter after you; that was a sort of shooting flying: add to this the demand Homer had upon me, to write fifty verses a day, besides learned notes, all which are at a conclusion for this year. Rejoice with me, O my friend! that my labour is over; come and make merry with me in much feasting. We will feed among the lilies (by the lilies I mean the ladies). Are not the Rosa-

lived, and was lapped in cotton, and had his plate of chicken, and his saucer of cream, and frisked, and barked, and wheezed, and grew fat, and so ended.* He became very melancholy and lazy, sadly plethoric, and only occasionally diverting in his latter days. But everybody loved him, and the remembrance of his pretty little tricks; and the raging old Dean of Saint Patrick's, chafing in his banishment, was afraid to open the letter which Pope wrote him announcing the sad news of the death of Gay.†

Swift's letters to him are beautiful; and having no purpose but

lindas of Britain as charming as the Blousalindas of the Hague? or have the two great Pastoral poets of our nation renounced love at the same time? for Philips, immortal Philips, hath deserted, yea, and in a rustic manner kicked his Rosalind. Dr. Parnell and I have been inseparable ever since you went. We are now at the Bath, where (if you are not, as I heartily hope, better engaged) your coming would be the greatest pleasure to us in the world. Talk not of expenses: Homer shall support his children. I beg a line from you, directed to the Post-house in Bath. Poor Parnell is in an ill state of health.

"Pardon me if I add a word of advice in the poetical way. Write something on the King, or Prince, or Princess. On whatsoever foot you may be with the Court, this can do no harm. I shall never know where to end, and am confounded in the many things I have to say to you, though they all amount but to this, that I am, entirely, as ever,

"Your," &c.

Gay took the advice "in the poetical way," and published "An Epistle to a Lady, occasioned by the arrival of her Royal Highness the Princess of Wales." But though this brought him access to Court, and the attendance of the Prince and Princess at his farce of the "What d'ye call it?" it did not bring him a place. On the accession of George II., he was offered the situation of Gentleman Usher to the Princess Louisa (her Highness being then two years old); but "by this offer," says Johnson, "he thought himself insulted."

* "Gay was a great eater.—As the French philosopher used to prove his existence by *Cogito, ergo sum*, the greatest proof of Gay's existence is, *Edit, ergo est*."—CONGREVE, *in a letter to Pope. Spence's Anecdotes*

† Swift endorsed the letter—"On my dear friend Mr. Gay's death; received Dec. 15, but not read till the 20th, by an impulse foreboding some misfortune."

"It was by Swift's interest that Gay was made known to Lord Bolingbroke, and obtained his patronage."—SCOTT'S *Swift*, vol. i. p. 156.

Pope wrote on the occasion of Gay's death, to Swift, thus:—

"[*Dec.* 5, 1732.]

". . . One of the nearest and longest ties I have ever had is broken all on a sudden by the unexpected death of poor Mr. Gay. An inflammatory fever hurried him out of this life in three days. . . . He asked of you a few hours before when in acute torment by the inflammation in his bowels and breast. . . . His sisters, we suppose, will be his heirs, who are two widows. . . . Good God! how often are we to die before we go quite off this stage? In every friend we lose a part of ourselves, and the best part. God keep those we have left! few are worth praying for, and one's self the least of all."

kindness in writing to him, no party aim to advocate, or slight or anger to wreak, every word the Dean says to his favourite is natural, trustworthy, and kindly. His admiration for Gay's parts and honesty, and his laughter at his weaknesses, were alike just and genuine. He paints his character in wonderful pleasant traits of jocular satire. "I writ lately to Mr. Pope," Swift says, writing to Gay: "I wish you had a little villakin in his neighbourhood; but you are yet too volatile, and any lady with a coach and six horses would carry you to Japan." "If your ramble," says Swift, in another letter, "was on horseback, I am glad of it, on account of your health; but I know your arts of patching up a journey between stage-coaches and friends' coaches—for you are as arrant a cockney as any hosier in Cheapside. I have often had it in my head to put it into yours, that you ought to have some great work in scheme, which may take up seven years to finish, besides two or three under-ones that may add another thousand pounds to your stock. And then I shall be in less pain about you. I know you can find dinners, but you love twelvepenny coaches too well, without considering that the interest of a whole thousand pounds brings you but half-a-crown a day." And then Swift goes off from Gay to pay some grand compliments to her Grace the Duchess of Queensberry, in whose sunshine Mr. Gay was basking, and in whose radiance the Dean would have liked to warm himself too.

But we have Gay here before us, in these letters—lazy, kindly, uncommonly idle; rather slovenly, I'm afraid; for ever eating and saying good things; a little round French abbé of a man, sleek, soft-handed, and soft-hearted.

Our object in these lectures is rather to describe the men than their works; or to deal with the latter only in as far as they seem to illustrate the character of their writers. Mr. Gay's "Fables" which were written to benefit that amiable Prince the Duke of Cumberland, the warrior of Dettingen and Culloden, I have not, I own, been able to peruse since a period of very early youth; and it must be confessed that they did not effect much benefit upon the illustrious young Prince, whose manners they were intended to mollify, and whose natural ferocity our gentle-hearted Satirist perhaps proposed to restrain. But the six pastorals called the "Shepherd's Week," and the burlesque poem of "Trivia," any man fond of lazy literature will find delightful at the present day, and must read from beginning to end with pleasure. They are to poetry what charming little Dresden china figures are to sculpture: graceful, minikin, fantastic; with a certain beauty always accompanying them. The pretty little personages of the pastoral, with gold clocks to their stockings, and fresh satin ribands to their crooks and waistcoats and bodices, danced their loves to a minuet-tune played on a bird-organ, approach the charmer, or rush from the false one daintily on their red-heeled tiptoes, and die of despair or rapture, with the most pathetic little grins and ogles; or repose, simpering at each other, under an arbour of pea-green crockery; or piping to pretty flocks that have just been washed with the best Naples in a stream of bergamot. Gay's gay plan seems to me far pleasanter than that of Philips—his rival and Pope's—a serious and dreary idyllic cockney; not that Gay's "Bumkinets" and "Hobnelias" are a whit more natural than the would-be serious characters of the other posture-master; but the quality of this true humourist was to laugh and make laugh, though always with a secret kindness and tenderness, to perform the drollest little antics and capers, but always with a certain grace, and to sweet music—as you may have seen a Savoyard boy abroad, with a hurdy-gurdy and a monkey, turning over head and heels, or clattering and pirouetting in a pair of wooden shoes, yet always with a look of love and appeal in his bright eyes, and a smile that asks and wins affection and protection. Happy they who have that sweet gift of nature! It was this which made the great folk and Court ladies free and friendly with John Gay—which made Pope and Arbuthnot love him—which melted the savage heart of Swift when he thought of him—and drove away, for a moment or two, the dark frenzies which obscured the lonely tyrant's brain, as he heard Gay's voice with its simple melody and artless ringing laughter.

What used to be said about Rubini,* *qu'il avait des larmes dans la voix*, may be said of Gay,† and of one other humourist of whom we shall have to speak. In almost every ballad of his, however slight,‡

* [This was said earlier of Mdlle. Duchesnois of the Théâtre Français, who was not beautiful, but had a most beautiful voice].

† "Gay, like Goldsmith, had a musical talent. 'He could play on the flute,' says Malone, 'and was, therefore, enabled to adapt so happily some of the airs in the *Beggar's Opera.*'"—*Notes to Spence.*

‡ "'Twas when the seas were roaring
With hollow blasts of wind,
A damsel lay deploring
All on a rock reclined.
Wide o'er the foaming billows
She cast a wistful look;
Her head was crown'd with willows
That trembled o'er the brook.

'Twelve months are gone and over,
And nine long tedious days;
Why didst thou, venturous lover—
Why didst thou trust the seas?

in the "Beggar's Opera"* and in its wearisome continuation (where the verses are to the full as pretty as in the first piece, however), there is a peculiar, hinted, pathetic sweetness and melody. It charms and melts you. It's indefinable, but it exists; and is the property of John Gay's and Oliver Goldsmith's best verse as fragrance is of a violet, or freshness of a rose.

Let me read a piece from one of his letters, which is so famous

Cease, cease, thou cruel Ocean,
  And let my lover rest;
Ah! what's thy troubled motion
  To that within my breast?

'The merchant, robb'd of pleasure,
  Sees tempests in despair;
But what's the loss of treasure
  To losing of my dear?
Should you some coast be laid on,
  Where gold and diamonds grow,
You'd find a richer maiden,
  But none that loves you so.

'How can they say that Nature
  Has nothing made in vain;
Why, then, beneath the water
  Should hideous rocks remain?
No eyes the rocks discover
  That lurk beneath the deep,
To wreck the wandering lover,
  And leave the maid to weep?'

All melancholy lying,
  Thus wailed she for her dear;
Repay'd each blast with sighing,
  Each billow with a tear;
When o'er the white wave stooping,
  His floating corpse she spy'd;
Then like a lily drooping,
  She bow'd her head, and died."

—*A Ballad from the "What d'ye call it?"*

"What can be prettier than Gay's ballad, or, rather, Swift's, Arbuthnot's, Pope's, and Gay's, in the 'What d'ye call it?' ''Twas when the seas were roaring'? I have been well informed that they all contributed."—*Cowper to Unwin*, 1783.

* "Dr. Swift had been observing once to Mr. Gay, what an odd pretty sort of thing a Newgate Pastoral might make. Gay was inclined to try at such a thing for some time, but afterwards thought it would be better to write a comedy on the same plan. This was what gave rise to the *Beggar's Opera*. He began on it, and when he first mentioned it to Swift, the Doctor did not much like the project. As he carried it on, he showed what he wrote to both of us;

that most people here are no doubt familiar with it, but so delightful that it is always pleasant to hear :—

"I have just passed part of this summer at an old romantic seat of my Lord Harcourt's which he lent me. It overlooks a common field, where, under the shade of a haycock, sat two lovers as constant as ever were found in romance—beneath a spreading beech. The name of the one (let it sound as it will) was John Hewet; of the other Sarah Drew. John was a well-set man, about five-and-twenty; Sarah a brown woman of eighteen. John had for several months borne the labour of the day in the same field with Sarah; when she milked, it was his morning and evening charge to bring the cows to her pail. Their love was the talk, but not the scandal, of the whole neighbourhood, for all they aimed at was the blameless possession of each other in marriage. It was but this very morning that he had obtained her parents' consent, and it was but till the next week that they were to wait to be happy. Perhaps this very day, in the intervals of their work, they were talking of their wedding-clothes; and John was now matching several kinds of poppies and field-flowers to her complexion, to make her a present of knots for the day. While they were thus employed (it was on the last of July) a terrible storm of thunder and lightning arose, that drove the labourers to what shelter the trees or hedges afforded. Sarah, frightened and out of breath, sunk on a haycock; and John (who never separated from her), sat by her side, having raked two or three heaps together, to secure her. Immediately there was heard so loud a crack, as if heaven had burst asunder. The labourers, all solicitous for each other's safety, called to one another: those that were nearest our lovers, hearing no answer, stepped to the place where they lay: they first saw a little smoke, and after, this faithful pair—John, with one arm about his Sarah's neck, and the other held over her face, as if to screen her from the lightning. They were struck dead, and already grown stiff and

and we now and then gave a correction, or a word or two of advice; but it was wholly of his own writing. When it was done, neither of us thought it would succeed. We showed it to Congreve, who, after reading it over, said, 'It would either take greatly, or be damned confoundedly.' We were all at the first night of it, in great uncertainty of the event, till we were very much encouraged by overhearing the Duke of Argyle, who sat in the next box to us, say, 'It will do—it must do!—I see it in the eyes of them!' This was a good while before the first act was over, and so gave us ease soon; for the Duke [besides his own good taste] has a more particular knack than any one now living in discovering the taste of the public. He was quite right in this as usual; the good-nature of the audience appeared stronger and stronger every act, and ended in a clamour of applause."—POPE. *Spence's Anecdotes.*

cold in this tender posture. There was no mark or discolouring on their bodies—only that Sarah's eyebrow was a little singed, and a small spot between her breasts. They were buried the next day in one grave."

And the proof that this description is delightful and beautiful is, that the great Mr. Pope admired it so much that he thought proper to steal it and to send it off to a certain lady and wit, with whom he pretended to be in love in those days—my Lord Duke of Kingston's daughter, and married to Mr. Wortley Montagu, then his Majesty's Ambassador at Constantinople.*

We are now come to the greatest name on our list—the highest among the poets, the highest among the English wits and humourists with whom we have to rank him. If the author of the "Dunciad" be not a humourist, if the poet of the "Rape of the Lock" be not a wit, who deserves to be called so? Besides that brilliant genius and immense fame, for both of which we should respect him, men of letters should admire him as being the greatest literary *artist* that England has seen. He polished, he refined, he thought; he took thoughts from other works to adorn and complete his own; borrowing an idea or a cadence from another poet as he would a figure or a simile from a flower, or a river, stream, or any object which struck him in his walk, or contemplation of nature. He began to imitate at an early age;† and taught himself to write by copying printed books. Then he passed into the hands of the priests, and from his first clerical master, who came to him when he was eight years old, he went to a school at Twyford, and another school at Hyde Park, at which places he unlearned all that he had got from his first instructor. At twelve years old, he went with his father into Windsor Forest, and there learned for a few months

* [This was a natural conjecture, but now appears to be erroneous. The letter seems to have been a joint composition of Gay and Pope, who were staying together at Lord Harcourt's house. Gay wrote to Fortescue, while Pope sent substantially the same letter to Martha Blount, Lord Bathurst, and Lady Mary Wortley Montagu.—See Mr. Courthope's notes in Pope's Works, vol. ix., 284, 399.]

† "Waller, Spenser, and Dryden were Mr. Pope's great favourites, in the order they are named, in his first reading, till he was about twelve years old." —POPE. *Spence's Anecdotes.*

"Mr. Pope's father (who was an honest merchant, and dealt in hollands, wholesale) was no poet, but he used to set him to make English verses when very young. He was pretty difficult in being pleased; and used often to send him back to new turn them. 'These are not good rhimes;' for that was my husband's word for verses."—POPE'S MOTHER. *Spence.*

"I wrote things, I'm ashamed to say how soon. Part of an Epic Poem

under a fourth priest. "And this was all the teaching I ever had," he said, "and God knows it extended a very little way."

When he had done with his priests he took to reading by himself, for which he had a very great eagerness and enthusiasm, especially for poetry. He learnt versification from Dryden, he said. In his youthful poem of "Alcander," he imitated every poet, Cowley, Milton, Spenser, Statius, Homer, Virgil. In a few years he had dipped into a great number of the English, French, Italian, Latin, and Greek poets. "This I did," he says, "without any design, except to amuse myself; and got the languages by hunting after the stories in the several poets I read, rather than read the books to get the languages. I followed everywhere as my fancy led me, and was like a boy gathering flowers in the fields and woods, just as they fell in his way. These five or six years I looked upon as the happiest in my life." Is not here a beautiful holiday picture? The forest and the fairy story-book—the boy spelling Ariosto or Virgil under the trees, battling with the Cid for the love of Chimène, or dreaming of Armida's garden—peace and sunshine round about—the kindest love and tenderness waiting for him at his quiet home yonder—and Genius throbbing in his young heart, and whispering to him, "You shall be great, you shall be famous; you too shall love and sing; you will sing her so nobly that some kind heart shall forget you are weak and ill formed. Every poet had a love. Fate must give one to you too,"—and day by day he walks the forest, very likely looking out for that charmer. "They were the happiest days of his life," he says, when he was only dreaming of his fame: when he had gained that mistress she was no consoler.

That charmer made her appearance, it would seem, about the year 1705, when Pope was seventeen. Letters of his are extant,

when about twelve. The scene of it lay at Rhodes and some of the neighbouring islands; and the poem opened under water with a description of the Court of Neptune."—POPE. *Ibid.*

"His perpetual application (after he set to study of himself) reduced him in four years' time to so bad a state of health, that, after trying physicians for a good while in vain, he resolved to give way to his distemper; and sat down calmly in a full expectation of death in a short time. Under this thought, he wrote letters to take a last farewell of some of his more particular friends, and, among the rest, one to the Abbé Southcote. The Abbé was extremely concerned both for his very ill state of health and the resolution he said he had taken. He thought there might yet be hope, and went immediately to Dr. Radcliffe, with whom he was well acquainted, told him Mr. Pope's case, got full directions from him, and carried them down to Pope in Windsor Forest. The chief thing the Doctor ordered him was to apply less, and to ride every day. The following his advice soon restored him to his health."—POPE. *Spence.*

addressed to a certain Lady M——, whom the youth courted, and to whom he expressed his ardour in language, to say no worse of it, that is entirely pert, odious, and affected. He imitated love-compositions as he had been imitating love-poems just before—it was a sham mistress he courted, and a sham passion, expressed as became it. These unlucky letters found their way into print years afterwards, and were sold to the congenial Mr. Curll. If any of my hearers, as I hope they may, should take a fancy to look at Pope's correspondence, let them pass over that first part of it; over, perhaps, almost all Pope's letters to women; in which there is a tone of not pleasant gallantry, and, amidst a profusion of compliments and politenesses, a something which makes one distrust the little pert, prurient bard. There is very little indeed to say about his loves, and that little not edifying. He wrote flames and raptures and elaborate verse and prose for Lady Mary Wortley Montagu; but that passion probably came to a climax in an impertinence, and was extinguished by a box on the ear, or some such rebuff, and he began on a sudden to hate her with a fervour much more genuine than that of his love had been. It was a feeble puny grimace of love, and paltering with passion. After Mr. Pope had sent off one of his fine compositions to Lady Mary, he made a second draft from the rough copy, and favoured some other friend with it. He was so charmed with the letter of Gay's that I have just quoted, that he had copied that and amended it, and sent it to Lady Mary as his own.* A gentleman who writes letters *à deux fins*, and after having poured out his heart to the beloved, serves up the same dish *réchauffé* to a friend, is not very much in earnest about his loves, however much he may be in his piques and vanities when his impertinence gets its due.

But, save that unlucky part of the "Pope Correspondence," I do not know, in the range of our literature, volumes more delightful.† You live in them in the finest company in the

* [See note on p. 534. Pope, however, was capable of very similar performances.]

† *Mr. Pope to the Rev. Mr. Broom, Pulham, Norfolk.*

"*Aug.* 29*th*, 1730.

"DEAR SIR,—I intended to write to you on this melancholy subject, the death of Mr. Fenton, before yours came, but stayed to have informed myself and you of the circumstances of it. All I hear is, that he felt a gradual decay, though so early in life, and was declining for five or six months. It was not, as I apprehended, the gout in his stomach, but, I believe, rather a complication first of gross humours, as he was naturally corpulent, not discharging themselves, as he used no sort of exercise. No man better bore the approaches of his dissolution (as I am told), or with less ostentation yielded up his being. The great modesty which you know was natural to him, and the great con-

world. A little stately, perhaps; a little *apprêté* and conscious that they are speaking to whole generations who are listening; but in the tone of their voices—pitched, as no doubt they are, beyond the mere conversation key—in the expression of their thoughts, their various views and natures, there is something generous, and cheering, and ennobling. You are in the society of men who have filled the greatest parts in the world's story—you

tempt he had for all sorts of vanity and parade, never appeared more than in his last moments: he had a conscious satisfaction (no doubt) in acting right, in feeling himself honest, true, and unpretending to more than his own. So he died as he lived, with that secret, yet sufficient contentment.

"As to any papers left behind him, I dare say they can be but few; for this reason, he never wrote out of vanity, or thought much of the applause of men. I know an instance when he did his utmost to conceal his own merit that way; and if we join to this his natural love of ease, I fancy we must expect little of this sort: at least, I have heard of none, except some few further remarks on Waller (which his cautious integrity made him leave an order to be given to Mr. Tonson), and perhaps, though it is many years since I saw it, a translation of the first book of *Oppian*. He had begun a tragedy of *Dion*, but made small progress in it.

"As to his other affairs, he died poor but honest, leaving no debts or legacies, except of a few pounds to Mr. Trumbull and my lady, in token of respect, gratefulness, and mutual esteem.

"I shall with pleasure take upon me to draw this amiable, quiet, deserving, unpretending, Christian, and philosophical character in his epitaph. There truth may be spoken in a few words; as for flourish, and oratory, and poetry, I leave them to younger and more lively writers, such as love writing for writing's sake, and would rather show their own fine parts than report the valuable ones of any other man. So the elegy I renounce.

"I condole with you from my heart on the loss of so worthy a man, and a friend to us both. . . .

"Adieu; let us love his memory and profit by his example. Am very sincerely, dear sir,

"Your affectionate and real servant."

To the Earl of Burlington.

"*August* 1714.

"MY LORD,—If your mare could speak, she would give you an account of what extraordinary company she had on the road, which, since she cannot do, I will.

"It was the enterprising Mr. Lintot, the redoubtable rival of Mr. Tonson, who, mounted on a stone-horse, overtook me in Windsor Forest. He said he heard I designed for Oxford, the seat of the Muses, and would, as my bookseller, by all means accompany me thither.

"I asked him where he got his horse? He answered he got it of his publisher; 'for that rogue, my printer,' said he, 'disappointed me. I hoped to put him in good humour by a treat at the tavern of a brown fricassée of rabbits, which cost ten shillings, with two quarts of wine, besides my conversation. I thought myself cock-sure of his horse, which he readily promised me, but said

are with St. John the statesman; Peterborough the conqueror; Swift, the greatest wit of all times; Gay, the kindliest laughter,—it is a privilege to sit in that company. Delightful and generous banquet! with a little faith and a little fancy any one of us here may enjoy it, and conjure up those great figures out of the past, and listen to their wit and wisdom. Mind that there is always a certain *cachet* about great men—they may be as mean on many

that Mr. Tonson had just such another design of going to Cambridge, expecting there the copy of a new kind of Horace from Dr. ——; and if Mr. Tonson went, he was pre-engaged to attend him, being to have the printing of the said copy. So, in short, I borrowed this stone-horse of my publisher, which he had of Mr. Oldmixon for a debt. He lent me, too, the pretty boy you see after me. He was a smutty dog yesterday, and cost me more than two hours to wash the ink off his face; but the devil is a fair-conditioned devil, and very forward in his catechism. If you have any more bags, he shall carry them.'

"I thought Mr. Lintot's civility not to be neglected, so gave the boy a small bag containing three shirts and an Elzevir Virgil, and, mounting in an instant, proceeded on the road, with my man before, my courteous stationer beside, and the aforesaid devil behind.

"Mr. Lintot began in this manner: 'Now, damn them! What if they should put it into the newspaper how you and I went together to Oxford? What would I care? If I should go down into Sussex, they would say I was gone to the Speaker; but what of that? If my son were but big enough to go on with the business, by G-d, I would keep as good company as old Jacob.'

"Hereupon, I inquired of the son. 'The lad,' says he, 'has fine parts, but is somewhat sickly, much as you are. I spare for nothing in his education at Westminster. Pray, don't you think Westminster to be the best school in England? Most of the late Ministry came out of it; so did many of this Ministry. I hope the boy will make his fortune.'

"'Don't you design to let him pass a year at Oxford?' 'To what purpose?' said he. 'The Universities do but make pedants, and I intend to breed him a man of business.'

"As Mr. Lintot was talking I observed he sat uneasy on his saddle, for which I expressed some solicitude. 'Nothing,' says he. 'I can bear it well enough; but, since we have the day before us, methinks it would be very pleasant for you to rest awhile under the woods.' When we were alighted, 'See, here, what a mighty pretty Horace I have in my pocket! What if you amused yourself in turning an ode till we mount again? Lord! if you pleased, what a clever miscellany might you make at leisure hours!' 'Perhaps I may,' said I, 'if we ride on: the motion is an aid to my fancy; a round trot very much awakens my spirits; then jog on apace, and I'll think as hard as I can.'

"Silence ensued for a full hour; after which Mr. Lintot lugged the reins, stopped short, and broke out, 'Well, sir, how far have you gone?' I answered, seven miles. 'Z—ds, sir,' said Lintot, 'I thought you had done seven stanzas. Oldisworth, in a ramble round Wimbledon Hill, would translate a whole ode in half this time. I'll say that for Oldisworth [though I lost by his Timothy's], he translates an ode of Horace the quickest of any man in England. I

points as you or I, but they carry their great air—they speak of common life more largely and generously than common men do—they regard the world with a manlier countenance, and see its real features more fairly than the timid shufflers who only dare to look up at life through blinkers, or to have an opinion when there is a crowd to back it. He who reads these noble records of a past age, salutes and reverences the great spirits who adorn it. You may

remember Dr. King would write verses in a tavern, three hours after he could not speak: and there is Sir Richard, in that rumbling old chariot of his, between Fleet Ditch and St. Giles's Pound, shall make you half a Job.'

"'Pray, Mr. Lintot,' said I, 'now you talk of translators, what is your method of managing them?' 'Sir,' replied he, 'these are the saddest pack of rogues in the world: in a hungry fit, they'll swear they understand all the languages in the universe. I have known one of them take down a Greek book upon my counter and cry, "Ah, this is Hebrew, and must read it from the latter end." By G-d, I can never be sure in these fellows, for I neither understand Greek, Latin, French, nor Italian myself. But this is my way: I agree with them for ten shillings per sheet, with a proviso that I will have their doings corrected with whom I please; so by one or the other they are led at last to the true sense of an author; my judgment giving the negative to all my translators.' 'Then how are you sure these correctors may not impose upon you?' 'Why, I get any civil gentleman (especially any Scotchman) that comes into my shop, to read the original to me in English; by this I know whether my first translator be deficient, and whether my corrector merits his money or not.

"'I'll tell you what happened to me last month. I bargained with S—— for a new version of *Lucretius*, to publish against Tonson's, agreeing to pay the author so many shillings at his producing so many lines. He made a great progress in a very short time, and I gave it to the corrector to compare with the Latin; but he went directly to Creech's translation, and found it the same, word for word, all but the first page. Now, what d'ye think I did? I arrested the translator for a cheat; nay, and I stopped the corrector's pay, too, upon the proof that he had made use of Creech instead of the original.'

"'Pray tell me next how you deal with the critics?' 'Sir,' said he, 'nothing more easy. I can silence the most formidable of them: the rich ones for a sheet apiece of the blotted manuscript, which cost me nothing; they'll go about with it to their acquaintance, and pretend they had it from the author, who submitted it to their correction: this has given some of them such an air, that in time they come to be consulted with and dedicated to as the tiptop critics of the town.—As for the poor critics, I'll give you one instance of my management, by which you may guess the rest: A lean man, that looked like a very good scholar, came to me t'other day; he turned over your Homer, shook his head, shrugged up his shoulders, and pish'd at every line of it. "One would wonder," says he, "at the strange presumption of some men; Homer is no such easy task as every stripling, every versifier——" he was going on when my wife called to dinner. "Sir," said I, "will you please to eat a piece of beef with me?" "Mr. Lintot," said he, "I am very sorry you should be at the expense of this great book: I am really concerned on your account." "Sir, I am much obliged to you: if you can dine upon a piece of beef, together with

go home now and talk with St. John; you may take a volume from your library and listen to Swift and Pope.

Might I give counsel to any young hearer, I would say to him, Try to frequent the company of your betters. In books and life that is the most wholesome society; learn to admire rightly; the great pleasure of life is that. Note what the great men admired; they admired great things: narrow spirits admire basely, and worship meanly. I know nothing in any story more gallant and

a slice of pudding——?"—"Mr. Lintot, I do not say but Mr. Pope, if he would condescend to advise with men of learning——"—"Sir, the pudding is upon the table, if you please to go in." My critic complies; he comes to a taste of your poetry, and tells me in the same breath that the book is commendable, and the pudding excellent.

"'Now, sir,' continued Mr. Lintot, 'in return for the frankness I have shown, pray tell me, is it the opinion of your friends at Court that my Lord Lansdowne will be brought to the bar or not?' I told him I heard he would not, and I hoped it, my Lord being one I had particular obligations to.—'That may be,' replied Mr. Lintot; 'but by G— if he is not, I shall lose the printing of a very good trial.'

"These, my Lord, are a few traits with which you discern the genius of Mr. Lintot, which I have chosen for the subject of a letter. I dropped him as soon as I got to Oxford, and paid a visit to my Lord Carlton, at Middleton. . . . I am," &c.

Dr. Swift to Mr. Pope.

"*Sept.* 29, 1725.

"I am now returning to the noble scene of Dublin—into the *grand monde*—for fear of burying my parts; to signalise myself among curates and vicars, and correct all corruptions crept in relating to the weight of bread-and-butter through those dominions where I govern. I have employed my time (besides ditching) in finishing, correcting, amending, and transcribing my 'Travels' [Gulliver's], in four parts complete, newly augmented, and intended for the press when the world shall deserve them, or rather, when a printer shall be found brave enough to venture his ears. I like the scheme of our meeting after distresses and dispersions; but the chief end I propose to myself in all my labours is to vex the world rather than divert it; and if I could compass that design without hurting my own person or fortune, I would be the most indefatigable writer you have ever seen without reading. I am exceedingly pleased that you have done with translations; Lord Treasurer Oxford often lamented that a rascally world should lay you under a necessity of misemploying your genius for so long a time; but since you will now be so much better employed, when you think of the world, give it one lash the more at my request. I have ever hated all nations, professions, and communities; and all my love is towards individuals—for instance, I hate the tribe of lawyers, but I love Councillor Such-a-one and Judge Such-a-one: it is so with physicians (I will not speak of my own trade), soldiers, English, Scotch, French, and the rest. But principally I hate and detest that animal called man—although I heartily love John, Peter, Thomas, and so forth.

". . . I have got materials towards a treatise proving the falsity of that

cheering than the love and friendship which this company of famous men bore towards one another. There never has been a society of men more friendly, as there never was one more illustrious. Who dares quarrel with Mr. Pope, great and famous himself, for liking the society of men great and famous? and for liking them for the qualities which made them so? A mere pretty fellow from White's could not have written the "Patriot King," and would very likely have despised little Mr. Pope, the decrepit Papist, whom the great St. John held to be one of the best and greatest of men: a mere

definition *animal rationale*, and to show it should be only *rationis capax*. . . . The matter is so clear that it will admit of no dispute—nay, I will hold a hundred pounds that you and I agree in the point. . . .

"Mr. Lewis sent me an account of Dr. Arbuthnot's illness, which is a very sensible affliction to me, who, by living so long out of the world, have lost that hardness of heart contracted by years and general conversation. I am daily losing friends, and neither seeking nor getting others. Oh! if the world had but a dozen of Arbuthnots in it, I would burn my 'Travels'!"

Mr. Pope to Dr. Swift.

"*October* 15, 1725.

"I am wonderfully pleased with the suddenness of your kind answer. It makes me hope you are coming towards us, and that you incline more and more to your old friends. . . . Here is one [Lord Bolingbroke] who was once a powerful planet, but has now (after long experience of all that comes of shining) learned to be content with returning to his first point without the thought or ambition of shining at all. Here is another [Edward, Earl of Oxford], who thinks one of the greatest glories of his father was to have distinguished and loved you, and who loves you hereditarily. Here is Arbuthnot, recovered from the jaws of death, and more pleased with the hope of seeing you again than of reviewing a world, every part of which he has long despised but what is made up of a few men like yourself. . . .

"Our friend Gay is used as the friends of Tories are by Whigs—and generally by Tories too. Because he had humour, he was supposed to have dealt with Dr. Swift, in like manner as when any one had learning formerly, he was thought to have dealt with the devil. . . .

"Lord Bolingbroke had not the least harm by his fall; I wish he had received no more by his other fall. But Lord Bolingbroke is the most improved mind since you saw him, that ever was improved without shifting into a new body, or being *paullo minus ab angelis*. I have often imagined to myself, that if ever all of us meet again, after so many varieties and changes, after so much of the old world and of the old man in each of us has been altered, that scarce a single thought of the one, any more than a single atom of the other, remains just the same; I have fancied, I say, that we should meet like the righteous in the millennium, quite in peace, divested of all our former passions, smiling at our past follies, and content to enjoy the kingdom of the just in tranquillity.

. . . .

"I designed to have left the following page for Dr. Arbuthnot to fill, but he is so touched with the period in yours to me, concerning him, that he intends to answer it by a whole letter. . . ."

nobleman of the Court could no more have won Barcelona, than he could have written Peterborough's letters to Pope,* which are as witty as Congreve: a mere Irish Dean could not have written "Gulliver"; and all these men loved Pope, and Pope loved all these men. To name his friends is to name the best men of his time. Addison had a senate; Pope reverenced his equals. He spoke of Swift with respect and admiration always. His admiration for Bolingbroke was so great, that when some one said of his friend, "There is something in that great man which looks as if he was placed here by mistake." "Yes," Pope answered, "and when the comet appeared to us a month or two ago, I had sometimes an imagination that it might possibly be come to carry him home as a coach comes to one's door for visitors." So these great spirits spoke of one another. Show me six of the dullest middle-aged gentlemen that ever dawdled round a club table so faithful and so friendly.

We have said before that the chief wits of this time, with the exception of Congreve, were what we should now call men's men.

* Of the Earl of Peterborough, Walpole says:—"He was one of those men of careless wit and negligent grace, who scatter a thousand *bon-mots* and idle verses, which we painful compilers gather and hoard, till the authors stare to find themselves authors. Such was this lord, of an advantageous figure and enterprising spirit; as gallant as Amadis and as brave; but a little more expeditious in his journeys: for he is said to have seen more kings and more postillions than any man in Europe. . . . He was a man, as his friend said, who would neither live nor die like any other mortal."

From the Earl of Peterborough to Pope.

"You must receive my letters with a just impartiality, and give grains of allowance for a gloomy or rainy day; I sink grievously with the weather-glass, and am quite spiritless when oppressed with the thoughts of a birthday or a return.

"Dutiful affection was bringing me to town; but undutiful laziness, and being much out of order, keep me in the country: however, if alive, I must make my appearance at the birthday. . . .

"You seem to think it vexatious that I shall allow you but one woman at a time either to praise or love. If I dispute with you upon this point, I doubt every jury will give a verdict against me. So, sir, with a Mahometan indulgence, I allow your pluralities, the favourite privilege of our church.

"I find you don't mend upon correction; again I tell you you must not think of women in a reasonable way; you know we always make goddesses of those we adore upon earth; and do not all the good men tell us we must lay aside reason in what relates to the Deity?

". . . I should have been glad of anything of Swift's. Pray, when you write to him next, tell him I expect him with impatience, in a place as odd and as much out of the way as himself. Yours."

Peterborough married Mrs. Anastasia Robinson, the celebrated singer.

They spent many hours of the four-and-twenty, a fourth part of each day nearly, in clubs and coffee-houses, where they dined, drank, and smoked. Wit and news went by word of mouth; a journal of 1710 contained the very smallest portion of one or the other. The chiefs spoke, the faithful *habitués* sat round; strangers came to wonder and listen. Old Dryden had his headquarters at "Will's," in Russell Street, at the corner of Bow Street: at which place Pope saw him when he was twelve years old. The company used to assemble on the first floor—what was called the dining-room floor in those days—and sat at various tables smoking their pipes. It is recorded that the beaux of the day thought it a great honour to be allowed to take a pinch out of Dryden's snuffbox. When Addison began to reign, he with a certain crafty propriety—a policy let us call it—which belonged to his nature, set up his court, and appointed the officers of his royal house. His palace was "Button's," opposite "Will's."* A quiet opposition, a silent assertion of empire, distinguished this great man. Addison's ministers were Budgell, Tickell, Philips, Carey; his master of the horse, honest Dick Steele, who was what Duroc was to Napoleon, or Hardy to Nelson: the man who performed his master's bidding, and would have cheerfully died in his quarrel. Addison lived with these people for seven or eight hours every day. The male society passed over their punch-bowls and tobacco-pipes about as much time as ladies of that age spent over spadille and manille.

For a brief space, upon coming up to town, Pope formed part of King Joseph's court, and was his rather too eager and obsequious humble servant.† Dick Steele, the editor of the *Tatler*,

* "Button had been a servant in the Countess of Warwick's family, who, under the patronage of Addison, kept a coffee-house on the south side of Russell Street, about two doors from Covent Garden. Here it was that the wits of that time used to assemble. It is said that when Addison had suffered any vexation from the Countess, he withdrew the company from Button's house.

"From the coffee-house he went again to a tavern, where he often sat late and drank too much wine."—*Dr. Johnson.*

Will's Coffee-house was on the west side of Bow Street, and "corner of Russell Street."—See *Handbook of London.*

† "My acquaintance with Mr. Addison commenced in 1712: I liked him then as well as I liked any man, and was very fond of his conversation. It was very soon after that Mr. Addison advised me 'not to be content with the applause of half the nation.' He used to talk much and often to me, of moderation in parties: and used to blame his dear friend Steele for being too much of a party man. He encouraged me in my design of translating the *Iliad*, which was begun that year, and finished in 1718."—POPE. *Spence's Anecdotes.*

"Addison had Budgell, and I think Philips, in the house with him.—Gay they would call one of my *élèves*.—They were angry with me for keeping so much with Dr. Swift and some of the late Ministry."—POPE. *Spence's Anecdotes.*

Mr. Addison's man, and his own man too—a person of no little figure in the world of letters—patronised the young poet, and set him a task or two. Young Mr. Pope did the tasks very quickly and smartly (he had been at the feet, quite as a boy, of Wycherley's * decrepit reputation, and propped up for a year that doting old wit): he was anxious to be well with the men of letters, to get a footing and a recognition. He thought it an honour to be admitted into their company; to have the confidence of Mr. Addison's friend Captain Steele. His eminent parts obtained for him the honour of heralding Addison's triumph of "Cato" with his admirable prologue, and heading the victorious procession as it were. Not content with this act of homage and admiration, he wanted to distinguish himself

* *To Mr. Blount.*

"*Jan.* 21, 1715–16.

"I know of nothing that will be so interesting to you at present as some circumstances of the last act of that eminent comic poet and our friend, Wycherley. He had often told me, and I doubt not he did all his acquaintance, that he would marry as soon as his life was despaired of. Accordingly, a few days before his death, he underwent the ceremony, and joined together those two sacraments which wise men say we should be the last to receive; for, if you observe, matrimony is placed after extreme unction in our catechism, as a kind of hint of the order of time in which they are to be taken. The old man then lay down, satisfied in the consciousness of having, by this one act, obliged a woman who (he was told) had merit, and shown an heroic resentment of the ill-usage of his next heir. Some hundred pounds which he had with the lady discharged his debts; a jointure of £500 a year made her a recompence; and the nephew was left to comfort himself as well as he could with the miserable remains of a mortgaged estate. I saw our friend twice after this was done—less peevish in his sickness than he used to be in his health; neither much afraid of dying, nor (which in him had been more likely) much ashamed of marrying. The evening before he expired, he called his young wife to the bedside, and earnestly entreated her not to deny him one request—the last he should make. Upon her assurances of consenting to it, he told her: 'My dear, it is only this—that you will never marry an old man again.' I cannot help remarking that sickness, which often destroys both wit and wisdom, yet seldom has power to remove that talent which we call humour. Mr. Wycherley showed his even in his last compliment; though I think his request a little hard, for why should he bar her from doubling her jointure on the same easy terms?

"So trivial as these circumstances are, I should not be displeased myself to know such trifles when they concern or characterize any eminent person. The wisest and wittiest of men are seldom wiser or wittier than others in these sober moments; at least, our friend ended much in the same character he had lived in; and Horace's rule for play may as well be applied to him as a playwright:—

"'Servetur ad imum
Qualis ab incepto processerit et sibi constet.'

"I am," &c.

by assaulting Addison's enemies, and attacked John Dennis with a prose lampoon, which highly offended his lofty patron. Mr. Steele was instructed to write to Mr. Dennis, and inform him that Mr. Pope's pamphlet against him was written quite without Mr. Addison's approval.* Indeed, "The Narrative of Dr. Robert Norris on the Phrenzy of J. D." is a vulgar and mean satire, and such a blow as the magnificent Addison could never desire to see any partisan of his strike in any literary quarrel. Pope was closely allied with Swift when he wrote this pamphlet. It is so dirty that it has been printed in Swift's works, too. It bears the foul marks of the master hand. Swift admired and enjoyed with all his heart the prodigious genius of the young Papist lad out of Windsor Forest, who had never seen a university in his life, and came and conquered the Dons and the doctors with his wit. He applauded, and loved him, too, and protected him, and taught him mischief. I wish Addison could have loved him better. The best satire that ever has been penned would never have been written then; and one of the best characters the world ever knew would have been without a flaw. But he who had so few equals could not bear one, and Pope was more than that. When Pope, trying for himself, and soaring on his immortal young wings, found that his, too, was a genius, which no pinion of that age could follow, he rose and left Addison's company, settling on his own eminence, and singing his own song.

It was not possible that Pope should remain a retainer of Mr. Addison; nor likely that after escaping from his vassalage and assuming an independent crown, the sovereign whose allegiance he quitted should view him amicably.† They did not do wrong to mislike each other. They but followed the impulse of nature, and the consequence of position. When Bernadotte became heir to a throne, the Prince Royal of Sweden was naturally Napoleon's enemy. "There are many passions and tempers of mankind," says Mr. Addison in the *Spectator*, speaking a couple of years before

* "Addison, who was no stranger to the world, probably saw the sefishness of Pope's friendship; and resolving that he should have the consequences of his officiousness to himself, informed Dennis by Steele that he was sorry for the insult."—JOHNSON. *Life of Addison.*

† "While I was heated with what I heard, I wrote a letter to Mr. Addison, to let him know 'that I was not unacquainted with this behaviour of his; that if I was to speak of him severely in return for it, it should not be in such a dirty way; that I should rather tell him himself fairly of his faults, and allow his good qualities; and that it should be something in the following manner.' I then subjoined the first sketch of what has since been called my satire on Addison. He used me very civilly ever after; and never did me any injustice, that I know of, from that time to his death, which was about three years after."—POPE. *Spence's Anecdotes.*

the little differences between him and Mr. Pope took place, "which naturally dispose us to depress and vilify the merit of one rising in the esteem of mankind. All those who made their entrance into the world with the same advantages, and were once looked on as his equals, are apt to think the fame of his merits a reflection on their own deserts. Those who were once his equals envy and defame him, because they now see him the superior; and those who were once his superiors, because they look upon him as their equal." Did Mr. Addison, justly perhaps thinking that, as young Mr. Pope had not had the benefit of a university education, he couldn't know Greek, therefore he couldn't translate Homer, encourage his young friend Mr. Tickell, of Queen's, to translate that poet, and aid him with his own known scholarship and skill?* It was natural that Mr. Addison should doubt of the learning of an amateur Grecian, should have a high opinion of Mr. Tickell, of Queen's, and should help that ingenious young man. It was natural, on the other hand, that Mr. Pope and Mr. Pope's friends should believe that his counter-translation, suddenly advertised and so long written, though Tickell's college friends had never heard of it—though, when Pope first wrote to Addison regarding his scheme, Mr. Addison knew nothing of the similar project of Tickell, of Queen's—it was natural that Mr. Pope and his friends, having interests, passions, and prejudices of their own, should believe that Tickell's translation was but an act of opposition against Pope, and that they should call Mr. Tickell's emulation Mr. Addison's envy—if envy it were.

> "And were there one whose fires
> True genius kindles and fair fame inspires,
> Blest with each talent and each art to please,
> And born to write, converse, and live with ease;
> Should such a man, too fond to rule alone,
> Bear, like the Turk, no brother near the throne;
> View him with scornful yet with jealous eyes,
> And hate, for arts that caused himself to rise;
> Damn with faint praise, assent with civil leer,
> And, without sneering, teach the rest to sneer;
> Willing to wound, and yet afraid to strike,
> Just hint a fault, and hesitate dislike;
> Alike reserved to blame as to commend
> A timorous foe and a suspicious friend;
> Dreading even fools, by flatterers besieged,
> And so obliging that he ne'er obliged:

* "That Tickell should have been guilty of a villainy seems to us highly improbable; that Addison should have been guilty of a villainy seems to us highly improbable; but that these two men should have conspired together to commit a villainy, seems, to us, improbable in a tenfold degree."—*Macaulay.*

> Like Cato give his little senate laws,
> And sit attentive to his own applause;
> While wits and templars every sentence raise,
> And wonder with a foolish face of praise;
> Who but must laugh if such a man there be,
> Who would not weep if Atticus were he?"

"I sent the verses to Mr. Addison," said Pope, "and he used me very civilly ever after." No wonder he did. It was shame very likely more than fear that silenced him. Johnson recounts an interview between Pope and Addison after their quarrel, in which Pope was angry, and Addison tried to be contemptuous and calm. Such a weapon as Pope's must have pierced any scorn. It flashes for ever, and quivers in Addison's memory. His great figure looks out on us from the past—stainless but for that—pale, calm, and beautiful: it bleeds from that black wound. He should be drawn, like Saint Sebastian, with that arrow in his side. As he sent to Gay and asked his pardon, as he bade his stepson come and see his death, be sure he had forgiven Pope, when he made ready to show how a Christian could die.*

Pope then formed part of the Addisonian court for a short time, and describes himself in his letters as sitting with that coterie until two o'clock in the morning over punch and burgundy amidst the fumes of tobacco. To use an expression of the present day, the "pace" of those *viveurs* of the former age was awful. Peterborough lived into the very jaws of death; Godolphin laboured all day and gambled at night; Bolingbroke,† writing to Swift, from

* [This story has been now upset by the researches of Mr. Dilke, Mr. Elwin, and others; though, when Thackeray wrote, it was the accepted version. There is no reason to suppose that Addison ever saw the verses. The statement is part of an elaborate fiction concocted by Pope, and supported by manufacturing letters to Addison out of letters really written to another correspondent. The whole story may be found in the edition of Pope by Elwin and Courthope, and is one of the most curious cases of literary imposture on record. It is enough to say that all stain has been removed from Addison's character. Thackeray would have rejoiced at that result, though he would have had to modify some of the eulogy bestowed upon Pope.]

† *Lord Bolingbroke to the Three Yahoos of Twickenham.*

"*July* 23, 1726.

"JONATHAN, ALEXANDER, JOHN, MOST EXCELLENT TRIUMVIRS OF PARNASSUS,—Though you are probably very indifferent where I am, or what I am doing, yet I resolve to believe the contrary. I persuade myself that you have sent at least fifteen times within this fortnight to Dawley farm, and that you are extremely mortified at my long silence. To relieve you, therefore, from this great anxiety of mind, I can do no less than write a few lines to you; and I please myself beforehand with the vast pleasure which this epistle must needs give you. That I may add to this pleasure, and give further proofs of my

Dawley, in his retirement, dating his letter at six o'clock in the morning, and rising, as he says, refreshed, serene, and calm, calls to mind the time of his London life; when about that hour he used to be going to bed, surfeited with pleasure, and jaded with business; his head often full of schemes, and his heart as often full of anxiety. It was too hard, too coarse a life for the sensitive, sickly Pope. He was the only wit of the day, a friend writes to me, who wasn't fat.* Swift was fat; Addison was fat; Steele was fat; Gay and Thomson were preposterously fat—all that fuddling and punch-drinking, that club and coffee-house boozing, shortened the lives and enlarged the waistcoats of the men of that age. Pope withdrew in a great measure from this boisterous London company, and being put into an independence by the gallant exertions of Swift † and his private friends, and by the enthusiastic national admiration which justly rewarded his great achievement of the "Iliad," purchased that famous villa of Twickenham which his song and life celebrated; duteously bringing his old parent to live and die there, entertaining his friends there, and making occasional visits to London in his little chariot, in which Atterbury compared him to "Homer in a nutshell."

"Mr. Dryden was not a genteel man," Pope quaintly said to Spence, speaking of the manner and habits of the famous old patriarch of "Will's." With regard to Pope's own manners, we have the best contemporary authority that they were singularly refined and polished. With his extraordinary sensibility, with his known tastes, with his delicate frame, with his power and dread of ridicule, Pope could have been no other than what we call a highly-bred person.‡ His closest friends, with the exception of Swift, were among the delights and ornaments of the polished society of

beneficent temper, I will likewise inform you, that I shall be in your neighbourhood again by the end of next week: by which time I hope that Jonathan's imagination of business will be succeeded by some imagination more becoming a professor of that divine science, *la bagatelle*. Adieu. Jonathan, Alexander, John, mirth be with you!"

* Prior must be excepted from this observation. "He was lank and lean."

† Swift exerted himself very much in promoting the *Iliad* subscription; and also introduced Pope to Harley and Bolingbroke. Pope realised by the *Iliad* upwards of £5000, which he laid out partly in annuities, and partly in the purchase of his famous villa. Johnson remarks that "it would be hard to find a man so well entitled to notice by his wit, that ever delighted so much in talking of his money."

‡ "His (Pope's) voice in common conversation was so naturally musical, that I remember honest Tom Southerne used always to call him 'the little nightingale.'"—*Orrery.*

their age. Garth,* the accomplished and benevolent, whom Steele has described so charmingly, of whom Codrington said that his character was "all beauty," and whom Pope himself called the best of Christians without knowing it; Arbuthnot,† one of the

* Garth, whom Dryden calls "generous as his Muse," was a Yorkshireman. He graduated at Cambridge, and was made M.D. in 1691. He soon distinguished himself in his profession, by his poem of the "Dispensary," and in society, and pronounced Dryden's funeral oration. He was a strict Whig, a notable member of the "Kit-Cat," and a friendly, convivial, able man. He was knighted by George I., with the Duke of Marlborough's sword. He died in 1718.

† "Arbuthnot was the son of an Episcopal clergyman in Scotland, and belonged to an ancient and distinguished Scotch family. He was educated at Aberdeen; and, coming up to London—according to a Scotch practice often enough alluded to—to make his fortune, first made himself known by *An Examination of Dr. Woodward's Account of the Deluge.* He became physician successively to Prince George of Denmark and to Queen Anne. He is usually allowed to have been the most learned, as well as one of the most witty and humorous members of the Scriblerus Club. The opinion entertained of him by the humourists of the day is abundantly evidenced in their correspondence. When he found himself in his last illness, he wrote thus, from his retreat at Hampstead, to Swift:—

"'HAMPSTEAD: *Oct.* 4, 1734.

"'MY DEAR AND WORTHY FRIEND,—You have no reason to put me among the rest of your forgetful friends, for I wrote two long letters to you, to which I never received one word of answer. The first was about your health; the last I sent a great while ago, by one De la Mar. I can assure you with great truth that none of your friends or acquaintance has a more warm heart towards you than myself. I am going out of this troublesome world, and you, among the rest of my friends, shall have my last prayers and good wishes.

"'. . . I came out to this place so reduced by a dropsy and an asthma, that I could neither sleep, breathe, eat, nor move. I most earnestly desired and begged of God that He would take me. Contrary to my expectation, upon venturing to ride (which I had forborne for some years) I recovered my strength to a pretty considerable degree, slept, and had my stomach again. . . . What I did, I can assure you was not for life, but ease; for I am at present in the case of a man that was almost in harbour, and then blown back to sea—who has a reasonable hope of going to a good place, and an absolute certainty of leaving a very bad one. Not that I have any particular disgust at the world; for I have as great comfort in my own family and from the kindness of my friends as any man; but the world, in the main, displeases me, and I have too true a presentiment of calamities that are to befall my country. However, if I should have the happiness to see you before I die, you will find that I enjoy the comforts of life with my usual cheerfulness. I cannot imagine why you are frightened from a journey to England: the reasons you assign are not sufficient—the journey, I am sure, would do you good. In general, I recommend riding, of which I have always had a good opinion, and can now confirm it from my own experience.

"'My family give you their love and service. The great loss I sustained in one of them gave me my first shock, and the trouble I have with the rest to bring them to a right temper to bear the loss of a father who loves them, and whom they love, is really a most sensible affliction to me. I am afraid, my

wisest, wittiest, most accomplished, gentlest of mankind; Bolingbroke, the Alcibiades of his age; the generous Oxford; the magnificent, the witty, the famous, and chivalrous Peterborough: these were the fast and faithful friends of Pope, the most brilliant company of friends, let us repeat, that the world has ever seen. The favourite recreation of his leisure hours was the society of painters, whose art he practised. In his correspondence are letters between him and Jervas, whose pupil he loved to be—Richardson, a celebrated artist of his time, and who painted for him a portrait of his old mother, and for whose picture he asked and thanked Richardson in one of the most delightful letters that ever were penned,*—and

dear friend, we shall never see one another more in this world. I shall, to the last moment, preserve my love and esteem for you, being well assured you will never leave the paths of virtue and honour; for all that is in this world is not worth the least deviation from the way. It will be great pleasure to me to hear from you sometimes; for none are with more sincerity than I am, my dear friend, your most faithful friend and humble servant.'"

"Arbuthnot," Johnson says, "was a man of great comprehension, skilful in his profession, versed in the sciences, acquainted with ancient literature, and able to animate his mass of knowledge by a bright and active imagination; a scholar with great brilliance of wit; a wit who, in the crowd of life, retained and discovered a noble ardour of religious zeal."

Dugald Stewart has testified to Arbuthnot's ability in a department of which he was particularly qualified to judge: "Let me add, that, in the list of philosophical reformers, the authors of *Martinus Scriblerus* ought not to be overlooked. Their happy ridicule of the scholastic logic and metaphysics is universally known; but few are aware of the acuteness and sagacity displayed in their allusions to some of the most vulnerable passages in Locke's *Essay*. In this part of the work it is commonly understood that Arbuthnot had the principal share."—See *Preliminary Dissertation to Encyclopædia Britannica*, note to p. 242, and also note B. B. B., p. 285.

* *To Mr. Richardson.*

"TWICKENHAM, *June* 10, 1733.

"As I know you and I mutually desire to see one another, I hoped that this day our wishes would have met, and brought you hither. And this for the very reason, which possibly might hinder you coming, that my poor mother is dead. I thank God her death was as easy as her life was innocent; and as it cost her not a groan, or even a sigh, there is yet upon her countenance such an expression of tranquillity, nay, almost of pleasure, that it is even amiable to behold it. It would afford the finest image of a saint expired that ever painting drew; and it would be the greatest obligation which even that obliging art could ever bestow on a friend, if you could come and sketch it for me. I am sure, if there be no very prevalent obstacle, you will leave any common business to do this; and I hope to see you this evening, as late as you will, or to-morrow morning as early, before this winter flower is faded. I will defer her interment till to-morrow night. I know you love me, or I could not have written this—I could not (at this time) have written at all. Adieu! May you die as happily! Yours,' &c.

the wonderful Kneller, who bragged more, spelt worse, and painted better than any artist of his day.*

It is affecting to note, through Pope's correspondence, the marked way in which his friends, the greatest, the most famous, and wittiest men of the time—generals and statesmen, philosophers and divines—all have a kind word and a kind thought for the good simple old mother, whom Pope tended so affectionately. Those men would have scarcely valued her, but that they knew how much he loved her, and that they pleased him by thinking of her. If his early letters to women are affected and insincere, whenever he speaks about this one, it is with a childish tenderness and an almost sacred simplicity. In 1713, when young Mr. Pope had, by a series of the most astonishing victories and dazzling achievements, seized the crown of poetry, and the town was in an uproar of admiration, or hostility, for the young chief; when Pope was issuing his famous decrees for the translation of the "Iliad"; when Dennis and the lower critics were hooting and assailing him; when Addison and the gentlemen of his court were sneering with sickening hearts at the prodigious triumphs of the young conqueror; when Pope, in a fever of victory, and genius, and hope, and anger, was struggling through the crowd of shouting friends and furious detractors to his temple of Fame, his old mother writes from the country, "My deare," says she—"my deare, there's Mr. Blount, of Mapel Durom, dead the same day that Mr. Inglefield died. Your sister is well; but your brother is sick. My service to Mrs. Blount, and all that ask of me. I hope to hear from you, and that you are well, which is my daily prayer; and this with my blessing." The triumph marches by, and the car of the young conqueror, the hero of a hundred brilliant victories: the fond mother sits in the quiet cottage at home and says, "I send you my daily prayers, and I bless you, my deare."

In our estimate of Pope's character, let us always take into account that constant tenderness and fidelity of affection which pervaded and sanctified his life, and never forget that maternal benediction.†

* "Mr. Pope was with Sir Godfrey Kneller one day, when his nephew, a Guinea trader, came in. 'Nephew,' said Sir Godfrey, 'you have the honour of seeing the two greatest men in the world.' 'I don't know how great you may be,' said the Guinea man, 'but I don't like your looks: I have often bought a man much better than both of you together, all muscles and bones, for ten guineas.'"—DR. WARBURTON. *Spence's Anecdotes.*

† Swift's mention of him as one

"whose filial piety excels
Whatever Grecian story tells,"

is well known. And a sneer of Walpole's may be put to a better use than he ever intended it for, *à propos* of this subject. He charitably sneers, in one of his letters, at Spence's "fondling an old mother—in imitation of Pope!"

It accompanied him always: his life seems purified by those artless and heartfelt prayers. And he seems to have received and deserved the fond attachment of the other members of his family. It is not a little touching to read in Spence of the enthusiastic admiration with which his half-sister regarded him, and the simple anecdote by which she illustrates her love. "I think no man was ever so little fond of money." Mrs. Rackett says about her brother, "I think my brother when he was young read more books than any man in the world;" and she falls to telling stories of his schooldays, and the manner in which his master at Twyford ill-used him. "I don't think my brother knew what fear was," she continues; and the accounts of Pope's friends bear out this character for courage. When he had exasperated the dunces, and threats of violence and personal assault were brought to him, the dauntless little champion never for one instant allowed fear to disturb him, or condescended to take any guard in his daily walks except occasionally his faithful dog to bear him company. "I had rather die at once," said the gallant little cripple, "than live in fear of those rascals."

As for his death, it was what the noble Arbuthnot asked and enjoyed for himself—a euthanasia—a beautiful end. A perfect benevolence, affection, serenity hallowed the departure of that high soul. Even in the very hallucinations of his brain, and weaknesses of his delirium, there was something almost sacred. Spence describes him in his last days, looking up and with a rapt gaze as if something had suddenly passed before him. "He said to me, 'What's that?' pointing into the air with a very steady regard, and then looked down and said, with a smile of the greatest softness, ''Twas a vision!'" He laughed scarcely ever, but his companions describe his countenance as often illuminated by a peculiar sweet smile.

"When," said Spence,* the kind anecdotist whom Johnson despised—"when I was telling Lord Bolingbroke that Mr. Pope, on every catching and recovery of his mind, was always saying something kindly of his present or absent friends; and that this was so surprising, as it seemed to me as if humanity had outlasted understanding, Lord Bolingbroke said, 'It has so,' and then added,

* Joseph Spence was the son of a clergyman, near Winchester. He was a short time at Eton, and afterwards became a Fellow of New College, Oxford, a clergyman, and professor of poetry. He was a friend of Thomson's, whose reputation he aided. He published an *Essay on the Odyssey* in 1726, which introduced him to Pope. Everybody liked him. His *Anecdotes* were placed, while still in MS., at the service of Johnson and also of Malone. They were published by Mr. Singer in 1820.

'I never in my life knew a man who had so tender a heart for his particular friends, or a more general friendship for mankind. I have known him these thirty years, and value myself more for that man's love than——' Here," Spence says, "St. John sunk his head and lost his voice in tears." The sob which finishes the epitaph is finer than words. It is the cloak thrown over the father's face in the famous Greek picture, which hides the grief and heightens it.

In Johnson's "Life of Pope" you will find described, with rather a malicious minuteness, some of the personal habits and infirmities of the great little Pope. His body was crooked, he was so short that it was necessary to raise his chair in order to place him on a level with other people at table.* He was sewed up in a buckram suit every morning, and required a nurse like a child. His contemporaries reviled these misfortunes with a strange acrimony, and made his poor deformed person the butt for many a bolt of heavy wit. The facetious Mr. Dennis, in speaking of him, says, "If you take the first letter of Mr. Alexander Pope's Christian name, and the first and last letters of his surname, you have A. P. E." Pope catalogues, at the end of the "Dunciad," with a rueful precision, other pretty names, besides Ape, which Dennis called him. That great critic pronounced Mr. Pope a little ass, a fool, a coward, a Papist, and therefore a hater of Scripture, and so forth. It must be remembered that the pillory was a flourishing and popular institution in those days. Authors stood in it in the body sometimes: and dragged their enemies thither morally, hooted them with foul abuse and assailed them with garbage of the gutter. Poor Pope's figure was an easy one for those clumsy caricaturists to draw. Any stupid hand could draw a hunchback and write Pope underneath. They did. A libel was published against Pope, with such a frontispiece. This kind of rude jesting was an evidence not only of an ill nature, but a dull one. When a child makes a pun, or a lout breaks out into a laugh, it is some very obvious combination of words, or discrepancy of objects, which provokes the infantine satirist, or tickles the boorish wag; and many of Pope's revilers laughed not so much because they were wicked, as because they knew no better.

* He speaks of Arbuthnot's having helped him through "that long disease, my life." But not only was he so feeble as is implied in his use of the "buckram," but "it now appears," says Mr. Peter Cunningham, "from his unpublished letters that, like Lord Hervey, he had recourse to ass's milk for the preservation of his health." It is to his lordship's use of that simple beverage that he alludes when he says—

> "Let Sporus tremble !—A. What, that thing of silk
> Sporus, that mere white-curd of ass's milk?"

Without the utmost sensibility, Pope could not have been the poet he was; and through his life, however much he protested that he disregarded their abuse, the coarse ridicule of his opponents stung and tore him. One of Cibber's pamphlets coming into Pope's hands, whilst Richardson the painter was with him, Pope turned round and said, "These things are my diversions;" and Richardson, sitting by whilst Pope perused the libel, said he saw his features "writhing with anguish." How little human nature changes! Can't one see that little figure? Can't one fancy one is reading Horace? Can't one fancy one is speaking of to-day?"

The tastes and sensibilities of Pope, which led him to cultivate the society of persons of fine manners, or wit, or taste, or beauty, caused him to shrink equally from that shabby and boisterous crew which formed the rank and file of literature in his time: and he was as unjust to these men as they to him. The delicate little creature sickened at habits and company which were quite tolerable to robuster men: and in the famous feud between Pope and the Dunces, and without attributing any peculiar wrong to either, one can quite understand how the two parties should so hate each other. As I fancy, it was a sort of necessity that when Pope's triumph passed, Mr. Addison and his men should look rather contemptuously down on it from their balcony; so it was natural for Dennis and Tibbald, and Welsted and Cibber, and the worn and hungry pressmen in the crowd below, to howl at him and assail him. And Pope was more savage to Grub Street than Grub Street was to Pope. The thong with which he lashed them was dreadful; he fired upon that howling crew such shafts of flame and poison, he slew and wounded so fiercely, that in reading the "Dunciad" and the prose lampoons of Pope, one feels disposed to side against the ruthless little tyrant, at least to pity those wretched folk on whom he was so unmerciful. It was Pope, and Swift to aid him, who established among us the Grub Street tradition. He revels in base descriptions of poor men's want; he gloats over poor Dennis's garret, and flannel nightcap and red stockings; he gives instructions how to find Curll's authors—the historian at the tallow-chandler's under the blind arch in Petty France, the two translators in bed together, the poet in the cock-loft in Budge Row, whose landlady keeps the ladder. It was Pope, I fear, who contributed, more than any man who ever lived, to depreciate the literary calling. It was not an unprosperous one before that time, as we have seen; at least there were great prizes in the profession which had made Addison a Minister, and Prior an Ambassador, and Steele a Commissioner, and Swift all but a Bishop. The profession of letters was ruined by that libel of the "Dunciad."* If authors were wretched and poor before, if some of them lived in haylofts, of which their landladies kept the ladders, at least nobody came to disturb them in their straw; if three of them had but one coat between them, the two remained invisible in the garret, the third, at any rate, appeared decently at the coffee-house and paid his two-pence like a gentleman. It was Pope that dragged into light all this poverty and meanness, and held up those wretched shifts and rags to public ridicule. It was Pope that has made generations of the reading world (delighted with the mischief, as who would not be that reads it?) believe that author and wretch, author and rags, author and dirt, author and drink, gin, cowheel, tripe, poverty, duns, bailiffs, squalling children and clamorous landladies, were always associated together. The condition of authorship began to fall from the days of the "Dunciad": and I believe in my heart that much of that obloquy which has since pursued our calling was occasioned by Pope's libels and wicked wit. Everybody read those. Everybody was familiarised with the idea of the poor devil, the author. The manner is so captivating that young authors practise it, and begin their career with satire. It is so easy to write, and so pleasant to read! to fire a shot that makes a giant wince, perhaps; and fancy one's self his conqueror. It is easy to shoot—but not as Pope did. The shafts of his satire rise sublimely: no poet's verse ever mounted higher than that wonderful flight with which the "Dunciad" concludes:—†

> "She comes, she comes! the sable throne behold
> Of Night primeval and of Chaos old;
> Before her, Fancy's gilded clouds decay,
> And all its varying rainbows die away;
> Wit shoots in vain its momentary fires,
> The meteor drops, and in a flash expires.
> As, one by one, at dread Medea's strain
> The sick'ning stars fade off the ethereal plain;
> As Argus' eyes, by Hermes' wand oppress'd,
> Closed, one by one, to everlasting rest;—
> Thus, at her fell approach and secret might,
> Art after Art goes out, and all is night.

---

* [This statement would require qualification. The Grub Street author was probably worse off in the time of Queen Anne than in the time of George II., and the "Dunciad" really showed that he could make himself more effectually unpleasant to his superiors. The prizes of Queen Anne's time did not go to the professional author, but to the authors who were in a good enough position to be on friendly terms with ministers.]

† "He (Johnson) repeats to us, in his forcible melodious manner, the concluding lines of the 'Dunciad.'"—*Boswell.*

See skulking Truth to her old cavern fled,
Mountains of casuistry heaped o'er her head;
Philosophy, that leaned on Heaven before,
Shrinks to her second cause and is no more.
Religion, blushing, veils her sacred fires,
And, unawares, Morality expires.
Nor public flame, nor private, dares to shine,
Nor human spark is left, nor glimpse divine.
Lo! thy dread empire, Chaos, is restored,
Light dies before thy uncreating word;
Thy hand, great Anarch, lets the curtain fall,
And universal darkness buries all." *

In these astonishing lines Pope reaches, I think, to the very greatest height which his sublime art has attained, and shows himself the equal of all poets of all times. It is the brightest ardour, the loftiest assertion of truth, the most generous wisdom illustrated by the noblest poetic figure, and spoken in words the aptest, grandest, and most harmonious. It is heroic courage speaking: a splendid declaration of righteous wrath and war. It is the gage flung down, and the silver trumpet ringing defiance to falsehood and tyranny, deceit, dulness, superstition. It is Truth, the champion, shining and intrepid, and fronting the great world-tyrant with armies of slaves at his back. It is a wonderful and victorious single combat, in that great battle which has always been waging since society began.

In speaking of a work of consummate art one does not try to show what it actually is, for that were vain; but what it is like, and what are the sensations produced in the mind of him who views it. And in considering Pope's admirable career, I am forced into similitudes drawn from other courage and greatness, and into comparing him with those who achieved triumphs in actual war. I think of the works of young Pope as I do of the actions of young Bonaparte or young Nelson. In their common life you will find frailties and meannesses, as great as the vices and follies of the meanest men. But in the presence of the great occasion, the great soul flashes out, and conquers transcendent. In thinking of the splendour of Pope's young victories, of his merit, unequalled as his renown, I hail and salute the achieving genius, and do homage to the pen of a hero.

* "Mr. Langton informed me that he once related to Johnson (on the authority of Spence), that Pope himself admired these lines so much that when he repeated them his voice faltered. 'And well it might, sir,' said Johnson, 'for they are noble lines.'"—*J. Boswell, junior.*

HOGARTH, SMOLLETT, AND FIELDING

I SUPPOSE, as long as novels last and authors aim at interesting their public, there must always be in the story a virtuous and gallant hero, a wicked monster his opposite, and a pretty girl who finds a champion; bravery and virtue conquer beauty; and vice, after seeming to triumph through a certain number of pages, is sure to be discomfited in the last volume, when justice overtakes him and honest folk come by their own. There never was perhaps a greatly popular story but this simple plot was carried through it: mere satiric wit is addressed to a class of readers and thinkers quite different to those simple souls who laugh and weep over the novel. I fancy very few ladies, indeed, for instance, could be brought to like "Gulliver" heartily, and (putting the coarseness and difference of manners out of the question) to relish the wonderful satire of "Jonathan Wild." In that strange apologue, the author takes for a hero the greatest rascal, coward, traitor, tyrant, hypocrite, that his wit and experience, both large in this matter, could enable him to devise or depict; he accompanies this villain through all the actions of his life, with a grinning deference and a wonderful mock respect; and doesn't leave him till he is dangling at the gallows, when the satirist makes him a low bow and wishes the scoundrel good-day.

It was not by satire of this sort, or by scorn and contempt, that Hogarth achieved his vast popularity and acquired his reputation.* His art is quite simple; † he speaks popular parables to interest

* Coleridge speaks of the "beautiful female faces" in Hogarth's pictures, "in whom," he says, "the satirist never extinguished that love of beauty which belonged to him as a poet."—*The Friend.*

† "I was pleased with the reply of a gentleman, who, being asked which book he esteemed most in his library, answered 'Shakspeare': being asked which he esteemed next best, replied 'Hogarth.' His graphic representations are indeed books: they have the teeming, fruitful, suggestive meaning of *words.* Other pictures we look at—his prints we read. . . .

"The quantity of thought which Hogarth crowds into every picture would almost unvulgarise every subject which he might choose. . . .

"I say not that all the ridiculous subjects of Hogarth have necessarily

simple hearts, and to inspire them with pleasure or pity or warning and terror. Not one of his tales but is as easy as "Goody Two-Shoes"; it is the moral of Tommy was a naughty boy and the master flogged him, and Jacky was a good boy and had plum-cake, which pervades the whole works of the homely and famous English moralist. And if the moral is written in rather too large letters after the fable, we must remember how simple the scholars and schoolmaster both were, and like neither the less because they are so artless and honest. "It was a maxim of Doctor Harrison's," Fielding says, in "Amelia,"—speaking of the benevolent divine and

something in them to make us like them; some are indifferent to us, some in their nature repulsive, and only made interesting by the wonderful skill and truth to nature in the painter; but I contend that there is in most of them that sprinkling of the better nature, which, like holy water, chases away and disperses the contagion of the bad. They have this in them, besides, that they bring us acquainted with the every-day human face,—they give us skill to detect those gradations of sense and virtue (which escape the careless or fastidious observer) in the circumstances of the world about us; and prevent that disgust at common life, that *tædium quotidianarum formarum*, which an unrestricted passion for ideal forms and beauties is in danger of producing. In this, as in many other things, they are analogous to the best novels of Smollett and Fielding."—*Charles Lamb.*

"It has been observed that Hogarth's pictures are exceedingly unlike any other representations of the same kind of subjects—that they form a class, and have a character peculiar to themselves. It may be worth while to consider in what this general distinction consists.

"In the first place, they are, in the strictest sense, *historical* pictures; and if what Fielding says be true, that his novel of *Tom Jones* ought to be regarded as an epic prose-poem, because it contained a regular development of fable, manners, character, and passion, the compositions of Hogarth will, in like manner, be found to have a higher claim to the title of epic pictures than many which have of late arrogated that denomination to themselves. When we say that Hogarth treated his subjects historically, we mean that his works represent the manners and humours of mankind in action, and their characters by varied expression. Everything in his pictures has life and motion in it. Not only does the business of the scene never stand still, but every feature and muscle is put into full play; the exact feeling of the moment is brought out, and carried to its utmost height, and then instantly seized and stamped on the canvas for ever. The expression is always taken *en passant*, in a state of progress or change, and, as it were, at the salient point. . . . His figures are not like the background on which they are painted: even the pictures on the wall have a peculiar look of their own. Again, with the rapidity, variety, and scope of history, Hogarth's heads have all the reality and correctness of portraits. He gives the extremes of character and expression, but he gives them with perfect truth and accuracy. This is, in fact, what distinguishes his compositions from all others of the same kind, that they are equally remote from caricature, and from mere still life. . . . His faces go to the very verge of caricature, and yet never (we believe in any single instance) go beyond it."—*Hazlitt.*

philosopher who represents the good principle in that novel—"that no man can descend below himself, in doing any act which may contribute to protect an innocent person, *or to bring a rogue to the gallows.*" The moralists of that age had no compunction, you see; they had not begun to be sceptical about the theory of punishment, and thought that the hanging of a thief was a spectacle for edification. Masters sent their apprentices, fathers took their children, to see Jack Sheppard or Jonathan Wild hanged, and it was as undoubting subscribers to this moral law, that Fielding wrote and Hogarth painted. Except in one instance, where, in the madhouse scene in the "Rake's Progress," the girl whom he has ruined is represented as still tending and weeping over him in his insanity, a glimpse of pity for his rogues never seems to enter honest Hogarth's mind. There's not the slightest doubt in the breast of the jolly Draco.

The famous set of pictures called "Marriage à la Mode," and which are now exhibited in the National Gallery in London, contains the most important and highly wrought of the Hogarth comedies. The care and method with which the moral grounds of these pictures are laid is as remarkable as the wit and skill of the observing and dexterous artist. He has to describe the negotiations for a marriage pending between the daughter of a rich citizen Alderman and young Lord Viscount Squanderfield, the dissipated son of a gouty old Earl. Pride and pomposity appear in every accessory surrounding the Earl. He sits in gold lace and velvet—as how should such an Earl wear anything but velvet and gold lace? His coronet is everywhere: on his footstool, on which reposes one gouty toe turned out; on the sconces and looking-glasses; on the dogs;* on his lordship's very crutches; on his great chair of state and the great baldaquin behind him; under which he sits pointing majestically to his pedigree, which shows that his race is sprung from the loins of William the Conqueror, and confronting the old Alderman from the City, who has mounted his sword for the occasion, and wears his Alderman's chain, and has brought a bag full of money, mortgage-deeds and thousand-pound notes, for the arrangement of the transaction pending between them. Whilst the steward † (a Methodist—therefore a hypocrite and cheat: for Hogarth scorned a Papist and a Dissenter) is negotiating between the old couple, their children sit together, united but apart. My lord is admiring his countenance

* [There is no coronet on the dogs in the picture. A coronet was conferred upon one dog in the engraving.]

† [This person is the Alderman's clerk or cashier. The Methodist steward (a different person) appears in the next picture—the breakfast scene.]

in the glass, while his bride is twiddling her marriage ring on her pocket-handkerchief, and listening with rueful countenance to Counsellor Silvertongue, who has been drawing the settlements. The girl is pretty, but the painter, with a curious watchfulness, has taken care to give her a likeness to her father; as in the young Viscount's face you see a resemblance to the Earl his noble sire. The sense of the coronet pervades the picture, as it is supposed to do the mind of its wearer. The pictures round the room are sly hints indicating the situation of the parties about to marry. A martyr is led to the fire; Andromeda * is offered to sacrifice; Judith is going to slay Holofernes. There is the ancestor of the house (in the picture it is the Earl himself as a young man), with a comet over his head, indicating that the career of the family is to be brilliant and brief. In the second picture † the old lord must be dead, for Madam has now the Countess's coronet over her bed and toilet-glass, and sits listening to that dangerous Counsellor Silvertongue, whose portrait now actually hangs up in her room, whilst the counsellor takes his ease on the sofa by her side, evidently the familiar of the house, and the confidant of the mistress. My Lord takes his pleasure elsewhere than at home, whither he returns jaded and tipsy from the "Rose," to find his wife yawning in her drawing-room, her whist-party over, and the daylight streaming in; or he amuses himself with the very worst company abroad, whilst his wife sits at home listening to foreign singers, or wastes her money at auctions, or, worse still, seeks amusement at masquerades. The dismal end is known. My Lord draws upon the counsellor, who kills him, and is apprehended whilst endeavouring to escape. My lady goes back perforce to the Alderman in the City, and faints ‡ upon reading Counsellor Silvertongue's dying speech at Tyburn, where the counsellor has been executed for sending his Lordship out of the world. Moral:—Don't listen to evil silver-tongued counsellors: don't marry a man for his rank, or a woman for her money: don't frequent foolish auctions and masquerade balls unknown to your husband: don't have wicked companions abroad and neglect your wife, otherwise you will be run through the body, and ruin will ensue, and disgrace, and Tyburn. The people are all naughty, and Bogey carries them all off. In the "Rake's Progress," a loose life is ended by a similar sad catastrophe. It is the spendthrift coming into possession of the wealth of the paternal miser; the prodigal surrounded by

* [This is a mistake. The only person likely to be intended is St. Sebastian. Any reference to the incidents is very doubtful.]

† [Really the fourth.]

‡ [She has taken laudanum and is dead.]

flatterers, and wasting his substance on the very worst company; the bailiffs, the gambling-house, and Bedlam for an end. In the famous story of "Industry and Idleness," the moral is pointed in a manner similarly clear. Fair-haired Frank Goodchild smiles at his work, whilst naughty Tom Idle snores over his loom. Frank reads the edifying ballads of "Whittington" and the "London 'Prentice," whilst that reprobate Tom Idle prefers "Moll Flanders," and drinks hugely of beer. Frank goes to church of a Sunday, and warbles hymns from the gallery; while Tom lies on a tombstone outside playing at "halfpenny-under-the-hat" with street blackguards, and is deservedly caned by the beadle. Frank is made overseer of the business, whilst Tom is sent to sea. Frank is taken into partnership and marries his master's daughter, sends out broken victuals to the poor, and listens in his nightcap and gown, with the lovely Mrs. Goodchild by his side, to the nuptial music of the City bands and the marrow-bones and cleavers; whilst idle Tom, returned from sea, shudders in a garret lest the officers are coming to take him for picking pockets. The Worshipful Francis Goodchild, Esquire, becomes Sheriff of London, and partakes of the most splendid dinners which money can purchase or Alderman devour; whilst poor Tom is taken up in a night-cellar, with that one-eyed and disreputable accomplice who first taught him to play chuck-farthing on a Sunday. What happens next? Tom is brought up before the justice of his country, in the person of Mr. Alderman Goodchild, who weeps as he recognises his old brother 'prentice, as Tom's one-eyed friend peaches on him, and the clerk makes out the poor rogue's ticket for Newgate. Then the end comes. Tom goes to Tyburn in a cart with a coffin in it; whilst the Right Honourable Francis Goodchild, Lord Mayor of London, proceeds to his Mansion House, in his gilt coach with four footmen and a sword-bearer, whilst the Companies of London march in the august procession, whilst the trainbands of the City fire their pieces and get drunk in his honour; and—O crowning delight and glory of all—whilst his Majesty the King* looks out from his royal balcony, with his riband on his breast, and his Queen and his star by his side, at the corner house of Saint Paul's Churchyard.

How the times have changed! The new Post Office now not disadvantageously occupies that spot where the scaffolding is in the picture, where the tipsy trainband-man is lurching against the post, with his wig over one eye, and the 'prentice-boy is trying to kiss the pretty girl in the gallery. Passed away 'prentice-boy and pretty girl! Passed away tipsy trainband-man with wig and bandolier! On the spot where Tom Idle (for whom I have an

* [Really Frederick, Prince of Wales, with the Princess of Wales.]

unaffected pity) made his exit from this wicked world, and where you see the hangman smoking his pipe as he reclines on the gibbet and views the hills of Harrow or Hampstead beyond, a splendid marble arch, a vast and modern city—clean, airy, painted drab, populous with nursery-maids and children, the abode of wealth and comfort—the elegant, the prosperous, the polite Tyburnia rises, the most respectable district in the habitable globe.

In that last plate of the London Apprentices, in which the apotheosis of the Right Honourable Francis Goodchild is drawn, a ragged fellow is represented in the corner of the simple, kindly piece, offering for sale a broadside, purporting to contain an account of the appearance of the ghost of Tom Idle executed at Tyburn. Could Tom's ghost have made its appearance in 1847, and not in 1747, what changes would have been remarked by that astonished escaped criminal! Over that road which the hangman used to travel constantly, and the Oxford stage twice a week, go ten thousand carriages every day: over yonder road, by which Dick Turpin fled to Windsor, and Squire Western journeyed into town, when he came to take up his quarters at the "Hercules Pillars" on the outskirts of London, what a rush of civilisation and order flows now! What armies of gentlemen with umbrellas march to banks, and chambers, and counting-houses! What regiments of nursery-maids and pretty infantry; what peaceful processions of policeman, what light broughams and what gay carriages, what swarms of busy apprentices and artificers, riding on omnibus-roofs, pass daily and hourly! Tom Idle's times are quite changed: many of the institutions gone into disuse which were admired in his day. There's more pity and kindness and a better chance for poor Tom's successors now than at that simpler period when Fielding hanged him and Hogarth drew him.

To the student of history, these admirable works must be invaluable, as they give us the most complete and truthful picture of the manners, and even the thoughts, of the past century. We look, and see pass before us the England of a hundred years ago—the peer in his drawing-room, the lady of fashion in her apartment, foreign singers surrounding her, and the chamber filled with gewgaws in the mode of that day; the church, with its quaint florid architecture and singing congregation; the parson with his great wig, and the beadle with his cane: all these are represented before us, and we are sure of the truth of the portrait. We see how the Lord Mayor dines in state; how the prodigal drinks and sports at the bagnio; how the poor girl beats hemp in Bridewell; how the thief divides his booty and drinks his punch at the night-cellar, and how he finishes his career at the gibbet. We may depend upon the perfect accuracy of these strange and varied portraits of the bygone generation: we see one of Walpole's Members of Parliament chaired after his election, and the lieges celebrating the event, and drinking confusion to the Pretender: we see the grenadiers and trainbands of the City marching out to meet the enemy; and have before us, with sword and firelock, and "White Hanoverian Horse" embroidered on the cap, the very figures of the men who ran away with Johnny Cope, and who conquered at Culloden. The Yorkshire waggon rolls into the inn yard; the country parson, in his jack-boots, and his bands and short cassock, comes trotting into town, and we fancy it is Parson Adams, with his sermons in his pocket. The Salisbury fly sets forth from the old "Angel"—you see the passengers entering the great heavy vehicle, up the wooden steps, their hats tied down with handkerchiefs over their faces, and under their arms, sword, hanger, and case-bottle; the landlady—apoplectic with the liquors in her own bar—is tugging at the bell; the hunchbacked postillion—he may have ridden the leaders to Humphrey Clinker—is begging a gratuity; the miser is grumbling at the bill; Jack of the "Centurion" lies on the top of the clumsy vehicle, with a soldier by his side *—it may be Smollett's Jack Hatchway—it has a likeness to Lismahago. You see the surburban fair and the strolling company of actors; the pretty milkmaid singing under the windows of the enraged French musician: it is such a girl as Steele charmingly described in the *Guardian*, a few years before this date,† singing, under Mr. Ironside's window in Shire Lane, her pleasant carol of a May morning. You see noblemen and blacklegs bawling and betting in the Cockpit: you see Garrick as he was arrayed in "King Richard"; Macheath and Polly in the dresses which they wore when they charmed our ancestors, and when noblemen in blue ribands sat on the stage and listened to their delightful music. You see the ragged French soldiery, in their white coats and cockades, at Calais Gate: they are of the regiment, very likely, which friend Roderick Random joined before he was rescued by his preserver Monsieur de Strap, with whom he fought on the famous day of Dettingen. You see the judges on the bench; the audience laughing in the pit; the student in the Oxford theatre; the citizen on his country walk; you see Broughton the boxer, Sarah Malcolm the murderess, Simon Lovat the traitor, John Wilkes the demagogue, leering at you with that squint which has become historical, and that face which, ugly as it was, he said he could make as captivating to woman as the countenance of the

* [The commentators say that the soldier is a Frenchman.]

† [The *Guardian* ended in 1713. The "enraged musician" is dated 1741.]

handsomest beau in town. All these sights and people are with you. After looking in the "Rake's Progress" at Hogarth's picture of Saint James's Palace Gate, you may people the street, but little altered within these hundred years, with the gilded carriages and thronging chairmen that bore the courtiers your ancestors to Queen Caroline's drawing-room more than a hundred years ago.

What manner of man * was he who executed these portraits

* Hogarth (whose family name was Hogart) was the grandson of a Westmoreland yeoman. His father came to London, and was an author and schoolmaster. William was born 10th November 1697, in the parish of Saint Martin, Ludgate. He was early apprenticed to an engraver of arms on plate. The following touches are from his *Anecdotes of Himself* (Edition of 1833):—

"As I had naturally a good eye, and a fondness for drawing, shows of all sorts gave me uncommon pleasure when an infant; and mimicry, common to all children, was remarkable in me. An early access to a neighbouring painter drew my attention from play; and I was, at every possible opportunity, employed in making drawings. I picked up an acquaintance of the same turn, and soon learnt to draw the alphabet with great correctness. My exercises, when at school, were more remarkable for the ornaments which adorned them, than for the exercise itself. In the former, I soon found that blockheads with better memories could much surpass me; but for the latter I was particularly distinguished. . . .

"I thought it still more unlikely that by pursuing the common method, and copying *old* drawings, I could ever attain the power of making *new* designs, which was my first and greatest ambition. I therefore endeavoured to habituate myself to the exercise of a sort of technical memory; and by repeating in my own mind the parts of which objects were composed, I could by degrees combine and put them down with my pencil. Thus, with all the drawbacks which resulted from the circumstances I have mentioned, I had one material advantage over my competitors, viz., the early habit I thus acquired of retaining in my mind's eye, without coldly copying it on the spot, whatever I intended to imitate.

"The instant I became master of my own time, I determined to qualify myself for engraving on copper. In this I readily got employment; and frontispieces to books, such as prints to *Hudibras*, in twelves, &c., soon brought me into the way. But the tribe of booksellers remained as my father had left them . . . which put me upon publishing on my own account. But here again I had to encounter a monopoly of printsellers, equally mean and destructive to the ingenious; for the first plate I published, called 'The Taste of the Town,' in which the reigning follies were lashed, had no sooner begun to take a run, than I found copies of it in the print-shops, vending at half-price, while the original prints were returned to me again, and I was thus obliged to sell the plate for whatever these pirates pleased to give me, as there was no place of sale but at their shops. Owing to this, and other circumstances, by engraving, until I was near thirty, I could do little more than maintain myself; *but even then I was a punctual paymaster*.

"I then married, and——"

[But William is going too fast here. He made a "stolen union," on

—so various, so faithful, and so admirable? In the National Collection of Pictures most of us have seen the best and most carefully finished series of his comic paintings, and the portrait of his own honest face, of which the bright blue eyes shine out from the

March 23, 1729, with Jane, daughter of Sir James Thornhill, serjeant-painter. For some time Sir James kept his heart and his purse-strings close, but "soon after became both reconciled and generous to the young couple."—*Hogarth's Works*, by NICHOLS and STEEVENS, vol. i. p. 44.]

"—commenced painter of small Conversation Pieces, from twelve to fifteen inches high. This, being a novelty, succeeded for a few years."

[About this time Hogarth had summer lodgings at South Lambeth, and did all kinds of work, "embellishing" the "Spring Gardens" at "Vauxhall," and the like. In 1731 he published a satirical plate against Pope, founded on the well-known imputation against him of his having satirised the Duke of Chandos, under the name of *Timon*, in his poem on "Taste." The plate represented a view of Burlington House, with Pope whitewashing it, and bespattering the Duke of Chandos's coach. Pope made no retort, and has never mentioned Hogarth.]

"Before I had done anything of much consequence in this walk, I entertained some hopes of succeeding in what the puffers in books call *The Great Style of History Painting*; so that without having had a stroke of this *grand* business before, I quitted small portraits and familiar conversations, and with a smile at my own temerity, commenced history-painter, and on a great staircase at St. Bartholomew's Hospital, painted two Scripture stories, the 'Pool of Bethesda' and the 'Good Samaritan,' with figures seven feet high. . . . But as religion, the great promoter of this style in other countries, rejected it in England, I was unwilling to sink into a *portrait manufacturer*; and, still ambitious of being singular, dropped all expectations of advantage from that source, and returned to the pursuit of my former dealings with the public at large.

"As to portrait-painting, the chief branch of the art by which a painter can procure himself a tolerable livelihood, and the only one by which a lover of money can get a fortune, a man of very moderate talents may have great success in it, as the artifice and address of a mercer is infinitely more useful than the abilities of a painter. By the manner in which the present race of professors in England conduct it, that also becomes still life."

. . . .

"By this inundation of folly and puff" (*he has been speaking of the success of Vanloo, who came over here in* 1737), "I must confess I was much disgusted, and determined to try if by any means I could stem the torrent, and, *by opposing, end it.* I laughed at the pretensions of these quacks in colouring, ridiculed their productions as feeble and contemptible, and asserted that it required neither taste nor talents to excel their most popular performances. This interference excited much enmity, because, as my opponents told me, my studies were in another way. 'You talk,' added they, 'with ineffable contempt of portrait-painting; if it is so easy a task, why do not you convince the world by painting a portrait yourself?' Provoked at this language, I, one day at the Academy in St. Martin's Lane, put the following question: 'Supposing any man, at this time, were to paint a portrait as well as Vandyke, would it be

canvas and give you an idea of that keen and brave look with which William Hogarth regarded the world. No man was ever less of a hero; you see him before you, and can fancy what he was—a jovial, honest London citizen, stout and sturdy; a hearty, plain-spoken

seen or acknowledged, and could the artist enjoy the benefit or acquire the reputation due to his performance?'

"They asked me in reply, if I could paint one as well; and I frankly answered, I believed I could. . . .

"Of the mighty talents said to be requisite for portrait painting I had not the most exalted opinion."

Let us now hear him on the question of the Academy:—

"To pester the three great estates of the empire, about twenty or thirty students drawing after a man or a horse, appears, as must be acknowledged, foolish enough: but the real motive is, that a few bustling characters, who have access to people of rank, think they can thus get a superiority over their brethren, be appointed to places, and have salaries, as in France, for telling a lad when a leg or an arm is too long or too short. . . .

"France, ever aping the magnificence of other nations, has in its turn assumed a foppish kind of splendour sufficient to dazzle the eyes of the neighbouring states, and draw vast sums of money from this country. . . .

"To return to our Royal Academy: I am told that one of their leading objects will be, sending young men abroad to study the antique statues, for such kind of studies may sometimes improve an exalted genius, but they will not create it; and whatever has been the cause, this same travelling to Italy has, in several instances that I have seen, seduced the student from nature and led him to paint marble figures, in which he has availed himself of the great works of antiquity, as a coward does when he puts on the armour of an Alexander; for, with similar pretensions and similar vanity, the painter supposes he shall be adored as a second Raphael Urbino."

We must now hear him on his "Sigismunda":—

"As the most violent and virulent abuse thrown on 'Sigismunda' was from a set of miscreants, with whom I am proud of having been ever at war—I mean the expounders of the mysteries of old pictures—I have been sometimes told they were beneath my notice. This is true of them individually; but as they have access to people of rank, who seem as happy in being cheated as these *merchants* are in cheating them, they have a power of doing much mischief to a modern artist. However mean the vendor of poisons, the mineral is destructive:—to me its operation was troublesome enough. Ill nature spreads so fast that now was the time for every little dog in the profession to bark!"

Next comes a characteristic account of his controversy with Wilkes and Churchill.

"The stagnation rendered it necessary that I should do some *timed thing*, to recover my lost time, and stop a gap in my income. This drew forth my print of 'The Times,' a subject which tended to the restoration of peace and unanimity, and put the opposers of these humane objects in a light which gave great offence to those who were trying to foment disaffection in the minds of the populace. One of the most notorious of them, till now my friend and flatterer, attacked me in the *North Briton*, in so infamous and malign a style,

man,* loving his laugh, his friend, his glass, his roast beef of Old England, and having a proper *bourgeois* scorn for French frogs, for mounseers, and wooden shoes in general, for foreign fiddlers, foreign singers, and, above all, for foreign painters, whom he held in the most amusing contempt.

It must have been great fun to hear him rage against Correggio and the Caracci; to watch him thump the table and snap his fingers, and say, "Historical painters be hanged! here's the man that will paint against any of them for a hundred pounds. Correggio's 'Sigismunda"! Look at Bill Hogarth's 'Sigismunda'; look at my altar-piece at Saint Mary Redcliffe, Bristol; look at my

that he himself, when pushed even by his best friends, was driven to so poor an excuse as to say he was drunk when he wrote it. . . .

"This renowned patriot's portrait, drawn like as I could as to features, and marked with some indications of his mind, fully answered my purpose. The ridiculous was apparent to every eye! A Brutus! A saviour of his country with such an aspect—was so arrant a farce, that though it gave rise to much laughter in the lookers-on, galled both him and his adherents to the bone. . . .

"Churchill, Wilkes's toad-echo, put the *North Briton* attack into verse, in an Epistle to Hogarth; but as the abuse was precisely the same, except a little poetical heightening, which goes for nothing, it made no impression. . . . However, having an old plate by me, with some parts ready, such as the background and a dog, I began to consider how I could turn so much work laid aside to some account, and so patched up a print of Master Churchill in the character of a Bear. The pleasure and pecuniary advantage which I derived from these two engravings, together with occasionally riding on horseback, restored me to as much health as can be expected at my time of life."

* "It happened in the early part of Hogarth's life, that a nobleman who was uncommonly ugly and deformed came to sit to him for his picture. It was executed with a skill that did honour to the artist's abilities; but the likeness was rigidly observed, without even the necessary attention to compliment or flattery. The peer, disgusted at this counterpart of himself, never once thought of paying for a reflection that would only disgust him with his deformities. Some time was suffered to elapse before the artist applied for his money; but afterwards many applications were made by him (who had then no need of a banker) for payment, without success. The painter, however, at last hit upon an expedient. . . . It was couched in the following card:—

"'Mr. Hogarth's dutiful respects to Lord ——. Finding that he does not mean to have the picture which was drawn for him, is informed again of Mr. Hogarth's necessity for the money. If, therefore, his Lordship does not send for it, in three days it will be disposed of, with the addition of a tail, and some other little appendages, to Mr. Hare, the famous wild-beast man: Mr. Hogarth having given that gentleman a conditional promise of it, for an exhibition-picture, on his Lordship's refusal.'

"This intimation had the desired effect."—*Works*, by NICHOLS and STEEVENS, vol. i. p. 25.

'Paul before Felix,' and see whether I'm not as good as the best of them." *

Posterity has not quite confirmed honest Hogarth's opinion about his talents for the sublime. Although Swift could not see the difference between tweedle-dee and tweedle-dum, posterity has not shared the Dean's contempt for Handel; the world has discovered a difference between tweedle-dee and tweedle-dum, and given a hearty applause and admiration to Hogarth, too, but not exactly as a painter of scriptural subjects, or as a rival of Correggio. It does not take away from one's liking for the man, or from the moral of his story, or the humour of it—from one's admiration for the prodigious merit of his performances, to remember that he persisted to the last in believing that the world was in a conspiracy against him with respect to his talents as an historical painter, and that a set of miscreants, as he called them, were employed to run his genius down. They say it was Liston's firm belief, that he was a great and neglected tragic actor; they say that every one of us believes in his heart, or would like to have others believe, that he is something which he is not. One of the most notorious of the "miscreants," Hogarth says, was Wilkes, who assailed him in the *North Briton*; the other was Churchill, who put the *North Briton* attack into heroic verse, and published his "Epistle to Hogarth." Hogarth replied by that caricature of Wilkes, in which the patriot still figures before us, with his Satanic grin and squint, and by a caricature of Churchill, in which he is represented as a bear with a staff, on which lie the first, lie the second—lie the tenth, are engraved in unmistakable letters. There is very little mistake about honest Hogarth's satire: if he has to paint a man with his throat cut, he draws him with his head almost off; and he tried to

* "Garrick himself was not more ductile to flattery. A word in favour of 'Sigismunda' might have commanded a proof-print or forced an original print out of our artist's hands. . . .

"The following authenticated story of our artist (furnished by the late Mr. Belchier, F.R.S., a surgeon of eminence) will also serve to show how much more easy it is to detect ill-placed or hyperbolical adulation respecting others, than when applied to ourselves. Hogarth, being at dinner with the great Cheselden and some other company, was told that Mr. John Freke, surgeon of St. Bartholomew's Hospital, a few evenings before at Dick's Coffee-house, had asserted that Greene was as eminent in composition as Handel. 'That fellow Freke,' replied Hogarth, 'is always shooting his bolt absurdly, one way or another. Handel is a giant in music; Greene only a light Florimel kind of a composer.' 'Ay,' says our artist's informant, 'but at the same time Mr. Freke declared you were as good a portrait-painter as Vandyke.' '*There* he was right,' adds Hogarth, 'and so, by G——, I am, give me my time and let me choose my subject.'"—*Works*, by NICHOLS and STEEVENS, vol. i. pp. 236, 237.

do the same for his enemies in this little controversy. "Having an old plate by me," says he, "with some parts ready, such as the background, and a dog, I began to consider how I could turn so much work laid aside to some account, and so patched up a print of Master Churchill, in the character of a bear; the pleasure and pecuniary advantage which I derived from these two engravings, together with occasionally riding on horseback, restored me to as much health as I can expect at my time of life."

And so he concludes his queer little book of Anecdotes: "I have gone through the circumstances of a life which till lately passed pretty much to my own satisfaction, and I hope in no respect injurious to any other man. This I may safely assert, that I have done my best to make those about me tolerably happy, and my greatest enemy cannot say I ever did an intentional injury. What may follow, God knows." *

A queer account still exists of a holiday jaunt taken by Hogarth and four friends of his, who set out like the redoubted Mr. Pickwick and his companions, but just a hundred years before those heroes; and made an excursion to Gravesend, Rochester, Sheerness, and adjacent places.† One of the gentlemen noted down the proceedings of the journey, for which Hogarth and a brother artist made drawings. The book is chiefly curious at this moment from showing the citizen life of those days, and the rough jolly style of merriment, not of the five companions merely, but of thousands of jolly fellows of their time. Hogarth and his friends, quitting the "Bedford Arms," Covent Garden, with a song, took water to Billingsgate, exchanging compliments with the bargemen as they went down the river. At Billingsgate Hogarth made a "caracatura" of a facetious porter, called the Duke of Puddledock, who agreeably entertained the party with the humours of the place. Hence they took a Gravesend boat for themselves; had straw to lie upon, and a tilt over their heads, they say, and went down the river at night, sleeping and singing jolly choruses.

They arrived at Gravesend at six, when they washed their faces and hands, and had their wigs powdered. Then they sallied forth for Rochester on foot, and drank by the way three pots of ale. At

* Of Hogarth's kindliness of disposition, the story of his rescue of the drummer-girl from the ruffian at Southwark Fair is an illustration; and in this case virtue was not its own reward, since her pretty face afterwards served him for a model in many a picture.

† He made this excursion in 1732, his companions being John Thornhill (son of Sir James), Scott the landscape-painter, Tothall, and Forrest. [The account was first published in 1782, and is in the third volume of the "Genuine Works," 1817.]

one o'clock they went to dinner with excellent port, and a quantity more beer, and afterwards Hogarth and Scott played at hopscotch in the town hall. It would appear that they slept most of them in one room, and the chronicler of the party describes them all as waking at seven o'clock, and telling each other their dreams. You have rough sketches by Hogarth of the incidents of this holiday excursion. The sturdy little painter is seen sprawling over a plank to a boat at Gravesend; the whole company are represented in one design, in a fisherman's room, where they had all passed the night. One gentleman in a nightcap is shaving himself; another is being shaved by the fisherman; a third, with a handkerchief over his bald pate, is taking his breakfast; and Hogarth is sketching the whole scene.

They describe at night how they returned to their quarters, drank to their friends, as usual, emptied several cans of good flip, all singing merrily.

It is a jolly party of tradesmen engaged at high jinks. These were the manners and pleasures of Hogarth, of his time very likely, of men not very refined, but honest and merry. It is a brave London citizen, with John Bull habits, prejudices, and pleasures.*

* Doctor Johnson made four lines once, on the death of poor Hogarth, which were equally true and pleasing; I know not why Garrick's were preferred to them:—

"'The hand of him here torpid lies,
That drew th' essential forms of grace;
Here, closed in death, th' attentive eyes,
That saw the manners in the face.'"

[Johnson's lines were only a suggested emendation upon the first form of the verses, submitted to him by Garrick for criticism.—BOSWELL'S *Johnson* (Birkbeck Hill), i. 187.]

"Mr. Hogarth, among the variety of kindnesses shown to me when I was too young to have a proper sense of them, was used to be very earnest that I should obtain the acquaintance, and if possible the friendship, of Doctor Johnson; whose conversation was, to the talk of other men, like Titian's painting compared to Hudson's, he said: 'but don't you tell people now that I say so,' continued he, 'for the connoisseurs and I are at war, you know; and because I hate *them*, they think I hate *Titian*—and let them!' . . . Of Dr. Johnson, when my father and he were talking about him one day, 'That man,' says Hogarth, 'is not contented with believing the Bible; but he fairly resolves, I think, to believe nothing *but* the Bible. Johnson,' added he, 'though so wise a fellow, is more like King David than King Solomon, for he says in his haste, *All men are liars.*'"—*Mrs. Piozzi.*

Hogarth died on the 26th of October 1764. The day before his death, he was removed from his villa at Chiswick to Leicester Fields, "in a very weak condition, yet remarkably cheerful." He had just received an agreeable letter from Franklin. He lies buried at Chiswick.

Of SMOLLETT's associates and manner of life the author of the admirable "Humphrey Clinker" has given us an interesting account in that most amusing of novels.*

* *To Sir Watkin Phillips, Bart., of Jesus College, Oxon.*

"DEAR PHILLIPS,—In my last, I mentioned my having spent an evening with a society of authors, who seemed to be jealous and afraid of one another. My uncle was not at all surprised to hear me say I was disappointed in their conversation. 'A man may be very entertaining and instructive upon paper,' said he, 'and exceedingly dull in common discourse. I have observed, that those who shine most in private company are but secondary stars in the constellation of genius. A small stock of ideas is more easily managed, and sooner displayed, than a great quantity crowded together. There is very seldom anything extraordinary in the appearance and address of a good writer; whereas a dull author generally distinguishes himself by some oddity or extravagance. For this reason I fancy that an assembly of grubs must be very diverting.'

"My curiosity being excited by this hint, I consulted my friend Dick Ivy, who undertook to gratify it the very next day, which was Sunday last. He carried me to dine with S——, whom you and I have long known by his writings. He lives in the skirts of the town; and every Sunday his house is open to all unfortunate brothers of the quill, whom he treats with beef, pudding, and potatoes, port, punch, and Calvert's entire butt beer. He has fixed upon the first day of the week for the exercise of his hospitality, because some of his guests could not enjoy it on any other, for reasons that I need not explain. I was civilly received in a plain, yet decent habitation, which opened backwards into a very pleasant garden, kept in excellent order; and, indeed, I saw none of the outward signs of authorship either in the house or the landlord, who is one of those few writers of the age that stand upon their own foundation, without patronage, and above dependence. If there was nothing characteristic in the entertainer, the company made ample amends for his want of singularity.

"At two in the afternoon, I found myself one of ten messmates seated at table; and I question if the whole kingdom could produce such another assemblage of originals. Among their peculiarities, I do not mention those of dress, which may be purely accidental. What struck me were oddities originally produced by affectation, and afterwards confirmed by habit. One of them wore spectacles at dinner, and another his hat flapped; though (as Ivy told me) the first was noted for having a seaman's eye when a bailiff was in the wind; and the other was never known to labour under any weakness or defect of vision, except about five years ago, when he was complimented with a couple of black eyes by a player, with whom he had quarrelled in his drink. A third wore a laced stocking, and made use of crutches, because, once in his life, he had been laid up with a broken leg, though no man could leap over a stick with more agility. A fourth had contracted such an antipathy to the country, that he insisted upon sitting with his back towards the window that looked into the garden; and when a dish of cauliflower was set upon the table, he snuffed up volatile salts to keep him from fainting; yet this delicate person was the son of a cottager, born under a hedge, and had many years run wild among asses on a common. A fifth affected distraction: when spoke to, he always answered from the purpose. Sometimes he suddenly started up, and rapped out a dreadful

I have no doubt that this picture by Smollett is as faithful a one as any from the pencil of his kindred humourist, Hogarth.

We have before us, and painted by his own hand, Tobias Smollett, the manly, kindly, honest, and irascible; worn and battered, but still brave and full of heart, after a long struggle against a hard fortune. His brain had been busied with a hundred different schemes; he had been reviewer and historian, critic, medical writer, poet, pamphleteer. He had fought endless literary

oath; sometimes he burst out a laughing; then he folded his arms, and sighed; and then he hissed like fifty serpents.

"At first, I really thought he was mad; and, as he sat near me, began to be under some apprehensions for my own safety; when our landlord, perceiving me alarmed, assured me aloud that I had nothing to fear. 'The gentleman,' said he, 'is trying to act a part for which he is by no means qualified; if he had all the inclination in the world, it is not in his power to be mad; his spirits are too flat to be kindled into phrenzy.' ''Tis no bad p-p-puff, how-owever," observed a person in a tarnished laced coat: 'aff-ffected m-madness w-ill p-pass for w-wit w-with nine-nineteen out of t-twenty.' 'And affected stuttering for humour,' replied our landlord; 'though, God knows! there is no affinity between them.' It seems this wag, after having made some abortive attempts in plain speaking, had recourse to this defect, by means of which he frequently extorted the laugh of the company, without the least expense of genius; and that imperfection, which he had at first counterfeited, was now become so habitual, that he could not lay it aside.

"A certain winking genius, who wore yellow gloves at dinner, had, on his first introduction, taken such offence at S——, because he looked and talked, and ate and drank, like any other man, that he spoke contemptuously of his understanding ever after, and never would repeat his visit, until he had exhibited the following proof of his caprice. Wat Wyvil, the poet, having made some unsuccessful advances towards an intimacy with S——, at last gave him to understand, by a third person, that he had written a poem in his praise, and a satire against his person: that if he would admit him to his house, the first should be immediately sent to press; but that if he persisted in declining his friendship, he would publish the satire without delay. S—— replied, that he looked upon Wyvil's panegyric as, in effect, a species of infamy, and would resent it accordingly with a good cudgel; but if he published the satire, he might deserve his compassion, and had nothing to fear from his revenge. Wyvil having considered the alternative, resolved to mortify S—— by printing the panegyric, for which he received a sound drubbing. Then he swore the peace against the aggressor, who, in order to avoid a prosecution at law, admitted him to his good graces. It was the singularity in S——'s conduct on this occasion, that reconciled him to the yellow-gloved philosopher, who owned he had some genius; and from that period cultivated his acquaintance.

"Curious to know upon what subjects the several talents of my fellow-guests were employed, I applied to my communicative friend Dick Ivy, who gave me to understand that most of them were, or had been, understrappers, or journeymen, to more creditable authors, for whom they translated, collated, and compiled, in the business of bookmaking; and that all of them had, at different

battles; and braved and wielded for years the cudgels of controversy. It was a hard and savage fight in those days, and a niggard pay. He was oppressed by illness, age, narrow fortune; but his spirit was still resolute, and his courage steady; the battle over, he could do justice to the enemy with whom he had been so fiercely engaged, and give a not unfriendly grasp to the hand that had mauled him. He is like one of those Scotch cadets, of whom history gives us so many examples, and whom, with a national

times, laboured in the service of our landlord, though they had now set up for themselves in various departments of literature. Not only their talents, but also their nations and dialects, were so various, that our conversation resembled the confusion of tongues at Babel. We had the Irish brogue, the Scotch accent, and foreign idiom, twanged off by the most discordant vociferation; for as they all spoke together, no man had any chance to be heard, unless he could bawl louder than his fellows. It must be owned, however, there was nothing pedantic in their discourse; they carefully avoided all learned disquisitions, and endeavoured to be facetious: nor did their endeavours always miscarry; some droll repartee passed, and much laughter was excited; and if any individual lost his temper so far as to transgress the bounds of decorum, he was effectually checked by the master of the feast, who exerted a sort of paternal authority over this irritable tribe.

"The most learned philosopher of the whole collection, who had been expelled the university for atheism, has made great progress in a refutation of Lord Bolingbroke's metaphysical works, which is said to be equally ingenious and orthodox; but, in the meantime, he has been presented to the grand jury as a public nuisance for having blasphemed in an alehouse on the Lord's day. The Scotchman gives lectures on the pronunciation of the English language, which he is now publishing by subscription.

"The Irishman is a political writer, and goes by the name of My Lord Potatoe. He wrote a pamphlet in vindication of a Minister, hoping his zeal would be rewarded with some place or pension; but finding himself neglected in that quarter, he whispered about that the pamphlet was written by the Minister himself, and he published an answer to his own production. In this he addressed the author under the title of 'your Lordship,' with such solemnity, that the public swallowed the deceit, and bought up the whole impression. The wise politicians of the metropolis declared they were both masterly performances, and chuckled over the flimsy reveries of an ignorant garreteer, as the profound speculations of a veteran statesman, acquainted with all the secrets of the cabinet. The imposture was detected in the sequel, and our Hibernian pamphleteer retains no part of his assumed importance but the bare title of 'my Lord,' and the upper part of the table at the potatoe-ordinary in Shoe Lane.

"Opposite to me sat a Piedmontese, who had obliged the public with a humorous satire, entitled *The Balance of the English Poets;* a performance which evinced the great modesty and taste of the author, and, in particular, his intimacy with the elegancies of the English language. The sage, who laboured under the ἀγροφοβία, or 'horror of green fields,' had just finished a treatise on practical agriculture, though, in fact, he had never seen corn growing in his life, and was so ignorant of grain, that our entertainer, in the face of the whole

fidelity, the great Scotch novelist has painted so charmingly. Of gentle birth * and narrow means, going out from his northern home to win his fortune in the world, and to fight his way, armed with courage, hunger, and keen wits. His crest is a shattered oak-tree,

company, made him own that a plate of hominy was the best rice-pudding he had ever eat.

"The stut erer had almost finished his travels through Europe and part of Asia, without ever budging beyond the liberties of the King's Bench, except in term-time with a tipstaff for his companion; and as for little Tim Cropdale, the most facetious member of the whole society, he had happily wound up the catastrophe of a virgin tragedy, from the exhibition of which he promised himself a large fund of profit and reputation. Tim had made shift to live many years by writing novels, at the rate of five pounds a volume; but that branch of business is now engrossed by female authors, who publish merely for the propagation of virtue, with so much ease, and spirit, and delicacy, and knowledge of the human heart, and all in the serene tranquillity of high life, that the reader is not only enchanted by their genius, but reformed by their morality.

"After dinner, we adjourned into the garden, where I observed Mr. S—— give a short separate audience to every individual in a small remote filbert-walk, from whence most of them dropped off one after another, without further ceremony."

Smollett's house was in Lawrence Lane, Chelsea, and is now destroyed.—See *Handbook of London*, p. 115.

"The person of Smollett was eminently handsome, his features prepossessing, and, by the joint testimony of all his surviving friends, his conversation, in the highest degree, instructive and amusing. Of his disposition, those who have read his works (and who has not?) may form a very accurate estimate; for in each of them he has presented, and sometimes under various points of view, the leading features of his own character without disguising the most unfavourable of them. . . . When unseduced by his satirical propensities, he was kind, generous, and humane to others; bold, upright, and independent in his own character; stooped to no patron, sued for no favour, but honestly and honourably maintained himself on his literary labours. . . . He was a doting father and an affectionate husband; and the warm zeal with which his memory was cherished by his surviving friends showed clearly the reliance which they placed upon his regard."—*Sir Walter Scott.*

* Smollett of Bonhill, in Dumbartonshire. *Arms*, azure, a bend, or, between a lion rampant, ppr., holding in his paw a banner, argent, and a bugle-horn, also ppr. *Crest*, an oak-tree, ppr. *Motto*, *Viresco.*

Smollett's father, Archibald, was the fourth son of Sir James Smollett of Bonhill, a Scotch Judge and Member of Parliament, and one of the commissioners for framing the Union with England. Archibald married, without the old gentleman's consent, and died early, leaving his children dependent on their grandfather. Tobias, the second son, was born in 1721, in the old house of Dalquharn in the valley of Leven; and all his life loved and admired that valley and Loch Lomond beyond all the valleys and lakes in Europe. He learned the "rudiments" at Dumbarton Grammar School, and studied at Glasgow.

But when he was only ten, his grandfather died, and left him without pro-

with green leaves yet springing from it. On his ancient coat-of-arms there is a lion and a horn; this shield of his was battered and dinted in a hundred fights and brawls,* through which the stout Scotchman bore it courageously. You see somehow that he is a gentleman,

vision (figuring as the old judge in *Roderick Random* in consequence, according to Sir Walter). Tobias, armed with the *Regicide, a Tragedy*—a provision precisely similar to that with which Doctor Johnson had started, just before—came up to London. The *Regicide* came to no good, though at first patronised by Lord Lyttelton ("one of those little fellows who are sometimes called great men," Smollett says); and Smollett embarked as "surgeon's mate" on board a line-of-battle ship, and served in the Carthagena expedition, in 1741. He left the service in the West Indies, and, after residing some time in Jamaica, returned to England in 1746.

He was now unsuccessful as a physician, to begin with; published the satires, *Advice* and *Reproof*, without any luck; and (1747) married the "beautiful and accomplished Miss Lascelles."

In 1748 he brought out his *Roderick Random*, which at once made a "hit." The subsequent events of his life may be presented, chronologically, in a bird's-eye view:—

1750. Made a tour to Paris, where he chiefly wrote *Peregrine Pickle.*
1751. Published *Peregrine Pickle.*
1753. Published *Adventures of Ferdinand Count Fathom.*
1755 Published version of *Don Quixote.*
1756. Began the *Critical Review.*
1758. Published his *History of England.*
1763–1766. Travelling in France and Italy; published his *Travels.*
1769. Published *Adventures of an Atom.*
1770. Set out for Italy; died at Leghorn, 21st of October 1771, in the fifty-first year of his age.

* A good specimen of the old "slashing" style of writing is presented by the paragraph on Admiral Knowles, which subjected Smollett to prosecution and imprisonment. The admiral's defence on the occasion of the failure of the Rochefort expedition came to be examined before the tribunal of the *Critical Review.*

"He is," said our author, "an admiral without conduct, an engineer without knowledge, an officer without resolution, and a man without veracity!"

Three months' imprisonment in the King's Bench avenged this stinging paragraph.

But the *Critical* was to Smollett a perpetual fountain of "hot water." Among less important controversies may be mentioned that with Grainger, the translator of Tibullus. Grainger replied in a pamphlet; and in the next number of the Review we find him threatened with "castigation," as an "owl that has broken from his mew!"

In Doctor Moore's biography of him is a pleasant anecdote. After publishing the *Don Quixote*, he returned to Scotland to pay a visit to his mother:—

"On Smollett's arrival, he was introduced to his mother with the connivance of Mrs. Telfer (her daughter), as a gentleman from the West Indies, who was intimately acquainted with her son. The better to support his assumed character, he endeavoured to preserve a serious countenance, approaching to a

through all his battling and struggling, his poverty, his hard-fought successes, and his defeats. His novels are recollections of his own adventures; his characters drawn, as I should think, from personages with whom he became acquainted in his own career of life. Strange companions he must have had; queer acquaintances he made in the Glasgow College—in the country apothecary's shop; in the gun-room of the man-of-war where he served as surgeon; and in the hard life on shore, where the sturdy adventurer struggled for fortune. He did not invent much, as I fancy, but had the keenest perceptive faculty, and described what he saw with wonderful relish and delightful broad humour. I think Uncle Bowling, in "Roderick Random," is as good a character as Squire Western himself; and Mr. Morgan, the Welsh apothecary, is as pleasant as Doctor Caius. What man who has made his inestimable acquaintance—what novel-reader who loves Don Quixote and Major Dalgetty—will refuse his most cordial acknowledgments to the admirable Lieutenant Lismahago? The novel of "Humphrey Clinker" is, I do think, the most laughable story that has ever been written since the goodly art of novel-writing began. Winifred Jenkins and Tabitha Bramble must keep Englishmen on the grin for ages yet to come; and in their letters and the story of their loves there is a perpetual fount of sparkling laughter, as inexhaustible as Bladud's well.

FIELDING, too, has described, though with a greater hand, the characters and scenes which he knew and saw. He had more than ordinary opportunities for becoming acquainted with life. His family and education, first—his fortunes and misfortunes afterwards, brought him into the society of every rank and condition of man.

frown; but while his mother's eyes were riveted on his countenance, he could not refrain from smiling: she immediately sprung from her chair, and throwing her arms round his neck, exclaimed, 'Ah, my son! my son! I have found you at last!'

"She afterwards told him, that if he had kept his austere looks and continued to *gloom*, he might have escaped detection some time longer, but 'your old roguish smile,' added she, 'betrayed you at once.'"

"Shortly after the publication of *The Adventures of an Atom*, disease again attacked Smollett with redoubled violence. Attempts being vainly made to obtain for him the office of Consul in some part of the Mediterranean, he was compelled to seek a warmer climate, without better means of provision than his own precarious finances could afford. The kindness of his distinguished friend and countryman, Dr. Armstrong (then abroad), procured for Dr. and Mrs. Smollett a house at Monte Nero, a village situated on the side of a mountain overlooking the sea, in the neighbourhood of Leghorn, a romantic and salutary abode, where he prepared for the press the last, and, like music 'sweetest in the close,' the most pleasing of his compositions, *The Expedition of Humphrey Clinker*. This delightful work was published in 1771."—*Sir Walter Scott*.

He is himself the hero of his books: he is wild Tom Jones, he is wild Captain Booth; less wild, I am glad to think, than his predecessor: at least heartily conscious of demerit, and anxious to amend.

When Fielding first came upon the town in 1727, the recollection of the great wits was still fresh in the coffee-houses and assemblies, and the judges there declared that young Harry Fielding had more spirits and wit than Congreve or any of his brilliant successors. His figure was tall and stalwart; his face handsome, manly, and noble-looking; to the very last days of his life he retained a grandeur of air, and although worn down by disease, his aspect and presence imposed respect upon the people round about him.

A dispute took place between Mr. Fielding and the captain * of the ship in which he was making his last voyage, and Fielding relates how the man finally went down on his knees, and begged his passenger's pardon. He was living up to the last days of his life, and his spirit never gave in. His vital power must have been immensely strong. Lady Mary Wortley Montagu † prettily characterises Fielding and this capacity for happiness which he

* The dispute with the captain arose from the wish of that functionary to intrude on his right to his cabin, for which he had paid thirty pounds. After recounting the circumstances of the apology, he characteristically adds:—

"And here, that I may not be thought the sly trumpeter of my own praises, I do utterly disclaim all praise on the occasion. Neither did the greatness of my mind dictate, nor the force of my Christianity exact this forgiveness. To speak truth, I forgave him from a motive which would make men much more forgiving, if they were much wiser than they are: because it was convenient for me so to do."

† Lady Mary was his second cousin—their respective grandfathers being sons of George Fielding, Earl of Desmond, son of William, Earl of Denbigh.

In a letter dated just a week before his death, she says:—

"H. Fielding has given a true picture of himself and his first wife in the characters of *Mr.* and *Mrs. Booth*, some compliments to his own figure excepted; and I am persuaded, several of the incidents he mentions are real matters of fact. I wonder he does not perceive *Tom Jones* and *Mr. Booth* are sorry scoundrels. . . . Fielding has really a fund of true humour, and was to be pitied at his first entrance into the world, having no choice, as he said himself, but to be a hackney writer or a hackney coachman. His genius deserved a better fate; but I cannot help blaming that continued indiscretion, to give it the softest name, that has run through his life, and I am afraid still remains. . . . Since I was born no original has appeared excepting Congreve, and Fielding, who would, I believe, have approached nearer to his excellences, if not forced by his necessities to publish without correction, and throw many productions into the world he would have thrown into the fire, if meat could have been got without money, or money without scribbling. . . . I am sorry not to see any more of Peregrine Pickle's performances; I wish you would tell me his name."—*Letters and Works* (Lord Wharncliffe's ed.), vol. iii. pp. 93, 94.

possessed, in a little notice of his death when she compares him to Steele, who was as improvident and as happy as he was, and says that both should have gone on living for ever. One can fancy the eagerness and gusto with which a man of Fielding's frame, with his vast health and robust appetite, his ardent spirits, his joyful humour, and his keen and healthy relish for life, must have seized and drunk that cup of pleasure which the town offered to him. Can any of my hearers remember the youthful feats of a college breakfast—the meats devoured and the cups quaffed in that Homeric feast? I can call to mind some of the heroes of those youthful banquets, and fancy young Fielding from Leyden rushing upon the feast, with his great laugh, and immense healthy young appetite, eager and vigorous to enjoy. The young man's wit and manners made him friends everywhere: he lived with the grand Man's society of those days; he was courted by peers and men of wealth and fashion. As he had a paternal allowance from his father, General Fielding, which, to use Henry's own phrase, any man might pay who would; as he liked good wine, good clothes, and good company, which are all expensive articles to purchase, Harry Fielding began to run into debt, and borrow money in that easy manner in which Captain Booth borrows money in the novel: was in nowise particular in accepting a few pieces from the purses of his rich friends, and bore down upon more than one of them, as Walpole tells us only too truly, for a dinner or a guinea. To supply himself with the latter, he began to write theatrical pieces, having already, no doubt, a considerable acquaintance amongst the Oldfields and Bracegirdles behind the scenes. He laughed at these pieces and scorned them. When the audience upon one occasion began to hiss a scene which he was too lazy to correct, and regarding which, when Garrick remonstrated with him, he said that the public was too stupid to find out the badness of his work: when the audience began to hiss, Fielding said with characteristic coolness—"They have found it out, have they?" He did not prepare his novels in this way, and with a very different care and interest laid the foundations and built up the edifices of his future fame.

Time and shower have very little damaged those. The fashion and ornaments are, perhaps, of the architecture of that age, but the buildings remain strong and lofty, and of admirable proportions—masterpieces of genius and monuments of workmanlike skill.

I cannot offer or hope to make a hero of Harry Fielding. Why hide his faults? Why conceal his weaknesses in a cloud of periphrases? Why not show him, like him as he is, not robed in a marble toga, and draped and polished in an heroic attitude, but with inked ruffles, and claret stains on his tarnished laced coat, and on his manly face the marks of good fellowship, of illness, of kindness, of care and wine? Stained as you see him, and worn by care and dissipation, that man retains some of the most precious and splendid human qualities and endowments. He has an admirable natural love of truth, the keenest instinctive antipathy to hypocrisy, the happiest satirical gift of laughing it to scorn. His wit is wonderfully wise and detective; it flashes upon a rogue and lightens up a rascal like a policeman's lantern. He is one of the manliest and kindliest of human beings: in the midst of all his imperfections, he respects female innocence and infantine tenderness as you would suppose such a great-hearted, courageous soul would respect and care for them. He could not be so brave, generous, truth-telling as he is, were he not infinitely merciful, pitiful, and tender. He will give any man his purse—he can't help kindness and profusion. He may have low tastes, but not a mean mind; he admires with all his heart good and virtuous men, stoops to no flattery, bears no rancour, disdains all disloyal arts, does his public duty uprightly, is fondly loved by his family, and dies at his work.*

If that theory be—and I have no doubt it is—the right and safe one, that human nature is always pleased with the spectacle of innocence rescued by fidelity, purity, and courage, I suppose that of the heroes of Fielding's three novels, we should like honest Joseph Andrews the best, and Captain Booth the second, and Tom Jones the third.†

Joseph Andrews, though he wears Lady Booby's cast-off livery, is, I think, to the full as polite as Tom Jones in his fustian suit, or Captain Booth in regimentals. He has, like those heroes, large calves, broad shoulders, a high courage, and a handsome face. The accounts of Joseph's bravery and good qualities; his voice, too musical to halloo to the dogs; his bravery in riding races for the gentlemen of the county, and his constancy in refusing bribes and temptation, have something affecting in their *naïveté* and freshness, and prepossess one in favour of that handsome young hero. The

* He sailed for Lisbon, from Gravesend, on Sunday morning, June 30th, 1754; and began *The Journal of a Voyage* during the passage. He died at Lisbon, in the beginning of October of the same year. He lies buried there, in the English Protestant churchyard, near the Estrella Church, with this inscription over him:—

"HENRICUS FIELDING
LUGET BRITANNIA GREMIO NON DARI
FOVERE NATUM."

† Fielding himself is said by Doctor Warton to have preferred *Joseph Andrews* to his other writings.

rustic bloom of Fanny, and the delightful simplicity of Parson Adams, are described with a friendliness which wins the reader of their story; we part from them with more regret than from Booth and Jones.

Fielding, no doubt, began to write this novel in ridicule of "Pamela," for which work one can understand the hearty contempt and antipathy which such an athletic and boisterous genius as Fielding's must have entertained. He couldn't do otherwise than laugh at the puny cockney bookseller, pouring out endless volumes of sentimental twaddle, and hold him up to scorn as a mollcoddle and a milksop. *His* genius had been nursed on sack posset, and not on dishes of tea. *His* muse had sung the loudest in tavern choruses, had seen the daylight streaming in over thousands of emptied bowls, and reeled home to chambers on the shoulders of the watchman. Richardson's goddess was attended by old maids and dowagers, and fed on muffins and bohea. "Milksop!" roars Harry Fielding, clattering at the timid shop-shutters. "Wretch! Monster! Mohock!" shrieks the sentimental author of "Pamela"; * and all the ladies of his court cackle out an affrighted chorus. Fielding proposes to write a book in ridicule of the author, whom he disliked and utterly scorned and laughed at; but he is himself of so generous, jovial, and kindly a turn that he begins to like the characters which he invents, can't help making them manly and pleasant as well as ridiculous, and before he has done with them all, loves them heartily every one.

Richardson's sickening antipathy for Harry Fielding is quite as natural as the other's laughter and contempt at the sentimentalist. I have not learned that these likings and dislikings have ceased in the present day: and every author must lay his account not only to misrepresentation, but to honest enmity among critics, and to being hated and abused for good as well as for bad reasons. Richardson disliked Fielding's works quite honestly: Walpole quite honestly spoke of them as vulgar and stupid. Their squeamish stomachs sickened at the rough fare and the rough guests assembled at Fielding's jolly revel. Indeed the cloth might have been cleaner:

* "Richardson," says worthy Mrs. Barbauld, in her Memoir of him, prefixed to his Correspondence, "was exceedingly hurt at this (*Joseph Andrews*), the more so as they had been on good terms, and he was verv intimate with Fielding's two sisters. He never appears cordially to have forgiven it (perhaps it was not in human nature he should), and he always speaks in his letters with a great deal of asperity of *Tom Jones*, more indeed than was quite graceful in a rival author. No doubt he himself thought his indignation was solely excited by the loose morality of the work and of its author, but he could tolerate Cibber."

and the dinner and the company were scarce such as suited a dandy. The kind and wise old Johnson would not sit down with him.* But a greater scholar than Johnson could afford to admire that astonishing genius of Harry Fielding; and we all know the lofty panegyric which Gibbon wrote of him, and which remains a towering monument to the great novelist's memory. "Our immortal Fielding," Gibbon writes, "was of the younger branch of the Earls of Denbigh, who drew their origin from the Counts of Hapsburgh. The successors of Charles V. may disdain their brethren of England, but the romance of 'Tom Jones,' that exquisite picture of humour and manners, will outlive the palace of the Escurial and the Imperial Eagle of Austria."

There can be no gainsaying the sentence of this great judge. To have your name mentioned by Gibbon, is like having it written on the dome of St. Peter's. Pilgrims from all the world admire and behold it.

As a picture of manners, the novel of "Tom Jones" is indeed exquisite: as a work of construction, quite a wonder: the by-play of wisdom; the power of observation; the multiplied felicitous turns and thoughts; the varied character of the great Comic Epic: keep the reader in a perpetual admiration and curiosity.† But against Mr. Thomas Jones himself we have a right to put in a protest, and quarrel with the esteem the author evidently has for that character. Charles Lamb says finely of Jones, that a single hearty laugh from him "clears the air"—but then it is in a certain

* It must always be borne in mind, that besides that the Doctor couldn't be expected to like Fielding's wild life (to say nothing of the fact that they were of opposite sides in politics), Richardson was one of his earliest and kindest friends. Yet Johnson too (as Boswell tells us) read *Amelia* through without stopping.

† "Manners change from generation to generation, and with manners morals appear to change—actually change with some, but appear to change with all but the abandoned. A young man of the present day who should act as Tom Jones is supposed to act at Upton, with Lady Bellaston, &c., would not be a Tom Jones; and a Tom Jones of the present day, without perhaps being in the ground a better man, would have perished rather than submit to be kept by a harridan of fortune. Therefore, this novel is, and indeed pretends to be, no example of conduct. But, notwithstanding all this, I do loathe the cant which can recommend *Pamela* and *Clarissa Harlowe* as strictly moral, although they poison the imagination of the young with continued doses of *tinct. lyttæ*, while *Tom Jones* is prohibited as loose. I do not speak of young women; but a young man whose heart or feelings can be injured, or even his passions excited by this novel, is already thoroughly corrupt. There is a cheerful, sunshiny, breezy spirit, that prevails everywhere, strongly contrasted with the close, hot, day-dreamy continuity of Richardson."—COLERIDGE. *Literary Remains*, vol. ii. p. 374.

state of the atmosphere. It might clear the air when such personages as Blifil or Lady Bellaston poison it. But I fear very much that (except until the very last scene of the story), when Mr. Jones enters Sophia's drawing-room, the pure air there is rather tainted with the young gentleman's tobacco-pipe and punch. I can't say that I think Mr. Jones a virtuous character; I can't say but that I think Fielding's evident liking and admiration for Mr. Jones shows that the great humourist's moral sense was blunted by his life, and that here, in Art and Ethics, there is a great error. If it is right to have a hero whom we may admire, let us at least take care that he is admirable: if, as is the plan of some authors (a plan decidedly against their interests, be it said), it is propounded that there exists in life no such being, and therefore that in novels, the picture of life, there should appear no such character; then Mr. Thomas Jones becomes an admissible person, and we examine his defects and good qualities, as we do those of Parson Thwackum, or Miss Seagrim. But a hero with a flawed reputation; a hero spunging for a guinea; a hero who can't pay his landlady, and is obliged to let his honour out to hire, is absurd, and his claim to heroic rank untenable. I protest against Mr. Thomas Jones holding such rank at all. I protest even against his being considered a more than ordinary young fellow, ruddy-cheeked, broad-shouldered, and fond of wine and pleasure. He would not rob a church, but that is all; and a pretty long argument may be debated, as to which of these old types—the spendthrift, the hypocrite, Jones and Blifil, Charles and Joseph Surface—is the worst member of society and the most deserving of censure. The prodigal Captain Booth is a better man than his predecessor Mr. Jones, in so far as he thinks much more humbly of himself than Jones did: goes down on his knees, and owns his weaknesses, and cries out, "Not for my sake, but for the sake of my pure and sweet and beautiful wife Amelia, I pray you, O critical reader, to forgive me." That stern moralist regards him from the bench (the judge's practice out of court is not here the question), and says, "Captain Booth, it is perfectly true that your life has been disreputable, and that on many occasions you have shown yourself to be no better than a scamp—you have been tippling at the tavern, when the kindest and sweetest lady in the world has cooked your little supper of boiled mutton and awaited you all the night; you have spoilt the little dish of boiled mutton thereby, and caused pangs and pains to Amelia's tender heart.* You have got into debt without the

* "Nor was she (Lady Mary Wortley Montagu) a stranger to that beloved first wife, whose picture he drew in his 'Amelia,' when, as she said, even the glowing language he knew how to employ did not do more than justice to the

means of paying it. You have gambled the money with which you ought to have paid your rent. You have spent in drink or in worse amusements the sums which your poor wife has raised upon her little home treasures, her own ornaments, and the toys of her children. But, you rascal! you own humbly that you are no better than you should be; you never for one moment pretend that you are anything but a miserable weak-minded rogue. You do in your heart adore that angelic woman your wife, and for her sake, sirrah, you shall have your discharge. Lucky for you, and for others like you, that in spite of your failings and imperfections, pure hearts pity and love you. For your wife's sake you are permitted to go hence without a remand; and I beg you, by the way, to carry to that angelical lady the expression of the cordial respect and admiration of this court." Amelia pleads for her husband, Will Booth: Amelia pleads for her reckless kindly old father, Harry Fielding. To have invented that character is not only a triumph of art, but it is a good action. They say it was in his own home that Fielding knew her and loved her: and from his own wife that he drew the most charming character in English fiction. Fiction! why fiction? why not history? I know Amelia

amiable qualities of the original, or to her beauty, although this had suffered a little from the accident related in the novel—a frightful overturn, which destroyed the gristle of her nose. He loved her passionately, and she returned his affection. . . .

"His biographers seem to have been shy of disclosing that, after the death of this charming woman, he married her maid. And yet the act was not so discreditable to his character as it may sound. The maid had few personal charms, but was an excellent creature, devotedly attached to her mistress, and almost broken-hearted for her loss. In the first agonies of his own grief, which approached to frenzy, he found no relief but from weeping along with her; nor solace when a degree calmer, but in talking to her of the angel they mutually regretted. This made her his habitual confidential associate, and in process of time he began to think he could not give his children a tenderer mother, or secure for himself a more faithful housekeeper and nurse. At least, this was what he told his friends; and it is certain that her conduct as his wife confirmed it, and fully justified his good opinion."—*Letters and Works of Lady Mary Wortley Montagu.* Edited by Lord Wharncliffe. *Introductory Anecdotes*, vol. i. pp. 80, 81.

Fielding's first wife was Miss Craddock, a young lady from Salisbury, with a fortune of £1500, whom he married in 1736. About the same time he succeeded, himself, to an estate of £200 per annum, and on the joint amount he lived for some time as a splendid country gentleman in Dorsetshire. Three years brought him to the end of his fortune; when he returned to London, and became a theatrical manager. [Recent researches have not confirmed the report as to the "estate of £200 a year"; nor can he have spent three years in the country.]

just as well as Lady Mary Wortley Montagu. I believe in Colonel Bath almost as much as in Colonel Gardiner or the Duke of Cumberland. I admire the author of "Amelia," and thank the kind master who introduced me to that sweet and delightful companion and friend. "Amelia" perhaps is not a better story than "Tom Jones," but it has the better ethics; the prodigal repents, at least, before forgiveness—whereas that odious broad-backed Mr. Jones carries off his beauty with scarce an interval of remorse for his manifold errors and shortcomings; and is not half punished enough before the great prize of fortune and love falls to his share. I am angry with Jones. Too much of the plum-cake and rewards of life fall to that boisterous, swaggering young scapegrace. Sophia actually surrenders without a proper sense of decorum; the fond, foolish palpitating little creature!—"Indeed, Mr. Jones," she says,—"it rests with you to appoint the day." I suppose Sophia is drawn from life as well as Amelia; and many a young fellow, no better than Mr. Thomas Jones, has carried by a *coup de main* the heart of many a kind girl who was a great deal too good for him.

What a wonderful art! What an admirable gift of nature was it by which the author of these tales was endowed, and which enabled him to fix our interest, to waken our sympathy, to seize upon our credulity, so that we believe in his people—speculate gravely upon their faults or their excellences, prefer this one or that, deplore Jones's fondness for play and drink, Booth's fondness for play and drink, and the unfortunate position of the wives of both gentlemen—love and admire those ladies with all our hearts, and talk about them as faithfully as if we had breakfasted with them this morning in their actual drawing-rooms, or should meet them this afternoon in the Park! What a genius! what a vigour! what a bright-eyed intelligence and observation! what a wholesome hatred for meanness and knavery! what a vast sympathy! what a cheerfulness! what a manly relish of life! what a love of human kind! what a poet is here!—watching, meditating, brooding, creating! What multitudes of truths has that man left behind him! What generations he has taught to laugh wisely and fairly! What scholars he has formed and accustomed to the exercise of thoughtful humour and the manly play of wit! What a courage he had! What a dauntless and constant cheerfulness of intellect, that burned bright and steady through all the storms of his life, and never deserted its last wreck! It is wonderful to think of the pains and misery which the man suffered; the pressure of want, illness, remorse which he endured! and that the writer was neither malignant nor melancholy, his view of truth never warped, and his generous human kindness never surrendered.*

In the quarrel mentioned before, which happened on Fielding's last voyage to Lisbon, and when the stout captain of the ship fell down on his knees, and asked the sick's man's pardon—"I did not suffer," Fielding says, in his hearty, manly way, his eyes lighting up as it were with their old fire—"I did not suffer a brave man and an old man to remain a moment in that posture, but immediately forgave him." Indeed, I think, with his noble spirit and

* In the *Gentleman's Magazine* for 1786, an anecdote is related of Harry Fielding, "in whom," says the correspondent, "good-nature and philanthropy in their extreme degree were known to be the prominent features." It seems that "some parochial taxes" for his house in Beaufort Buildings had long been demanded by the collector. "At last, Harry went off to Johnson, and obtained by a process of literary mortgage the needful sum. He was returning with it, when he met an old college chum whom he had not seen for many years. He asked the chum to dinner with him at a neighbouring tavern; and learning that he was in difficulties, emptied the contents of his pocket into his. On returning home he was informed that the collector had been twice for the money. 'Friendship has called for the money and had it,' said Fielding; 'let the collector call again.'"

It is elsewhere told of him, that being in company with the Earl of Denbigh, his kinsman, and the conversation turning upon their relationship, the Earl asked him how it was that he spelled his name "Fielding," and not "Feilding," like the head of the house? "I cannot tell, my Lord," said he, "except it be that my branch of the family were the first that knew how to spell."

In 1748, he was made Justice of the Peace for Westminster and Middlesex, an office then paid by fees and very laborious, without being particularly reputable. It may be seen from his own words, in the Introduction to the "Voyage," what kind of work devolved upon him, and in what a state he was during these last years; and still more clearly, how he comported himself through all.

"Whilst I was preparing for my journey, and when I was almost fatigued to death with several long examinations, relating to five different murders, all committed within the space of a week, by different gangs of street-robbers, I received a message from his Grace the Duke of Newcastle, by Mr. Carrington, the King's messenger, to attend his Grace the next morning in Lincoln's Inn Fields, upon some business of importance: but I excused myself from complying with the message, as, besides being lame, I was very ill with the great fatigues I had lately undergone, added to my distemper.

"His Grace, however, sent Mr. Carrington the very next morning with another summons, with which, though in the utmost distress, I immediately complied; but the Duke happening, unfortunately for me, to be then particularly engaged, after I had waited some time, sent a gentleman to discourse with me on the best plan which could be invented for these murders and robberies, which were every day committed in the streets; upon which I promised to transmit my opinion in writing to his Grace, who, as the gentleman informed me, intended to lay it before the Privy Council.

"Though this visit cost me a severe cold, I, notwithstanding, set myself down

unconquerable generosity, Fielding reminds one of those brave men of whom one reads in stories of English shipwrecks and disasters—of the officer on the African shore, when disease had destroyed the crew, and he himself is seized by fever, who throws the lead with a death-stricken hand, takes the soundings, carries the ship out of the river or off the dangerous coast, and dies in the manly endeavour—of the wounded captain, when the vessel founders, who never loses his heart, who eyes the danger steadily, and has a cheery word for all, until the inevitable fate overwhelms him, and the gallant ship goes down. Such a brave and gentle heart, such an intrepid and courageous spirit, I love to recognise in the manly, the English Harry Fielding.

to work, and in about four days sent the Duke as regular a plan as I could form, with all the reasons and arguments I could bring to support it, drawn out on several sheets of paper; and soon received a message from the Duke, by Mr. Carrington, acquainting me that my plan was highly approved of, and that all the terms of it would be complied with.

"The principal and most material of these terms was the immediately depositing £600 in my hands; at which small charge I undertook to demolish the then reigning gangs, and to put the civil policy into such order, that no such gangs should ever be able for the future to form themselves into bodies, or at least to remain any time formidable to the public.

"I had delayed my Bath journey for some time, contrary to the repeated advice of my physical acquaintances and the ardent desire of my warmest friends, though my distemper was now turned to a deep jaundice; in which case the Bath waters are generally reputed to be almost infallible. But I had the most eager desire to demolish this gang of villains and cut-throats. . . .

"After some weeks the money was paid at the Treasury, and within a few days after £200 of it had come into my hands, the whole gang of cut-throats was entirely dispersed. . . ."

Further on, he says—

"I will confess that my private affairs at the beginning of the winter had but a gloomy aspect; for I had not plundered the public or the poor of those sums which men, who are always ready to plunder both as much as they can, have been pleased to suspect me of taking; on the contrary, by composing, instead of inflaming, the quarrels of porters and beggars (which I blush when I say hath not been universally practised), and by refusing to take a shilling from a man who most undoubtedly would not have had another left, I had reduced an income of about £500 a year of the dirtiest money upon earth to little more than £300, a considerable portion of which remained with my clerk."

STERNE AND GOLDSMITH

ROGER STERNE, Sterne's father, was the second son of a numerous race, descendants of Richard Sterne, Archbishop of York, in the reign of Charles II.;* and children of Simon Sterne and Mary Jaques, his wife, heiress of Elvington, near York.† Roger was an ensign in Colonel Hans Hamilton's regiment, and engaged in Flanders in Queen Anne's wars.‡ He married the daughter of a noted sutler. "*N.B.*, he was in debt to him," his son writes, pursuing the paternal biography—and marched through the world with this companion; she following the regiment and bringing many children to poor Roger Sterne. The Captain was an irascible but kind and simple little man, Sterne says, and he informs us that his sire was run through the body at Gibraltar, by a brother officer, in a duel which arose out of a dispute about a goose. Roger never entirely recovered from the effects of this rencontre, but died presently at Jamaica,§ whither he had followed the drum.

Laurence, his second child, was born at Clonmel, in Ireland, in 1713, and travelled for the first ten years of his life, on his father's march, from barrack to transport, from Ireland to England.||

One relative of his mother's took her and her family under shelter for ten months at Mullingar; another collateral descendant of the Archbishop's housed them for a year at his castle near Carrickfergus. Larry Sterne was put to school at Halifax in England, finally was adopted by his kinsman of Elvington, and

* [1664 to 1683.]

† He came of a Suffolk family—one of whom settled in Nottinghamshire. The famous "starling" was actually the family crest.

‡ [He was appointed ensign about 1710. The regiment became Colonel Chudleigh's in 1711, and afterwards the 34th Foot. He did not become lieutenant till late in life.]

§ [March 1731.]

|| "It was in this parish (of Animo, in Wicklow), during our stay, that I had that wonderful escape in falling through a mill-race, whilst the mill was going, and of being taken up unhurt: the story is incredible, but known for truth in all that part of Ireland, where hundreds of the common people flocked to see me."—*Sterne.*

parted company with his father, the Captain, who marched on his path of life till he met the fatal goose which closed his career. The most picturesque and delightful parts of Laurence Sterne's writings we owe to his recollections of the military life. Trim's montero cap, and Le Fevre's sword, and dear Uncle Toby's roquelaure are doubtless reminiscences of the boy, who had lived with the followers of William and Marlborough, and had beat time with his little feet to the fifes of Ramillies in Dublin barrack-yard, or played with the torn flags and halberds of Malplaquet on the parade-ground at Clonmel.

Laurence remained at Halifax school till he was eighteen years old. His wit and cleverness appear to have acquired the respect of his master here; for when the usher whipped Laurence for writing his name on the newly whitewashed schoolroom ceiling, the pedagogue in chief rebuked the understrapper, and said that the name should never be effaced, for Sterne was a boy of genius, and would come to preferment.

His cousin, the Squire of Elvington, sent Sterne to Jesus College, Cambridge, where he remained some years,* and, taking orders, got, through his uncle's interest, the living of Sutton and a prebendal stall at York.† Through his wife's connections he got the living of Stillington. He married her in 1741, having ardently courted the young lady for some years previously. It was not until the young lady fancied herself dying, that she made Sterne acquainted with the extent of her liking for him. One evening when he was sitting with her, with an almost broken heart to see her so ill (the reverend Mr. Sterne's heart was a good deal broken in the course of his life), she said—"My dear Laurey, I never can be yours, for I verily believe I have not long to live; but I have left you every shilling of my fortune;" a generosity which overpowered Sterne. She recovered: and so they were married, and grew heartily tired of each other before many years were over. "Nescio quid est materia cum me," Sterne writes to one of his friends (in dog-Latin, and very sad dog-Latin too); "sed sum fatigatus et ægrotus de meâ uxore plus quam unquam:" which means, I am sorry to say, "I don't know what is the matter with me; but I am more tired and sick of my wife than ever." ‡

* [He was admitted sizar on 6th July 1733, became an exhibitioner in 1734, graduated B.A. in 1736, and M.A. 1740.]

† [Sterne was presented to Sutton, where he generally lived till 1760, in 1738. He became prebendary of York in January 1740-41. In 1760 he moved to Coxwold, on being presented to the perpetual curacy. He held a stall at York, and the three livings, Sutton, Stillington, and Coxwold, till his death.]

‡ "My wife returns to Toulouse, and proposes to pass the summer at Bagnères. I, on the contrary, go and visit my wife, the church, in Yorkshire. We all live the longer at least the happier, for having things our own way;

This to be sure was five-and-twenty years * after Laurey had been overcome by her generosity, and she by Laurey's love. Then he wrote to her of the delights of marriage, saying, "We will be as merry and as innocent as our first parents in Paradise, before the arch-fiend entered that indescribable scene. The kindest affections will have room to expand in our retirement: let the human tempest and hurricane rage at a distance, the desolation is beyond the horizon of peace. My L. has seen a polyanthus blow in December?—Some friendly wall has sheltered it from the biting wind. No planetary influence shall reach us but that which presides and cherishes the sweetest flowers. The gloomy family of care and distrust shall be banished from our dwelling, guarded by thy kind and tutelar deity. We will sing our choral songs of gratitude and rejoice to the end of our pilgrimage. Adieu, my L. Return to one who languishes for thy society!—As I take up my pen, my poor pulse quickens, my pale face glows, and tears are trickling down on my paper as I trace the word L."

And it is about this woman, with whom he finds no fault but that she bores him, that our philanthropist writes, "Sum fatigatus et ægrotus"—*Sum mortaliter in amore* with somebody else! That fine flower of love, that polyanthus over which Sterne snivelled so many tears, could not last for a quarter of a century!

Or rather it could not be expected that a gentleman with such a fountain at command should keep it to *arroser* one homely old lady, when a score of younger and prettier people might be refreshed from the same gushing source.† It was in December 1767, that the Reverend Laurence Sterne, the famous Shandean, the charming Yorick, the delight of the fashionable world, the

this is my conjugal maxim. I own 'tis not the best of maxims, but I maintain 'tis not the worst."—STERNE'S *Letters:* 20th January 1764. [His wife was Elizabeth, only daughter of Richard Lumley, formerly rector of Bedale. Both parents died in her infancy.]

* [This is probably a mistake. The Latin letter addressed to John Hall Stevenson is now known to have been written in 1758. Mrs. Sterne had a fit of insanity next year, and was for a time at a private asylum in York.]

† In a collection of "Seven Letters by Sterne and his Friends" (printed for private circulation in 1844), is a letter of M. Tollot, who was in France with Sterne and his family in 1764. Here is a paragraph:—

"Nous arrivâmes le lendemain à Montpellier, où nous trouvâmes notre ami Mr. Sterne, sa femme, sa fille, Mr. Huet, et quelques autres Anglaises. J'eus, je vous l'avoue, beaucoup de plaisir en revoyant le bon et agréable Tristram. . . . Il avait été assez longtemps à Toulouse, où il se serait amusé sans sa femme, qui le poursuivit partout, et qui voulait être de tout. Ces dispositions dans cette bonne dame lui ont fait passer d'assez mauvais momens; il supporte tous ces désagrémens avec une patience d'ange."

About four months after this very characteristic letter, Sterne wrote to the delicious divine for whose sermons the whole polite world was subscribing,* the occupier of Rabelais's easy-chair, only fresh stuffed and more elegant than when in possession of the cynical old curate of Meudon,†—the more than rival of the Dean of Saint Patrick's, wrote the above-quoted respectable letter to his

same gentleman to whom Tollot had written; and from his letter we may extract a companion paragraph:—

". . . . . . All which being premised, I have been for eight weeks smitten with the tenderest passion that ever tender wight underwent. I wish, dear cousin, thou couldst conceive (perhaps thou canst without my wishing it) how deliciously I cantered away with it the first month, two up, two down, always upon my *hanches*, along the streets from my hotel to hers, at first once—then twice, then three times a day, till at length I was within an ace of setting up my hobby-horse in her stable for good and all. I might as well, considering how the enemies of the Lord have blasphemed thereupon. The last three weeks we were every hour upon the doleful ditty of parting; and thou may'st conceive, dear cousin, how it altered my gait and air: for I went and came like any louden'd carl, and did nothing but *jouer des sentimens* with her from sun-rising even to the setting of the same; and now she is gone to the south of France: and to finish the *comédie*, I fell ill, and broke a vessel in my lungs, and half bled to death. Voilà mon histoire!"

Whether husband or wife had most of the "patience d'ange" may be uncertain; but there can be no doubt which needed it most!

* "'Tristram Shandy' is still a greater object of admiration, the man as well as the book: one is invited to dinner, where he dines, a fortnight before. As to the volumes yet published, there is much good fun in them and humour sometimes hit and sometimes missed. Have you read his 'Sermons,' with his own comick figure, from a painting by Reynolds, at the head of them? They are in the style I think most proper for the pulpit, and show a strong imagination and a sensible heart; but you see him often tottering on the verge of laughter, and ready to throw his periwig in the face of the audience."—GRAY'S *Letters:* June 22nd, 1760.

"It having been observed that there was little hospitality in London—Johnson: 'Nay, sir, any man who has a name, or who has the power of pleasing, will be very generally invited in London. The man, Sterne, I have been told, has had engagements for three months.' Goldsmith: 'And a very dull fellow.' Johnson: 'Why, no, sir.'"—BOSWELL'S *Life of Johnson.*

"Her [Miss Monckton's] vivacity enchanted the sage, and they used to talk together with all imaginable ease. A singular instance happened one evening, when she insisted that some of Sterne's writings were very pathetic. Johnson bluntly denied it. 'I am sure,' said she, 'they have affected me.' 'Why,' said Johnson, smiling, and rolling himself about—'that is because, dearest, you're a dunce.' When she some time afterwards mentioned this to him, he said with equal truth and politeness, 'Madam, if I had thought so, I certainly should not have said it.'"—*Ibid.*

† A passage or two from Sterne's Sermons may not be without interest here. Is not the following, levelled against the cruelties of the Church of Rome, stamped with the autograph of the author of the *Sentimental Journey?*—

"To be convinced of this, go with me for a moment into the prisons of the

friend in London: and it was in April of the same year that he was pouring out his fond heart to Mrs. Elizabeth Draper, wife of "Daniel Draper, Esquire, Councillor of Bombay, and, in 1775, chief of the factory of Surat—a gentleman very much respected in that quarter of the globe." *

"I got thy letter last night, Eliza," Sterne writes, "on my return from Lord Bathurst's, where I dined"—(the letter has this

Inquisition—behold *religion* with mercy and justice chained down under her feet—there, sitting ghastly upon a black tribunal, propped up with racks, and instruments of torment.—Hark!—what a piteous groan!—See the melancholy wretch who uttered it, just brought forth to undergo the anguish of a mock-trial, and endure the utmost pain that a studied system of *religious cruelty* has been able to invent. Behold this helpless victim delivered up to his tormentors. *His body so wasted with sorrow and long confinement, you'll see every nerve and muscle as it suffers.*—Observe the last movement of that horrid engine.—What convulsions it has thrown him into! Consider the nature of the posture in which he now lies stretched.—What exquisite torture he endures by it!—'Tis all nature can bear.—Good GOD! see how it keeps his weary soul hanging upon his trembling lips, willing to take its leave, but not suffered to depart. Behold the unhappy wretch led back to his cell—dragg'd out of it again to meet the flames—and the insults in his last agonies, which this principle—this principle, that there can be religion without morality—has prepared for him."—*Sermon 27th.*

The next extract is preached on a text to be found in Judges xix. vv. 1, 2, 3, concerning a "certain Levite":—

"Such a one the Levite wanted to share his solitude and fill up that uncomfortable blank in the heart in such a situation: for, notwithstanding all we meet with in books, in many of which, no doubt, there are a good many handsome things said upon the sweets of retirement, &c. . . yet still 'it *is not good for man to be alone;*' nor can all which the cold-hearted pedant stuns our ears with upon the subject, ever give one answer of satisfaction to the mind; in the midst of the loudest vauntings of philosophy, nature will have her yearnings for society and friendship;' a good heart wants some object to be kind to—and the best parts of our blood, and the purest of our spirits, suffer most under the destitution.

"Let the torpid monk seek Heaven comfortless and alone. God speed him! For my own part, I fear I should never so find the way: *let me be wise and religious, but let me be* MAN; wherever thy Providence places me, or whatever be the road I take to Thee, give me some companion in my journey, be it only to remark to, 'How our shadows lengthen as our sun goes down!'—to whom I may say, 'How fresh is the face of Nature! how sweet the flowers of the field! how delicious are these fruits!'"—*Sermon 18th.*

The first of these passages gives us another drawing of the famous "Captive." The second shows that the same reflection was suggested to the Reverend Laurence by a text in Judges as by the *fille-de-chambre.*

Sterne's Sermons were published as those of "Mr. Yorick."

* [Mrs. Draper, daughter of May Sclater, of a good west-country family, was married at Bombay in 1758, when little more than fourteen. She first met Sterne when on a visit to England in December 1766.]

merit in it, that it contains a pleasant reminiscence of better men than Sterne, and introduces us to a portrait of a kind old gentleman)—"I got thy letter last night, Eliza, on my return from Lord Bathurst's; and where I was heard—as I talked of thee an hour without intermission—with so much pleasure and attention, that the good old Lord toasted your health three different times; and now he is in his 85th year, says he hopes to live long enough to be introduced as a friend to my fair Indian disciple, and to see her eclipse all other Nabobesses as much in wealth as she does already in exterior and, what is far better" (for Sterne is nothing without his morality), "in interior merit. This nobleman is an old friend of mine. You know he was always the protector of men of wit and genius, and has had those of the last century, Addison, Steele, Pope, Swift, Prior, &c., always at his table. The manner in which his notice began of me was as singular as it was polite. He came up to me one day as I was at the Princess of Wales's Court, and said, 'I want to know you, Mr. Sterne, but it is fit you also should know who it is that wishes this pleasure. You have heard of an old Lord Bathurst, of whom your Popes and Swifts have sung and spoken so much? I have lived my life with geniuses of that cast; but have survived them; and, despairing ever to find their equals, it is some years since I have shut up my books and closed my accounts; but you have kindled a desire in me of opening them once more before I die: which I now do: so go home and dine with me.' This nobleman, I say, is a prodigy, for he has all the wit and promptness of a man of thirty; a disposition to be pleased, and a power to please others, beyond whatever I knew: added to which a man of learning, courtesy, and feeling.

"He heard me talk of thee, Eliza, with uncommon satisfaction—for there was only a third person, *and of sensibility*, with us: and a most sentimental afternoon till nine o'clock have we passed! *

* "I am glad that you are in love: 'twill cure you at least of the spleen, which has a bad effect on both man and woman. I myself must ever have some Dulcinea in my head; it harmonises the soul; and in these cases I first endeavour to make the lady believe so, or rather, I begin first to make myself believe that I am in love; but I carry on my affairs quite in the French way, sentimentally: 'L'amour,' say they, 'n'est rien sans sentiment.' Now, notwithstanding they make such a pother about the *word*, they have no precise idea annexed to it. And so much for that same subject called love."—STERNE'S *Letters:* May 23, 1765.

"*P.S.*—My *Sentimental Journey* will please Mrs. J(ames) and my Lydia" [his daughter, afterwards Mrs. Medalle]—"I can answer for those two. It is a subject which works well, and suits the frame of mind I have been in for some time past. I told you my design in it was to teach us to love the world and our fellow-creatures better than we do—so it runs most upon those gentler passions and affections which aid so much to it."—*Letters* [1767].

LORD BATHURST INTRODUCES HIMSELF TO MR. STERNE.

But thou, Eliza, wert the star that conducted and enlivened the discourse! And when I talked not of thee, still didst thou fill my mind, and warm every thought I uttered, for I am not ashamed to acknowledge I greatly miss thee. Best of all good girls!—the sufferings I have sustained all night in consequence of thine, Eliza, are beyond the power of words. . . . And so thou hast fixed thy Bramin's portrait over thy writing-desk, and wilt consult it in all doubts and difficulties?—Grateful and good girl! Yorick smiles contentedly over all thou dost: his picture does not do justice to his own complacency. I am glad your shipmates are friendly beings" (Eliza was at Deal, going back to the Councillor at Bombay, and indeed it was high time she should be off). "You could least dispense with what is contrary to your own nature, which is soft and gentle, Eliza; it would civilise savages—though pity were it thou shouldst be tainted with the office. Write to me, my child, thy delicious letters. Let them speak the easy carelessness of a heart that opens itself anyhow, everyhow. Such, Eliza, I write to thee!" (The artless rogue, of course he did!) "And so I should ever love thee, most artlessly, most affectionately, if Providence permitted thy residence in the same section of the globe: for I am all that honour and affection can make me 'THY BRAMIN.'"

The Bramin continues addressing Mrs. Draper until the departure of the *Earl of Chatham* Indiaman from Deal, on the 3rd of April 1767. He is amiably anxious about the fresh paint for Eliza's cabin; he is uncommonly solicitous about her companions on board:—

"I fear the best of your shipmates are only genteel by comparison with the contrasted crew with which thou beholdest them. So was—you know who—from the same fallacy which was put upon your judgment when—but I will not mortify you!"

"You know who" was, of course, Daniel Draper, Esquire, of Bombay—a gentleman very much respected in that quarter of the globe, and about whose probable health our worthy Bramin writes with delightful candour:—

"I honour you, Eliza, for keeping secret some things which, if explained, had been a panegyric on yourself. There is a dignity in venerable affliction which will not allow it to appeal to the world for pity or redress. Well have you supported that character, my amiable, my philosophic friend! And, indeed, I begin to think you have as many virtues as my Uncle Toby's widow. Talking of widows—pray, Eliza, if ever you are such, do not think of giving yourself to some wealthy Nabob, because I design to marry you myself. My wife cannot live long, and I know not the woman I should like so well for her substitute as yourself. 'Tis true I am ninety-five in constitution, and you but twenty-five; but what I want in youth, I will make up in wit and good-humour. Not Swift so loved his Stella, Scarron his Maintenon, or Waller his Saccharissa. Tell me, in answer to this, that you approve and honour the proposal."

Approve and honour the proposal! The coward was writing gay letters to his friends this while, with sneering allusions to this poor foolish *Bramine.* Her ship was not out of the Downs and the charming Sterne was at the "Mount Coffee-house," with a sheet of gilt-edged paper before him, offering that precious treasure his heart to Lady P——,* asking whether it gave her pleasure to see him unhappy? whether it added to her triumph that her eyes and lips had turned a man into a fool?—quoting the Lord's Prayer, with a horrible baseness of blasphemy, as a proof that he had desired not to be led into temptation, and swearing himself the most tender and sincere fool in the world. It was from his home at Coxwold that he wrote the Latin Letter, which, I suppose, he was ashamed to put into English. I find in my copy of the Letters that there is a note of, I can't call it admiration, at Letter 112, which seems to announce that there was a No. 3 to whom the wretched worn-out old scamp was paying his addresses; † and the year after, having come back to his lodgings in Bond Street, with his "Sentimental Journey" to launch upon the town, eager as ever

* [*i.e.* Lady Percy, daughter of Lord Bute.]

† *To Mrs. H——.*

"COXWOULD: *Nov.* 15, 1767.

"Now be a good dear woman, my H——, and execute those commissions well, and when I see you I will give you a kiss—there's for you! But I have something else for you which I am fabricating at a great rate, and that is my 'Sentimental Journey,' which shall make you cry as much as it has affected me, or I will give up the business of sentimental writing. . . .

"I am yours, &c. &c.,

"T. SHANDY."

To the Earl of ——.

"COXWOULD: *Nov.* 28, 1767.

"MY LORD,—'Tis with the greatest pleasure I take my pen to thank your lordship for your letter of inquiry about Yorick: he was worn out, both his spirits and body, with the 'Sentimental Journey.' 'Tis true, then, an author must feel himself, or his reader will not; but I have torn my whole frame into pieces by my feelings: I believe the brain stands as much in need of recruiting

for praise and pleasure—as vain, as wicked, as witty, as false as he had ever been—death at length seized the feeble wretch, and on the 18th of March 1768, that "bale of cadaverous goods," as he calls his body, was consigned to Pluto.* In his last letter there is one sign of grace—the real affection with which he entreats a friend to be a guardian to his daughter Lydia. All his letters to her are artless, kind, affectionate, and *not* sentimental; as a hundred pages in his writings are beautiful, and full, not of surprising humour merely, but of genuine love and kindness. A perilous trade, indeed, is that of a man who has to bring his tears and laughter, his recol-

as the body. Therefore I shall set out for town the twentieth of next month, after having recruited myself a week at York. I might indeed solace myself with my wife (who is come from France); but, in fact, I have long been a sentimental being, whatever your lordship may think to the contrary."

[From April to August 1767, Sterne wrote a "Journal to Eliza," which he called the "Bramine's Journal," and described as a "diary of the miserable feelings of a person separated from a lady for whose society he languished." It has never been printed. It was bequeathed to the British Museum by Mr. Thomas Washbourne Gibbs, of Bath, who, in 1851, showed it to Thackeray with a view to this lecture. Thackeray returned it without using it, and told the owner that it made him think worse of Sterne than any of the published writings.]

* "In February 1768, Laurence Sterne, his frame exhausted by long debilitating illness, expired at his lodgings in Bond Street, London. There was something in the manner of his death singularly resembling the particulars detailed by *Mrs. Quickly* as attending that of *Falstaff*, the compeer of *Yorick*, for infinite jest, however unlike in other particulars. As he lay on his bed totally exhausted, he complained that his feet were cold, and requested the female attendant to chafe them. She did so, and it seemed to relieve him. He complained that the cold came up higher; and whilst the assistant was in the act of chafing his ankles and legs, he expired without a groan. It was also remarkable that his death took place much in the manner which he himself had wished; and that the last offices were rendered him, not in his own house, or by the hand of kindred affection, but in an inn, and by strangers.

"We are well acquainted with Sterne's features and personal appearance, to which he himself frequently alludes. He was tall and thin, with a hectic and consumptive appearance."—*Sir Walter Scott.*

"It is known that Sterne died in hired lodgings, and I have been told that his attendants robbed him even of his gold sleeve-buttons while he was expiring." —*Dr. Ferriar.*

"He died at No. 41 (now a cheesemonger's), on the west side of Old Bond Street."—*Handbook of London.* [At Sterne's death it is said to have been a "silk-bag shop"; it is now Agnew's Picture Gallery. At his death, John Crawford of Erroll, who was entertaining some of Sterne's friends, sent a footman to James Macdonald to inquire after his health. Macdonald, who published memoirs, was sent to Sterne's bedside, and heard the dying man say, "Now it has come." A few minutes later he was dead. He was buried in St. George's burial-ground in the Bayswater Road, which has recently been put in order.]

lections, his personal griefs and joys, his private thoughts and feelings to market, to write them on paper, and sell them for money. Does he exaggerate his grief, so as to get his reader's pity for a false sensibility? feign indignation, so as to establish a character for virtue? elaborate repartees, so that he may pass for a wit? steal from other authors, and put down the theft to the credit side of his own reputation for ingenuity and learning? feign originality? affect benevolence or misanthropy? appeal to the gallery gods with claptraps and vulgar baits to catch applause?

How much of the paint and emphasis is necessary for the fair business of the stage, and how much of the rant and rouge is put on for the vanity of the actor? His audience trusts him: can he trust himself? How much was deliberate calculation and imposture—how much was false sensibility—and how much true feeling? Where did the lie begin, and did he know where? and where did the truth end in the art and scheme of this man of genius, this actor, this quack? Some time since, I was in the company of a French actor who began after dinner, and at his own request, to sing French songs of the sort called *des chansons grivoises*, and which he performed admirably, and to the dissatisfaction of most persons present. Having finished these, he commenced a sentimental ballad—it was so charmingly sung that it touched all persons present, and especially the singer himself, whose voice trembled, whose eyes filled with emotion, and who was snivelling and weeping quite genuine tears by the time his own ditty was over. I suppose Sterne had this artistical sensibility; he used to blubber perpetually in his study, and finding his tears infectious, and that they brought him a great popularity, he exercised the lucrative gift of weeping: he utilised it, and cried on every occasion. I own that I don't value or respect much the cheap dribble of those fountains. He fatigues me with his perpetual disquiet and his uneasy appeals to my risible or sentimental faculties. He is always looking in my face, watching his effect, uncertain whether I think him an impostor or not; posture-making, coaxing, and imploring me. "See what sensibility I have—own now that I'm very clever—do cry now, you can't resist this." The humour of Swift and Rabelais, whom he pretended to succeed, poured from them as naturally as song does from a bird; they lose no manly dignity with it, but laugh their hearty great laugh out of their broad chests as nature bade them. But this man—who can make you laugh, who can make you cry too—never lets his reader alone, or will permit his audience repose: when you are quiet, he fancies he must rouse you, and turns over head and heels, or sidles up and whispers a nasty story. The man is a great jester, not a great humourist. He goes to work systematically and of cold blood; paints his face, puts on his ruff and motley clothes, and lays down his carpet and tumbles on it.

For instance, take the "Sentimental Journey," and see in the writer the deliberate propensity to make points and seek applause. He gets to "Dessein's Hotel," he wants a carriage to travel to Paris, he goes to the inn-yard, and begins what the actors call "business" at once. There is that little carriage (the *désobligeante*).

"Four months had elapsed since it had finished its career of Europe in the corner of Monsieur Dessein's coach-yard, and having sallied out thence but a vamped-up business at first, though it had been twice taken to pieces on Mont Cenis, it had not profited much by its adventures, but by none so little as the standing so many months unpitied in the corner of Monsieur Dessein's coach-yard. Much, indeed, was not to be said for it—but something might—and when a few words will rescue misery out of her distress, I hate the man who can be a churl of them."

Le tour est fait! Paillasse has tumbled! Paillasse has jumped over the *désobligeante*, cleared it, hood and all, and bows to the noble company. Does anybody believe that this is a real Sentiment? that this luxury of generosity, this gallant rescue of Misery—out of an old cab, is genuine feeling? It is as genuine as the virtuous oratory of Joseph Surface when he begins, "The man who," &c. &c., and wishes to pass off for a saint with his credulous, good-humoured dupes.

Our friend purchases the carriage: after turning that notorious old monk to good account, and effecting (like a soft and good-natured Paillasse as he was, and very free with his money when he had it) an exchange of snuffboxes with the old Franciscan, jogs out of Calais; sets down in immense figures on the credit side of his account the sous he gives away to the Montreuil beggars; and, at Nampont, gets out of the chaise and whimpers over that famous dead donkey, for which any sentimentalist may cry who will. It is agreeably and skilfully done—that dead jackass: like Monsieur de Soubise's cook on the campaign, Sterne dresses it, and serves it up quite tender and with a very piquant sauce. But tears and fine feelings, and a white pocket-handkerchief, and a funeral sermon, and horses and feathers, and a procession of mutes, and a hearse with a dead donkey inside! Psha, mountebank! I'll not give thee one penny more for that trick, donkey and all!

This donkey had appeared once before with signal effect. In 1765, three years before the publication of the "Sentimental Journey," the seventh and eighth volumes of "Tristram Shandy" were given to the world, and the famous Lyons donkey makes his entry in those volumes (pp. 315, 316):—

"'Twas by a poor ass, with a couple of large panniers at his back, who had just turned in to collect eleemosynary turnip-tops and cabbage-leaves, and stood dubious, with his two forefeet at the inside of the threshold, and with his two hinder feet towards the street, as not knowing very well whether he was to go in or no.

"Now 'tis an animal (be in what hurry I may) I cannot bear to strike: there is a patient endurance of suffering wrote so unaffectedly in his looks and carriage which pleads so mightily for him, that it always disarms me, and to that degree that I do not like to speak unkindly to him: on the contrary, meet him where I will, whether in town or country, in cart or under panniers, whether in liberty or bondage, I have ever something civil to say to him on my part; and, as one word begets another (if he has as little to do as I), I generally fall into conversation with him; and surely never is my imagination so busy as in framing responses from the etchings of his countenance; and where those carry me not deep enough, in flying from my own heart into his, and seeing what is natural for an ass to think—as well as a man, upon the occasion. In truth, it is the only creature of all the classes of beings below me with whom I can do this. . . . With an ass I can commune for ever.

"'Come, Honesty,' said I, seeing it was impracticable to pass betwixt him and the gate, 'art thou for coming in or going out?'

"The ass twisted his head round to look up the street.

"'Well!' replied I, 'we'll wait a minute for thy driver.'

"He turned his head thoughtfully about, and looked wistfully the opposite way.

"'I understand thee perfectly,' answered I: 'if thou takest a wrong step in this affair, he will cudgel thee to death. Well! a minute is but a minute; and if it saves a fellow-creature a drubbing, it shall not be set down as ill spent.'

"He was eating the stem of an artichoke as this discourse went on, and, in the little peevish contentions between hunger and unsavouriness, had dropped it out of his mouth half-a-dozen times, and had picked it up again. 'God help thee, Jack!' said I, 'thou hast a bitter breakfast on't—and many a bitter day's labour, and many a bitter blow, I fear, for its wages! 'Tis all, all bitterness to thee—whatever life is to others! And now thy mouth, if one knew the truth of it, is as bitter, I dare say, as soot' (for he had cast aside the stem), 'and thou hast not a friend perhaps in all this world that will give thee a macaroon.' In saying this, I pulled out a paper of 'em, which I had just bought, and gave him one; and at this moment that I am telling it, my heart smites me that there was more of pleasantry in the conceit of seeing *how* an ass would eat a macaroon than of benevolence in giving him one, which presided in the act.

"When the ass had eaten his macaroon, I pressed him to come in. The poor beast was heavy loaded—his legs seemed to tremble under him—he hung rather backwards, and, as I pulled at his halter, it broke in my hand. He looked up pensive in my face: 'Don't thrash me with it; but if you will you may.' 'If I do,' said I, 'I'll be d——.'"

A critic who refuses to see in this charming description wit, humour, pathos, a kind nature speaking, and a real sentiment, must be hard indeed to move and to please. A page or two farther we come to a description not less beautiful—a landscape and figures, deliciously painted by one who had the keenest enjoyment and the most tremulous sensibility:—

"'Twas in the road between Nismes and Lunel, where is the best Muscatto wine in all France: the sun was set, they had done their work: the nymphs had tied up their hair afresh, and the swains were preparing for a carousal. My mule made a dead point. ''Tis the pipe and tambourine,' said I—'I never will argue a point with one of your family as long as I live;' so leaping off his back, and kicking off one boot into this ditch and t'other into that, 'I'll take a dance,' said I, 'so stay you here.'

"A sunburnt daughter of labour rose up from the group to meet me as I advanced towards them; her hair, which was of a dark chestnut approaching to a black, was tied up in a knot, all but a single tress.

"'We want a cavalier,' said she, holding out both her hands, as if to offer them. 'And a cavalier you shall have,' said I, taking hold of both of them. 'We could not have done without you,' said she, letting go one hand, with self-taught politeness, and leading me up with the other.

"A lame youth, whom Apollo had recompensed with a pipe, and to which he had added a tambourine of his own accord, ran sweetly over the prelude, as he sat upon the bank. 'Tie me up this tress instantly,' said Nannette, putting a piece of string into my hand. It taught me to forget I was a stranger. The whole knot fell down—we had been seven years acquainted. The youth struck the note upon the tambourine, his pipe followed, and off we bounded.

"The sister of the youth—who had stolen her voice from heaven—sang alternately with her brother. 'Twas a Gascoigne roundelay: '*Viva la joia, fidon la tristessa.*' The nymphs joined in unison, and their swains an octave below them.

"*Viva la joia* was in Nannette's lips, *viva la joia* in her eyes. A transient spark of amity shot across the space betwixt us. She looked amiable. Why could I not live and end my days thus? 'Just Disposer of our joys and sorrows!' cried I, 'why could not a man sit down in the lap of content here, and dance, and sing, and say his prayers, and go to heaven with this nut-brown maid?' Capriciously did she bend her head on one side, and dance up insidious. 'Then 'tis time to dance off,' quoth I."

And with this pretty dance and chorus, the volume artfully concludes. Even here one can't give the whole description. There is not a page in Sterne's writing but has something that were better away, a latent corruption—a hint, as of an impure presence.*

Some of that dreary *double entendre* may be attributed to freer times and manners than ours, but not all. The foul satyr's eyes

* "With regard to Sterne, and the charge of licentiousness which presses so seriously upon his character as a writer, I would remark that there is a sort of knowingness, the wit of which depends, 1st, on the modesty it gives pain to; or, 2ndly, on the innocence and innocent ignorance over which it triumphs; or, 3rdly, on a certain oscillation in the individual's own mind between the remaining good and the encroaching evil of his nature—a sort of dallying with the devil—a fluxionary art of combining courage and cowardice, as when a man snuffs a candle with his fingers for the first time, or better still, perhaps, like that trembling daring with which a child touches a hot tea-urn, because it has been forbidden; so that the mind has its own white and black angel; the same or similar amusement as may be supposed to take place between an old debauchee and a prude—the feeling resentment, on the one hand, from a prudential anxiety to preserve appearances and have a character; and, on the other, an inward sympathy with the enemy. We have only to suppose society innocent, and then nine-tenths of this sort of wit would be like a stone that falls in snow, making no sound, because exciting no resistance; the remainder rests on its being an offence against the good manners of human nature itself.

"This source, unworthy as it is, may doubtless be combined with wit, drollery, fancy, and even humour; and we have only to regret the misalliance; but that the latter are quite distinct from the former, may be made evident by abstracting in our imagination the morality of the characters of Mr. Shandy, my Uncle Toby, and Trim, which are all antagonists to this spurious sort of wit, from the rest of 'Tristram Shandy,' and by supposing, instead of them, the presence of two or three callous debauchees. The result will be pure disgust. Sterne cannot be too severely censured for thus using the best dispositions of our nature as the panders and condiments for the basest."—COLERIDGE. *Literary Remains*, vol. i. pp. 141, 142.

leer out of the leaves constantly: the last words the famous author wrote were bad and wicked—the last lines the poor stricken wretch penned were for pity and pardon. I think of these past writers and of one who lives amongst us now, and am grateful for the innocent laughter and the sweet and unsullied page which the author of "David Copperfield" gives to my children.

"Jeté sur cette boule,
Laid, chétif et souffrant;
Etouffé dans la foule,
Faute d'être assez grand:

Une plainte touchante
De ma bouche sortit.
Le bon Dieu me dit: Chante,
Chante, pauvre petit!

Chanter ou je m'abuse,
Est ma tâche ici-bas.
Tous ceux qu'ainsi j'amuse
Ne m'aimeront-ils pas?"

In those charming lines of Béranger, one may fancy described the career, the sufferings, the genius, the gentle nature of GOLDSMITH, and the esteem in which we hold him. Who, of the millions whom he has amused, doesn't love him? To be the most beloved of English writers, what a title that is for a man! * A wild youth, wayward, but full of tenderness and affection, quits the country village, where his boyhood has been passed in happy musing, in idle shelter, in fond longing to see the great world out of doors, and achieve name and fortune: and after years of dire struggle, and neglect and poverty, his heart turning back as fondly to his native place as it had longed eagerly for change when sheltered there, he writes a book and a poem, full of the recollections and feelings of home: he paints the friends and scenes of his youth, and

* "He was a friend to virtue, and in his most playful pages never forgets what is due to it. A gentleness, delicacy, and purity of feeling distinguishes whatever he wrote, and bears a correspondence to the generosity of a disposition which knew no bounds but his last guinea. . . .

"The admirable ease and grace of the narrative, as well as the pleasing truth with which the principal characters are designed, make the 'Vicar of Wakefield' one of the most delicious morsels of fictitious composition on which the human mind was ever employed.

". . . We read the 'Vicar of Wakefield' in youth and in age—we return to it again and again, and bless the memory of an author who contrives so well to reconcile us to human nature."—*Sir Walter Scott.*

peoples Auburn and Wakefield with remembrances of Lissoy. Wander he must, but he carries away a home-relic with him, and dies with it on his breast. His nature is truant; in repose it longs for change: as on the journey it looks back for friends and quiet. He passes to-day in building an air-castle for to-morrow, or in writing yesterday's elegy; and he would fly away this hour, but that a cage and necessity keep him. What is the charm of his verse, of his style, and humour? His sweet regrets, his delicate compassion, his soft smile, his tremulous sympathy, the weakness which he owns? Your love for him is half pity. You come hot and tired from the day's battle, and this sweet minstrel sings to you. Who could harm the kind vagrant harper? Whom did he ever hurt? He carries no weapon, save the harp on which he plays to you; and with which he delights great and humble, young and old, the captains in the tents, or the soldiers round the fire, or the women and children in the villages, at whose porches he stops and sings his simple songs of love and beauty. With that sweet story of the "Vicar of Wakefield" * he has found entry into every castle and every hamlet

* "Now Herder came," says Goethe in his Autobiography, relating his first acquaintance with Goldsmith's masterpiece, "and together with his great knowledge brought many other aids, and the later publications besides. Among these he announced to us the 'Vicar of Wakefield' as an excellent work, with the German translation of which he would make us acquainted by reading it aloud to us himself. . . .

"A Protestant country clergyman is perhaps the most beautiful subject for a modern idyl; he appears like Melchizedeck, as priest and king in one person. To the most innocent situation which can be imagined on earth, to that of a husbandman, he is, for the most part, united by similarity of occupation as well as by equality in family relationships; he is a father, a master of a family, an agriculturist, and thus perfectly a member of the community. On this pure, beautiful earthly foundation rests his higher calling; to him is it given to guide men through life, to take care of their spiritual education, to bless them at all the leading epochs of their existence, to instruct, to strengthen, to console them, and, if consolation is not sufficient for the present, to call up and guarantee the hope of a happier future. Imagine such a man with pure human sentiments, strong enough not to deviate from them under any circumstances, and by this already elevated above the multitude of whom one cannot expect purity and firmness; give him the learning necessary for his office, as well as a cheerful, equable activity, which is even passionate, as it neglects no moment to do good—and you will have him well endowed. But at the same time add the necessary limitation, so that he must not only pause in a small circle, but may also, perchance, pass over to a smaller; grant him good-nature, placability, resolution, and everything else praiseworthy that springs from a decided character, and over all this a cheerful spirit of compliance, and a smiling toleration of his own failings and those of others,—then you will have put together pretty well the image of our excellent Wakefield.

"The delineation of this character on his course of life through joys and sorrows, the ever-increasing interest of the story, by the combination of the

in Europe. Not one of us, however busy or hard, but once or twice in our lives has passed an evening with him, and undergone the charm of his delightful music.

Goldsmith's father was no doubt the good Doctor Primrose, whom we all of us know.* Swift was yet alive, when the little Oliver

entirely natural with the strange and the singular, make this novel one of the best which have ever been written; besides this, it has the great advantage that it is quite moral, nay, in a pure sense, Christian—represents the reward of a good-will and perseverance in the right, strengthens an unconditional confidence in God, and attests the final triumph of good over evil; and all this without a trace of cant or pedantry. The author was preserved from both of these by an elevation of mind that shows itself throughout in the form of irony, by which this little work must appear to us as wise as it is amiable. The author, Dr. Goldsmith, has, without question, a great insight into the moral world, into its strength and its infirmities; but at the same time he can thankfully acknowledge that he is an Englishman, and reckon highly the advantages which his country and his nation afford him. The family, with the delineation of which he occupies himself, stands upon one of the last steps of citizen comfort, and yet comes in contact with the highest; its narrow circle, which becomes still more contracted, touches upon the great world through the natural and civil course of things; this little skiff floats on the agitated waves of English life, and in weal or woe it has to expect injury or help from the vast fleet which sails around it.

"I may suppose that my readers know this work, and have it in memory; whoever hears it named for the first time here, as well as he who is induced to read it again, will thank me."—GOETHE. *Truth and Poetry; from my own Life.* (English Translation, vol. i. pp. 378, 379.)

"He seems from infancy to have been compounded of two natures, one bright, the other blundering; or to have had fairy gifts laid in his cradle by the 'good people' who haunted his birthplace, the old goblin mansion on the banks of the Inny. "He carries with him the wayward elfin spirit, if we may so term it, throughout his career. His fairy gifts are of no avail at school, academy, or college: they unfit him for close study and practical science, and render him heedless of everything that does not address itself to his poetical imagination and genial and festive feelings; they dispose him to break away from restraint, to stroll about hedges, green lanes, and haunted streams, to revel with jovial companions, or to rove the country like a gipsy in quest of odd adventures. . . . Though his circumstances often compelled him to associate with the poor, they never could betray him into companionship with the depraved. His relish for humour, and for the study of character, as we have before observed, brought him often into convivial company of a vulgar kind; but he discriminated between their vulgarity and their amusing qualities, or rather wrought from the whole store familiar features of life which form the staple of his most popular writings." —*Washington Irving.*

* "The family of Goldsmith, Goldsmyth, or, as it was occasionally written, Gouldsmith, is of considerable standing in Ireland, and seems always to have held a respectable station in society. Its origin is English, supposed to be derived from that which was long settled at Crayford in Kent."—PRIOR'S *Life of Goldsmith.*

Oliver's father, great-grandfather, and great-great-grandfather were clergymen; and two of them married clergymen's daughters.

was born at Pallas, or Pallasmore, in the county of Longford, in Ireland. In 1730, two years after the child's birth, Charles Goldsmith removed his family to Lissoy, in the county Westmeath, that sweet "Auburn" which every person who hears me has seen in fancy. Here the kind parson * brought up his eight children; and loving all the world, as his son says, fancied all the world loved him. He had a crowd of poor dependants besides those hungry children. He kept an open table; round which sat flatterers and poor friends, who laughed at the honest rector's many jokes, and ate the produce of his seventy acres of farm. Those who have seen an Irish house in the present day can fancy that one of Lissoy. The old beggar still has his allotted corner by the kitchen turf; the maimed old soldier still gets his potatoes and buttermilk; the poor cottier still asks his honour's charity, and prays God bless his reverence for the sixpence; the ragged pensioner still takes his place by right and sufferance. There's still a crowd in the kitchen, and a crowd round the parlour table, profusion, confusion, kindness, poverty. If an Irishman comes to London to make his fortune, he has a half-dozen of Irish dependants who take a percentage of his earnings. The good Charles Goldsmith † left but little provision for his hungry race when death summoned him; and one of his

* "At church, with meek and unaffected grace,
His looks adorn'd the venerable place;
Truth from his lips prevail'd with double sway,
And fools who came to scoff remain'd to pray.
The service past, around the pious man,
With steady zeal each honest rustic ran;
E'en children follow'd with endearing wile,
And pluck'd his gown to share the good man's smile.
His ready smile a parent's warmth exprest,
Their welfare pleased him, and their cares distrest;
To them his heart, his love, his griefs were given,
But all his serious thoughts had rest in heaven.
As some tall cliff that lifts its awful form,
Swells from the vale, and midway leaves the storm,
Though round its breast the rolling clouds are spread,
Eternal sunshine settles on its head."—*The Deserted Village.*

† "In May this year (1768), he lost his brother, the Rev. Henry Goldsmith, for whom he had been unable to obtain preferment in the Church. . . .

". . . To the curacy of Kilkenny West, the moderate stipend of which, forty pounds a year, is sufficiently celebrated by his brother's lines. It has been stated that Mr. Goldsmith added a school, which, after having been held at more than one place in the vicinity, was finally fixed at Lissoy. Here his talents and industry gave it celebrity, and under his care the sons of many of the neighbouring gentry received their education. A fever breaking out among the boys about 1765, they dispersed for a time, but re-assembling at Athlone,

daughters being engaged to a Squire of rather superior dignity, Charles Goldsmith impoverished the rest of his family to provide the girl with a dowry.

The smallpox, which scourged all Europe at that time, and ravaged the roses off the cheeks of half the world, fell foul of poor little Oliver's face, when the child was eight years old, and left him scarred and disfigured for his life. An old woman in his father's village taught him his letters, and pronounced him a dunce: Paddy Byrne, the hedge-schoolmaster, took him in hand: and from Paddy Byrne he was transmitted to a clergyman at Elphin. When a child was sent to school in those days, the classic phrase was that he was placed under Mr. So-and-so's *ferule*. Poor little ancestors! It is hard to think how ruthlessly you were birched; and how much of needless whipping and tears our small forefathers had to undergo! A relative—kind uncle Contarine—took the main charge of little Noll; who went through his schooldays righteously doing as little work as he could: robbing orchards, playing at ball, and making his pocket-money fly about whenever fortune sent it to him. Everybody knows the story of that famous "Mistake of a Night," when the young schoolboy, provided with a guinea and a nag, rode up to the "best house" in Ardagh, called for the landlord's company over a bottle of wine at supper, and for a hot cake for breakfast in the morning; and found, when he asked for the bill, that the best house was Squire Featherstone's, and not the inn for which he mistook it. Who does not know every story about Goldsmith? That is a delightful and fantastic picture of the child dancing and capering about in the kitchen at home, when the old fiddler gibed at him for his ugliness, and called him Æsop; and little Noll made his repartee of "Heralds proclaim aloud this saying—See Æsop dancing and his monkey playing." One can fancy a queer pitiful look of humour and appeal upon that little scarred face—the funny little dancing figure, the funny little brogue. In his life, and his writings, which are the honest expression of it, he is constantly bewailing that homely face and person; anon he surveys them in the glass ruefully; and presently assumes the most comical

he continued his scholastic labours there until the time of his death, which happened, like that of his brother, about the forty-fifth year of his age. He was a man of an excellent heart and an amiable disposition."—PRIOR'S *Goldsmith*.

> "Where'er I roam, whatever realms to see,
> My heart, untravell'd, fondly turns to thee:
> Still to my brother turns with ceaseless pain,
> And drags at each remove a lengthening chain."
>
> —*The Traveller.*

dignity. He likes to deck out his little person in splendour and fine colours. He presented himself to be examined for ordination in a pair of scarlet breeches, and said honestly that he did not like to go into the Church, because he was fond of coloured clothes. When he tried to practise as a doctor, he got by hook or by crook a black velvet suit, and looked as big and grand as he could, and kept his hat over a patch on the old coat: in better days he bloomed out in plum-colour, in blue silk, and in new velvet. For some of those splendours the heirs and assignees of Mr. Filby, the tailor, have never been paid to this day: perhaps the kind tailor and his creditor have met and settled their little account in Hades.*

They showed until lately a window at Trinity College,† Dublin, on which the name of O. Goldsmith was engraved with a diamond. Whose diamond was it? Not the young sizar's, who made but a poor figure in that place of learning. He was idle, penniless, and fond of pleasure: ‡ he learned his way early to the pawnbroker's shop. He wrote ballads, they say, for the street-singers, who paid him a crown for a poem: and his pleasure was to steal out at night and hear his verses sung. He was chastised by his tutor for giving a dance in his rooms, and took the box on the ear so much to heart, that he packed up his all, pawned his books and little property, and disappeared from college and family. He said he intended to go to America, but when his money was spent, the young prodigal came home ruefully, and the good folks there killed their calf—it was but a lean one—and welcomed him back.

After college he hung about his mother's house, and lived for some years the life of a buckeen—passed a month with this relation and that, a year with one patron, a great deal of time at the public-house.§ Tired of this life, it was resolved that he should go to London, and study at the Temple; but he got no farther on the road to London and the woolsack than Dublin, where he gambled

* "When Goldsmith died, half the unpaid bill he owed to Mr. William Filby (amounting in all to £79) was for clothes supplied to this nephew Hodson."—FORSTER'S *Goldsmith*, p. 520.

As this nephew Hodson ended his days (see the same page) "a prosperous Irish gentleman," it is not unreasonable to wish that he had cleared off Mr. Filby's bill.

† [The pane is still preserved in the library of Trinity College.]

‡ "Poor fellow! He hardly knew an ass from a mule, nor a turkey from a goose, but when he saw it on the table."—CUMBERLAND'S *Memoirs*.

§ "These youthful follies, like the fermentation of liquors, often disturb the mind only in order to its future refinement: a life spent in phlegmatic apathy resembles those liquors which never ferment, and are consequently always muddy."—GOLDSMITH. *Memoir of Voltaire*.

"He [Johnson] said 'Goldsmith was a plant that flowered late. There appeared nothing remarkable about him when he was young.'"—*Boswell*.

away the fifty pounds given to him for his outfit, and whence he returned to the indefatigable forgiveness of home. Then he determined to be a doctor, and uncle Contarine helped him to a couple of years at Edinburgh. Then from Edinburgh he felt that he ought to hear the famous professors of Leyden and Paris, and wrote most amusing pompous letters to his uncle about the great Farheim, Du Petit, and Duhamel du Monceau, whose lectures he proposed to follow. If uncle Contarine believed those letters—if Oliver's mother believed that story which the youth related of his going to Cork, with the purpose of embarking for America, of his having paid his passage-money, and having sent his kit on board; of the anonymous captain sailing away with Oliver's valuable luggage in a nameless ship, never to return; if uncle Contarine and the mother at Ballymahon believed his stories, they must have been a very simple pair; as it was a very simple rogue indeed who cheated them. When the lad, after failing in his clerical examination, after failing in his plan for studying the law, took leave of these projects and of his parents, and set out for Edinburgh, he saw mother, and uncle, and lazy Ballymahon, and green native turf, and sparkling river for the last time. He was never to look on old Ireland more, and only in fancy revisit her.

"But me not destined such delights to share,
My prime of life in wandering spent and care,
Impelled, with steps unceasing to pursue
Some fleeting good that mocks me with the view;
That like the circle bounding earth and skies
Allures from far, yet, as I follow, flies:
My fortune leads to traverse realms alone,
And find no spot of all the world my own."

I spoke in a former lecture of that high courage which enabled Fielding, in spite of disease, remorse, and poverty, always to retain a cheerful spirit and to keep his manly benevolence and love of truth intact, as if these treasures had been confided to him for the public benefit, and he was accountable to posterity for their honourable employ; and a constancy equally happy and admirable I think was shown by Goldsmith, whose sweet and friendly nature bloomed kindly always in the midst of a life's storm, and rain, and bitter weather.* The poor fellow was never so friendless but he could

* "An 'inspired idiot,' Goldsmith, hangs strangely about him [Johnson]. . . . Yet, on the whole, there is no evil in the 'gooseberry fool,' but rather much good; of a finer, if of a weaker sort than Johnson's; and all the more genuine that he himself could never become *conscious* of it,—though unhappily never cease *attempting* to become so: the author of the genuine 'Vicar of Wakefield,' nill he will he, must needs fly towards such a mass of genuine manhood."—CARLYLE's *Essays* (2nd ed.), vol. iv. p. 91.

befriend some one; never so pinched and wretched but he could give of his crust, and speak his word of compassion. If he had but his flute left, he could give that, and make the children happy in the dreary London court. He could give the coals in that queer coal-scuttle we read of to his poor neighbour: he could give away his blankets in college to the poor widow, and warm himself as he best might in the feathers: he could pawn his coat to save his landlord from gaol: when he was a school-usher he spent his earnings in treats for the boys, and the good-natured schoolmaster's wife said justly that she ought to keep Mr. Goldsmith's money as well as the young gentlemen's. When he met his pupils in later life, nothing would satisfy the Doctor but he must treat them still. "Have you seen the print of me after Sir Joshua Reynolds?" he asked of one of his old pupils. "Not seen it? not bought it? Sure, Jack, if your picture had been published, I'd not have been without it half-an-hour." His purse and his heart were everybody's, and his friends' as much as his own. When he was at the height of his reputation, and the Earl of Northumberland, going as Lord Lieutenant to Ireland, asked if he could be of any service to Doctor Goldsmith, Goldsmith recommended his brother, and not himself, to the great man. "My patrons," he gallantly said, "are the booksellers, and I want no others."* Hard patrons they were, and hard work he did; but he did not complain much: if in his early writings some bitter words escaped him, some allusions to neglect and poverty, he withdrew these expressions when his works were republished, and better days seemed to open for him; and he did not care to complain that printer or publisher had overlooked his merit, or left him poor. The Court face was turned from honest Oliver, the Court patronised Beattie;

* "At present, the few poets of England no longer depend on the great for subsistence; they have now no other patrons but the public, and the public, collectively considered, is a good and generous master. It is indeed too frequently mistaken as to the merits of every candidate for favour; but to make amends it is never mistaken long. A performance indeed may be forced for a time into reputation, but, destitute of real merit, it soon sinks; time, the touchstone of what is truly valuable, will soon discover the fraud, and an author should never arrogate to himself any share of success till his works have been read at least ten years with satisfaction.

"A man of letters at present, whose works are valuable, is perfectly sensible of their value. Every polite member of the community, by buying what he writes, contributes to reward him. The ridicule, therefore, of living in a garret might have been wit in the last age, but continues such no longer, because no longer true. A writer of real merit now may easily be rich, if his heart be set only on fortune; and for those who have no merit, it is but fit that such should remain in merited obscurity."—GOLDSMITH. *Citizen of the World*, Let. 84.

the fashion did not shine on him—fashion adored Sterne.* Fashion pronounced Kelly to be the great writer of comedy of his day. A little — not ill-humour, but plaintiveness — a little betrayal of wounded pride which he showed render him not the less amiable. The author of the "Vicar of Wakefield" had a right to protest when Newbery kept back the manuscript for two years; had a right to be a little peevish with Sterne; a little angry when Colman's actors declined their parts in his delightful comedy, when the manager refused to have a scene painted for it, and pronounced its damnation before hearing. He had not the great public with him; but he had the noble Johnson, and the admirable Reynolds, and the great Gibbon, and the great Burke, and the great Fox—friends and admirers illustrious indeed, as famous as those who, fifty years before, sat round Pope's table.

Nobody knows, and I dare say Goldsmith's buoyant temper kept no account of, all the pains which he endured during the early period of his literary career. Should any man of letters in our day have to bear up against such, Heaven grant he may come out of the period of misfortune with such a pure kind heart as that which Goldsmith obstinately bore in his breast. The insults to which he had to submit are shocking to read of—slander, contumely, vulgar satire, brutal malignity perverting his commonest motives and actions; he had his share of these, and one's anger is roused at reading of them, as it is at seeing a woman insulted or a child assaulted, at the notion that a creature so very gentle and weak,

* Goldsmith attacked Sterne obviously enough, censuring his indecency, and slighting his wit, and ridiculing his manner, in the 53rd letter in the "Citizen of the World."

"As in common conversation," says he, "the best way to make the audience laugh is by first laughing yourself; so in writing, the properest manner is to show an attempt at humour, which will pass upon most for humour in reality. To effect this, readers must be treated with the most perfect familiarity; in one page the author is to make them a low bow, and in the next to pull them by the nose; he must talk in riddles, and then send them to bed in order to dream for the solution," &c.

Sterne's humourous *mot* on the subject of the gravest part of the charges, then, as now, made against him, may perhaps be quoted here, from the excellent, the respectable Sir Walter Scott:—

"Soon after 'Tristram' had appeared, Sterne asked a Yorkshire lady of fortune and condition, whether she had read his book. 'I have not, Mr. Sterne,' was the answer; 'and to be plain with you, I am informed it is not proper for female perusal.' 'My dear good lady,' replied the author, 'do not be gulled by such stories; the book is like your young heir there' (pointing to a child of three years old, who was rolling on the carpet in his white tunic): 'he shows at times a good deal that is usually concealed, but it is all in perfect innocence.'"

and full of love, should have had to suffer so. And he had worse than insult to undergo—to own to fault and deprecate the anger of ruffians. There is a letter of his extant to one Griffiths, a bookseller, in which poor Goldsmith is forced to confess that certain books sent by Griffiths are in the hands of a friend from whom Goldsmith had been forced to borrow money. "He was wild, sir," Johnson said, speaking of Goldsmith to Boswell, with his great, wise benevolence and noble mercifulness of heart—"Dr. Goldsmith was wild, sir; but he is so no more." Ah! if we pity the good and weak man who suffers undeservedly, let us deal very gently with him from whom misery extorts not only tears, but shame; let us think humbly and charitably of the human nature that suffers so sadly and falls so low. Whose turn may it be to-morrow? What weak heart, confident before trial, may not succumb under temptation invincible? Cover the good man who has been vanquished—cover his face and pass on.

For the last half-dozen years of his life, Goldsmith was far removed from the pressure of any ignoble necessity: and in the receipt, indeed, of a pretty large income from the booksellers his patrons. Had he lived but a few years more, his public fame would have been as great as his private reputation, and he might have enjoyed alive a part of that esteem which his country has ever since paid to the vivid and versatile genius who has touched on almost every subject of literature, and touched nothing that he did not adorn. Except in rare instances, a man is known in our profession, and esteemed as a skilful workman, years before the lucky hit which trebles his usual gains, and stamps him a popular author. In the strength of his age, and the dawn of his reputation, having for backers and friends the most illustrious literary men of his time,* fame and prosperity might have been in store for Goldsmith, had fate so willed it, and, at forty-six, had not sudden disease carried him off. I say prosperity rather than competence, for it is probable that no sum could have put order into his affairs, or sufficed for his irreclaimable habits of dissipation. It must be remembered that he owed £2000 when he died. "Was ever poet," Johnson asked,

* "Goldsmith told us that he was now busy in writing a Natural History; and that he might have full leisure for it, he had taken lodgings at a farmer's house, near to the six-mile stone in the Edgware Road, and had carried down his books in two returned post-chaises. He said he believed the farmer's family thought him an odd character, similar to that in which the *Spectator* appeared to his landlady and her children; he was *The Gentleman*. Mr. Mickle, the translator of the *Lusiad*, and I, went to visit him at this place a few days afterwards. He was not at home; but having a curiosity to see his apartment, we went in, and found curious scraps of descriptions of animals scrawled upon the wall with a blacklead pencil."—*Boswell.*

"so trusted before?" As has been the case with many another good fellow of his nation, his life was tracked and his substance wasted by crowds of hungry beggars and lazy dependants. If they came at a lucky time (and be sure they knew his affairs better than he did himself, and watched his pay-day), he gave them of his money: if they begged on empty-purse days, he gave them his promissory bills: or he treated them to a tavern where he had credit; or he obliged them with an order upon honest Mr. Filby for coats, for which he paid as long as he could earn, and until the shears of Filby were to cut for him no more. Staggering under a load of debt and labour, tracked by bailiffs and reproachful creditors, running from a hundred poor dependants, whose appealing looks were perhaps the hardest of all pains for him to bear, devising fevered plans for the morrow, new histories, new comedies, all sorts of new literary schemes, flying from all these into seclusion, and out of seclusion into pleasure—at last, at five-and-forty, death seized him and closed his career.* I have been many a time in the chambers in the Temple which were his, and passed up the staircase, which Johnson and Burke and Reynolds trod to see their friend, their poet, their kind Goldsmith—the stair on which the poor women sat weeping bitterly when they heard that the greatest and most generous of all men was dead within the black oak door.† Ah! it was a different lot from that for which the poor fellow sighed, when he wrote with heart yearning for

* "When Goldsmith was dying, Dr. Turton said to him, 'Your pulse is in greater disorder than it should be, from the degree of fever which you have; is your mind at ease?' Goldsmith answered it was not."—*Dr. Johnson* (*in Boswell*).

"Chambers, you find, is gone far, and poor Goldsmith is gone much further. He died of a fever, exasperated, as I believe, by the fear of distress. He had raised money and squandered it, by every artifice of acquisition and folly of expense. But let not his failings be remembered; he was a very great man."—*Dr. Johnson* to *Boswell*, July 5th, 1774.

† "When Burke was told [of Goldsmith's death] he burst into tears. Reynolds was in his painting-room when the messenger went to him; but at once he laid his pencil aside, which in times of great family distress he had not been known to do, left his painting-room, and did not re-enter it that day. . . .

"The staircase of Brick Court is said to have been filled with mourners, the reverse of domestic; women without a home, without domesticity of any kind, with no friend but him they had come to weep for; outcasts of that great, solitary, wicked city, to whom he had never forgotten to be kind and charitable. And he had domestic mourners, too. His coffin was reopened at the request of Miss Horneck and her sister (such was the regard he was known to have for them!) that a lock might be cut from his hair. It was in Mrs. Gwyn's possession when she died, after nearly seventy years."—FORSTER'S *Goldsmith*.

home those most charming of all fond verses, in which he fancies he revisits Auburn:—

"Here, as I take my solitary rounds,
Amidst thy tangling walks and ruined grounds,
And, many a year elapsed, return to view
Where once the cottage stood, the hawthorn grew,
Remembrance wakes, with all her busy train,
Swells at my breast, and turns the past to pain.

In all my wanderings round this world of care,
In all my griefs—and God has given my share—
I still had hopes, my latest hours to crown,
Amidst these humble bowers to lay me down;
To husband out life's taper at the close,
And keep the flame from wasting by repose;
I still had hopes—for pride attends us still—
Amidst the swains to show my book-learned skill,
Around my fire an evening group to draw,
And tell of all I felt and all I saw;
And, as a hare, whom hounds and horns pursue,
Pants to the place from whence at first he flew—
I still had hopes, my long vexations past,
Here to return, and die at home at last.

O blest retirement, friend to life's decline!
Retreats from care that never must be mine—
How blest is he who crowns, in shades like these,
A youth of labour with an age of ease;
Who quits a world where strong temptations try,
And, since 'tis hard to combat, learns to fly!
For him no wretches born to work and weep
Explore the mine or tempt the dangerous deep;
No surly porter stands in guilty state
To spurn imploring famine from the gate:
But on he moves to meet his latter end,
Angels around befriending virtue's friend;
Sinks to the grave with unperceived decay,
Whilst resignation gently slopes the way;
And all his prospects brightening to the last,
His heaven commences ere the world be past."

In these verses, I need not say with what melody, with what touching truth, with what exquisite beauty of comparison—as indeed in hundreds more pages of the writings of this honest soul—the whole character of the man is told—his humble confession of faults and weakness; his pleasant little vanity, and desire that his village should admire him; his simple scheme of good in which everybody was to be happy—no beggar was to be refused his dinner—nobody in fact was to work much, and he to be the harmless chief of the Utopia, and the monarch of the Irish Yvetot. He would have told again, and without fear of their failing, those famous jokes * which had hung fire in London; he would have talked of his great friends of the Club—of my Lord Clare and my Lord Bishop, my Lord Nugent—sure he knew them intimately,

* "Goldsmith's incessant desire of being conspicuous in company was the occasion of his sometimes appearing to such disadvantage, as one should hardly have supposed possible in a man of his genius. When his literary reputation had risen deservedly high, and his society was much courted, he became very jealous of the extraordinary attention which was everywhere paid to Johnson. One evening, in a circle of wits, he found fault with me for talking of Johnson as entitled to the honour of unquestionable superiority, 'Sir,' said he, 'you are for making a monarchy of what should be a republic.'

"He was still more mortified, when, talking in a company with fluent vivacity, and, as he flattered himself, to the admiration of all present, a German who sat next him, and perceived Johnson rolling himself as if about to speak, suddenly stopped him, saying, 'Stay, stay—Toctor Shonson is going to zay zomething.' This was no doubt very provoking, especially to one so irritable as Goldsmith, who frequently mentioned it with strong expressions of indignation.

"It may also be observed that Goldsmith was sometimes content to be treated with an easy familiarity, but upon occasions would be consequential and important. An instance of this occurred in a small particular. Johnson had a way of contracting the names of his friends, as Beauclerk, Beau; Boswell, Bozzy. . . . I remember one day, when Tom Davies was telling that Doctor Johnson said—'We are all in labour for a name to *Goldy's* play,' Goldsmith seemed displeased that such a liberty should be taken with his name, and said, 'I have often desired him not to call me *Goldy*.'"

This is one of several of Boswell's depreciatory mentions of Goldsmith—which may well irritate biographers and admirers, and also those who take that more kindly and more profound view of Boswell's own character, which was opened up by Mr. Carlyle's famous article on his book. No wonder that Mr. Irving calls Boswell an "incarnation of toadyism." And the worst of it is, that Johnson himself has suffered from this habit of the Laird of Auchinleck's. People are apt to forget under what Boswellian stimulus the great Doctor uttered many hasty things:—things no more indicative of the nature of the depths of his character than the phosphoric gleaming of the sea, when struck at night, is indicative of radical corruption of nature! In truth, it is clear enough on the whole that both Johnson and Goldsmith *appreciated* each other, and that they mutually knew it. They were, as it were, tripped up and flung against each other, occasionally, by the blundering and silly gambolling of people in company.

Something must be allowed for Boswell's "rivalry for Johnson's good graces" with Oliver (as Sir Walter Scott has remarked), for Oliver was intimate with the Doctor before his biographer was,—and, as we all remember, marched off with him to "take tea with Mrs. Williams" before Boswell had advanced to that honourable degree of intimacy. But, in truth, Boswell—though he perhaps showed more talent in his delineation of the Doctor than is generally ascribed to him—had not faculty to take a fair view of *two* great men at a time. Besides, as Mr. Forster justly remarks, "he was impatient of Goldsmith from the first hour of their acquaintance."—*Life and Adventures*, p. 292.

and was hand and glove with some of the best men in town—and he would have spoken of Johnson and of Burke, and of Sir Joshua who had painted him—and he would have told wonderful sly stories of Ranelagh and the Pantheon, and the masquerades at Madame Cornelys; and he would have toasted, with a sigh, the Jessamy Bride—the lovely Mary Horneck.

The figure of that charming young lady forms one of the prettiest recollections of Goldsmith's life. She and her beautiful sister, who married Bunbury, the graceful and humorous amateur artist of those days, when Gilray had but just begun to try his powers, were among the kindest and dearest of Goldsmith's many friends, cheered and pitied him, travelled abroad with him, made him welcome at their home, and gave him many a pleasant holiday. He bought his finest clothes to figure at their country-house at Barton—he wrote them droll verses. They loved him, laughed at him, played him tricks and made him happy. He asked for a loan from Garrick, and Garrick kindly supplied him, to enable him to go to Barton: but there were to be no more holidays and only one brief struggle more for poor Goldsmith. A lock of his hair was taken from the coffin and given to the Jessamy Bride. She lived quite into our time. Hazlitt saw her an old lady, but beautiful still, in Northcote's painting-room, who told the eager critic how proud she always was that Goldsmith had admired her. The younger Colman has left a touching reminiscence of him (vol. i. 63, 64):—

"I was only five years old," he says, "when Goldsmith took me on his knee one evening whilst he was drinking coffee with my father, and began to play with me, which amiable act I returned, with the ingratitude of a peevish brat, by giving him a very smart slap on the face: it must have been a tingler, for it left the marks of my spiteful paw on his cheek. This infantile outrage was followed by summary justice, and I was locked up by my indignant father in an adjoining room to undergo solitary imprisonment in the dark. Here I began to howl and scream most abominably, which was no bad step towards my liberation, since those who were not inclined to pity me might be likely to set me free for the purpose of abating a nuisance.

"At length a generous friend appeared to extricate me from jeopardy, and that generous friend was no other than the man I had so wantonly molested by assault and battery—it was the tender-hearted Doctor himself, with a lighted candle in his hand and a smile upon his countenance, which was still partially red from the effects of my petulance. I sulked and sobbed as he fondled and soothed, till I began to brighten. Goldsmith seized the propitious

GOLDSMITH AT PLAY.

moment of returning good-humour, when he put down the candle and began to conjure. He placed three hats, which happened to be in the room, and a shilling under each. The shillings, he told me, were England, France, and Spain. 'Hey presto cockalorum!' cried the Doctor, and lo, on uncovering the shillings, which had been dispersed each beneath a separate hat, they were all found congregated under one. I was no politician at five years old, and therefore might not have wondered at the sudden revolution which brought England, France, and Spain all under one crown; but as also I was no conjurer, it amazed me beyond measure. . . . From that time, whenever the Doctor came to visit my father, 'I plucked his gown to share the good man's smile;' a game at romps constantly ensued, and we were always cordial friends and merry playfellows. Our unequal companionship varied somewhat as to sports as I grew older; but it did not last long: my senior playmate died in his forty-fifth year, when I had attained my eleventh. . . . In all the numerous accounts of his virtues and foibles, his genius and absurdities, his knowledge of nature and ignorance of the world, his 'compassion for another's woe' was always predominant; and my trivial story of his humouring a froward child weighs but as a feather in the recorded scale of his benevolence."

Think of him reckless, thriftless, vain, if you like—but merciful, gentle, generous, full of love and pity. He passes out of our life, and goes to render his account beyond it. Think of the poor pensioners weeping at his grave; think of the noble spirits that admired and deplored him; think of the righteous pen that wrote his epitaph—and of the wonderful and unanimous response of affection with which the world has paid back the love he gave it. His humour delighting us still: his song fresh and beautiful as when first he charmed with it: his words in all our mouths: his very weaknesses beloved and familiar—his benevolent spirit seems still to smile upon us; to do gentle kindnesses: to succour with sweet charity: to soothe, caress, and forgive: to plead with the fortunate for the unhappy and the poor.

His name is the last in the list of those men of humour who have formed the themes of the discourses which you have heard so kindly.

Long before I had ever hoped for such an audience, or dreamed of the possibility of the good fortune which has brought me so many friends, I was at issue with some of my literary brethren upon a point—which they held from tradition I think rather than experience—that our profession was neglected in this country; and that men of letters were ill received and held in slight esteem. It would hardly be grateful of me now to alter my old opinion that we do meet with good-will and kindness, with generous helping hands in the time of our necessity, with cordial and friendly recognition. What claim had any one of these of whom I have been speaking, but genius? What return of gratitude, fame, affection, did it not bring to all?

What punishment befell those who were unfortunate among them, but that which follows reckless habits and careless lives? For these faults a wit must suffer like the dullest prodigal that ever ran in debt. He must pay the tailor if he wears the coat; his children must go in rags if he spends his money at the tavern; he can't come to London and be made Lord Chancellor if he stops on the road and gambles away his last shilling at Dublin. And he must pay the social penalty of these follies too, and expect that the world will shun the man of bad habits, that women will avoid the man of loose life, that prudent folks will close their doors as a precaution, and before a demand should be made on their pockets by the needy prodigal. With what difficulty had any one of these men to contend, save that eternal and mechanical one of want of means and lack of capital, and of which thousands of young lawyers, young doctors, young soldiers and sailors, of inventors, manufacturers, shopkeepers, have to complain? Hearts as brave and resolute as ever beat in the breast of any wit or poet, sicken and break daily in the vain endeavour and unavailing struggle against life's difficulty. Don't we see daily ruined inventors, grey-haired midshipmen, balked heroes, blighted curates, barristers pining a hungry life out in chambers, the attorneys never mounting to their garrets, whilst scores of them are rapping at the door of the successful quack below? If these suffer, who is the author, that he should be exempt? Let us bear our ills with the same constancy with which others endure them, accept our manly part in life, hold our own, and ask no more. I can conceive of no kings or laws causing or curing Goldsmith's improvidence, or Fielding's fatal love of pleasure, or Dick Steele's mania for running races with the constable. You never can outrun that sure-footed officer—not by any swiftness or by dodges devised by any genius, however great; and he carries off the Tatler to the spunging-house, or taps the Citizen of the World on the shoulder as he would any other mortal.

Does society look down on a man because he is an author? I suppose if people want a buffoon they tolerate him only in so far as he is amusing; it can hardly be expected that they should respect him as an equal. Is there to be a guard of honour provided for the author of the last new novel or poem? how long is he to reign, and keep other potentates out of possession? He retires, grumbles, and prints a lamentation that literature is despised. If Captain A. is left out of Lady B.'s parties, he does not state that the army is despised: if Lord C. no longer asks Counsellor D. to dinner, Counsellor D. does not announce that the bar is insulted. He is not fair to society if he enters it with this suspicion hankering about him; if he is doubtful about his reception, how hold up his head honestly, and look frankly in the face that world about which he is full of suspicion? Is he place-hunting, and thinking in his mind that he ought to be made an Ambassador like Prior, or a Secretary of State like Addison? his pretence of equality falls to the ground at once; he is scheming for a patron, not shaking the hand of a friend, when he meets the world. Treat such a man as he deserves; laugh at his buffoonery, and give him a dinner and a *bon jour;* laugh at his self-sufficiency and absurd assumptions of superiority, and his equally ludicrous airs of martyrdom: laugh at his flattery and his scheming, and buy it, if it's worth the having. Let the wag have his dinner and the hireling his pay, if you want him, and make a profound bow to the *grand homme incompris*, and the boisterous martyr, and show him the door. The great world, the great aggregate experience, has its good sense, as it has its good humour. It detects a pretender, as it trusts a loyal heart. It is kind in the main: how should it be otherwise than kind, when it is so wise and clear-headed? To any literary man who says, "It despises my profession," I say, with all my might—no, no, no. It may pass over your individual case—how many a brave fellow has failed in the race and perished unknown in the struggle!—but it treats you as you merit in the main. If you serve it, it is not unthankful; if you please it, it is pleased; if you cringe to it, it detects you, and scorns you if you are mean; it returns your cheerfulness with its good humour; it deals not ungenerously with your weaknesses; it recognises most kindly your merits; it gives you a fair place and fair play. To any one of those men of whom we have spoken was it in the main ungrateful? A king might refuse Goldsmith a pension, as a publisher might keep his masterpiece and the delight of all the world in his desk for two years; but it was mistake, and not ill-will. Noble and illustrious names of Swift, and Pope, and Addison! dear and honoured memories of Goldsmith and Fielding! kind friends, teachers, benefactors! who shall say that our country, which continues to bring you such an unceasing tribute of applause, admiration, love, sympathy, does not do honour to the literary calling in the honour which it bestows upon *you?*

THE FOUR GEORGES

SKETCHES OF MANNERS, MORALS,
COURT AND TOWN LIFE

THE FOUR GEORGES

GEORGE THE FIRST

A VERY few years since, I knew familiarly a lady who had been asked in marriage by Horace Walpole, who had been patted on the head by George I. This lady had knocked at Doctor Johnson's door; had been intimate with Fox, the beautiful Georgina of Devonshire, and that brilliant Whig society of the reign of George III.; had known the Duchess of Queensberry, the patroness of Gay and Prior, the admired young beauty of the Court of Queen Anne. I often thought, as I took my kind old friend's hand, how with it I held on to the old society of wits and men of the world. I could travel back for sevenscore years of time—have glimpses of Brummel, Selwyn, Chesterfield, and the men of pleasure; of Walpole and Conway; of Johnson, Reynolds, Goldsmith; of North, Chatham, Newcastle; of the fair maids of honour of George II.'s Court; of the German retainers of George I.'s; where Addison was Secretary of State; where Dick Steele held a place; whither the great Marlborough came with his fiery spouse; when Pope, and Swift, and Bolingbroke yet lived and wrote. Of a society so vast, busy, brilliant, it is impossible in four brief chapters to give a complete notion; but we may peep here and there into that bygone world of the Georges, see what they and their Courts were like; glance at the people round about them; look at past manners, fashions, pleasures, and contrast them with our own. I have to say thus much by way of preface, because the subject of these lectures has been misunderstood, and I have been taken to task for not having given grave historical treatises, which it never was my intention to attempt. Not about battles, about politics, about statesmen and measures of State, did I ever think to lecture you: but to sketch the manners and life of the old world; to amuse for a few hours with talk about the old society; and, with the result of many a day's and night's pleasant reading, to try and while away a few winter evenings for my hearers.

Among the German princes who sat under Luther at Wittenberg was Duke Ernest of Celle, whose younger son, William of Lüneburg, was the progenitor of the illustrious Hanoverian House at present reigning in Great Britain. Duke William held his Court at Celle, a little town of ten thousand people that lies on the railway line between Hamburg and Hanover, in the midst of great plains of sand, upon the river Aller. When Duke William had it, it was a very humble wood-built place, with a great brick church, which he sedulously frequented, and in which he and others of his house lie buried. He was a very religious lord, and was called William the Pious by his small circle of subjects, over whom he ruled till fate deprived him both of sight and reason. Sometimes, in his latter days, the good Duke had glimpses of mental light, when he would bid his musicians play the psalm-tunes which he loved. One thinks of a descendant of his, two hundred years afterwards, blind, old, and lost of wits, singing Handel in Windsor Tower.

William the Pious had fifteen children, eight daughters and seven sons, who, as the property left among them was small, drew lots to determine which one of them should marry, and continue the stout race of the Guelphs. The lot fell on Duke George, the sixth brother. The others remained single, or contracted left-handed marriages after the princely fashion of those days. It is a queer picture—that of the old Prince dying in his little wood-built capital, and his seven sons tossing up which should inherit and transmit the crown of Brentford. Duke George, the lucky prize-man, made the tour of Europe, during which he visited the Court of Queen Elizabeth; and in the year 1617, came back and settled at Zell, with a wife out of Darmstadt. His remaining brothers all kept their house at Zell, for economy's sake. And presently, in due course, they all died—all the honest Dukes: Ernest, and Christian, and Augustus, and Magnus, and George, and John—and they are buried in the brick church of Brentford yonder, by the sandy banks of the Aller.

Dr. Vehse gives a pleasant glimpse of the way of life of our Dukes in Zell. "When the trumpeter on the tower has blown," Duke Christian orders—viz., at nine o'clock in the morning, and four in the evening—every one must be present at meals, and those who are not must go without. None of the servants, unless it be a knave who has been ordered to ride out, shall eat or drink in the kitchen or cellar; or, without special leave, fodder his horses at the

Prince's cost. When the meal is served in the Court-room, a page shall go round and bid every one be quiet and orderly, forbidding all cursing, swearing, and rudeness; all throwing about of bread, bones, or roast, or pocketing of the same. Every morning, at seven, the squires shall have their morning soup, along with which, and dinner, they shall be served with their under-drink — every morning, except Friday morning, when there was sermon, and no drink. Every evening they shall have their beer, and at night their sleep-drink. The butler is especially warned not to allow noble or simple to go into the cellar: wine shall only be served at the Prince's or Councillor's table; and every Monday, the honest old Duke Christian ordains the accounts shall be ready, and the expenses in the kitchen, the wine and beer cellar, the bakehouse and stable, made out.

Duke George, the marrying Duke, did not stop at home to partake of the beer and wine, and the sermons. He went about fighting wherever there was profit to be had. He served as general in the army of the circle of Lower Saxony, the Protestant army; then he went over to the Emperor, and fought in his armies in Germany and Italy; and when Gustavus Adolphus appeared in Germany, George took service as a Swedish general, and seized the Abbey of Hildesheim, as his share of the plunder. Here, in the year 1641, Duke George died, leaving four sons behind him, from the youngest of whom descend our Royal Georges.

Under these children of Duke George, the old God-fearing simple ways of Zell appear to have gone out of mode. The second brother was constantly visiting Venice, and leading a jolly wicked life there. It was the most jovial of all places at the end of the seventeenth century; and military men, after a campaign, rushed thither, as the warriors of the Allies rushed to Paris in 1814, to gamble, and rejoice, and partake of all sorts of godless delights. This prince, then, loving Venice and its pleasures, brought Italian singers and dancers back with him to quiet old Zell; and, worse still, demeaned himself by marrying a French lady of birth quite inferior to his own—Eleanor d'Olbreuse, from whom our Queen is descended. Eleanor had a pretty daughter, who inherited a great fortune, which inflamed her cousin, George Louis of Hanover, with a desire to marry her; and so, with her beauty and her riches, she came to a sad end.

It is too long to tell how the four sons of Duke George divided his territories amongst them, and how, finally, they came into possession of the son of the youngest of the four. In this generation the Protestant faith was very nearly extinguished in the family: and then where should we in England have gone for a king? The third brother also took delight in Italy, where the priests converted him and his Protestant chaplain too. Mass was said in Hanover once more; and Italian soprani piped their Latin rhymes in place of the hymns which William the Pious and Doctor Luther sang. Louis XIV. gave this and other converts a splendid pension. Crowds of Frenchmen and brilliant French fashions came to his Court. It is incalculable how much that Royal bigwig cost Germany. Every prince imitated the French King, and had his Versailles, his Wilhelmshöhe or Ludwigslust; his Court and its splendours; his gardens laid out with statues; his fountains, and waterworks, and Tritons; his actors, and dancers, and singers, and fiddlers; his harem, with its inhabitants; his diamonds and duchies for these latter; his enormous festivities, his gaming-tables, tournaments, masquerades, and banquets lasting a week long, for which the people paid with their money, when the poor wretches had it; with their bodies and very blood when they had none; being sold in thousands by their lords and masters, who gaily dealt in soldiers, staked a regiment upon the red at the gambling-table; swapped a battalion against a dancing-girl's diamond necklace; and, as it were, pocketed their people.

As one views Europe, through contemporary books of travel, in the early part of the last century, the landscape is awful—wretched wastes, beggarly and plundered; half-burned cottages and trembling peasants gathering piteous harvests: gangs of such tramping along with bayonets behind them, and corporals with canes and cats-of-nine-tails to flog them to barracks. By these passes my Lord's gilt carriage floundering through the ruts, as he swears at the postillions, and toils on to the Residenz. Hard by, but away from the noise and brawling of the citizens and buyers, is Wilhelmslust or Ludwigsruhe, or Monbijou, or Versailles—it scarcely matters which,—near to the city, shut out by woods from the beggared country, the enormous, hideous, gilded, monstrous marble palace, where the Prince is, and the Court, and the trim gardens, and huge fountains, and the forest where the ragged peasants are beating the game in (it is death to them to touch a feather); and the jolly hunt sweeps by with its uniform of crimson and gold; and the Prince gallops ahead puffing his Royal horn; and his lords and mistresses ride after him; and the stag is pulled down; and the grand huntsman gives the knife in the midst of a chorus of bugles; and 'tis time the Court go home to dinner; and our noble traveller, it may be the Baron of Pöllnitz, or the Count de Königsmarck, or the excellent Chevalier de Seingalt, sees the procession gleaming through the trim avenues of the wood, and hastens to the inn, and sends his noble name to the marshal of the Court. Then our nobleman arrays himself in green and gold, or pink and silver, in the richest Paris mode, and is introduced by the chamberlain, and makes his bow to the jolly Prince, and the gracious Princess; and is presented to the chief lords and ladies, and then comes supper and a bank at Faro, where he loses or wins a thousand pieces by daylight. If it is a German Court, you may add not a little drunkenness to this picture of high life; but German, or French, or Spanish, if you can see out of your palace-windows beyond the trim-cut forest vistas, misery is lying outside; hunger is stalking about the bare villages, listlessly following precarious husbandry; ploughing stony fields with starved cattle; or fearfully taking in scanty harvests. Augustus is fat and jolly on his throne; he can knock down an ox, and eat one almost; his mistress, Aurora von Königsmarck, is the loveliest, the wittiest creature; his diamonds are the biggest and most brilliant in the world, and his feasts as splendid as those of Versailles. As for Louis the Great, he is more than mortal. Lift up your glances respectfully, and mark him eyeing Madame de Fontanges or Madame de Montespan from under his sublime periwig, as he passes through the great gallery where Villars and Vendôme, and Berwick, and Bossuet, and Massillon are waiting. Can Court be more splendid; nobles and knights more gallant and superb; ladies more lovely? A grander monarch, or a more miserable starved wretch than the peasant his subject, you cannot look on. Let us bear both these types in mind, if we wish to estimate the old society properly. Remember the glory and the chivalry? Yes! Remember the grace and beauty, the splendour and lofty politeness; the gallant courtesy of Fontenoy, where the French line bids the gentlemen of the English guard to fire first; the noble constancy of the old King and Villars his general, who fits out the last army with the last crownpiece from the treasury, and goes to meet the enemy and die or conquer for France at Denain. But round all that Royal splendour lies a nation enslaved and ruined: there are people robbed of their rights—communities laid waste—faith, justice, commerce trampled upon, and well-nigh destroyed—nay, in the very centre of Royalty itself, what horrible stains and meanness, crime and shame! It is but to a silly harlot that some of the noblest gentlemen, and some of the proudest women in the world are bowing down; it is the price of a miserable province that the King ties in diamonds round his mistress's white neck. In the first half of the last century, I say, this is going on all Europe over. Saxony is a waste as well as Picardy or Artois; and Versailles is only larger and not worse than Herrenhausen.

It was the first Elector of Hanover who made the fortunate match which bestowed the race of Hanoverian Sovereigns upon us Britons. Nine years after Charles Stuart lost his head, his niece Sophia, one of many children of another luckless dethroned sovereign, the Elector Palatine, married Ernest Augustus of Brunswick, and brought the reversion to the crown of the three kingdoms in her scanty trousseau.

One of the handsomest, the most cheerful, sensible, shrewd, accomplished of women was Sophia, daughter of poor Frederick, the winter King of Bohemia. The other daughters of lovely unhappy Elizabeth Stuart went off into the Catholic Church; this one, luckily for her family, remained, I cannot say faithful to the Reformed Religion, but at least she adopted no other. An agent of the French King's, Gourville, a convert himself, strove to bring her and her husband to a sense of the truth; and tells us that he one day asked Madame the Duchess of Hanover of what religion her daughter was, then a pretty girl of thirteen years old. The Duchess replied that the princess *was of no religion as yet.* They were waiting to know of what religion her husband would be, Protestant or Catholic, before instructing her! And the Duke of Hanover having heard all Gourville's proposal, said that a change would be advantageous to his house, but that he himself was too old to change.

This shrewd woman had such keen eyes that she knew how to shut them upon occasion, and was blind to many faults which it appeared that her husband the Bishop of Osnaburg and Duke of Hanover committed. He loved to take his pleasure like other sovereigns—was a merry prince, fond of dinner and the bottle; liked to go to Italy, as his brothers had done before him: and we read how he jovially sold 6700 of his Hanoverians to the Seigniory of Venice. They went bravely off to the Morea, under command of Ernest's son, Prince Max, and only 1400 of them ever came home again. The German princes sold a good deal of this kind of stock. You may remember how George III.'s Government purchased Hessians, and the use we made of them during the War of Independence.

The ducats Duke Ernest got for his soldiers he spent in a series of the most brilliant entertainments. Nevertheless, the jovial Prince was economical, and kept a steady eye upon his own interests. He achieved the electoral dignity for himself: he married his eldest son George to his beautiful cousin of Zell; and sending his sons out in command of armies to fight—now on this side, now on that—he lived on, taking his pleasure, and scheming his schemes, a merry wise prince enough—not, I fear, a moral prince, of which kind we shall have but very few specimens in the course of these lectures.

Ernest Augustus had seven children in all, some of whom were scapegraces, and rebelled against the parental system of primogeniture and non-division of property which the Elector ordained. "Gustchen," the Electress writes about her second son:—"Poor Gus is thrust out, and his father will give him no more keep. I laugh in the day, and cry all night about it; for I am a fool with my children." Three of the six died fighting against Turks, Tartars, Frenchmen. One of them conspired, revolted, fled to Rome, leaving an agent behind him, whose head was taken off. The daughter, of whose early education we have made mention, was married to the Elector of Brandenburg, and so her religion settled finally on the Protestant side.

A niece of the Electress Sophia—who had been made to change her religion, and marry the Duke of Orleans, brother of the French King; a woman whose honest heart was always with her friends and dear old Deutschland, though her fat little body was confined at Paris, or Marly, or Versailles—has left us, in her enormous correspondence (part of which has been printed in German and French), recollections of the Electress, and of George her son. Elizabeth Charlotte was at Osnaburgh when George was born (1660). She narrowly escaped a whipping for being in the way on that auspicious day. She seems not to have liked little George, nor George grown up; and represents him as odiously hard, cold, and silent. Silent he may have been: not a jolly Prince like his father before him, but a prudent, quiet, selfish potentate, going his own way, managing his own affairs, and understanding his own interests remarkably well.

In his father's lifetime, and at the head of the Hanover forces of 8000 or 10,000 men, George served the Emperor, on the Danube against Turks, at the siege of Vienna, in Italy, and on the Rhine. When he succeeded to the Electorate, he handled its affairs with great prudence and dexterity. He was very much liked by his people of Hanover. He did not show his feelings much, but he cried heartily on leaving them; as they used for joy when he came back. He showed an uncommon prudence and coolness of behaviour when he came into his kingdom; exhibiting no elation; reasonably doubtful whether he should not be turned out some day; looking upon himself only as a lodger, and making the most of his brief tenure of St. James's and Hampton Court; plundering, it is true, somewhat, and dividing amongst his German followers; but what could be expected of a sovereign who at home could sell his subjects at so many ducats per head, and make no scruple in so disposing of them? I fancy a considerable shrewdness, prudence, and even moderation in his ways. The German Protestant was a cheaper, and better, and kinder king than the Catholic Stuart in whose chair he sat, and so far loyal to England that he let England govern herself.

Having these lectures in view, I made it my business to visit that ugly cradle in which our Georges were nursed. The old town of Hanover must look still pretty much as in the time when George Louis left it. The gardens and pavilions of Herrenhausen are scarce changed since the day when the stout old Electress Sophia fell down in her last walk there, preceding by but a few weeks to the tomb James II.'s daughter, whose death made way for the Brunswick Stuarts in England.

The first two Royal Georges, and their father, Ernest Augustus, had quite Royal notions regarding marriage; and Louis XIV. and Charles II. scarce distinguished themselves more at Versailles or St. James's than these German Sultans in their little city on the banks of the Leine. You may see at Herrenhausen the very rustic theatre in which the Platens danced and performed masques, and sang before the Elector and his sons. There are the very fauns and dryads of stone still glimmering through the branches, still grinning and piping their ditties of no tone, as in the days when painted nymphs hung garlands round them; appeared under their leafy arcades with gilt crooks, guiding rams with gilt horns; descended from "machines" in the guise of Diana or Minerva; and delivered immense allegorical compliments to the princes returned home from the campaign.

That was a curious state of morals and politics in Europe; a queer consequence of the triumph of the monarchical principle. Feudalism was beaten down. The nobility, in its quarrels with the Crown, had pretty well succumbed, and the monarch was all in all. He became almost divine: the proudest and most ancient gentry of the land did menial service for him. Who should carry Louis XIV.'s candle when he went to bed? what prince of the blood should hold the King's shirt when his Most Christian Majesty changed that garment?—the French memoirs of the seventeenth century are full of such details and squabbles. The tradition is not yet extinct in Europe. Any of you who were present, as myriads were, at that splendid pageant, the opening of our Crystal Palace in London, must have seen two noble lords, great officers of the household, with ancient pedigrees, with embroidered coats, and stars on their breasts and wands in their hands, walking backwards for near the space of a mile, while the Royal procession made its progress. Shall we wonder—shall we be angry—shall we laugh at these old-world ceremonies? View them as you will, according to your mood; and with scorn or with respect, or with anger and sorrow, as your temper leads you. Up goes Gessler's hat upon the pole. Salute that symbol of sovereignty with heartfelt awe; or with a sulky shrug of acquiescence, or with a grinning obeisance; or with a stout rebellious No—clap your own beaver down on your pate, and refuse to doff it to that spangled velvet and flaunting feather. I make no comment upon the spectators' behaviour; all I say is, that Gessler's cap is still up in the market-place of Europe, and not a few folks are still kneeling to it.

Put clumsy High Dutch statues in place of the marbles of Versailles: fancy Herrenhausen waterworks in place of those of Marly: spread the tables with Schweinskopf, Specksuppe, Leberkuchen, and the like delicacies, in place of the French *cuisine;* and fancy Frau von Kielmansegge dancing with Count Kammerjunker Quirini, or singing French songs with the most awful German accent: imagine a coarse Versailles, and we have a Hanover before us. "I am now got into the region of beauty," writes Mary Wortley, from Hanover, in 1716; "all the women have literally rosy cheeks, snowy foreheads and necks, jet eyebrows, to which may generally be added coal-black hair. These perfections never leave them to the day of their death, and have a very fine effect by candlelight: but I could wish they were handsome with a little variety. They resemble one another as Mrs. Salmon's Court of Great Britain, and are in as much danger of melting away by too nearly approaching the fire." The sly Mary Wortley saw this painted seraglio of the first George of Hanover, the year after his accession to the British throne. There were great doings and feasts there. Here Lady Mary saw George II. too. "I can tell you, without flattery or partiality," she says, "that our young prince has all the accomplishments that it is possible to have at his age, with an air of sprightliness and understanding, and a something so very engaging in his behaviour that needs not the advantage of his rank to appear charming." I find elsewhere similar panegyrics upon Frederick Prince of Wales, George II.'s son; and upon George III., of course; and upon George IV. in an eminent degree. It was the rule to be dazzled by princes, and people's eyes winked quite honestly at that Royal radiance.

The Electoral Court of Hanover was numerous; pretty well paid, as times went; above all, paid with a regularity which few other European Courts could boast of. Perhaps you will be amused to know how the Electoral Court was composed. There were the princes of the house in the first class; in the second, the single field-marshal of the army (the contingent was 18,000, Pöllnitz says, and the Elector had other 14,000 troops in his pay). Then follow, in due order, the authorities civil and military, the working privy councillors, the generals of cavalry and infantry, in the third class; the high chamberlain, high marshals of the Court, high masters of the horse, the major-generals of cavalry and infantry, in the fourth class; down to the majors, the hofjunkers or pages, the secretaries or assessors, of the tenth class, of whom all were noble.

We find the master of the horse had 1090 thalers of pay; the high chamberlain, 2000—a thaler being about three shillings of our money. There were two chamberlains, and one for the Princess; five gentlemen of the chamber, and five gentlemen ushers; eleven pages and personages to educate these young noblemen—such as a governor, a preceptor, a fecht-meister or fencing-master, and a dancing ditto, this latter with a handsome salary of 400 thalers. There were three body and Court physicians, with 800 and 500 thalers; a Court barber, 600 thalers; a Court organist; two musikanten; four French fiddlers; twelve trumpeters, and a bugler; so that there was plenty of music, profane and pious, in Hanover. There were ten chamber waiters, and twenty-four lacqueys in livery; a maître-d'hôtel, and attendants of the kitchen; a French cook; a body cook; ten cooks; six cooks' assistants; two Braten masters, or masters of the roast—(one fancies enormous spits turning slowly, and the honest masters of the roast beladling the dripping); a pastry-baker; a pie-baker; and, finally, three scullions, at the modest remuneration of eleven thalers. In the sugar-chamber there were four pastrycooks (for the ladies, no doubt); seven officers in the wine and beer cellars; four bread-bakers; and five men in the plate-room. There were 600 horses in the Serene stables—no less than twenty teams of princely carriage horses, eight to a team; sixteen coachmen; fourteen postillions; nineteen ostlers; thirteen helps, besides smiths, carriage-masters, horse-doctors, and other attendants of the stable. The female attendants were not so numerous: I grieve to find but a dozen or fourteen of them about the Electoral premises, and only two washer-women for all the Court. These functionaries had not so much to do as in the present age. I own to finding a pleasure in these small-beer chronicles. I like to people the old world with its every-day figures and inhabitants—not so much with heroes fighting immense battles and inspiring repulsed battalions to engage; or statesmen locked up in darkling cabinets and meditating ponderous laws or dire conspiracies—as with people occupied with their every-day work or pleasure; my lord and lady hunting in the forest, or dancing in the Court, or bowing to their Serene Highnesses as they pass in to dinner; John Cook and his procession bringing the meal from the kitchen; the jolly butlers bearing in the flagons from the cellar; the stout coachman driving the ponderous gilt waggon, with eight cream-coloured horses in housings of scarlet velvet and morocco leather; a postillion on the leaders, and a pair or a half-dozen of running footmen scudding along by the side of the vehicle, with conical caps, long silver-headed maces, which they poised as they ran, and splendid jackets laced all over with silver and gold. I fancy the citizens' wives and their daughters looking out from the balconies; and the burghers over their beer and mumm, rising up, cap in hand, as the cavalcade passes through the town with torch-bearers, trumpeters blowing their lusty cheeks out, and squadrons of jack-booted lifeguardsmen, girt with shining cuirasses, and bestriding thundering chargers, escorting his Highness's coach from Hanover to Herrenhausen; or halting, mayhap, at Madame Platen's country house of Monplaisir, which lies half-way between the summer-palace and the Residenz.

In the good old times of which I am treating, whilst common men were driven off by herds, and sold to fight the Emperor's enemies on the Danube, or to bayonet King Louis's troops of common men on the Rhine, noblemen passed from Court to Court, seeking service with one prince or the other, and naturally taking command of the ignoble vulgar of soldiery which battled and died almost without hope of promotion. Noble adventurers travelled from Court to Court in search of employment; not merely noble males, but noble females too; and if these latter were beauties, and obtained the favourable notice of princes, they stopped in the Courts, became the favourites of their Serene or Royal Highnesses; and received great sums of money and splendid diamonds; and were promoted to be duchesses, marchionesses, and the like; and did not fall much in public esteem for the manner in which they won their advancement. In this way Mademoiselle de Quérouailles, a beautiful French lady, came to London, on a special mission of Louis XIV., and was adopted by our grateful country and sovereign, and figured as Duchess of Portsmouth. In this way the beautiful Aurora of Königsmarck travelling about found favour in the eyes of Augustus of Saxony, and became the mother of Marshal Saxe, who gave us a beating at Fontenoy; and in this manner the lovely sisters Elizabeth and Melusina of Meissenbach (who had actually been driven out of Paris, whither they had travelled on a like errand, by the wise jealousy of the female favourite there in possession) journeyed to Hanover, and became favourites of the Serene house there reigning.

That beautiful Aurora von Königsmarck and her brother are wonderful as types of bygone manners, and strange illustrations of the morals of old days. The Königsmarcks were descended from an ancient noble family of Brandenburg, a branch of which passed into Sweden, where it enriched itself and produced several mighty men of valour.

The founder of the race was Hans Christof, a famous warrior and plunderer of the Thirty Years' War. One of Hans's sons, Otto, appeared as ambassador at the Court of Louis XIV., and had to make a Swedish speech at his reception before the Most Christian King. Otto was a famous dandy and warrior, but he forgot the speech, and what do you think he did? Far from being disconcerted, he recited a portion of the Swedish Catechism to His Most Christian Majesty and his Court, not one of whom understood his lingo with the exception of his own suite, who had to keep their gravity as best they might.

Otto's nephew, Aurora's elder brother, Carl Johann of Königsmarck, a favourite of Charles II., a beauty, a dandy, a warrior, a rascal of more than ordinary mark, escaped but deserved being hanged in England, for the murder of Tom Thynne of Longleat. He had a little brother in London with him at this time:—as great a beauty, as great a dandy, as great a villain as his elder. This lad, Philip of Königsmarck, also was implicated in the affair; and perhaps it is a pity he ever brought his pretty neck out of it. He went over to Hanover, and was soon appointed colonel of a regiment of H.E. Highness's dragoons. In early life he had been page in the Court of Celle; and it was said that he and the pretty Princess Sophia Dorothea, who by this time was married to her cousin George the Electoral Prince, had been in love with each other as children. Their loves were now to be renewed, not innocently, and to come to a fearful end.

A biography of the wife of George I., by Doctor Doran, has lately appeared and I confess I am astounded at the verdict which that writer has delivered, and at his acquittal of this most unfortunate lady. That she had a cold selfish libertine of a husband no one can doubt; but that the bad husband had a bad wife is equally clear. She was married to her cousin for money or convenience, as all princesses were married. She was most beautiful, lively, witty, accomplished: his brutality outraged her; his silence and coldness chilled her; his cruelty insulted her. No wonder she did not love him. How could love be a part of the compact in such a marriage as that? With this unlucky heart to dispose of, the poor creature bestowed it on Philip of Königsmarck, than whom a greater scamp does not walk the history of the seventeenth century. A hundred and eighty years after the fellow was thrust into his unknown grave, a Swedish professor lights upon a box of letters in the University

Library at Upsala, written by Philip and Dorothea to each other, and telling their miserable story.

The bewitching Königsmarck had conquered two female hearts in Hanover. Besides the Electoral Prince's lovely young wife Sophia Dorothea, Philip had inspired a passion in a hideous old Court lady, the Countess of Platen. The Princess seems to have pursued him with the fidelity of many years. Heaps of letters followed him on his campaigns, and were answered by the daring adventurer. The Princess wanted to fly with him; to quit her odious husband at any rate. She besought her parents to receive her back; had a notion of taking refuge in France, and going over to the Catholic religion; had absolutely packed her jewels for flight, and very likely arranged its details with her lover, in that last long night's interview, after which Philip of Königsmarck was seen no more

Königsmarck, inflamed with drink—there is scarcely any vice of which, according to his own showing, this gentleman was not a practitioner—had boasted at a supper at Dresden of his intimacy with the two Hanoverian ladies, not only with the Princess, but with another lady powerful in Hanover. Tho Countess Platen, the old favourite of the Elector, hated the young Electoral Princess. The young lady had a lively wit, and constantly made fun of the old one. The Princess's jokes were conveyed to the old Platen just as our idle words are carried about at this present day: and so they both hated each other.

The characters in the tragedy, of which the curtain was now about to fall, are about as dark a set as eye ever rested on. There is the jolly Prince, shrewd, selfish, scheming, loving his cups and his ease (I think his good-humour makes the tragedy but darker); his Princess, who speaks little, but observes all; his old painted Jezebel of a mistress; his son, the Electoral Prince, shrewd too, quiet, selfish, not ill-humoured, and generally silent, except when goaded into fury by the intolerable tongue of his lovely wife; there is poor Sophia Dorothea, with her coquetry and her wrongs, and her passionate attachment to her scamp of a lover, and her wild imprudences, and her mad artifices, and her insane fidelity, and her furious jealousy regarding her husband (though she loathed and cheated him), and her prodigious falsehoods; and the confidante, of course, into whose hands the letters are slipped; and there is Lothario, finally, than whom, as I have said, one can't imagine a more handsome, wicked, worthless reprobate.

How that perverse fidelity of passion pursues the villain! How madly true the woman is, and how astoundingly she lies! She has bewitched two or three persons who have taken her up, and they won't believe in her wrong. Like Mary of Scotland, she finds adherents ready to conspire for her even in history, and people who have to deal with her are charmed, and fascinated, and bedevilled. How devotedly Miss Strickland has stood by Mary's innocence! Are there not scores of ladies in this audience who persist in it too? Innocent! I remember as a boy how a great party persisted in declaring Caroline of Brunswick was a martyred angel. So was Helen of Greece innocent. She never ran away with Paris, the dangerous young Trojan. Menelaus, her husband, ill-used her; and there never was any siege of Troy at all. So was Bluebeard's wife innocent. She never peeped into the closet where the other wives were with their heads off. She never dropped the key, or stained it with blood; and her brothers were quite right in finishing Bluebeard, the cowardly brute! Yes, Caroline of Brunswick was innocent; and Madame Laffarge never poisoned her husband; and Mary of Scotland never blew up hers; and poor Sophia Dorothea was never unfaithful; and Eve never took the apple—it was a cowardly fabrication of the serpent's.

George Louis has been held up to execration as a murderous Bluebeard, whereas the Electoral Prince had no share in the transaction in which Philip of Königsmarck was scuffled out of this mortal scene. The Prince was absent when the catastrophe came. The Princess had had a hundred warnings; mild hints from her husband's parents; grim remonstrances from himself—but took no more heed of this advice than such besotted poor wretches do. On the night of Sunday, the 1st of July 1694, Königsmarck paid a long visit to the Princess, and left her to get ready for flight. Her husband was away at Berlin; her carriages and horses were prepared and ready for the elopement. Meanwhile, the spies of Countess Platen had brought the news to their mistress. She went to Ernest Augustus, and procured from the Elector an order for the arrest of the Swede. On the way by which he was to come, four guards were commissioned to take him. He strove to cut his way through the four men, and wounded more than one of them. They fell upon him; cut him down; and, as he was lying wounded on the ground, the Countess, his enemy, whom he had betrayed and insulted, came out and beheld him prostrate. He cursed her with his dying lips, and the furious woman stamped upon his mouth with her heel. He was despatched presently; his body burnt the next day; and all traces of the man disappeared. The guards who killed him were enjoined silence under severe penalties. The Princess was reported to be ill in her apartments, from which she was taken in October of the same year, being then eight-and-twenty years old, and consigned to the castle of Ahlden, where she remained a prisoner for no less

THE DEATH OF KÖNIGSMARK.

than thirty-two years. A separation had been pronounced previously between her and her husband. She was called henceforth the "Princess of Ahlden," and her silent husband no more uttered her name.

Four years after the Königsmarck catastrophe, Ernest Augustus, the first Elector of Hanover, died, and George Louis, his son, reigned in his stead. Sixteen years he reigned in Hanover, after which he became, as we know, King of Great Britain, France, and Ireland, Defender of the Faith. The wicked old Countess Platen died in the year 1706. She had lost her sight, but nevertheless the legend says that she constantly saw Königsmarck's ghost by her wicked old bed. And so there was an end of her.

In the year 1700 the little Duke of Gloucester, the last of poor Queen Anne's children, died, and the folks of Hanover straightway became of prodigious importance in England. The Electress Sophia was declared the next in succession to the English throne. George Louis was created Duke of Cambridge; grand deputations were sent over from our country to Deutschland; but Queen Anne, whose weak heart hankered after her relatives at Saint Germains, never could be got to allow her cousin, the Elector Duke of Cambridge, to come and pay his respects to her Majesty, and take his seat in her House of Peers. Had the Queen lasted a month longer; had the English Tories been as bold and resolute as they were clever and crafty; had the Prince whom the nation loved and pitied been equal to his fortune, George Louis had never talked German in Saint James's Chapel Royal.

When the crown did come to George Louis he was in no hurry about putting it on. He waited at home for a while; took an affecting farewell of his dear Hanover and Herrenhausen; and set out in the most leisurely manner to ascend "the throne of his ancestors," as he called it in his first speech to Parliament. He brought with him a compact body of Germans, whose society he loved, and whom he kept round the Royal person. He had his faithful German chamberlains; his German secretaries; his negroes, captives of his bow and spear in Turkish wars; his two ugly elderly German favourites, Mesdames of Kielmansegge and Schulenberg, whom he created respectively Countess of Darlington and Duchess of Kendal. The Duchess was tall, and lean of stature, and hence was irreverently nicknamed the Maypole. The Countess was a large-sized noblewoman, and this elevated personage was denominated the Elephant. Both of these ladies loved Hanover and its delights; clung round the linden trees of the great Herrenhausen avenue, and at first would not quit the place. Schulenberg, in fact, could not come on account of her debts; but finding the Maypole would not come, the Elephant packed up her trunk and slipped out of Hanover, unwieldy as she was. On this the Maypole straightway put herself in motion, and followed her beloved George Louis. One seems to be speaking of Captain Macheath, and Polly, and Lucy. The King we had selected; the courtiers who came in his train; the English nobles who came to welcome him, and on many of whom the shrewd old cynic turned his back—I protest it is a wonderful satirical picture. I am a citizen waiting at Greenwich pier, say, and crying hurrah for King George; and yet I can scarcely keep my countenance, and help laughing at the enormous absurdity of this advent!

Here we are, all on our knees. Here is the Archbishop of Canterbury prostrating himself to the Head of his Church, with Kielmansegge and Schulenberg wlth their ruddled cheeks grinning behind the Defender of the Faith. Here is my Lord Duke of Marlborough kneeling too, the greatest warrior of all times; he who betrayed King William—betrayed King James II.—betrayed Queen Anne—betrayed England to the French, the Elector to the Pretender, the Pretender to the Elector; and here are my Lords Oxford and Bolingbroke, the latter of whom has just tripped up the heels of the former; and if a month's more time had been allowed him, would have had King James at Westminster. The great Whig gentlemen made their bows and congées with proper decorum and ceremony; but yonder keen old schemer knows the value of their loyalty. "Loyalty," he must think, "as applied to me—it is absurd! There are fifty nearer heirs to the throne than I am. I am but an accident, and you fine Whig gentlemen take me for your own sake, not for mine. You Tories hate me; you archbishop, smirking on your knees, and prating about Heaven, you know I don't care a fig for your Thirty-nine Articles, and can't understand a word of your stupid sermons. You, my Lords Bolingbroke and Oxford—you know you were conspiring against me a month ago; and you, my Lord Duke of Marlborough—you would sell me or any man else, if you found your advantage in it. Come, my good Melusina, come, my honest Sophia, let us go into my private room, and have some oysters and some Rhine wine, and some pipes afterwards: let us make the best of our situation; let us take what we can get, and leave these bawling, brawling, lying English to shout, and fight, and cheat, in their own way!"

If Swift had not been committed to the statesmen of the losing side, what a fine satirical picture we might have had of that general *sauve qui peut* amongst the Tory party! How mum the Tories became; how the House of Lords and House of Commons chopped round; and how decorously the majorities welcomed King George!

Bolingbroke, making his last speech in the House of Lords, pointed out the shame of the Peerage, where several lords concurred to condemn in one general vote all that they had approved in former parliaments by many particular resolutions. And so their conduct was shameful. St. John had the best of the argument, but the worst of the vote. Bad times were come for him. He talked philosophy, and professed innocence. He courted retirement, and was ready to meet persecution; but, hearing that honest Mat Prior, who had been recalled from Paris, was about to peach regarding the past transactions, the philosopher bolted, and took that magnificent head of his out of the ugly reach of the axe. Oxford, the lazy and good-humoured, had more courage, and awaited the storm at home. He and Mat Prior both had lodgings in the Tower, and both brought their heads safe out of that dangerous menagerie. When Atterbury was carried off to the same den a few years afterwards, and it was asked, what next should be done with him? "Done with him? Fling him to the lions," Cadogan said, Marlborough's lieutenant. But the British lion of those days did not care much for drinking the blood of peaceful peers and poets, or crunching the bones of bishops. Only four men were executed in London for the rebellion of 1715; and twenty-two in Lancashire. Above a thousand taken in arms submitted to the King's mercy, and petitioned to be transported to his Majesty's colonies in America. I have heard that their descendants took the loyalist side in the disputes which arose sixty years after. It is pleasant to find that a friend of ours, worthy Dick Steele, was for letting off the rebels with their lives.

As one thinks of what might have been, how amusing the speculation is! We know how the doomed Scottish gentlemen came out at Lord Mar's summons, mounted the white cockade, that has been a flower of sad poetry ever since, and rallied round the ill-omened Stuart standard at Braemar. Mar, with 8000 men, and but 1500 opposed to him, might have driven the enemy over the Tweed, and taken possession of the whole of Scotland; but that the Pretender's Duke did not venture to move when the day was his own. Edinburgh Castle might have been in King's James's hands; but that the men who were to escalade it stayed to drink his health at the tavern, and arrived two hours too late at the rendezvous under the castle wall. There was sympathy enough in the town—the projected attack seems to have been known there—Lord Mahon quotes Sinclair's account of a gentleman not concerned, who told Sinclair, that he was in a house that evening where eighteen of them were drinking, as the facetious landlady said, "powdering their hair," for the attack on the castle. Suppose they had not stopped to powder their hair? Edinburgh Castle, and town, and all Scotland were King's James's. The North of England rises, and marches over Barnet Heath upon London. Wyndham is up in Somersetshire; Packington in Worcestershire; and Vivian in Cornwall. The Elector of Hanover and his hideous mistresses pack up the plate, and perhaps the Crown jewels, in London, and are off, *viâ* Harwich and Helvoetsluys, for dear old Deutschland. The King—God save him!—lands at Dover, with tumultuous applause; shouting multitudes, roaring cannon, the Duke of Marlborough weeping tears of joy, and all the bishops kneeling in the mud. In a few years mass is said in Saint Paul's; matins and vespers are sung in York Minster; and Doctor Swift is turned out of his stall and deanery house at Saint Patrick's to give place to Father Dominic from Salamanca. All these changes were possible then, and once thirty years afterwards—all this we might have had but for the *pulveris exigui jactu*, that little toss of powder for the hair which the Scotch conspirators stopped to take at the tavern.

You understand the distinction I would draw between history—of which I do not aspire to be an expounder—and manners and life such as these sketches would describe. The rebellion breaks out in the North; its story is before you in a hundred volumes, in none more fairly than in the excellent narrative of Lord Mahon. The clans are up in Scotland; Derwentwater, Nithsdale, and Forster are in arms in Northumberland—these are matters of history, for which you are referred to the due chroniclers. The Guards are set to watch the streets, and prevent the people wearing white roses. I read presently of a couple of soldiers almost flogged to death for wearing oak boughs in their hats on the 29th of May—another badge of the beloved Stuarts It is with these we have to do, rather than the marches and battles of the armies to which the poor fellows belonged—with statesmen, and how they looked, and how they lived, rather than with measures of State, which belong to history alone. For example, at the close of the old Queen's reign, it is known that the Duke of Marlborough left the kingdom—after what menaces, after what prayers, lies, bribes offered, taken, refused, accepted; after what dark doubling and tacking, let history, if she can or dare, say. The Queen dead: who so eager to return as my Lord Duke? Who shouts God save the King! so lustily as the great conqueror of Blenheim and Malplaquet? (By the way, he will send over some more money for the Pretender yet, on the sly.) Who lays his hand on his blue riband, and lifts his eyes more gracefully to Heaven than this hero? He makes a quasi-triumphal entrance into London, by Temple Bar, in his enormous gilt coach—and the enormous gilt coach breaks down somewhere by Chancery

Lane, and his Highness is obliged to get another. There it is we have him. We are with the mob in the crowd, not with the great folks in the procession. We are not the Historic Muse, but her Ladyship's attendant, tale-bearer—*valet de chambre*—for whom no man is a hero; and, as yonder one steps from his carriage to the next handy conveyance, we take the number of the hack; we look all over at his stars, ribands, embroidery; we think within ourselves, O you unfathomable schemer! O you warrior invincible! O you beautiful smiling Judas! What master would you not kiss or betray? What traitor's head, blackening on the spikes on yonder gate, ever hatched a tithe of the treason which has worked under your periwig?

We have brought our Georges to London city, and if we would behold its aspect, may see it in Hogarth's lively perspective of Cheapside, or read of it in a hundred contemporary books which paint the manners of that age. Our dear old *Spectator* looks smiling upon the streets, with their innumerable signs, and describes them with his charming humour. "Our streets are filled with Blue Boars, Black Swans, and Red Lions, not to mention Flying Pigs and Hogs in Armour, with other creatures more extraordinary than any in the deserts of Africa." A few of these quaint old figures still remain in London town. You may still see there, and over its old hostel in Ludgate Hill, the "Belle Sauvage" to whom the *Spectator* so pleasantly alludes in that paper; and who was, probably, no other than the sweet American Pocahontas, who rescued from death the daring Captain Smith. There is the "Lion's Head," down whose jaws the *Spectator's* own letters were passed; and over a great banker's in Fleet Street, the effigy of the wallet, which the founder of the firm bore when he came into London a country boy. People this street, so ornamented, with crowds of swinging chairmen, with servants bawling to clear the way, with Mr. Dean in his cassock, his lacquey marching before him; or Mrs. Dinah in her sack, tripping to chapel, her footboy carrying her Ladyship's great prayer-book; with itinerant tradesmen singing their hundred cries (I remember forty years ago, as boy in London city, a score of cheery familiar cries that are silent now). Fancy the beaux thronging to the chocolate-houses, tapping their snuffboxes as they issue thence, their periwigs appearing over the red curtains. Fancy Saccharissa beckoning and smiling from the upper windows, and a crowd of soldiers brawling and bustling at the door—gentlemen of the Life Guards, clad in scarlet, with blue facings, and laced with gold at the seams; gentlemen of the Horse Grenadiers, in their caps of sky-blue cloth, with the garter embroidered on the front in gold and silver; men of the Halberdiers, in their long red coats, as bluff Harry left them, with their ruff and velvet flat caps. Perhaps the King's Majesty himself is going to Saint James's as we pass. If he is going to Parliament, he is in his coach-and-eight, surrounded by his guards and the high officers of his crown. Otherwise his Majesty only uses a chair, with six footmen walking before, and six yeomen of the guard at the sides of the sedan. The officers in waiting follow the King in coaches. It must be rather slow work.

Our *Spectator* and *Tatler* are full of delightful glimpses of the town life of those days. In the company of that charming guide, we may go to the opera, the comedy, the puppet-show, the auction, even the cockpit: we can take boat at Temple Stairs, and accompany Sir Roger de Coverley and Mr. Spectator to Spring Garden—it will be called Vauxhall a few years hence, when Hogarth will paint for it. Would you not like to step back into the past, and be introduced to Mr. Addison?—not the Right Honourable Joseph Addison, Esquire, George I.'s Secretary of State, but to the delightful painter of contemporary manners; the man who, when in good-humour himself, was the pleasantest companion in all England. I should like to go into Lockit's with him, and drink a bowl along with Sir R. Steele (who has just been knighted by King George, and who does not happen to have any money to pay his share of the reckoning). I should not care to follow Mr. Addison to his secretary's office in Whitehall. There we get into politics. Our business is pleasure, and the town, and the coffee-house, and the theatre, and the Mall. Delightful Spectator! kind friend of leisure hours! happy companion! true Christian gentleman! How much greater, better, you are than the King Mr. Secretary kneels to!

You can have foreign testimony about old-world London if you like; and my before-quoted friend, Charles Louis, Baron de Pöllnitz, will conduct us to it.

"A man of sense," says he, "or a fine gentleman, is never at a loss for company in London, and this is the way the latter passes his time. He rises late, puts on a frock, and, leaving his sword at home, takes his cane, and goes where he pleases. The Park is commonly the place where he walks, because 'tis the Exchange for men of quality. 'Tis the same thing as the Tuileries at Paris, only the Park has a certain beauty of simplicity which cannot be described. The grand walk is called the Mall; is full of people at every hour of the day, but especially at morning and evening, when their Majesties often walk with the Royal family, who are attended only by half-a-dozen yeomen of the guard, and permit all persons to walk at the same time with them. The ladies and gentlemen always appear in rich dresses, for the English, who, twenty years ago, did not wear gold lace but in their army, are now embroidered and bedaubed as much as the French. I speak of persons of quality; for the citizen still contents himself with a suit of fine cloth, a good hat and wig, and fine linen. Everybody is well clothed here, and even the beggars don't make so ragged an appearance as they do elsewhere."

After our friend, the man of quality, has had his morning or undress walk in the Mall, he goes home to dress, and then saunters to some coffee-house or chocolate-house frequented by the persons he would see.

"For 'tis a rule with the English to go once a day at least to houses of this sort, where they talk of business and news, read the papers, and often look at one another without opening their lips. And 'tis very well they are so mute: for were they all as talkative as people of other nations, the coffee-houses would be intolerable, and there would be no hearing what one man said where they are so many. The chocolate-house in St. James's Street, where I go every morning to pass away the time, is always so full that a man can scarce turn about in it."

Delightful as London city was, King George I. liked to be out of it as much as ever he could; and when there, passed all his time with his Germans. It was with them as with Blucher, a hundred years afterwards, when the bold old Reiter looked down from Saint Paul's, and sighed out, "Was für Plunder!" The German women plundered; the German secretaries plundered; the German cooks and intendants plundered; even Mustapha and Mahomet, the German negroes, had a share of the booty. Take what you can get, was the old monarch's maxim. He was not a lofty monarch, certainly: he was not a patron of the fine arts: but he was not a hypocrite, he was not revengeful, he was not extravagant. Though a despot in Hanover, he was a moderate ruler in England. His aim was to leave it to itself as much as possible, and to live out of it as much as he could. His heart was in Hanover. When taken ill on his last journey, as he was passing through Holland, he thrust his livid head out of the coach-window, and gasped out, "Osnaburg, Osnaburg!" He was more than fifty years of age when he came amongst us: we took him because we wanted him, because he served our turn; we laughed at his uncouth German ways, and sneered at him. He took our loyalty for what it was worth; laid hands on what money he could; kept us assuredly from Popery and wooden shoes. I, for one, would have been on his side in those days. Cynical and selfish as he was, he was better than a king out of Saint Germains with the French King's orders in his pocket, and a swarm of Jesuits in his train.

The Fates are supposed to interest themselves about Royal personages; and so this one had omens and prophecies specially regarding him. He was said to be much disturbed at a prophecy that he should die very soon after his wife; and sure enough, pallid Death, having seized upon the luckless Princess in her castle of Ahlden, presently pounced upon H.M. King George I., in his travelling chariot, on the Hanover road. What postillion can outride that pale horseman? It is said, George promised one of his left-handed widows to come to her after death, if leave were granted to him to revisit the glimpses of the moon; and soon after his demise, a great raven actually flying or hopping in at the Duchess of Kendal's window at Twickenham, she chose to imagine the King's spirit inhabited these plumes, and took special care of her sable visitor. Affecting metempsychosis—funereal Royal bird! How pathetic is the idea of the Duchess weeping over it! When this chaste addition to our English aristocracy died, all her jewels, her plate, her plunder went over to her relations in Hanover. I wonder whether her heirs took the bird, and whether it is still flapping its wings over Herrenhausen!

The days are over in England of that strange religion of king-worship, when priests flattered princes in the Temple of God; when servility was held to be ennobling duty; when beauty and youth tried eagerly for Royal favour; and woman's shame was held to be no dishonour. Mended morals and mended manners in Courts and people are among the priceless consequences of the freedom which George I. came to rescue and secure. He kept his compact with his English subjects; and if he escaped no more than other men and monarchs from the vices of his age, at least we may thank him for preserving and transmitting the liberties of ours. In our free air, Royal and humble homes have alike been purified; and Truth, the birthright of high and low among us, which quite fearlessly judges our greatest personages, can only speak of them now in words of respect and regard. There are stains in the portrait of the first George, and traits in it which none of us need admire; but among the nobler features are justice, courage, moderation—and these we may recognise ere we turn the picture to the wall.

GEORGE THE SECOND

ON the afternoon of the 14th of June 1727, two horsemen might have been perceived galloping along the road from Chelsea to Richmond. The foremost, cased in the jackboots of the period, was a broad-faced, jolly-looking, and very corpulent cavalier; but, by the manner in which he urged his horse, you might see that he was a bold as well as a skilful rider. Indeed, no man loved sport better; and in the hunting-fields of Norfolk, no squire rode more boldly after the fox, or cheered Ringwood and Sweetlips more lustily, than he who now thundered over the Richmond road.

He speedily reached Richmond Lodge, and asked to see the owner of the mansion. The mistress of the house and her ladies, to whom our friend was admitted, said he could not be introduced to the master, however pressing the business might be. The master was asleep after his dinner; he always slept after his dinner: and woe be to the person who interrupted him! Nevertheless, our stout friend of the jackboots put the affrighted ladies aside, opened the forbidden door of the bedroom, wherein upon the bed lay a little gentleman; and here the eager messenger knelt down in his jackboots.

He on the bed started up, and with many oaths and a strong German accent asked who was there, and who dared to disturb him?

"I am Sir Robert Walpole," said the messenger. The awakened sleeper hated Sir Robert Walpole. "I have the honour to announce to your Majesty that your Royal father, King George I., died at Osnaburg, on Saturday last, the 10th instant."

"*Dat is one big lie!*" roared out his Sacred Majesty King George II.: but Sir Robert Walpole stated the fact, and from that day until three-and-thirty years after, George, the second of the name, ruled over England.

How the King made away with his father's will under the astonished nose of the Archbishop of Canterbury; how he was a choleric little sovereign; how he shook his fist in the face of his father's courtiers; how he kicked his coat and wig about in his rages, and called everybody thief, liar, rascal, with whom he differed,—you will read in all the history books; and how he speedily and shrewdly reconciled himself with the bold Minister, whom he had hated during his father's life, and by whom he was served during fifteen years of his own with admirable prudence, fidelity, and success. But for Sir Robert Walpole, we should have had the Pretender back again. But for his obstinate love of peace, we should have had wars, which the nation was not strong enough nor united enough to endure. But for his resolute counsels and good-humoured resistance, we might have had German despots attempting a Hanoverian regimen over us: we should have had revolt, commotion, want, and tyrannous misrule, in place of a quarter of a century of peace, freedom, and material prosperity, such as the country never enjoyed, until that corrupter of parliaments, that dissolute tipsy cynic, that courageous lover of peace and liberty, that great citizen, patriot, and statesman governed it. In religion he was little better than a heathen; cracked ribald jokes at bigwigs and bishops, and laughed at High Church and Low. In private life the old pagan revelled in the lowest pleasures; he passed his Sundays tippling at Richmond; and his holidays bawling after dogs, or boozing at Houghton with boors over beef and punch. He cared for letters no more than his master did: he judged human nature so meanly that one is ashamed to have to own that he was right, and that men could be corrupted by means so base. But, with his hireling House of Commons, he defended liberty for us; with his incredulity he kept Church-craft down. There were parsons at Oxford as double-dealing and dangerous as any priests out of Rome, and he routed them both. He gave Englishmen no conquests, but he gave them peace and ease and freedom; the Three per Cents nearly at par; and wheat at five and six and twenty shillings a quarter.

It was lucky for us that our first Georges were not more high-minded men; especially fortunate that they loved Hanover so much as to leave England to have her own way. Our chief troubles began when we got a King who gloried in the name of Briton, and, being born in the country, proposed to rule it. He was no more fit to govern England than his grandfather and great-grandfather, who did not try. It was righting itself during their occupation. The dangerous noble old spirit of Cavalier loyalty was dying out; the stately old English High Church was emptying itself; the questions dropping which, on one side and the other—the side of loyalty, prerogative, Church, and King,—the side of right, truth, civil and religious freedom,—had set generations of brave men in arms. By the time when George III. came to the throne the combat between loyalty and liberty was come to an end; and Charles Edward, old, tipsy, and childless, was dying in Italy.

Those who are curious about European Court history of the last age know the memoirs of the Margravine of Bayreuth, and what a Court was that of Berlin, where George II.'s cousins ruled sovereign. Frederick the Great's father knocked down his sons, daughters, officers of state; he kidnapped big men all Europe over to make grenadiers of: his feasts, his parades, his wine-parties, his tobacco-parties, are all described. Jonathan Wild the Great in language, pleasures, and behaviour is scarcely more delicate than this German sovereign. Louis XV., his life, and reign, and doings, are told in a thousand French memoirs. Our George II., at least, was not a worse king than his neighbours. He claimed and took the Royal exemption from doing right which sovereigns assumed. A dull little man of low tastes he appears to us in England; yet Hervey tells us that this choleric prince was a great sentimentalist, and that his letters—of which he wrote prodigious quantities—were quite dangerous in their powers of fascination. He kept his sentimentalities for his Germans and his queen. With us English he never chose to be familiar. He has been accused of avarice, yet he did not give much money, and did not leave much behind him. He did not love the fine arts, but he did not pretend to love them. He was no more a hypocrite about religion than his father. He judged men by a low standard; yet, with such men as were near him, was he wrong in judging as he did? He readily detected lying and flattery, and liars and flatterers were perforce his companions. Had he been more of a dupe he might have been more amiable. A dismal experience made him cynical. No boon was it to him to be clear-sighted, and see only selfishness and flattery round about him. What could Walpole tell him about his Lords and Commons, but that they were all venal? Did not his clergy, his courtiers, bring him the same story? Dealing with men and women in his rude sceptical way, he came to doubt about honour, male and female, about patriotism, about religion. "He is wild, but he fights like a man," George I., the taciturn, said of his son and successor. Courage George II. certainly had. The Electoral Prince, at the head of his father's contingent, had approved himself a good and brave soldier under Eugene and Marlborough. At Oudenarde he specially distinguished himself. At Malplaquet the other claimant to the English throne won but little honour. There was always a question about James's courage. Neither then in Flanders, nor afterwards in his own ancient kingdom of Scotland, did the luckless Pretender show much resolution. But dapper little George had a famous tough spirit of his own, and fought like a Trojan. He called out his brother of Prussia with sword and pistol; and I wish, for the interest of romancers in general, that that famous duel could have taken place. The two sovereigns hated each other with all their might; their seconds were appointed; the place of meeting was settled; and the duel was only prevented by strong representations made to the two, of the European laughter which would have been caused by such a transaction.

Whenever we hear of dapper George at war, it is certain that he demeaned himself like a little man of valour. At Dettingen his horse ran away with him, and with difficulty was stopped from carrying him into the enemy's lines. The King, dismounting from the fiery quadruped, said bravely, "Now I know I shall not run away;" and placed himself at the head of the foot, drew his sword, brandishing it at the whole of the French army, and calling out to his own men to come on, in bad English, but with the most famous pluck and spirit. In '45, when the Pretender was at Derby, and many people began to look pale, the King never lost his courage—not he. "Pooh! don't talk to me that stuff!" he said, like a gallant little prince as he was, and never for one moment allowed his equanimity, or his business, or his pleasures, or his travels, to be disturbed. On public festivals he always appeared in the hat and coat he wore on the famous day of Oudenarde; and the people laughed, but kindly, at the odd old garment, for bravery never goes out of fashion.

In private life the Prince showed himself a worthy descendant of his father. In this respect, so much has been said about the first George's manners, that we need not enter into a description of the son's German harem. In 1705 he married a princess remarkable for beauty, for cleverness, for learning, for good temper—one of the truest and fondest wives ever prince was blessed with, and who loved him and was faithful to him, and he, in his coarse fashion, loved her to the last. It must be told to the honour of Caroline of Anspach, that, at the time when German princes thought no more of changing their religion than you of altering your cap, she refused to give up Protestantism for the other creed, although an archduke, afterwards to be an emperor, was offered to her for a bridegroom. Her Protestant relations in Berlin were angry at her rebellious spirit; it was they who tried to convert her (it is droll to think that Frederick the Great, who had no religion at all, was known for a long time in England as the Protestant hero), and these good Protestants set upon Caroline a certain Father Urban, a very skilful Jesuit, and famous winner of souls. But she routed the Jesuit; and she refused Charles VI.; and she married the little Electoral Prince of Hanover, whom she tended with love, and with every manner of sacrifice, with artful kindness, with tender flattery, with entire self-devotion, thenceforward until her life's end.

When George I. made his first visit to Hanover, his son was appointed Regent during the Royal absence. But this honour was never again conferred on the Prince of Wales; he and his father fell out presently. On the occasion of the christening of his second son, a Royal row took place, and the Prince, shaking his fist in the Duke of Newcastle's face, called him a rogue, and provoked his august father. He and his wife were turned out of Saint James's, and their princely children taken from them, by order of the Royal head of the family. Father and mother wept piteously at parting from their little ones. The young ones sent some cherries, with their love, to papa and mamma; the parents watered the fruit with tears. They had no tears thirty-five years afterwards, when Prince Frederick died—their eldest son, their heir, their enemy.

The King called his daughter-in-law "cette diablesse Madame la Princesse." The frequenters of the latter's Court were forbidden to appear at the King's: their Royal Highnesses going to Bath, we read how the courtiers followed them thither, and paid that homage in Somersetshire which was forbidden in London. That phrase of "cette diablesse Madame la Princesse" explains one cause of the wrath of her Royal papa. She was a very clever woman: she had a keen sense of humour: she had a dreadful tongue: she turned into ridicule the antiquated sultan and his hideous harem. She wrote savage letters about him home to members of her family. So, driven out from the Royal presence, the Prince and Princess set up for themselves in Leicester Fields, "where," says Walpole, "the most promising of the young gentlemen of the next party, and the prettiest and liveliest of the young ladies, formed the new Court." Besides Leicester House, they had their lodge at Richmond, frequented by some of the pleasantest company of those days. There were the Herveys, and Chesterfield, and little Mr. Pope from Twickenham, and with him, sometimes, the savage Dean of Saint Patrick's, and quite a bevy of young ladies whose pretty faces smile on us out of history. There was Lepell, famous in ballad song; and the saucy charming Mary Bellenden, who would have none of the Prince of Wales's fine compliments, who folded her arms across her breast, and bade H.R.H. keep off; and knocked his purse of guineas into his face, and told him she was tired of seeing him count them. He was not an august monarch, this Augustus. Walpole tells how, one night at the Royal card-table, the playful princesses pulled a chair away from under Lady Deloraine, who, in revenge, pulled the King's from under him, so that his Majesty fell on the carpet. In whatever posture one sees this Royal George, he is ludicrous somehow; even at Dettingen, where he fought so bravely, his figure is absurd—calling out in his broken English, and lunging with his rapier, like a fencing master. In contemporary caricatures, George's son, "the Hero of Culloden," is also made an object of considerable fun.

I refrain to quote from Walpole regarding George—for those charming volumes are in the hands of all who love the gossip of the last century. Nothing can be more cheery than Horace's letters. Fiddles sing all through them: wax-lights, fine dresses, fine jokes, fine plate, fine equipages, glitter and sparkle there: never was such a brilliant, jigging, smirking Vanity Fair as that through which he leads us. Hervey, the next great authority, is a darker spirit. About him there is something frightful: a few years since his heirs opened the lid of the Ickworth box; it was as if a Pompeii was opened to us—the last century dug up, with its temples and its games, its chariots, its public places—lupanaria. Wandering through that city of the dead, that dreadfully selfish time, through those godless intrigues and feasts, through those crowds, pushing, and eager, and struggling—rouged, and lying, and fawning—I have wanted some one to be friends with. I have said to friends conversant with that history, "Show me some good person about that Court; find me, among those selfish courtiers, those dissolute gay people, some one being that I can love and regard." There is that strutting little sultan George II.; there is that hunchbacked beetle-browed Lord Chesterfield; there is John Hervey, with his deadly smile, and ghastly painted face—I hate them. There is Hoadly, cringing from one bishopric to another; yonder comes little Mr. Pope from Twickenham, with his friend the Irish Dean, in his new cassock, bowing, too, but with rage flashing from under his bushy eyebrows, and scorn and hate quivering in his smile. Can you be fond of these? Of Pope I might: at least I might love his genius, his wit, his greatness, his sensibility—with a certain conviction that at some fancied slight, some sneer which he imagined, he would turn upon me and stab me. Can you trust the Queen? She is not of our order: their very position makes kings and queens lonely. One inscrutable attachment that inscrutable woman has. To that she is faithful, through all trial, neglect, pain, and time. Save her husband, she really cares for no created being. She is good enough to her children, and even fond enough of them; but she would chop them all up into little pieces to please him. In her intercourse with all around her she was perfectly kind, gracious, and natural: but friends may die, daughters may depart, she will be as perfectly kind and gracious to the next set. If the King wants her, she will smile upon him, be she ever so sad; and walk with him, be she ever so weary; and laugh at his brutal jokes, be she in ever so much pain of body or heart. Caroline's devotion to her husband is a prodigy to read of. What charm had the little man? What was there in those wonderful letters of thirty pages long, which he wrote to her when he was absent, and to his mistresses at Hanover, when he was in London with his wife? Why did Caroline, the most lovely and accomplished princess of Germany, take a little red-faced staring princeling for a husband, and refuse an emperor? Why, to her last hour, did she love him so? She killed herself because she loved him so. She had the gout, and would plunge her feet in cold water in order to walk with him. With the film of death over her eyes, writhing in intolerable pain, she yet had a livid smile and a gentle word for her master. You have read the wonderful history of that deathbed? How she bade him marry again, and the reply the old King blubbered out, "Non, non: j'aurai des maîtresses." There never was such a ghastly farce. I watch the astonishing scene—I stand by that awful bedside, wondering at the ways in which God has ordained the lives, loves, rewards, successes, passions, actions, ends of his creatures—and can't but laugh, in the presence of death, and with the saddest heart. In that often-quoted passage from Lord Hervey, in which the Queen's deathbed is described, the grotesque horror of the details surpasses all satire: the dreadful humour of the scene is more terrible than Swift's blackest pages, or Fielding's fiercest irony. The man who wrote the story had something diabolical about him: the terrible verses which Pope wrote respecting Hervey, in one of his own moods of almost fiendish malignity, I fear are true. I am frightened as I look back into the past, and fancy I behold that ghastly beautiful face; as I think of the Queen writhing on her deathbed, and crying out, "Pray!—pray!"—of the Royal old sinner by her side, who kisses her dead lips with frantic grief, and leaves her to sin more;—of the bevy of courtly clergymen, and the archbishop, whose prayers she rejects, and who are obliged for propriety's sake to shuffle off the anxious inquiries of the public, and vow that her Majesty quitted this life "in a heavenly frame of mind." What a life!—to what ends devoted! What a vanity of vanities! It is a theme for another pulpit than the lecturer's. For a pulpit?—I think the part which pulpits play in the deaths of kings is the most ghastly of all the ceremonial: the lying eulogies, the blinking of disagreeable truths, the sickening flatteries, the simulated grief, the falsehood and sycophancies—all uttered in the name of Heaven in our State churches: these monstrous threnodies have been sung from time immemorial over kings and queens, good, bad, wicked, licentious. The State parson must bring out his commonplaces; his apparatus of rhetorical black-hangings. Dead king or live king, the clergyman must flatter him—announce his piety whilst living, and when dead perform the obsequies of "Our Most Religious and Gracious King."

I read that Lady Yarmouth (my most religious and gracious King's favourite) sold a bishopric to a clergyman for £5000. (He betted her £5000 that he would not be made a bishop, and he lost, and paid her.) Was he the only prelate of his time led up by such hands for consecration? As I peep into George II.'s Saint James's, I see crowds of cassocks rustling up the back-stairs of the ladies of the Court; stealthy clergy slipping purses into their laps; that godless old King yawning under his canopy in his Chapel Royal, as the chaplain before him is discoursing. Discoursing about what? —about righteousness and judgment? Whilst the chaplain is preaching, the King is chattering in German almost as loud as the preacher; so loud that the clergyman—it may be one Doctor Young, he who wrote "Night Thoughts," and discoursed on the splendours of the stars, the glories of Heaven, and utter vanities of this world —actually burst out crying in his pulpit because the Defender of the Faith and dispenser of bishoprics would not listen to him! No wonder that the clergy were corrupt and indifferent amidst this indifference and corruption. No wonder that sceptics multiplied and morals degenerated, so far as they depended on the influence of such a king. No wonder that Whitfield cried out in the wilderness, that Wesley quitted the insulted temple to pray on the hill-side. I look with reverence on those men at that time. Which is the sublimer spectacle—the good John Wesley, surrounded by his congregation of miners at the pit's mouth, or the Queen's chaplains mumbling through their morning office in their ante-room, under the picture of the great Venus, with the door opened into the adjoining chamber, where the Queen is dressing, talking scandal to Lord Hervey, or uttering sneers at Lady Suffolk, who is kneeling with the basin at her mistress's side? I say I am scared as I look round at this society—at this King, at these courtiers, at these politicians, at these bishops—at this flaunting vice and levity. Whereabouts in this Court is the honest man? Where is the pure person one may like? The air stifles one with its sickly perfumes. There are some old-world follies and some absurd ceremonials about our Court of the present day, which I laugh at, but as an Englishman, contrasting it with the past, shall I not acknowledge the change of to-day? As the mistress of Saint James's passes me now, I salute the Sovereign, wise, moderate, exemplary of life; the good mother; the good wife; the accomplished lady; the enlightened friend of art; the tender sympathiser in her people's glories and sorrows.

Of all the Court of George and Caroline, I find no one but Lady Suffolk with whom it seems pleasant and kindly to hold converse. Even the misogynist Croker, who edited her letters, loves her, and has that regard for her with which her sweet graciousness seems to have inspired almost all men and some women who came near her. I have noted many little traits which go to prove the charms of her character (it is not merely because she is charming, but because she is characteristic, that I allude to her). She writes delightfully sober letters. Addressing Mr. Gay at Tunbridge (he was, you know, a poet, penniless and in disgrace), she says: "The place you are in has strangely filled your head with physicians and cures; but, take my word for it, many a fine lady has gone there to drink the waters without being sick; and many a man has complained of the loss of his heart, who had it in his own possession. I desire you will keep yours; for I shall not be very fond of a friend without one, and I have a great mind you should be in the number of mine."

When Lord Peterborough was seventy years old, that indomitable youth addressed some flaming love, or rather gallantry, letters to Mrs. Howard—curious relics they are of the romantic manner of wooing sometimes in use in those days. It is not passion; it is not love; it is gallantry: a mixture of earnest and acting; high-flown compliments, profound bows, vows, sighs, and ogles, in the manner of the Clélie romances, and Millamont and Doricourt in the comedy. There was a vast elaboration of ceremonies and etiquette, of raptures—a regulated form for kneeling and wooing which has quite passed out of our downright manners. Henrietta Howard accepted the noble old Earl's philandering; answered the queer love-letters with due acknowledgment; made a profound curtsey to Peterborough's profound bow; and got John Gay to help her in the composition of her letters in reply to her old knight. He wrote her charming verses, in which there was truth as well as grace. "O wonderful creature!" he writes:—

"O wonderful creature, a woman of reason!
Never grave out of pride, never gay out of season!
When so easy to guess who this angel should be,
Who would think Mrs. Howard ne'er dreamt it was she?"

The great Mr. Pope also celebrated her in lines not less pleasant, and painted a portrait of what must certainly have been a delightful lady:—

"I know a thing that's most uncommon—
Envy, be silent, and attend!—
I know a reasonable woman,
Handsome, yet witty, and a friend:

Not warp'd by passion, aw'd by rumour,
Not grave through pride, or gay through folly:
An equal mixture of good-humour
And exquisite soft melancholy.

Has she no faults, then (Envy says), sir?
Yes, she has one, I must aver—
When all the world conspires to praise her,
The woman's deaf, and does not hear!"

Even the women concurred in praising and loving her. The Duchess of Queensberry bears testimony to her amiable qualities, and writes to her: "I tell you so and so, because you love children, and to have children love you." The beautiful jolly Mary Bellenden, represented by contemporaries as "the most perfect creature ever known," writes very pleasantly to her "dear Howard," her "dear Swiss," from the country, whither Mary had retired after her marriage, and when she gave up being a maid of honour. "How do you do, Mrs. Howard?" Mary breaks out. "How do you do, Mrs. Howard? that is all I have to say. This afternoon I am taken with a fit of writing; but as to matter, I have nothing better to entertain you, than news of my farm. I therefore give you the following list of the stock of eatables that I am fatting for my private tooth. It is well known to the whole county of Kent, that I have four fat calves, two fat hogs, fit for killing, twelve promising black pigs, two young chickens, three fine geese, with thirteen eggs under each (several being duck-eggs, else the others do not come to maturity); all this, with rabbits, and pigeons, and carp in plenty, beef and mutton at reasonable rates. Now, Howard, if you have a mind to stick a knife into anything I have named, say so!"

A jolly set must they have been, those maids of honour. Pope introduces us to a whole bevy of them, in a pleasant letter. "I went," he says, "by water to Hampton Court, and met the Prince, with all his ladies, on horseback, coming from hunting. Mrs. Bellenden and Mrs. Lepell took me into protection, contrary to the laws against harbouring Papists, and gave me a dinner, with something I liked better, an opportunity of conversation with Mrs. Howard. We all agreed that the life of a maid of honour was of all things the most miserable, and wished that all women who envied it had a specimen of it. To eat Westphalia ham of a morning, ride over hedges and ditches on borrowed hacks, come home in the heat of the day with a fever, and (what is worse a hundred times) with a red mark on the forehead from an uneasy hat—all this may qualify them to make excellent wives for hunters.

As soon as they wipe off the heat of the day, they must simper an hour and catch cold in the Princess's apartment; from thence to dinner with what appetite they may; and after that till midnight, work, walk, or think which way they please. No lone house in Wales, with a mountain and rookery, is more contemplative than this Court. Miss Lepell walked with me three or four hours by moonlight, and we met no creature of any quality but the King, who gave audience to the Vice-chamberlain all alone under the garden wall."

I fancy it was a merrier England, that of our ancestors, than the island which we inhabit. People high and low amused themselves very much more. I have calculated the manner in which statesmen and persons of condition passed their time—and what with drinking, and dining, and supping, and cards, wonder how they got through their business at all. They played all sorts of games, which, with the exception of cricket and tennis, have quite gone out of our manners now. In the old prints of Saint James's Park, you still see the marks along the walk, to note the balls when the Court played at Mall. Fancy Birdcage Walk now so laid out, and Lord John and Lord Palmerston knocking balls up and down the avenue! Most of those jolly sports belong to the past, and the good old games of England are only to be found in old novels, in old ballads, or the columns of dingy old newspapers, which say how a main of cocks is to be fought at Winchester between the Winchester men and the Hampton men; or how the Cornwall men and the Devon men are going to hold a great wrestling-match at Totnes, and so on.

A hundred and twenty years ago there were not only country towns in England, but people who inhabited them. We were very much more gregarious; we were amused by very simple pleasures. Every town had its fair, every village its wake. The old poets have sung a hundred jolly ditties about great cudgel-playings, famous grinning through horse-collars, great maypole meetings, and morris-dances. The girls used to run races clad in very light attire; and the kind gentry and good parsons thought no shame in looking on. Dancing bears went about the country with pipe and tabor. Certain well-known tunes were sung all over the land for hundreds of years, and high and low rejoiced in that simple music. Gentlemen who wished to entertain their female friends constantly sent for a band. When Beau Fielding, a mighty fine gentleman, was courting the lady whom he married, he treated her and her companion at his lodgings to a supper from the tavern, and after supper they sent out for a fiddler—three of them. Fancy the three, in a great wainscoted room, in Covent Garden or Soho, lighted by two or three candles in silver sconces, some grapes, and a bottle of Florence wine on the table, and the honest fiddler playing old tunes in quaint old minor keys, as the Beau takes out one lady after the other, and solemnly dances with her!

The very great folks, young noblemen, with their governors, and the like, went abroad and made the great tour; the home satirists jeered at the Frenchified and Italian ways which they brought back; but the greater number of people never left the country. The jolly squire often had never been twenty miles from home. Those who did go went to the baths, to Harrogate, or Scarborough, or Bath, or Epsom. Old letters are full of these places of pleasure. Gay writes to us about the fiddlers of Tunbridge; of the ladies having merry little private balls amongst themselves; and the gentlemen entertaining them by turns with tea and music. One of the young beauties whom he met did not care for tea.

"We have a young lady here," he says, "that is very particular in her desires. I have known some young ladies, who, if ever they prayed, would ask for some equipage or title, a husband or matadores: but this lady, who is but seventeen, and has £30,000 to her fortune, places all her wishes on a pot of good ale. When her friends, for the sake of her shape and complexion, would dissuade her from it, she answers, with the truest sincerity, that by the loss of shape and complexion she could only lose a husband, whereas ale is her passion."

Every country town had its assembly-room—mouldy old tenements, which we may still see in deserted inn-yards, in decayed provincial cities, out of which the great wen of London has sucked all the life. York, at assize-times, and throughout the winter, harboured a large society of northern gentry. Shrewsbury was celebrated for its festivities. At Newmarket, I read of "a vast deal of good company, besides rogues and blacklegs;" at Norwich, of two assemblies, with a prodigious crowd in the hall, the rooms, and the gallery. In Cheshire (it is a maid of honour of Queen Caroline who writes, and who is longing to be back at Hampton Court, and the fun there) I peep into a country-house, and see a very merry party:—

"We meet in the work-room before nine, eat, and break a joke or two till twelve, then we repair to our own chambers and make ourselves ready, for it cannot be called dressing. At noon the great bell fetches us into a parlour, adorned with all sorts of fine arms, poisoned darts, several pair of old boots and shoes worn by men of might, with the stirrups of King Charles I., taken from him at Edgehill." And there they have their dinner, after which comes dancing and supper.

AN IMPROMPTU DANCE.

As for Bath, all history went and bathed and drank there. George II. and his Queen, Prince Frederick and his Court, scarce a character one can mention of the early last century but was seen in that famous Pump Room where Beau Nash presided, and his picture hung between the busts of Newton and Pope—

> "This picture, placed these busts between,
> Gives satire all its strength:
> Wisdom and Wit are little seen,
> But Folly at full length."

I should like to have seen the Folly. It was a splendid, embroidered, beruffled, snuffboxed, red-heeled, impertinent Folly, and knew how to make itself respected. I should like to have seen that noble old madcap Peterborough in his boots (he actually had the audacity to walk about Bath in boots!), with his blue riband and stars, and a cabbage under each arm, and a chicken in his hand, which he had been cheapening for his dinner. Chesterfield came there many a time and gambled for hundreds, and grinned through his gout. Mary Wortley was there, young and beautiful; and Mary Wortley, old, hideous, and snuffy. Miss Chudleigh came there, slipping away from one husband, and on the look-out for another. Walpole passed many a day there; sickly, supercilious, absurdly dandified, and affected; with a brilliant wit, a delightful sensibility; and for his friends, a most tender, generous, and faithful heart. And if you and I had been alive then, and strolling down Milsom Street—hush! we should have taken our hats off, as an awful, long, lean, gaunt figure, swathed in flannels, passed by in its chair, and a livid face looked out from the window—great fierce eyes staring from under a bushy powdered wig, a terrible frown, a terrible Roman nose—and we whisper to one another, "There he is! There's the great commoner! There is Mr. Pitt!" As we walk away, the abbey bells are set a-ringing; and we meet our testy friend Toby Smollett, on the arm of James Quin the actor, who tells us that the bells ring for Mr. Bullock, an eminent cow-keeper from Tottenham, who has just arrived to drink the waters; and Toby shakes his cane at the door of Colonel Ringworm—the Creole gentleman's lodgings next his own—where the colonel's two negroes are practising on the French horn.

When we try to recall social England, we must fancy it playing at cards for many hours every day. The custom is well-nigh gone out among us now, but fifty years ago was general, fifty years before that almost universal, in the country. "Gaming has become so much the fashion," writes Seymour, the author of the "Court Gamester," "that he who in company should be ignorant of the games in vogue would be reckoned low-bred, and hardly fit for conversation." There were cards everywhere. It was considered ill-bred to read in company. "Books were not fit articles for drawing-rooms," old ladies used to say. People were jealous, as it were, and angry with them. You will find in Hervey that George II. was always furious at the sight of books; and his Queen, who loved reading, had to practise it in secret in her closet. But cards were the resource of all the world. Every night for hours, kings and queens of England sat down and handled their majesties of spades and diamonds. In European Courts, I believe the practice still remains, not for gambling, but for pastime. Our ancestors generally adopted it. "Books! prithee, don't talk to me about books," said old Sarah Marlborough. "The only books I know are men and cards." "Dear old Sir Roger de Coverley sent all his tenants a string of hogs' puddings and a pack of cards at Christmas," says the *Spectator*, wishing to depict a kind landlord. One of the good old lady writers in whose letters I have been dipping cries out, "Sure, cards have kept us women from a great deal of scandal!" Wise old Johnson regretted that he had not learnt to play. "It is very useful in life," he says; "it generates kindness, and consolidates society." David Hume never went to bed without his whist. We have Walpole, in one of his letters, in a transport of gratitude for the cards. "I shall build an altar to Pam," says he, in his pleasant dandified way, "for the escape of my charming Duchess of Grafton." The Duchess had been playing cards at Rome, when she ought to have been at a cardinal's concert, where the floor fell in, and all the monsignors were precipitated into the cellar. Even the Nonconformist clergy looked not unkindly on the practice. "I do not think," says one of them, "that honest Martin Luther committed sin by playing at backgammon for an hour or two after dinner, in order by unbending his mind to promote digestion." As for the High Church parsons, they all played, bishops and all. On Twelfth-day the Court used to play in state.

"This being Twelfth-day, his Majesty, the Prince of Wales, and the Knights Companions of the Garter, Thistle, and Bath, appeared in the collars of their respective orders. Their Majesties, the Prince of Wales, and three eldest Princesses, went to the Chapel Royal, preceded by the heralds. The Duke of Manchester carried the sword of State. The King and Prince made offering at the altar of gold, frankincense, and myrrh, according to the annual custom. At night their Majesties played at hazard with the nobility, for the benefit of the groom porter; and 'twas said the King won 600 guineas; the Queen 360; Princess Amelia 20; Princess Caroline, 10; the Duke of Grafton and the Earl of Portmore, several thousands."

Let us glance at the same chronicle, which is of the year 1731, and see how others of our forefathers were engaged.

"*Cork, 15th January.*—This day, one Tim Croneen was, for the murder and robbery of Mr. St. Leger and his wife sentenced to be hanged two minutes, then his head to be cut off, and his body divided in four quarters, to be placed in four cross-ways. He was servant to Mr. St. Leger, and committed the murder with the privity of the servant-maid, who was sentenced to be burned; also of the gardener, whom he knocked on the head, to deprive him of his share of the booty."

"*January 3rd.*—A postboy was shot by an Irish gentleman on the road near Stone, in Staffordshire, who died in two days, for which the gentleman was imprisoned."

"A poor man was found hanging in a gentleman's stables at Bungay, in Suffolk, by a person who cut him down, and running for assistance, left his penknife behind him. The poor man recovering, cut his throat with the knife; and a river being nigh, jumped into it; but company coming, he was dragged out alive, and was like to remain so."

"The Honourable Thomas Finch, brother to the Earl of Nottingham, is appointed Ambassador at the Hague, in the room of the Earl of Chesterfield, who is on his return home."

"William Cowper, Esq., and the Rev. Mr. John Cowper, chaplain in ordinary to her Majesty, and rector of Great Berkhampstead, in the county of Hertford, are appointed clerks of the Commissioners of Bankruptcy."

"Charles Creagh, Esq., and —— Macnamara, Esq., between whom an old grudge of three years had subsisted, which had occasioned their being bound over about fifty times for breaking the peace, meeting in company with Mr. Eyres, of Galloway, they discharged their pistols, and all three were killed on the spot—to the great joy of their peaceful neighbours, say the Irish papers."

"Wheat is 26s. to 28s., and barley 20s. to 22s. a quarter; three per cents., 92; best loaf sugar, 9¼d.; Bohea, 12s. to 14s.; Pekoe, 18s.; and Hyson, 35s. per pound."

"At Exon was celebrated with great magnificence the birthday of the son of Sir W. Courtney, Bart., at which more than 1000 persons were present. A bullock was roasted whole; a butt of wine and several tuns of beer and cider were given to the populace. At the same time Sir William delivered to his son, then of age, Powdram Castle, and a great estate."

"Charlesworth and Cox, two solicitors, convicted of forgery, stood on the pillory at the Royal Exchange. The first was severely handled by the populace, but the other was very much favoured, and protected by six or seven fellows who got on the pillory to protect him from the insults of the mob."

"A boy killed by falling upon iron spikes, from a lamp-post, which he climbed to see Mother Needham stand in the pillory."

"Mary Lynn was burnt to ashes at the stake for being concerned in the murder of her mistress."

"Alexander Russell, the foot soldier, who was capitally convicted for a street robbery in January sessions, was reprieved for transportation; but having an estate fallen to him, obtained a free pardon."

"The Lord John Russell married to the Lady Diana Spencer, at Marlborough House. He has a fortune of £30,000 down, and is to have £100,000 at the death of the Duchess Dowager of Marlborough, his grandmother."

"March 1, being the anniversary of the Queen's birthday, when her Majesty entered the forty-ninth year of her age, there was a splendid appearance of nobility at St. James's. Her Majesty was magnificently dressed, and wore a flowered muslin head-edging, as did also her Royal Highness. The Lord Portmore was said to have had the richest dress, though an Italian Count had twenty-four diamonds instead of buttons."

New clothes on the birthday were the fashion for all loyal people. Swift mentions the custom several times. Walpole is constantly speaking of it; laughing at the practice, but having the very finest clothes from Paris, nevertheless. If the King and Queen were unpopular, there were very few new clothes at the drawing-room. In a paper in the *True Patriot*, No. 3, written to attack the Pretender, the Scotch, French, and Popery, Fielding supposes the Scotch and the Pretender in possession of London, and himself about to be hanged for loyalty,—when, just as the rope is round his neck, he says: "My little girl entered my bed-chamber, and put an end to my dream by pulling open my eyes, and telling me that the tailor had just brought home my clothes for his Majesty's birthday." In his "Temple Beau," the beau is dunned "for a birthday suit of velvet, £40." Be sure that Mr. Harry Fielding was dunned too.

The public days, no doubt, were splendid, but the private Court life must have been awfully wearisome.

"I will not trouble you," writes Hervey to Lady Sandon, "with any account of our occupations at Hampton Court. No mill-horse ever went in a more constant track, or a more unchanging circle; so that, by the assistance of an almanack for the day of the week, and a watch for the hour of the day, you may inform yourself fully, without any other intelligence but your memory, of every transaction within the verge of the Court. Walking, chaises, levées, and audiences fill the morning. At night the King plays at commerce and backgammon, and the Queen at quadrille, where poor Lady Charlotte runs her usual nightly gantlet, the Queen pulling her hood, and the Princess Royal rapping her knuckles. The Duke of Grafton takes his nightly opiate of lottery, and sleeps as usual between the Princesses Amelia and Caroline. Lord Grantham strolls from one room to another (as Dryden says), like some discontented ghost that oft appears, and is forbid to speak; and stirs himself about as people stir a fire, not with any design, but in hopes to make it burn brisker. At last the King gets up; the pool finishes; and everybody has their dismission. Their Majesties retire to Lady Charlotte and my Lord Lifford; my Lord Grantham, to Lady Frances and Mr. Clark: some to supper, some to bed; and thus the evening and the morning make the day."

The King's fondness for Hanover occasioned all sorts of rough jokes among his English subjects, to whom *sauerkraut* and sausages have ever been ridiculous objects. When our present Prince Consort came among us, the people bawled out songs in the streets indicative of the absurdity of Germany in general. The sausage-shops produced enormous sausages which we might suppose were the daily food and delight of German princes. I remember the caricatures at the marriage of Prince Leopold with the Princess Charlotte. The bridegroom was drawn in rags. George III.'s wife was called by the people a beggarly German duchess; the British idea being that all princes were beggarly except British princes. King George paid us back. He thought there were no manners out of Germany. Sarah Marlborough once coming to visit the Princess, whilst her Royal Highness was whipping one of the roaring Royal children, "Ah!" says George, who was standing by, "you have no good manners in England, because you are not properly brought up when you are young." He insisted that no English cook could roast, no English coachman could drive: he actually questioned the superiority of our nobility, our horses, and our roast beef!

Whilst he was away from his beloved Hanover, everything remained there exactly as in the Prince's presence. There were eight hundred horses in the stables, there was all the apparatus of chamberlains, Court-marshals, and equerries; and Court assemblies were held every Saturday, where all the nobility of Hanover assembled at what I can't but think a fine and touching ceremony.

A large arm-chair was placed in the assembly room, and on it the King's portrait. The nobility advanced, and made a bow to the arm-chair, and to the image which Nebuchadnezzar the king had set up; and spoke under their voices before the august picture, just as they would have done had the King Churfürst been present himself.

He was always going back to Hanover. In the year 1729, he went for two whole years, during which Caroline reigned for him in England, and he was not in the least missed by his British subjects. He went again in '35 and '36; and between the years 1740 and 1755 was no less than eight times on the Continent, which amusement he was obliged to give up at the outbreak of the Seven Years' War. Here every day's amusement was the same. "Our life is as uniform as that of a monastery," writes a courtier whom Vehse quotes. "Every morning at eleven, and every evening at six, we drive in the heat to Herrenhausen, through an enormous linden avenue; and twice a day cover our coats and coaches with dust. In the King's society there never is the least change. At table, and at cards, he sees always the same faces, and at the end of the game retires into his chamber. Twice a week there is a French theatre; the other days there is play in the gallery. In this way, were the King always to stop in Hanover, one could make a ten years' calendar of his proceedings; and settle beforehand what his time of business, meals, and pleasure would be."

The old pagan kept his promise to his dying wife. Lady Yarmouth was now in full favour, and treated with profound respect by the Hanover society, though it appears rather neglected in England when she came among us. In 1740, a couple of the King's daughters went to see him at Hanover; Anna, the Princess of Orange (about whom, and whose husband and marriage-day Walpole and Hervey have left us the most ludicrous descriptions), and Maria of Hesse-Cassel, with their respective lords. This made the Hanover Court very brilliant. In honour of his high guests, the King gave several *fêtes;* among others, a magnificent masked ball, in the green theatre at Herrenhausen—the garden theatre, with linden and box for screen, and grass for a carpet, where the Platens had danced to George and his father the late sultan. The stage and a great part of the garden were illuminated with coloured lamps. Almost the whole Court appeared in white dominoes, "like," says the describer of the scene, "like spirits in the Elysian fields. At night, supper was served in the gallery with three great tables, and the King was very merry. After supper dancing was resumed, and I did not get home till five o'clock by full daylight to Hanover. Some days afterwards we had, in the opera-house at

Hanover, a great assembly. The King appeared in a Turkish dress; his turban was ornamented with a magnificent *agrafe* of diamonds; the Lady Yarmouth was dressed as a sultana; nobody was more beautiful than the Princess of Hesse." So, while poor Caroline is resting in her coffin, dapper little George, with his red face and his white eyebrows and goggle-eyes, at sixty years of age, is dancing a pretty dance with Madame Walmoden, and capering about dressed up like a Turk! For twenty years more, that little old Bajazet went on in this Turkish fashion, until the fit came which choked the old man, when he ordered the side of his coffin to be taken out, as well as that of poor Caroline's who had preceded him, so that his sinful old bones and ashes might mingle with those of the faithful creature. O strutting Turkey-cock of Herrenhausen! O naughty little Mahomet! in what Turkish paradise are you now, and where be your painted houris? So Countess Yarmouth appeared as a sultana, and his Majesty in a Turkish dress wore an *agrafe* of diamonds, and was very merry, was he? Friends! he was your fathers' King as well as mine—let us drop a respectful tear over his grave.

He said of his wife that he never knew a woman who was worthy to buckle her shoe: he would sit alone weeping before her portrait, and when he had dried his eyes, he would go off to his Walmoden and talk of her. On the 25th day of October 1760, he being then in the seventy-seventh year of his age, and the thirty-fourth of his reign, his page went to take him his Royal chocolate, and behold! the Most Religious and Gracious King was lying dead on the floor. They went and fetched Walmoden; but Walmoden could not wake him. The Sacred Majesty was but a lifeless corpse. The King was dead; God save the King! But, of course, poets and clergymen decorously bewailed the late one. Here are some artless verses, in which an English divine deplored the famous departed hero, and over which you may cry or you may laugh, exactly as your humour suits:—

> "While at his feet expiring Faction lay,
> No contest left but who should best obey;
> Saw in his offspring all himself renewed;
> The same fair path of glory still pursued;
> Saw to young George Augusta's care impart
> Whate'er could raise and humanise the heart;
> Blend all his grandsire's virtues with his own,
> And form their mingled radiance for the throne—
> No farther blessing could on earth be given—
> The next degree of happiness was—heaven!"

If he had been good, if he had been just, if he had been pure in life, and wise in council, could the poet have said much more? It was a parson who came and wept over this grave, with Walmoden sitting on it, and claimed heaven for the poor old man slumbering below. Here was one who had neither dignity, learning, morals, nor wit—who tainted a great society by a bad example; who, in youth, manhood, old age, was gross, low, and sensual; and Mr. Porteus, afterwards my Lord Bishop Porteus, says the earth was not good enough for him, and that his only place was heaven! Bravo, Mr. Porteus! The divine who wept these tears over George the Second's memory wore George the Third's lawn. I don't know whether people still admire his poetry or his sermons.

GEORGE THE THIRD

WE have to glance over sixty years in as many minutes. To read the mere catalogue of characters who figured during that long period would occupy our allotted time, and we should have all text and no sermon. England has to undergo the revolt of the American colonies; to submit to defeat and separation; to shake under the volcano of the French Revolution; to grapple and fight for the life with her gigantic enemy Napoleon; to gasp and rally after that tremendous struggle. The old society, with its courtly splendours, has to pass away; generations of statesmen to rise and disappear; Pitt to follow Chatham to the tomb; the memory of Rodney and Wolfe to be superseded by Nelson's and Wellington's glory; the old poets who unite us to Queen Anne's time to sink into their graves; Johnson to die, and Scott and Byron to arise; Garrick to delight the world with his dazzling dramatic genius, and Kean to leap on the stage and take possession of the astonished theatre. Steam has to be invented; kings to be beheaded, banished, deposed, restored. Napoleon is to be but an episode, and George III. is to be alive through all these varied changes, to accompany his people through all these revolutions of thought, government, society; to survive out of the old world into ours.

When I first saw England, she was in mourning for the young Princess Charlotte, the hope of the empire. I came from India as a child, and our ship touched at an island on the way home, where my black servant took me a long walk over rocks and hills until we reached a garden, where we saw a man walking. "That is he," said the black man: "that is Bonaparte! He eats three sheep every day, and all the little children he can lay hands on!" There were people in the British dominions besides that poor Calcutta serving-man, with an equal horror of the Corsican ogre.

With the same childish attendant, I remember peeping through the colonnade at Carlton House, and seeing the abode of the great Prince Regent. I can see yet the guards pacing before the gates of the place. The place! What place? The palace exists no more than the palace of Nebuchadnezzar. It is but a name now. Where be the sentries who used to salute as the Royal chariots drove in and out? The chariots, with the kings inside, have driven to the realms of Pluto; the tall Guards have marched into darkness, and the echoes of their drums are rolling in Hades. Where the palace once stood, a hundred little children are paddling up and down the steps to Saint James's Park. A score of grave gentlemen are taking their tea at the "Athenæum Club;" as many grisly warriors are garrisoning the "United Service Club" opposite. Pall Mall is the great social Exchange of London now—the mart of news, of politics, of scandal, of rumour—the English Forum, so to speak, where men discuss the last despatch from the Crimea, the last speech of Lord Derby, the next move of Lord John. And, now and then, to a few antiquaries whose thoughts are with the past rather than with the present, it is a memorial of old times and old people, and Pall Mall is our Palmyra. Look! About this spot Tom of Ten Thousand was killed by Königsmarck's gang. In that great red house Gainsborough lived, and Culloden Cumberland, George III.'s uncle. Yonder is Sarah Marlborough's palace, just as it stood when that termagant occupied it. At 25, Walter Scott used to live; at the house, now No. 79,* and occupied by the Society for the Propagation of the Gospel in Foreign Parts, resided Mistress Eleanor Gwynn, comedian. How often has Queen Caroline's chair issued from under yonder arch! All the men of the Georges have passed up and down the street. It has seen Walpole's chariot and Chatham's sedan; and Fox, Gibbon, Sheridan, on their way to Brooks's; and stately William Pitt stalking on the arm of Dundas; and Hanger and Tom Sheridan reeling out of Raggett's; and Byron limping into Wattier's; and Swift striding out of Bury Street; and Mr. Addison and Dick Steele, both perhaps a little the better for liquor; and the Prince of Wales and the Duke of York clattering over the pavement; and Johnson counting the posts along the streets, after dawdling before Dodsley's window; and Horry Walpole hobbling into his carriage, with a gimcrack just bought at Christie's; and George Selwyn sauntering into White's.

In the published letters to George Selwyn we get a mass of correspondence by no means so brilliant and witty as Walpole's, or so bitter and bright as Hervey's, but as interesting, and even more descriptive of the time, because the letters are the work of many hands. You hear more voices speaking, as it were, and more natural than Horace's dandified treble, and Sporus's malignant whisper. As one reads the Selwyn letters — as one looks at Reynolds's noble pictures illustrative of those magnificent times and voluptuous people—one almost hears the voice of the dead past;

* 1856.

the laughter and the chorus; the toast called over the brimming cups; the shout of the racecourse or the gaming-table; the merry joke frankly spoken to the laughing fine lady. How fine those ladies were, those ladies who heard and spoke such coarse jokes; how grand those gentlemen!

I fancy that peculiar product of the past, the fine gentleman, has almost vanished off the face of the earth, and is disappearing like the beaver or the Red Indian. We can't have fine gentlemen any more, because we can't have the society in which they lived. The people will not obey: the parasites will not be as obsequious as formerly: children do not go down on their knees to beg their parents' blessing: chaplains do not say grace and retire before the pudding: servants do not say "your honour" and "your worship" at every moment: tradesmen do not stand hat in hand as the gentleman passes: authors do not wait for hours in gentlemen's anterooms with a fulsome dedication, for which they hope to get five guineas from his Lordship. In the days when there were fine gentlemen, Mr. Secretary Pitt's under-secretaries did not dare to sit down before him; but Mr. Pitt, in his turn, went down on his gouty knees to George II.; and when George III. spoke a few kind words to him, Lord Chatham burst into tears of reverential joy and gratitude; so awful was the idea of the monarch, and so great the distinctions of rank. Fancy Lord John Russell or Lord Palmerston on their knees whilst the Sovereign was reading a despatch, or beginning to cry because Prince Albert said something civil!

At the accession of George III., the patricians were yet at the height of their good fortune. Society recognised their superiority, which they themselves pretty calmly took for granted. They inherited not only titles and estates, and seats in the House of Peers, but seats in the House of Commons. There were a multitude of Government places, and not merely these, but bribes of actual £500 notes, which members of the House took not much shame in receiving. Fox went into Parliament at twenty: Pitt when just of age: his father when not much older. It was the good time for patricians. Small blame to them if they took and enjoyed, and over-enjoyed, the prizes of politics, the pleasures of social life.

In these letters to Selwyn, we are made acquainted with a whole society of these defunct fine gentlemen: and can watch with a curious interest a life which the novel-writers of that time, I think, have scarce touched upon. To Smollett, to Fielding even, a lord was a lord: a gorgeous being with a blue riband, a coroneted chair, and an immense star on his bosom, to whom commoners paid reverence. Richardson, a man of humbler birth than either of the above two, owned that he was ignorant regarding the manners of the aristocracy, and besought Mrs. Donnellan, a lady who had lived in the great world, to examine a volume of "Sir Charles Grandison," and point out any errors which she might see in this particular. Mrs. Donnellan found so many faults, that Richardson changed colour; shut up the book; and muttered that it were best to throw it in the fire. Here, in Selwyn, we have the real original men and women of fashion of the early time of George III. We can follow them to the new club at Almack's: we can travel over Europe with them: we can accompany them not only to the public places, but to their country-houses and private society. Here is a whole company of them; wits and prodigals; some persevering in their bad ways; some repentant, but relapsing; beautiful ladies, parasites, humble chaplains, led captains. Those fair creatures whom we love in Reynolds's portraits, and who still look out on us from his canvases with their sweet calm faces and gracious smiles — those fine gentlemen who did us the honour to govern us; who inherited their boroughs; took their ease in their patent places; and slipped Lord North's bribes so elegantly under their ruffles—we make acquaintance with a hundred of these fine folks, hear their talk and laughter, read of their loves, quarrels, intrigues, debts, duels, divorces; can fancy them alive if we read the book long enough. We can attend at Duke Hamilton's wedding, and behold him marry his bride with the curtain-ring: we can peep into her poor sister's deathbed: we can see Charles Fox cursing over the cards, or March bawling out the odds at Newmarket: we can imagine Burgoyne tripping off from Saint James's Street to conquer the Americans, and slinking back into the club somewhat crestfallen after his beating; we can see the young King dressing himself for the drawing-room and asking ten thousand questions regarding all the gentlemen: we can have high life or low, the struggle at the Opera to behold the Violetta or the Zamperini—the Macaronis and fine ladies in their chairs trooping to the masquerade or Madame Cornelys's—the crowd at Drury Lane to look at the body of Miss Ray, whom Parson Hackman has just pistolled—or we can peep into Newgate, where poor Mr. Rice the forger is waiting his fate and his supper. "You need not be particular about the sauce for his fowl," says one turnkey to another; "for you know he is to be hanged in the morning." "Yes," replies the second janitor, "but the chaplain sups with him, and he is a terrible fellow for melted butter."

Selwyn has a chaplain and parasite, one Doctor Warner, than whom Plautus, or Ben Jonson, or Hogarth, never painted a better character. In letter after letter he adds fresh strokes to the portrait of himself, and completes a portrait not a little curious to look at now that the man has passed away; all the foul pleasures and gambols in which he revelled, played out; all the rouged faces into which he leered, worms and skulls; all the fine gentlemen whose shoe-buckles he kissed, laid in their coffins. This worthy clergyman takes care to tell us that he does not believe in his religion, though, thank Heaven, he is not so great a rogue as a lawyer. He goes on Mr. Selwyn's errands, any errands, and is proud, he says, to be that gentleman's proveditor. He waits upon the Duke of Queensberry—old Q.—and exchanges pretty stories with that aristocrat. He comes home "after a hard day's christening," as he says, and writes to his patron before sitting down to whist and partridges for supper. He revels in the thoughts of ox-cheek and burgundy—he is a boisterous, uproarious parasite, licks his master's shoes with explosions of laughter and cunning smack and gusto, and likes the taste of that blacking as much as the best claret in old Q.'s cellar. He has Rabelais and Horace at his greasy fingers' ends. He is inexpressibly mean, curiously jolly; kindly and good-natured in secret—a tender-hearted knave, not a venomous lickspittle. Jesse says, that at his chapel in Long Acre, "he attained a considerable popularity by the pleasing, manly, and eloquent style of his delivery." Was infidelity endemic, and corruption in the air? Around a young King, himself of the most exemplary life and undoubted piety, lived a Court society as dissolute as our country ever knew. George II.'s bad morals bore their fruit in George III.'s early years; as I believe that a knowledge of that good man's example, his moderation, his frugal simplicity, and God-fearing life, tended infinitely to improve the morals of the country and purify the whole nation.

After Warner, the most interesting of Selwyn's correspondents is the Earl of Carlisle, grandfather of the amiable nobleman at present * Viceroy in Ireland. The grandfather, too, was Irish Viceroy, having previously been treasurer of the King's household; and, in 1778, the principal Commissioner for treating, consulting, and agreeing upon the means of quieting the divisions subsisting in his Majesty's colonies, plantations, and possessions in North America. You may read his Lordship's manifestoes in the *Royal New York Gazette.* He returned to England, having by no means quieted the colonies; and speedily afterwards the *Royal New York Gazette* somehow ceased to be published.

This good, clever, kind, highly-bred Lord Carlisle was one of the English fine gentlemen who was well-nigh ruined by the awful debauchery and extravagance which prevailed in the great English

* 1856.

society of those days. Its dissoluteness was awful: it had swarmed over Europe after the Peace; it had danced, and raced, and gambled in all the Courts. It had made its bow at Versailles; it had run its horses on the plain of Sablons, near Paris, and created the Anglomania there: it had exported vast quantities of pictures and marbles from Rome and Florence: it had ruined itself by building great galleries and palaces for the reception of the statues and pictures: it had brought over singing-women and dancing-women from all the operas of Europe, on whom my Lords lavished their thousands, whilst they left their honest wives and honest children languishing in the lonely deserted splendours of the castle and park at home.

Besides the great London society of those days, there was another unacknowledged world, extravagant beyond measure, tearing about in the pursuit of pleasure; dancing, gambling, drinking, singing; meeting the real society in the public places (at Ranelaghs, Vauxhalls, and Ridottos, about which our old novelists talk so constantly), and outvying the real leaders of fashion in luxury, and splendour, and beauty. For instance, when the famous Miss Gunning visited Paris as Lady Coventry, where she expected that her beauty would meet with the applause which had followed her and her sister through England, it appears she was put to flight by an English lady still more lovely in the eyes of the Parisians. A certain Mrs. Pitt took a box at the opera opposite the Countess; and was so much handsomer than her Ladyship, that the parterre cried out that this was the real English angel, whereupon Lady Coventry quitted Paris in a huff. The poor thing died presently of consumption, accelerated, it was said, by the red and white paint with which she plastered those luckless charms of hers. (We must represent to ourselves all fashionable female Europe, at that time, as plastered with white, and raddled with red.) She left two daughters behind her, whom George Selwyn loved (he was curiously fond of little children), and who are described very drolly and pathetically in these letters, in their little nursery, where passionate little Lady Fanny, if she had not good cards, flung hers into Lady Mary's face; and where they sat conspiring how they should receive a mother-in-law whom their papa presently brought home. They got on very well with their mother-in-law, who was very kind to them; and they grew up, and they were married, and they were both divorced afterwards—poor little souls! Poor painted mother, poor society, ghastly in its pleasures, its loves, its revelries!

As for my Lord Commissioner, we can afford to speak about him; because, though he was a wild and weak Commissioner at one time, though he hurt his estate, though he gambled and lost ten thousand pounds at a sitting—"five times more," says the unlucky gentleman, "than I ever lost before"; though he swore he never would touch a card again; and yet, strange to say, went back to the table and lost still more; yet he repented of his errors, sobered down, and became a worthy peer and a good country gentleman, and returned to the good wife and the good children whom he had always loved with the best part of his heart. He had married at one-and-twenty. He found himself, in the midst of a dissolute society, at the head of a great fortune. Forced into luxury, and obliged to be a great lord and a great idler, he yielded to some temptations, and paid for them a bitter penalty of manly remorse; from some others he fled wisely, and ended by conquering them nobly. But he always had the good wife and children in his mind, and they saved him. "I am very glad you did not come to me the morning I left London," he writes to G. Selwyn, as he is embarking for America. "I can only say, I never knew till that moment of parting, what grief was." There is no parting now, where they are. The faithful wife, the kind generous gentleman, have left a noble race behind them; an inheritor of his name and titles, who is beloved as widely as he is known; a man most kind, accomplished, gentle, friendly, and pure; and female descendants occupying high stations and embellishing great names; some renowned for beauty, and all for spotless lives, and pious matronly virtues.

Another of Selwyn's correspondents is the Earl of March, afterwards Duke of Queensberry, whose life lasted into this century; and who certainly as earl or duke, young man or greybeard, was not an ornament to any possible society. The legends about old Q. are awful. In Selwyn, in Wraxall, and contemporary chronicles, the observer of human nature may follow him, drinking, gambling intriguing to the end of his career; when the wrinkled, palsied, toothless old Don Juan died, as wicked and unrepentant as he had been at the hottest season of youth and passion. There is a house in Piccadilly, where they used to show a certain low window at which old Q. sat to his very last days, ogling through his senile glasses the women as they passed by.

There must have been a great deal of good about this lazy sleepy George Selwyn, which, no doubt, is set to his present credit. "Your friendship," writes Carlisle to him, "is so different from anything I have ever met with or seen in the world, that when I recollect the extraordinary proofs of your kindness, it seems to me like a dream." "I have lost my oldest friend and acquaintance, G. Selwyn," writes Walpole to Miss Berry: "I really loved him, not only for his infinite wit, but for a thousand good qualities." I am glad, for my part, that such a lover of cakes and ale should have had a thousand good qualities—that he should have been friendly, generous, warm-hearted, trustworthy. "I rise at six," writes Carlisle to him, from Spa (a great resort of fashionable people in our ancestors' days), "play at cricket till dinner, and dance in the evening, till I can scarcely crawl to bed at eleven. There is a life for you! You get up at nine; play with Raton your dog till twelve, in your dressing-gown; then creep down to 'White's'; are five hours at table; sleep till supper-time; and then make two wretches carry you in a sedan-chair, with three pints of claret in you, three miles for a shilling." Occasionally, instead of sleeping at "White's," George went down and snoozed in the House of Commons by the side of Lord North. He represented Gloucester for many years, and had a borough of his own, Ludgershall, for which, when he was too lazy to contest Gloucester, he sat himself. "I have given directions for the election of Ludgershall to be of Lord Melbourne and myself," he writes to the Premier, whose friend he was, and who was himself as sleepy, as witty, and as good-natured as George.

If, in looking at the lives of princes, courtiers, men of rank and fashion, we must perforce depict them as idle, profligate, and criminal, we must make allowances for the rich men's failings, and recollect that we, too, were very likely indolent and voluptuous, had we no motive for work, a mortal's natural taste for pleasure, and the daily temptation of a large income. What could a great peer, with a great castle and park, and a great fortune, do but be splendid and idle? In these letters of Lord Carlisle's from which I have been quoting, there is many a just complaint made by the kind-hearted young nobleman of the state which he is obliged to keep; the magnificence in which he must live; the idleness to which his position as a peer of England bound him. Better for him had he been a lawyer at his desk, or a clerk in his office;—a thousand times better chance for happiness, education, employment, security from temptation. A few years since the profession of arms was the only one which our nobles could follow. The Church, the Bar, medicine, literature, the arts, commerce, were below them. It is to the middle class we must look for the safety of England: the working educated men, away from Lord North's bribery in the senate; the good clergy not corrupted into parasites by hopes of preferment; the tradesmen rising into manly opulence; the painters pursuing their gentle calling; the men of letters in their quiet studies: these are the men whom we love and like to read of in the last age. How small the grandees and the men of pleasure look beside them! how contemptible the stories of the George III. Court squabbles are beside the recorded talk of dear old Johnson! What is the grandest entertainment at Windsor, compared to a night at the club over its modest cups, with Percy and Langton, and Goldsmith and poor Bozzy at the table? I declare I think, of all the polite men of that age, Joshua Reynolds was the finest gentleman. And they were good, as well as witty and wise, those dear old friends of the past. Their minds were not debauched by excess, or effeminate with luxury. They toiled their noble day's labour: they rested, and took their kindly pleasure: they cheered their holiday meetings with generous wit and hearty interchange of thought: they were no prudes, but no blush need follow their conversation: they were merry, but no riot came out of their cups. Ah! I would have liked a night at the "Turk's Head," even though bad news had arrived from the colonies, and Doctor Johnson was growling against the rebels; to have sat with him and Goldy; and to have heard Burke, the finest talker in the world; and to have had Garrick flashing in with a story from his theatre!—I like, I say, to think of that society; and not merely how pleasant and how wise, but how *good* they were. I think it was on going home one night from the club that Edmund Burke—his noble soul full of great thoughts, be sure, for they never left him; his heart full of gentleness—was accosted by a poor wandering woman, to whom he spoke words of kindness; and moved by the tears of this Magdalen, perhaps having caused them by the good words he spoke to her, he took her home to the house of his wife and children, and never left her until he had found the means of restoring her to honesty and labour. O you fine gentlemen! you Marches, and Selwyns, and Chesterfields, how small you look by the side of these great men! Good-natured Carlisle plays at cricket all day, and dances in the evening "till he can scarcely crawl," gaily contrasting his superior virtue with George Selwyn's, "carried to bed by two wretches at midnight with three pints of claret in him." Do you remember the verses—the sacred verses—which Johnson wrote on the death of his humble friend Levett?

"Well tried through many a varying year,
See Levett to the grave descend;
Officious, innocent, sincere,
Of every friendless name the friend.

In misery's darkest cavern known,
His useful care was ever nigh,
Where hopeless anguish poured the groan,
And lonely want retired to die.

No summons mocked by chill delay,
No petty gain disdained by pride,
The modest wants of every day
The toil of every day supplied.

> His virtues walked their narrow round,
> Nor made a pause, nor left a void;
> And sure the Eternal Master found
> His single talent well employed."

Whose name looks the brightest now, that of Queensberry the wealthy duke, or Selwyn the wit, or Levett the poor physician?

I hold old Johnson (and shall we not pardon James Boswell some errors for embalming him for us?) to be the great supporter of the British monarchy and Church during the last age—better than whole benches of bishops, better than Pitts, Norths, and the great Burke himself. Johnson had the ear of the nation: his immense authority reconciled it to loyalty, and shamed it out of irreligion. When George III. talked with him, and the people heard the great author's good opinion of the Sovereign, whole generations rallied to the King. Johnson was revered as a sort of oracle; and the oracle declared for Church and King. What a humanity the old man had! He was a kindly partaker of all honest pleasures: a fierce foe to all sin, but a gentle enemy to all sinners. What, boys, are you for a frolic?" he cries, when Topham Beauclerc comes and wakes him up at midnight: "I'm with you." And away he goes, tumbles on his homely old clothes, and trundles through Covent Garden with the young fellows. When he used to frequent Garrick's theatre, and had "the liberty of the scenes," he says, "All the actresses knew me, and dropped me a curtsey as they passed to the stage." That would make a pretty picture: it is a pretty picture, in my mind, of youth, folly, gaiety, tenderly surveyed by wisdom's merciful pure eyes.

George III. and his Queen lived in a very unpretending but elegant-looking house, on the site of the hideous pile under which his granddaughter at present reposes. The King's mother inhabited Carlton House, which contemporary prints represent with a perfect paradise of a garden, with trim lawns, green arcades, and vistas of classic statues. She admired these in company with my Lord Bute, who had a fine classic taste, and sometimes counsel took and sometimes tea in the pleasant green arbours along with that polite nobleman. Bute was hated with a rage of which there have been few examples in English history. He was the butt for everybody's abuse; for Wilkes's devilish mischief; for Churchill's slashing satire; for the hooting of the mob that roasted the boot, his emblem, in a thousand bonfires; that hated him because he was a favourite and a Scotchman, calling him "Mortimer," "Lothario," I know not what names, and accusing his Royal mistress of all sorts of crimes —the grave, lean, demure elderly woman, who, I dare say, was

DR. JOHNSON AND THE ACTRESSES.

quite as good as her neighbours. Chatham lent the aid of his great malice to influence the popular sentiment against her. He assailed, in the House of Lords, "the secret influence, more mighty than the throne itself, which betrayed and clogged every administration." The most furious pamphlets echoed the cry. "Impeach the King's mother," was scribbled over every wall at the Court end of the town, Walpole tells us. What had she done? What had Frederick, Prince of Wales, George's father, done, that he was so loathed by George II. and never mentioned by George III.? Let us not seek for stones to batter that forgotten grave, but acquiesce in the contemporary epitaph over him:—

> "Here lies Fred,
> Who was alive, and is dead.
> Had it been his father,
> I had much rather.
> Had it been his brother,
> Still better than another.
> Had it been his sister,
> No one would have missed her.
> Had it been the whole generation,
> Still better for the nation.
> But since 'tis only Fred,
> Who was alive, and is dead,
> There's no more to be said."

The widow with eight children round her prudently reconciled herself with the King, and won the old man's confidence and good will. A shrewd, hard, domineering, narrow-minded woman, she educated her children according to her lights, and spoke of the eldest as a dull good boy: she kept him very close: she held the tightest rein over him: she had curious prejudices and bigotries. His uncle, the burly Cumberland, taking down a sabre once, and drawing it to amuse the child—the boy started back and turned pale. The Prince felt a generous shock: "What must they have told him about me?" he asked.

His mother's bigotry and hatred he inherited with the courageous obstinacy of his own race; but he was a firm believer where his fathers had been freethinkers, and a true and fond supporter of the Church, of which he was the titular defender. Like other dull men, the King was all his life suspicious of superior people. He did not like Fox; he did not like Reynolds; he did not like Nelson, Chatham, Burke; he was testy at the idea of all innovations, and suspicious of all innovators. He loved mediocrities; Benjamin West was his favourite painter; Beattie was his poet. The King lamented, not without pathos, in his after life, that his education had been neglected. He was a dull lad brought up by narrow-minded people. The cleverest tutors in the world could have done little probably to expand that small intellect, though they might have improved his tastes, and taught his perceptions some generosity.

But he admired as well as he could. There is little doubt that a letter, written by the little Princess Charlotte of Mecklenburg-Strelitz,—a letter containing the most feeble commonplaces about the horrors of war, and the most trivial remarks on the blessings of peace,—struck the young monarch greatly, and decided him upon selecting the young Princess as the sharer of his throne. I pass over the stories of his juvenile loves—of Hannah Lightfoot, the Quakeress, to whom they say he was actually married (though I don't know who has ever seen the register)—of lovely black-haired Sarah Lennox, about whose beauty Walpole has written in raptures, and who used to lie in wait for the young Prince, and make hay at him on the lawn of Holland House. He sighed and he longed, but he rode away from her. Her picture still hangs in Holland House, a magnificent masterpiece of Reynolds, a canvas worthy of Titian. She looks from the castle window, holding a bird in her hand, at black-eyed young Charles Fox, her nephew. The Royal bird flew away from lovely Sarah. She had to figure as bridesmaid at her little Mecklenburg rival's wedding, and died in our own time, a quiet old lady, who had become the mother of the heroic Napiers.

They say the little Princess who had written the fine letter about the horrors of war—a beautiful letter without a single blot, for which she was to be rewarded, like the heroine of the old spelling-book story—was at play one day with some of her young companions in the gardens of Strelitz, and that the young ladies' conversation was, strange to say, about husbands. "Who will take such a poor little princess as me?" Charlotte said to her friend, Ida von Bulow, and at that very moment the postman's horn sounded, and Ida said, "Princess! there is the sweetheart." As she said, so it actually turned out. The postman brought letters from the splendid young King of all England, who said, "Princess! because you have written such a beautiful letter, which does credit to your head and heart, come and be Queen of Great Britain, France, and Ireland, and the true wife of your most obedient servant, George!" So she jumped for joy; and went upstairs and packed all her little trunks; and set off straightway for her kingdom in a beautiful yacht, with a harpsichord on board for her to play upon, and around her a beautiful fleet, all covered with flags and streamers: and the distinguished Madame Auerbach complimented her with an ode, a translation of which may be read in the *Gentleman's Magazine* to the present day:—

> "Her gallant navy through the main
> Now cleaves its liquid way.
> There to their queen a chosen train
> Of nymphs due reverence pay.
>
> Europa, when conveyed by Jove
> To Crete's distinguished shore,
> Greater attention scarce could prove,
> Or be respected more."

They met, and they were married, and for years they led the happiest simplest lives sure ever led by married couple. It is said the King winced when he first saw his homely little bride; but, however that may be, he was a true and faithful husband to her, as she was a faithful and loving wife. They had the simplest pleasures—the very mildest and simplest—little country dances, to which a dozen couples were invited, and where the honest King would stand up and dance for three hours at a time to one tune; after which delicious excitement they would go to bed without any supper (the Court people grumbling sadly at that absence of supper), and get up quite early the next morning, and perhaps the next night have another dance; or the Queen would play on the spinet —she played pretty well, Haydn said—or the King would read to her a paper out of the *Spectator*, or perhaps one of Ogden's sermons. O Arcadia! what a life it must have been! There used to be Sunday drawing-rooms at Court; but the young King stopped these, as he stopped all that godless gambling whereof we have made mention. Not that George was averse to any innocent pleasures, or pleasures which he thought innocent. He was a patron of the arts, after his fashion; kind and gracious to the artists whom he favoured, and respectful to their calling. He wanted once to establish an Order of Minerva for literary and scientific characters; the knights were to take rank after the Knights of the Bath, and to sport a straw-coloured ribbon and a star of sixteen points. But there was such a row among the *literati* as to the persons who should be appointed, that the plan was given up, and Minerva and her star never came down amongst us.

He objected to painting St. Paul's, as Popish practice; accordingly, the most clumsy heathen sculptures decorate that edifice at present. It is fortunate that the paintings, too, were spared, for painting and drawing were woefully unsound at the close of the last century; and it is far better for our eyes to contemplate whitewash (when we turn them away from the clergyman) than to look at Opie's pitchy canvases, or Fuseli's livid monsters.

And yet there is one day in the year—a day when old George loved with all his heart to attend it—when I think Saint Paul's presents the noblest sight in the whole world: when five thousand charity children with cheeks like nosegays, and sweet fresh voices, sing the hymn which makes every heart thrill with praise and happiness I have seen a hundred grand sights in the world—coronations, Parisian splendours, Crystal Palace openings, Pope's chapels with their processions of long-tailed cardinals and quavering choirs of fat soprani—but think in all Christendom there is no such sight as Charity Children's Day. *Non Angli, sed angeli.* As one looks at that beautiful multitude of innocents: as the first note strikes: indeed one may almost fancy that cherubs are singing.

Of Church music the King was always very fond, showing skill in it both as a critic and as a performer. Many stories, mirthful and affecting, are told of his behaviour at the concerts which he ordered. When he was blind and ill he chose the music for the Ancient Concerts once, and the music and words which he selected were from "Samson Agonistes," and all had reference to his blindness, his captivity, and his affliction. He would beat time with his music-roll as they sang the anthem in the Chapel Royal. If the page below was talkative or inattentive, down would come the music-roll on young scapegrace's powdered head. The theatre was always his delight. His bishops and clergy used to attend it, thinking it no shame to appear where that good man was seen. He is said not to have cared for Shakspeare or tragedy much; farces and pantomimes were his joy; and especially when clown swallowed a carrot or a string of sausages, he would laugh so outrageously that the lovely Princess by his side would have to say, "My gracious monarch, do compose yourself." But he continued to laugh, and at the very smallest farces, as long as his poor wits were left him.

There is something to me exceedingly touching in that simple early life of the King's. As long as his mother lived—a dozen years after his marriage with the little spinet-player—he was a great shy awkward boy under the tutelage of that hard parent. She must have been a clever, domineering, cruel woman. She kept her household lonely and in gloom, mistrusting almost all people who came about her children. Seeing the young Duke of Gloucester silent and unhappy once, she sharply asked him the cause of his silence. "I am thinking," said the poor child. "Thinking, sir! and of what?" "I am thinking if ever I have a son I will not make him so unhappy as you make me." The other sons were all wild, except George. Dutifully every evening George and Charlotte paid their visit to the King's mother at Carlton House. She had a throat-complaint, of which she died; but to the last persisted in driving about the streets to show she was alive. The night before her death the resolute woman talked with her son and daughter-in-law as usual, went to bed, and was found dead there in the morning. "George, be a King!" were the words which she was for ever croaking in the ears of her son: and a king the simple, stubborn, affectionate, bigoted man tried to be.

He did his best; he worked according to his lights; what virtue he knew, he tried to practise; what knowledge he could master, he strove to acquire. He was for ever drawing maps, for example, and learned geography with no small care and industry. He knew all about the family histories and genealogies of his gentry, and pretty histories he must have known. He knew the whole *Army List;* and all the facings, and the exact number of the buttons, and all the tags and laces, and the cut of all the cocked-hats, pig-tails, and gaiters in his army. He knew the *personnel* of the Universities; what doctors were inclined to Socinianism, and who were sound Churchmen; he knew the etiquettes of his own and his grandfather's Courts to a nicety, and the smallest particulars regarding the routine of ministers, secretaries, embassies, audiences; the humblest page in the ante-room, or the meanest helper in the stables or kitchen. These parts of the Royal business he was capable of learning, and he learned. But, as one thinks of an office, almost divine, performed by any mortal man—of any single being pretending to control the thoughts, to direct the faith, to order the implicit obedience of brother millions, to compel them into war at his offence or quarrel; to command, "In this way you shall trade, in this way you shall think; these neighbours shall be your allies whom you shall help, these others your enemies whom you shall slay at my orders; in this way you shall worship God;"—who can wonder that, when such a man as George took such an office on himself, punishment and humiliation should fall upon people and chief?

Yet there is something grand about his courage. The battle of the King with his aristocracy remains yet to be told by the historian who shall view the reign of George more justly than the trumpery panegyrists who wrote immediately after his decease. It was he, with the people to back him, who made the war with America; it was he and the people who refused justice to the Roman Catholics; and on both questions he beat the patricians. He bribed: he bullied: he darkly dissembled on occasion: he exercised a slippery perseverance, and a vindictive resolution, which one almost admires as one thinks his character over. His courage was never to be beat.

It trampled North under foot: it bent the stiff neck of the younger Pitt: even his illness never conquered that indomitable spirit. As soon as his brain was clear, it resumed the scheme, only laid aside when his reason left him: as soon as his hands were out of the strait-waistcoat, they took up the pen and the plan which had engaged him up to the moment of his malady. I believe it is by persons believing themselves in the right that nine-tenths of the tyranny of this world has been perpetrated. Arguing on that convenient premiss, the Dey of Algiers would cut off twenty heads of a morning; Father Dominic would burn a score of Jews in the presence of the Most Catholic King, and the Archbishops of Toledo and Salamanca sing Amen. Protestants were roasted, Jesuits hung and quartered at Smithfield, and witches burned at Salem, and all by worthy people, who believed they had the best authority for their actions.

And so, with respect to old George, even Americans, whom he hated and who conquered him, may give him credit for having quite honest reasons for oppressing them. Appended to Lord Brougham's biographical sketch of Lord North are some autograph notes of the King, which let us most curiously into the state of his mind. "The times certainly require," says he, "the concurrence of all who wish to prevent anarchy. I have no wish but the prosperity of my own dominions, therefore I must look upon all who would not heartily assist me as bad men, as well as bad subjects." That is the way he reasoned. "I wish nothing but good, therefore every man who does not agree with me is a traitor and a scoundrel." Remember that he believed himself anointed by a Divine commission; remember that he was a man of slow parts and imperfect education; that the same awful will of Heaven which placed a crown upon his head, which made him tender to his family, pure in his life, courageous and honest, made him dull of comprehension, obstinate of will, and at many times deprived him of reason. He was the father of his people; his rebellious children must be flogged into obedience. He was the defender of the Protestant faith; he would rather lay that stout head upon the block than that Catholics should have a share in the government of England. And you do not suppose that there are not honest bigots enough in all countries to back kings in this kind of statesmanship? Without doubt the American war was popular in England. In 1775 the address in favour of coercing the colonies was carried by 304 to 105 in the Commons, by 104 to 29 in the House of Lords. Popular?—so was the Revocation of the Edict of Nantes popular in France: so was the Massacre of Saint Bartholomew: so was the Inquisition exceedingly popular in Spain.

Wars and revolutions are, however, the politician's province. The great events of this long reign, the statesmen and orators who illustrated it, I do not pretend to make the subjects of an hour's light talk. Let us return to our humbler duty of Court gossip. Yonder sits our little Queen, surrounded by many stout sons and fair daughters whom she bore to her faithful George. The history of the daughters, as little Miss Burney has painted them to us, is delightful. They were handsome—she calls them beautiful; they were most kind, loving, and ladylike; they were gracious to every person, high and low, who served them. They had many little accomplishments of their own. This one drew: that one played the piano: they all worked most prodigiously, and fitted up whole suites of rooms—pretty smiling Penelopes,—with their busy little needles. As we picture to ourselves the society of eighty years ago, we must imagine hundreds of thousands of groups of women in great high caps, tight bodies and full skirts, needling away, whilst one of the number, or perhaps a favoured gentleman in a pigtail, reads out a novel to the company. Peep into the cottage at Olney, for example, and see there Mrs. Unwin and Lady Hesketh, those high-bred ladies, those sweet pious women, and William Cowper, that delicate wit, that trembling pietist, that refined gentleman, absolutely reading out "Jonathan Wild" to the ladies! What a change in our manners, in our amusements, since then!

King George's household was a model of an English gentleman's household. It was early; it was kindly; it was charitable; it was frugal; it was orderly; it must have been stupid to a degree which I shudder now to contemplate. No wonder all the princes ran away from the lap of that dreary domestic virtue. It always rose, rode, dined at stated intervals. Day after day was the same. At the same hour at night the King kissed his daughters' jolly cheeks; the Princesses kissed their mother's hand; and Madame Thielke brought the Royal nightcap. At the same hour the equerries and women in waiting had their little dinner, and cackled over their tea. The King had his backgammon or his evening concert; the equerries yawned themselves to death in the ante-room; or the King and his family walked on Windsor slopes, the King holding his darling little Princess Amelia by the hand; and the people crowded round quite good-naturedly; and the Eton boys thrust their chubby cheeks under the crowd's elbows; and the concert over, the King never failed to take his enormous cocked-hat off, and salute his band, and say, "Thank you, gentlemen."

A quieter household, a more prosaic life than this of Kew or Windsor, cannot be imagined. Rain or shine, the King rode every day for hours; poked his red face into hundreds of cottages round about, and showed that shovel hat and Windsor uniform to farmers, to pig-boys, to old women making apple-dumplings; to all sorts of people, gentle and simple, about whom countless stories are told. Nothing can be more undignified than these stories. When Haroun Alraschid visits a subject incog., the latter is sure to be very much the better for the caliph's magnificence. Old George showed no such Royal splendour. He used to give a guinea sometimes: sometimes feel in his pockets and find he had no money: often ask a man a hundred questions—about the number of his family, about his oats and beans, about the rent he paid for his house—and ride on. On one occasion he played the part of King Alfred, and turned a piece of meat with a string at a cottager's house. When the old woman came home, she found a paper with an enclosure of money, and a note written by the Royal pencil: "Five guineas to buy a jack." It was not splendid, but it was kind and worthy of Farmer George. One day, when the King and Queen were walking together, they met a little boy—they were always fond of children, the good folk—and patted the little white head. "Whose little boy are you?" asks the Windsor uniform. "I am the King's beefeater's little boy," replied the child. On which the King said, "Then kneel down, and kiss the Queen's hand." But the innocent offspring of the beefeater declined this treat. "No," said he, "I won't kneel, for if I do, I shall spoil my new breeches." The thrifty King ought to have hugged him and knighted him on the spot. George's admirers wrote pages and pages of such stories about him. One morning, before anybody else was up, the King walked about Gloucester town; pushed over Molly the housemaid with her pail, who was scrubbing the doorsteps; ran upstairs and woke all the equerries in their bedrooms; and then trotted down to the bridge, where, by this time, a dozen of louts were assembled. "What! is this Gloucester New Bridge?" asked our gracious monarch; and the people answered him, "Yes, your Majesty." "Why, then, my boys," said he, "let us have a huzzay!" After giving them which intellectual gratification, he went home to breakfast. Our fathers read these simple tales with fond pleasure; laughed at these very small jokes; liked the old man who poked his nose into every cottage; who lived on plain wholesome roast and boiled; who despised your French kickshaws; who was a true hearty old English gentleman. You may have seen Gilray's famous print of him—in the old wig, in the stout old hideous Windsor uniform—as the King of Brobdingnag, peering at a little Gulliver, whom he holds up in his hand, whilst in the other he has an opera-glass, through which he surveys the pigmy? Our fathers chose to set up George as the type of a great king; and the little Gulliver was the great Napoleon. We prided ourselves on our prejudices; we blustered and bragged with absurd vainglory; we dealt to our enemy a monstrous injustice of contempt and scorn; we fought him with all weapons, mean as well as heroic. There was no lie we would not believe; no charge of crime which our furious prejudice would not credit. I thought at one time of making a collection of the lies which the French had written against us, and we had published against them during the war: it would be a strange memorial of popular falsehood.

Their Majesties were very sociable potentates; and the Court Chronicler tells of numerous visits which they paid to their subjects, gentle and simple: with whom they dined; at whose great country-houses they stopped; or at whose poorer lodgings they affably partook of tea and bread-and-butter. Some of the great folk spent enormous sums in entertaining their Sovereigns. As marks of special favour, the King and Queen sometimes stood as sponsors for the children of the nobility. We find Lady Salisbury was so honoured in the year 1786; and in the year 1802, Lady Chesterfield. The *Court News* relates how her Ladyship received their Majesties on a state bed "dressed with white satin and a profusion of lace: the counterpane of white satin embroidered with gold, and the bed of crimson satin lined with white." The child was first brought by the nurse to the Marchioness of Bath, who presided as chief nurse. Then the Marchioness handed baby to the Queen. Then the Queen handed the little darling to the Bishop of Norwich, the officiating clergyman; and, the ceremony over, a cup of caudle was presented by the Earl to his Majesty on one knee, on a large gold waiter, placed on a crimson velvet cushion. Misfortunes would occur in these interesting genuflectory ceremonies of Royal worship. Bubb Doddington, Lord Melcombe, a very fat, puffy man, in a most gorgeous Court-suit, had to kneel, Cumberland says, and was so fat and so tight that he could not get up again. "Kneel, sir, kneel!" cried my Lord-in-waiting to a country mayor who had to read an address, but who went on with his compliment standing. "Kneel, sir, kneel!" cries my Lord, in dreadful alarm. "I can't!" says the mayor, turning round; "don't you see I have got a wooden leg?" In the capital "Burney Diary and Letters," the home and Court life of good old King George and good old Queen Charlotte are presented at portentous length. The King rose every morning at six: and had two hours to himself. He thought it effeminate to have a carpet in his bedroom. Shortly before eight, the Queen and the Royal family were always ready for him, and they proceeded to the King's chapel in the castle. There were no fires in the passages: the chapel was scarcely alight; princesses, governesses, equerries grumbled and caught cold: but cold or hot, it was their duty to go: and, wet or dry, light or dark, the stout old George was always in his place to say amen to the chaplain.

The Queen's character is represented in "Burney" at full length. She was a sensible, most decorous woman; a very grand lady on State occasions, simple enough in ordinary life; well read as times went, and giving shrewd opinions about books; stingy, but not unjust: not generally unkind to her dependants, but invincible in her notions of etiquette, and quite angry if her people suffered ill-health in her service. She gave Miss Burney a shabby pittance, and led the poor young woman a life which well-nigh killed her. She never thought but that she was doing Burney the greatest favour, in taking her from freedom, fame, and competence, and killing her off with languor in that dreary Court. It was not dreary to her. Had she been servant instead of mistress, her spirit would never have broken down: she never would have put a pin out of place, or been a moment from her duty. *She* was not weak, and she could not pardon those who were. She was perfectly correct in life, and she hated poor sinners with a rancour such as virtue sometimes has. She must have had awful private trials of her own: not merely with her children, but with her husband, in those long days about which nobody will ever know anything now; when he was not quite insane; when his incessant tongue was babbling folly, rage, persecution; and she had to smile and be respectful and attentive under this intolerable ennui. The Queen bore all her duties stoutly, as she expected others to bear them. At a State christening, the lady who held the infant was tired and looked unwell, and the Princess of Wales asked permission for her to sit down. "Let her stand," said the Queen, flicking the snuff off her sleeve. *She* would have stood, the resolute old woman, if she had had to hold the child till his beard was grown. "I am seventy years of age," the Queen said, facing a mob of ruffians who stopped her sedan: "I have been fifty years Queen of England, and I never was insulted before." Fearless, rigid, unforgiving little queen! I don't wonder that her sons revolted from her.

Of all the figures in that large family group which surrounds George and his Queen, the prettiest, I think, is the father's darling, the Princess Amelia, pathetic for her beauty, her sweetness, her early death, and for the extreme passionate tenderness with which her father loved her. This was his favourite amongst all the children: of his sons, he loved the Duke of York best. Burney tells a sad story of the poor old man at Weymouth, and how eager he was to have this darling son with him. The King's house was

THE LAST DAYS OF GEORGE THE THIRD.

not big enough to hold the Prince; and his father had a portable house erected close to his own, and at huge pains, so that his dear Frederick should be near him. He clung on his arm all the time of his visit: talked to no one else; had talked of no one else for some time before. The Prince, so long expected, stayed but a single night. He had business in London the next day, he said. The dulness of the old King's Court stupefied York and the other big sons of George III. They scared equerries and ladies, frightened the modest little circle, with their coarse spirits and loud talk. Of little comfort, indeed, were the King's sons to the King.

But the pretty Amelia was his darling; and the little maiden, prattling and smiling in the fond arms of that old father, is a sweet image to look on. There is a family picture in "Burney," which a man must be very hard-hearted not to like. She describes an after-dinner walk of the Royal family at Windsor.

"It was really a mighty pretty procession," she says. "The little Princess, just turned of three years old, in a robe-coat covered with fine muslin, a dressed close cap, white gloves, and fan, walked on alone and first, highly delighted with the parade, and turning from side to side to see everybody as she passed; for all the terracers stand up against the walls, to make a clear passage for the Royal family the moment they come in sight. Then followed the King and Queen, no less delighted with the joy of their little darling. The Princess Royal leaning on Lady Elizabeth Waldegrave, the Princess Augusta holding by the Duchess of Ancaster, the Princess Elizabeth led by Lady Charlotte Bertie, followed."

"Office here takes place of rank," says Burney,—to explain how it was that Lady Elizabeth Waldegrave, as lady of the bedchamber, walked before a duchess. "General Bude, and the Duke of Montague, and Major Price as equerry, brought up the rear of the procession."

One sees it: the band playing its old music, the sun shining on the happy loyal crowd; and lighting the ancient battlements, the rich elms, and purple landscape, and bright greensward; the Royal standard drooping from the great tower yonder; as old George passes, followed by his race, preceded by the charming infant, who caresses the crowd with her innocent smiles.

"On sight of Mrs. Delany, the King instantly stopped to speak to her; the Queen, of course, and the little Princess, and all the rest, stood still. They talked a good while with the sweet old lady, during which time the King once or twice addressed himself to me. I caught the Queen's eye, and saw in it a little surprise, but by no means any displeasure, to see me of the party. The little Princess went up to Mrs. Delany, of whom she is very fond and behaved like a little angel to her. She then, with a look of inquiry and recollection, came behind Mrs. Delany to look at me. 'I am afraid,' said I, in a whisper, and stooping down, 'your Royal Highness does not remember me?' Her answer was an arch little smile, and a nearer approach, with her lips pouted out to kiss me."

The Princess wrote verses herself, and there are some pretty plaintive lines attributed to her, which are more touching than better poetry:—

"Unthinking, idle, wild, and young,
I laughed, and danced, and talked, and sung:
And, proud of health, of freedom vain,
Dreamed not of sorrow, care, or pain;
Concluding, in those hours of glee,
That all the world was made for me.

But when the hour of trial came,
When sickness shook this trembling frame,
When folly's gay pursuits were o'er,
And I could sing and dance no more,
It then occurred, how sad 'twould be,
Were this world only made for me."

The poor soul quitted it—and ere yet she was dead the agonised father was in such a state, that the officers round about him were obliged to set watchers over him, and from November 1810 George III. ceased to reign. All the world knows the story of his malady: all history presents no sadder figure than that of the old man, blind and deprived of reason, wandering through the rooms of his palace, addressing imaginary parliaments, reviewing fancied troops, holding ghostly Courts. I have seen his picture as it was taken at this time, hanging in the apartment of his daughter, the Landgravine of Hesse Hombourg—amidst books and Windsor furniture, and a hundred fond reminiscences of her English home. The poor old father is represented in a purple gown, his snowy beard falling over his breast—the star of his famous Order still idly shining on it. He was not only sightless: he became utterly deaf. All light, all reason, all sound of human voices, all the pleasures of this world of God, were taken from him. Some slight lucid moments he had; in one of which the Queen, desiring to see him, entered the room, and found him singing a hymn, and accompanying himself at the harpsichord. When he had finished he knelt down and prayed aloud for her, and then for his family, and then for the nation, concluding with a prayer for himself, that it might please God to avert his heavy calamity from him, but if not, to give him resignation to submit. He then burst into tears, and his reason again fled.

What preacher need moralise on this story; what words save the simplest are requisite to tell it? It is too terrible for tears. The thought of such a misery smites me down in submission before the Ruler of kings and men, the Monarch Supreme over empires and republics, the inscrutable Dispenser of life, death, happiness, victory. "O brothers," I said to those who heard me first in America—"O brothers! speaking the same dear mother tongue—O comrades! enemies no more, let us take a mournful hand together as we stand by this Royal corpse, and call a truce to battle! Low he lies, to whom the proudest used to kneel once, and who was cast lower than the poorest: dead, whom millions prayed for in vain. Driven off his throne; buffeted by rude hands; with his children in revolt; the darling of his old age killed before him untimely; our Lear hangs over her breathless lips and cries, 'Cordelia, Cordelia, stay a little!'

> 'Vex not his ghost—oh! let him pass—he hates him
> That would upon the rack of this tough world
> Stretch him out longer!'

Hush! Strife and Quarrel, over the solemn grave! Sound, trumpets, a mournful march! Fall, dark curtain, upon his pageant, his pride, his grief, his awful tragedy!"

GEORGE THE FOURTH

IN Twiss's amusing "Life of Eldon," we read how, on the death of the Duke of York, the old Chancellor became possessed of a lock of the defunct Prince's hair; and so careful was he respecting the authenticity of the relic, that Bessy Eldon his wife sat in the room with the young man from Hamlet's who distributed the ringlet into separate lockets, which each of the Eldon family afterwards wore. You know how, when George IV. came to Edinburgh, a better man than he went on board the Royal yacht to welcome the King to his kingdom of Scotland, seized a goblet from which his Majesty had just drunk, vowed it should remain for ever as an heirloom in his family, clapped the precious glass in his pocket, and sat down on it and broke it when he got home. Suppose the good sheriff's prize unbroken now at Abbotsford, should we not smile with something like pity as we beheld it? Suppose one of those lockets of the no-Popery Prince's hair offered for sale at Christie's, *quot libras e duce summo invenies?* how many pounds would you find for the illustrious Duke? Madame Tussaud has got King George's coronation robes: is there any man now alive who would kiss the hem of that trumpery? He sleeps since thirty years: do not any of you, who remembered him, wonder that you once respected and huzza'd and admired him?

To make a portrait of him at first seemed a matter of small difficulty. There is his coat, his star, his wig, his countenance simpering under it: with a slate and a piece of chalk, I could at this very desk perform a recognisable likeness of him. And yet after reading of him in scores of volumes, hunting him through old magazines and newspapers, having him here at a ball, there at a public dinner, there at races and so forth, you find you have nothing—nothing but a coat and a wig and a mask smiling below it—nothing but a great simulacrum. His sire and grandsires were men. One knows what they were like: what they would do in given circumstances: that on occasion they fought and demeaned themselves like tough good soldiers. They had friends whom they liked according to their natures; enemies whom they hated fiercely;

passions, and actions, and individualities of their own. The sailor King who came after George was a man: the Duke of York was a man, big, burly, loud, jolly, cursing, courageous. But this George, what was he? I look through all his life, and recognise but a bow and a grin. I try and take him to pieces, and find silk stockings, padding, stays, a coat with frogs and a fur collar, a star and blue riband, a pocket handkerchief prodigiously scented, one of Truefitt's best nutty-brown wigs reeking with oil, a set of teeth and a huge black stock, underwaistcoats, more underwaistcoats, and then nothing. I know of no sentiment that he ever distinctly uttered. Documents are published under his name, but people wrote them—private letters, but people spelt them. He put a great George P. or George R. at the bottom of the page and fancied he had written the paper: some bookseller's clerk, some poor author, some *man* did the work; saw to the spelling, cleaned up the slovenly sentences, and gave the lax maudlin slipslop a sort of consistency. He must have had an individuality; the dancing-master whom he emulated, nay, surpassed—the wigmaker who curled his toupee for him—the tailor who cut his coats, had that. But about George, one can get at nothing actual. That outside, I am certain, is pad and tailor's work; there may be something behind, but what? We cannot get at the character; no doubt never shall. Will men of the future have nothing better to do than to unswathe and interpret that Royal old mummy? I own I once used to think it would be good sport to pursue him, fasten on him, and pull him down. But now I am ashamed to mount and lay good dogs on, to summon a full field, and then to hunt the poor game

On the 12th August 1762, the forty-seventh anniversary of the accession of the House of Brunswick to the English throne, all the bells in London pealed in gratulation, and announced that an heir to George III. was born. Five days afterwards the King was pleased to pass letters patent under the great seal, creating H.R.H. the Prince of Great Britain, Electoral Prince of Brunswick Luneburg, Duke of Cornwall and Rothesay, Earl of Carrick, Baron of Renfrew, Lord of the Isles, and Great Steward of Scotland, Prince of Wales and Earl of Chester.

All the people at his birth thronged to see this lovely child; and behind a gilt china-screen railing in Saint James's Palace, in a cradle surmounted by the three princely ostrich feathers, the Royal infant was laid to delight the eyes of the lieges. Among the earliest instances of homage paid to him, I read that "a curious Indian bow and arrows were sent to the Prince from his father's faithful subjects in New York." He was fond of playing with these toys: an old statesman, orator and wit of his grandfather's and great-grandfather's time, never tired of his business, still eager in his old age to be well at Court, used to play with the little Prince, and pretend to fall down dead when the Prince shot at him with his toy bow and arrows—and get up and fall down dead over and over again—to the increased delight of the child. So that he was flattered from his cradle upwards; and before his little feet could walk, statesmen and courtiers were busy kissing them.

There is a pretty picture of the Royal infant—a beautiful buxom child—asleep in his mother's lap; who turns round and holds a finger to her lip, as if she would bid the courtiers around respect the baby's slumbers. From that day until his decease, sixty-eight years after, I suppose there were more pictures taken of that personage than of any other human being who ever was born and died—in every kind of uniform and every possible Court-dress—in long fair hair, with powder, with and without a pigtail—in every conceivable cocked-hat—in dragoon uniform—in Windsor uniform—in a field-marshal's clothes—in a Scotch kilt and tartans, with dirk and claymore (a stupendous figure)—in a frogged frock-coat with a fur collar and tight breeches and silk stockings—in wigs of every colour, fair, brown, and black—in his famous coronation robes finally, with which performance he was so much in love that he distributed copies of the picture to all the Courts and British embassies in Europe, and to numberless clubs, town-halls, and private friends. I remember as a young man how almost every dining-room had his portrait.

There is plenty of biographical tattle about the Prince's boyhood. It is told with what astonishing rapidity he learned all languages, ancient and modern; how he rode beautifully, sang charmingly, and played elegantly on the violoncello. That he was beautiful was patent to all eyes. He had a high spirit; and once, when he had had a difference with his father, burst into the Royal closet and called out, "Wilkes and liberty for ever!" He was so clever, that he confounded his very governors in learning; and one of them, Lord Bruce, having made a false quantity in quoting Greek, the admirable young Prince instantly corrected him. Lord Bruce could not remain a governor after this humiliation; resigned his office, and, to soothe his feelings, was actually promoted to be an earl! It is the most wonderful reason for promoting a man that ever I heard. Lord Bruce was made an earl for a blunder in prosody; and Nelson was made a baron for the victory of the Nile.

Lovers of long sums have added up the millions and millions which in the course of his brilliant existence this single Prince consumed. Besides his income of £50,000, £70,000, £100,000, £120,000 a year, we read of three applications to Parliament; debts to the amount of £160,000, of £650,000; besides mysterious foreign loans, whereof he pocketed the proceeds. What did he do for all this money? Why was he to have it? If he had been a manufacturing town, or a populous rural district, or an army of five thousand men, he would not have cost more. He, one solitary stout man, who did not toil, nor spin, nor fight,—what had any mortal done that he should be pampered so?

In 1784, when he was twenty-one years of age, Carlton Palace was given to him, and furnished by the nation with as much luxury as could be devised. His pockets were filled with money: he said it was not enough; he flung it out of window: he spent £10,000 a year for the coats on his back. The nation gave him more money, and more, and more. The sum is past counting. He was a prince most lovely to look on, and was christened Prince Florizel on his first appearance in the world. That he was the handsomest prince in the whole world was agreed by men, and alas! by many women.

I suppose he must have been very graceful. There are so many testimonies to the charm of his manner, that we must allow him great elegance and powers of fascination. He, and the King of France's brother, the Count d'Artois, a charming young Prince who danced deliciously on the tight-rope—a poor old tottering exiled King, who asked hospitality of King George's successor, and lived awhile in the palace of Mary Stuart—divided in their youth the title of first gentlemen of Europe. We in England of course gave the prize to *our* gentleman. Until George's death the propriety of that award was scarce questioned, or the doubters voted rebels and traitors. Only the other day I was reading in the reprint of the delightful "Noctes" of Christopher North. The health of THE KING is drunk in large capitals by the loyal Scotsman. You would fancy him a hero, a sage, a statesman, a pattern for kings and men. It was Walter Scott who had that accident with the broken glass I spoke of anon. He was the King's Scottish champion, rallied all Scotland to him, made loyalty the fashion, and laid about him fiercely with his claymore upon all the Prince's enemies. The Brunswicks had no such defenders as those two Jacobite commoners, old Sam Johnson, the Lichfield chapman's son, and Walter Scott, the Edinburgh lawyer's.

Nature and circumstance had done their utmost to prepare the Prince for being spoiled: the dreadful dulness of papa's Court, its stupid amusements, its dreary occupations, the maddening humdrum, the stifling sobriety of its routine, would have made a scapegrace of a much less lively prince. All the big princes bolted from that castle of ennui where old King George sat, posting up his books and droning over his Handel; and old Queen Charlotte over her snuff and her tambour-frame. Most of the sturdy gallant sons settled down after sowing their wild oats, and became sober subjects of their father and brother—not ill liked by the nation, which pardons youthful irregularities readily enough, for the sake of pluck, and unaffectedness, and good-humour.

The boy is father of the man. Our Prince signalised his entrance into the world by a feat worthy of his future life. He invented a new shoe-buckle. It was an inch long and five inches broad. "It covered almost the whole instep, reaching down to the ground on either side of the foot." A sweet invention! lovely and useful as the Prince on whose foot it sparkled. At his first appearance at a Court ball, we read that "his coat was pink silk, with white cuffs; his waistcoat white silk, embroidered with various-coloured foil, and adorned with a profusion of French paste. And his hat was ornamented with two rows of steel beads, five thousand in number, with a button and loop of the same metal, and cocked in a new military style." What a Florizel! Do these details seem trivial? They are the grave incidents of his life. His biographers say that when he commenced housekeeping in that splendid new palace of his, the Prince of Wales had some windy projects of encouraging literature, science, and the arts; of having assemblies of literary characters; and societies for the encouragement of geography, astronomy, and botany. Astronomy, geography, and botany! Fiddlesticks! French ballet-dancers, French cooks, horse-jockeys, buffoons, procurers, tailors, boxers, fencing-masters, china, jewel, and gimcrack merchants—these were his real companions. At first he made a pretence of having Burke and Fox and Sheridan for his friends. But how could such men be serious before such an empty scapegrace as this lad? Fox might talk dice with him, and Sheridan wine; but what else had these men of genius in common with their tawdry young host of Carlton House? That fribble the leader of such men as Fox and Burke! That man's opinions about the Constitution, the India Bill, justice to the Catholics—about any question graver than the button for a waistcoat or the sauce for a partridge—worth anything! The friendship between the Prince and the Whig chiefs was impossible. They were hypocrites in pretending to respect him, and if he broke the hollow compact between them, who shall blame him? His natural companions were dandies and parasites. He could talk to a tailor or a cook; but, as the equal of great statesmen, to set up a creature, lazy, weak, indolent, besotted, of monstrous vanity, and levity incurable—it is absurd. They thought to use him, and did for a while; but they must have known how timid he was; how entirely heartless and treacherous, and have expected his desertion.

His next set of friends were mere table companions, of whom he grew tired too; then we hear of him with a very few select toadies, mere boys from school or the Guards, whose sprightliness tickled the fancy of the worn-out voluptuary. What matters what friends he had? He dropped all his friends; he never could have real friends. An heir to the throne has flatterers, adventurers who hang about him, ambitious men who use him; but friendship is denied him.

And women, I suppose, are as false and selfish in their dealings with such a character as men. Shall we take the Leporello part, flourish a catalogue of the conquests of this Royal Don Juan, and tell the names of the favourites to whom, one after the other, George Prince flung his pocket-handkerchief? What purpose would it answer to say how Perdita was pursued, won, deserted, and by whom succeeded? What good in knowing that he did actually marry Mrs. Fitz-Herbert according to the rites of the Roman Catholic Church; that her marriage settlements have been seen in London; that the names of the witnesses to her marriage are known? This sort of vice that we are now come to presents no new or fleeting trait of manners. Debauchees, dissolute, heartless, fickle, cowardly, have been ever since the world began. This one had more temptations than most, and so much may be said in extenuation for him.

It was an unlucky thing for this doomed one, and tending to lead him yet farther on the road to the deuce, that, besides being lovely, so that women were fascinated by him; and heir-apparent, so that all the world flattered him; he should have a beautiful voice, which led him directly in the way of drink: and thus all the pleasant devils were coaxing on poor Florizel; desire, and idleness, and vanity, and drunkenness, all clashing their merry cymbals and bidding him come on.

We first hear of his warbling sentimental ditties under the walls of Kew Palace by the moonlit banks of Thames, with Lord Viscount Leporello keeping watch lest the music should be disturbed.

Singing after dinner and supper was the universal fashion of the day. You may fancy all England sounding with choruses, but some ribald, some harmless, all occasioning the consumption of a prodigious deal of fermented liquor.

"The jolly Muse her wings to try no frolic flights need take,
But round the bowl would dip and fly, like swallows round a lake,"

sang Morris in one of his gallant Anacreontics, to which the Prince many a time joined in chorus, and of which the burden is,—

"And that I think's a reason fair to drink and fill again."

This delightful boon companion of the Prince's found "a reason fair" to forego filling and drinking, saw the error of his ways, gave up the bowl and chorus, and died retired and religious. The Prince's table no doubt was a very tempting one. The wits came and did their utmost to amuse him. It is wonderful how the spirits rise, the wit brightens, the wine has an aroma, when a great man is at the head of the table. Scott, the loyal Cavalier, the King's true liegeman, the very best *raconteur* of his time, poured out with an endless generosity his store of old-world learning, kindness, and humour. Grattan contributed to it his wondrous eloquence, fancy, feeling. Tom Moore perched upon it for a while, and piped his most exquisite little love-tunes on it, flying away in a twitter of indignation afterwards, and attacking the Prince with bill and claw. In such society, no wonder the sitting was long, and the butler tired of drawing corks. Remember what the usages of the time were, and that William Pitt, coming to the House of Commons after having drunk a bottle of port-wine at his own house, would go into Bellamy's with Dundas, and help finish a couple more.

You peruse volumes after volumes about our Prince, and find some half-dozen stock stories—indeed not many more—common to all the histories. He was good-natured; an indolent voluptuous prince, not unkindly. One story, the most favourable to him of all, perhaps, is that as Prince Regent he was eager to hear all that could be said in behalf of prisoners condemned to death, and anxious, if possible, to remit the capital sentence. He was kind to his servants. There is a story common to all the biographies, of Molly the housemaid, who, when his household was to be broken up, owing to some reforms which he tried absurdly to practise, was discovered crying as she dusted the chairs because she was to leave a master who had a kind word for all his servants. Another tale is that of a groom of the Prince's being discovered in corn and oat peculations, and dismissed by the personage at the head of the stables; the Prince had word of John's disgrace, remonstrated with him very kindly, generously reinstated him, and bade him promise to sin no more—a promise which John kept. Another story is very fondly told of the Prince as a young man hearing of an officer's family in distress, and how he straightway borrowed six or eight hundred pounds, put his long fair hair under his hat, and so disguised carried the money to the starving family. He sent money, too, to Sheridan on his deathbed, and would have sent more had not death ended the career of that man of genius. Besides these, there are a few pretty speeches, kind and graceful, to persons with whom he was brought in contact. But he turned upon twenty friends. He was fond and familiar with them one day, and he passed them on the next without recognition. He used them, liked them, loved them perhaps, in his way, and then separated from them. On Monday he kissed and fondled poor Perdita, and on Tuesday he met her and did not know her. On Wednesday he was very affectionate with that wretched Brummel, and on Thursday forgot him; cheated him even out of a snuffbox which he owed the poor dandy; saw him years afterwards in his downfall and poverty, when the bankrupt Beau sent him another snuffbox with some of the snuff he used to love, as a piteous token of remembrance and submission; and the King took the snuff, and ordered his horses, and drove on, and had not the grace to notice his old companion, favourite, rival, enemy, superior. In Wraxall there is some gossip about him. When the charming, beautiful, generous Duchess of Devonshire died—the lovely lady whom he used to call his dearest duchess once, and pretend to admire as all English society admired her—he said, "Then we have lost the best-bred woman in England." "Then we have lost the kindest heart in England," said noble Charles Fox. On another occasion, when three noblemen were to receive the Garter, says Wraxall, "A great personage observed that never did three men receive the order in so characteristic a manner. The Duke of A. advanced to the sovereign with a phlegmatic, cold, awkward air like a clown; Lord B. came forward fawning and smiling like a courtier; Lord C. presented himself easy, unembarrassed, like a gentleman!" These are the stories one has to recall about the Prince and King—kindness to a housemaid, generosity to a groom, criticism on a bow. There *are* no better stories about him: they are mean and trivial, and they characterise him. The great war of empires and giants goes on. Day by day victories are won and lost by the brave. Torn smoky flags and battered eagles are wrenched from the heroic enemy and laid at his feet; and he sits there on his throne and smiles, and gives the guerdon of valour to the conqueror. He! Elliston the actor, when the *Coronation* was performed, in which he took the principal part, used to fancy himself the King, burst into tears, and hiccup a blessing on the people. I believe it is certain about George IV., that he had heard so much of the war, knighted so many people, and worn such a prodigious quantity of marshal's uniforms, cocked-hats, cock's feathers, scarlet and bullion in general, that he actually fancied he had been present in some campaigns, and, under the name of General Brock, led a tremendous charge of the German legion at Waterloo.

He is dead but thirty years, and one asks how a great society could have tolerated him? Would we bear him now? In this quarter of a century, what a silent revolution has been working! how it has separated us from old times and manners! How it has changed men themselves! I can see old gentlemen now among us, of perfect good breeding, of quiet lives, with venerable grey heads, fondling their grandchildren; and look at them, and wonder what they were once. That gentleman of the grand old school, when he was in the 10th Hussars, and dined at the Prince's table, would fall under it night after night. Night after night that gentleman sat at Brooks's or Raggett's over the dice. If, in the petulance of play or drink, that gentleman spoke a sharp word to his neighbour, he and the other would infallibly go out and try to shoot each other the next morning. That gentleman would drive his friend Richmond, the black boxer, down to Moulsey, and hold his coat, and shout and swear, and hurrah with delight whilst the black man was beating Dutch Sam the Jew. That gentleman would take a manly pleasure in pulling his own coat off, and thrashing a bargeman in a street row. That gentleman has been in a watch-house. That gentleman, so exquisitely polite with ladies in a drawing-room, so loftily courteous, if he talked now as he used among men in his youth, would swear so as to make your hair stand on end. I met lately a very old German gentleman, who had served in our army at the beginning of the century. Since then he has lived on his own estate, but rarely meeting with an Englishman, whose language —the language of fifty years ago that is—he possesses perfectly. When this highly-bred old man began to speak English to me almost every other word he uttered was an oath: as they used (they swore dreadfully in Flanders) with the Duke of York before Valenciennes, or at Carlton House over the supper and cards. Read Byron's letters. So accustomed is the young man to oaths that he employs them even in writing to his friends, and swears by the post. Read his account of the doings of the young men at Cambridge, of the ribald professors, "one of whom could pour out Greek like a drunken Helot," and whose excesses surpassed even those of the young men. Read Matthews's description of the boyish lordling's housekeeping at Newstead, the skull-cup passed round, the monk's dresses from the masquerade warehouse, in which the young scapegraces used to sit until daylight, chanting appropriate songs round their wine. "We come to breakfast at two or three o'clock," Matthews says. "There are gloves and foils for those who like to amuse themselves, or we fire pistols at a mark in the hall, or we worry the wolf." A jolly life truly! The noble young owner of the mansion writes about such affairs himself in letters to his friend Mr. John Jackson, pugilist, in London.

All the Prince's time tells a similar strange story of manners and pleasure. In Wraxall we find the Prime Minister himself, the redoubted William Pitt, engaged in high jinks with personages of no less importance than Lord Thurlow the Lord Chancellor, and Mr. Dundas the Treasurer of the Navy. Wraxall relates how these three statesmen, returning after dinner from Addiscombe, found a turnpike open and galloped through it without paying the toll. The turnpike-man, fancying they were highwaymen, fired a blunderbuss after them, but missed them; and the poet sang—

> "How as Pitt wandered darkling o'er the plain,
> His reason drown'd in Jenkinson's champagne,
> A rustic's hand, but righteous Fate withstood,
> Had shed a Premier's for a robber's blood."

Here we have the Treasurer of the Navy, the Lord High Chancellor, and the Prime Minister, all engaged in a most undoubted lark. In Eldon's "Memoirs," about the very same time, I read that the bar loved wine, as well as the woolsack. Not John Scott himself; he was a good boy always; and though he loved port-wine, loved his business and his duty and his fees a great deal better.

He has a Northern Circuit story of those days, about a party at the house of a certain Lawyer Fawcett, who gave a dinner every year to the counsel.

"On one occasion," related Lord Eldon, "I heard Lee say, 'I cannot leave Fawcett's wine. Mind, Davenport, you will go home immediately after dinner, to read the brief in that cause that we have to conduct to-morrow.'

"'Not I,' said Davenport. 'Leave my dinner and my wine to read a brief! No, no, Lee; that won't do.'

"'Then,' said Lee, 'what is to be done? who else is employed?'

"*Davenport.* 'Oh! young Scott.'

"*Lee.* 'Oh! he must go. Mr. Scott, you must go home immediately, and make yourself acquainted with that cause, before our consultation this evening.'

"This was very hard upon me; but I did go, and there was an attorney from Cumberland, and one from Northumberland, and I do not know how many other persons. Pretty late, in came Jack Lee, as drunk as he could be.

"'I cannot consult to-night; I must go to bed,' he exclaimed, and away he went. Then came Sir Thomas Davenport.

"'We cannot have a consultation to-night, Mr. Wordsworth' (Wordsworth, I think, was the name; it was a Cumberland name), shouted Davenport. 'Don't you see how drunk Mr. Scott is? it is impossible to consult.' Poor me! who had scarce had any dinner, and lost all my wine—I was so drunk that I could not consult'

Well, a verdict was given against us, and it was all owing to Lawyer Fawcett's dinner. We moved for a new trial; and I must say, for the honour of the bar, that those two gentlemen, Jack Lee and Sir Thomas Davenport, paid all the expenses between them of the first trial. It is the only instance I ever knew; but they did. We moved for a new trial (on the ground, I suppose, of the counsel not being in their senses), and it was granted. When it came on, the following year, the judge rose and said—

"'Gentlemen, did any of you dine with Lawyer Fawcett yesterday? for, if you did, I will not hear this cause till next year.'

"There was great laughter. We gained the cause that time."

On another occasion, at Lancaster, where poor Bozzy must needs be going the Northern Circuit, "we found him," says Mr. Scott, "lying upon the pavement inebriated. We subscribed a guinea at supper for him, and a half-crown for his clerk"—(no doubt there was a large bar, so that Scott's joke did not cost him much)—"and sent him, when he waked next morning, a brief, with instructions to move for what we denominated the writ of *quare adhæsit pavimento;* with observations duly calculated to induce him to think that it required great learning to explain the necessity of granting it, to the judge before whom he was to move." Boswell sent all round the town to attorneys for books that might enable him to distinguish himself—but in vain. He moved, however, for the writ, making the best use he could of the observations in the brief. The judge was perfectly astonished, and the audience amazed. The judge said, "I never heard of such a writ—what can it be that adheres *pavimento?* Are any of you gentlemen at the bar able to explain this?"

The bar laughed. At last one of them said—

"My Lord, Mr. Boswell last night *adhæsit pavimento.* There was no moving him for some time. At last he was carried to bed, and he has been dreaming about himself and the pavement."

The canny old gentleman relishes these jokes. When the Bishop of Lincoln was moving from the deanery of Saint Paul's, he says he asked a learned friend of his, by name Will Hay, how he should move some especially fine claret, about which he was anxious.

"Pray, my Lord Bishop," says Hay, "how much of the wine have you?"

The Bishop said six dozen.

"If that is all," Hay answered, "you have but to ask me six times to dinner, and I will carry it all away myself."

There were giants in those days; but this joke about wine is not so fearful as one perpetrated by Orator Thelwall, in the heat of the French Revolution, ten years later, over a frothing pot of porter. He blew the head off, and said, "This is the way I would serve all kings."

Now we come to yet higher personages, and find their doings recorded in the blushing pages of timid little Miss Burney's "Memoirs." She represents a prince of the Blood in quite a Royal condition. The loudness, the bigness, boisterousness, creaking boots and rattling oaths of the young princes appear to have frightened the prim household of Windsor, and set all the teacups twittering on the tray. On the night of a ball and birthday, when one of the pretty kind princesses was to come out, it was agreed that her brother, Prince William Henry, should dance the opening minuet with her, and he came to visit the household at their dinner.

"At dinner, Mrs. Schwellenberg presided, attired magnificently; Miss Goldsworthy, Mrs. Stanforth, Messrs. Du Luc and Stanhope dined with us; and while we were still eating fruit, the Duke of Clarence entered.

"He was just risen from the King's table, and waiting for his equipage to go home and prepare for the ball. To give you an idea of the energy of His Royal Highness's language, I ought to set apart an objection to writing, or rather intimating, certain forcible words, and beg leave to show you in genuine colours a Royal sailor.

"We all rose, of course, upon his entrance, and the two gentlemen placed themselves behind their chairs, while the footmen left the room. But he ordered us all to sit down, and called the men back to hand about some wine. He was in exceeding high spirits, and in the utmost good-humour. He placed himself at the head of the table, next Mrs. Schwellenberg, and looked remarkably well, gay, and full of sport and mischief; yet clever withal, as well as comical.

"'Well, this is the first day I have ever dined with the King at Saint James's on his birthday. Pray, have you all drunk his Majesty's health?'

"'No, your Royal Highness; your Royal Highness might make dem do dat,' said Mrs. Schwellenberg.

"'Oh, by ——, I will! Here, you' (to the footman), 'bring champagne; I'll drink the King's health again, if I die for it. Yes, I have done it pretty well already; so has the King, I promise you! I believe his Majesty was never taken such good care of before; we have kept his spirits up, I promise you; we have enabled him to go through his fatigues; and I should have done more still, but for the ball and Mary;—I have promised to dance with Mary. I must keep sober for Mary.'"

Indefatigable Miss Burney continues for a dozen pages reporting H.R.H.'s conversation, and indicating, with a humour not unworthy of the clever little author of "Evelina," the increasing state of excitement of the young sailor Prince, who drank more and more champagne, stopped old Mrs. Schwellenberg's remonstrances by giving the old lady a kiss, and telling her to hold her potato-trap, and who did not "keep sober for Mary." Mary had to find another partner that night, for the Royal William Henry could not keep his legs.

Will you have a picture of the amusements of another Royal Prince? It is the Duke of York, the blundering general, the beloved Commander-in-chief of the army, the brother with whom George IV. had had many a midnight carouse, and who continued his habits of pleasure almost till death seized his stout body.

In Pückler Muskau's "Letters," that German prince describes a bout with H.R.H., who in his best time was such a powerful toper that "six bottles of claret after dinner scarce made a perceptible change in his countenance."

"I remember," says Pückler, "that one evening—indeed, it was past midnight—he took some of his guests, among whom were the Austrian ambassador, Count Meervelt, Count Beroldingen, and myself, into his beautiful armoury. We tried to swing several Turkish sabres, but none of us had a very firm grasp; whence it happened that the Duke and Meervelt both scratched themselves with a sort of straight Indian sword so as to draw blood. Meervelt then wished to try if the sword cut as well as a Damascus, and attempted to cut through one of the wax candles that stood on the table. The experiment answered so ill, that both the candles, candlesticks and all, fell to the ground and were extinguished. While we were groping in the dark and trying to find the door, the Duke's aide-de-camp stammered out in great agitation, 'By G—, sir, I remember the sword is poisoned!'

"You may conceive the agreeable feelings of the wounded at this intelligence! Happily, on further examination, it appeared that claret, and not poison, was at the bottom of the colonel's exclamation."

And now I have one more story of the bacchanalian sort, in which Clarence and York, and the very highest personage of the realm, the great Prince Regent, all play parts. The feast took place at the Pavilion at Brighton, and was described to me by a gentleman who was present at the scene. In Gilray's caricatures, and amongst Fox's jolly associates, there figures a great nobleman, the Duke of Norfolk, called Jocky of Norfolk in his time, and celebrated for his table exploits. He had quarrelled with the

THE FIRST GENTLEMAN OF EUROPE.

Prince, like the rest of the Whigs; but a sort of reconciliation had taken place; and now, being a very old man, the Prince invited him to dine and sleep at the Pavilion, and the old Duke drove over from his Castle of Arundel with his famous equipage of grey horses, still remembered in Sussex.

The Prince of Wales had concocted with his Royal brothers a notable scheme for making the old man drunk. Every person at table was enjoined to drink wine with the Duke—a challenge which the old toper did not refuse. He soon began to see that there was a conspiracy against him; he drank glass for glass; he overthrew many of the brave. At last the First Gentleman of Europe proposed bumpers of brandy. One of the Royal brothers filled a great glass for the Duke. He stood up and tossed off the drink. "Now," says he, "I will have my carriage, and go home." The Prince urged upon him his previous promise to sleep under the roof where he had been so generously entertained. "No," he said; he had had enough of such hospitality. A trap had been set for him; he would leave the place at once and never enter its doors more.

The carriage was called, and came; but, in the half-hour's interval, the liquor had proved too potent for the old man; his host's generous purpose was answered, and the Duke's old grey head lay stupefied on the table. Nevertheless, when his post-chaise was announced, he staggered to it as well as he could, and stumbling in, bade the postillions drive to Arundel. They drove him for half-an-hour round and round the Pavilion lawn; the poor old man fancied he was going home. When he awoke that morning he was in bed at the Prince's hideous house at Brighton. You may see the place now for sixpence: they have fiddlers there every day; and sometimes buffoons and mountebanks hire the Riding House and do their tricks and tumbling there. The trees are still there, and the gravel walks round which the poor old sinner was trotted. I can fancy the flushed faces of the Royal Princes as they support themselves at the portico pillars, and look on at old Norfolk's disgrace; but I can't fancy how the man who perpetrated it continued to be called a gentleman.

From drinking, the pleased Muse now turns to gambling, of which in his youth our Prince was a great practitioner. He was a famous pigeon for the play-men; they lived upon him. Egalité Orleans, it was believed, punished him severely. A noble lord, whom we shall call the Marquis of Steyne, is said to have mulcted him in immense sums. He frequented the clubs, where play was then almost universal; and as it was known his debts of honour were sacred, whilst he was gambling Jews waited outside to purchase his notes of hand. His transactions on the turf were unlucky as well as discreditable: though I believe he, and his jockey, and his horse, Escape, were all innocent in that affair which created so much scandal.

Arthur's, Almack's, Bootle's, and White's were the chief clubs of the young men of fashion. There was play at all, and decayed noblemen and broken-down senators fleeced the unwary there. In Selwyn's "Letters" we find Carlisle, Devonshire, Coventry, Queensberry all undergoing the probation. Charles Fox, a dreadful gambler, was cheated in very late times—lost £200,000 at play. Gibbon tells of his playing for twenty-two hours at a sitting, and losing £500 an hour. That indomitable punter said that the greatest pleasure in life, after winning, was losing. What hours, what nights, what health did he waste over the devil's books! I was going to say what peace of mind; but he took his losses very philosophically. After an awful night's play, and the enjoyment of the greatest pleasure but *one* in life, he was found on a sofa tranquilly reading an Eclogue of Virgil.

Play survived long after the wild Prince and Fox had given up the dice-box. The dandies continued it. Byron, Brummel—how many names could I mention of men of the world who have suffered by it! In 1837 occurred a famous trial which pretty nigh put an end to gambling in England. A peer of the realm was found cheating at whist, and repeatedly seen to practise the trick called *sauter la coupe.* His friends at the clubs saw him cheat, and went on playing with him. One greenhorn, who had discovered his foul play, asked an old hand what he should do. "Do!" said the Mammon of Unrighteousness. "*Back him, you fool!*" The best efforts were made to screen him. People wrote him anonymous letters and warned him; but he would cheat, and they were obliged to find him out. Since that day, when my Lord's shame was made public, the gaming-table has lost all its splendour. Shabby Jews and blacklegs prowl about race-courses and tavern parlours, and now and then inveigle silly yokels with greasy packs of cards in railroad cars; but Play is a deposed goddess, her worshippers bankrupt, and her table in rags.

So is another famous British institution gone to decay—the Ring: the noble practice of British boxing, which in my youth was still almost flourishing.

The Prince, in his early days, was a great patron of this national sport, as his grand-uncle Culloden Cumberland had been before him; but, being present at a fight at Brighton, where one of the combatants was killed, the Prince pensioned the boxer's widow, and declared he never would attend another battle. "But, nevertheless" —I read in the noble language of Pierce Egan (whose smaller work on Pugilism I have the honour to possess)—"he thought it a manly and decided English feature, which ought not to be destroyed. His Majesty had a drawing of the sporting characters in the Fives Court placed in his boudoir, to remind him of his former attachment and support of true courage; and when any fight of note occurred after he was king, accounts of it were read to him by his desire." That gives one a fine image of a king taking his recreation;—at ease in a Royal dressing-gown;—too majestic to read himself, ordering the Prime Minister to read him accounts of battles: how Cribb punched Molyneux's eye, or Jack Randall thrashed the Game Chicken.

Where my Prince *did* actually distinguish himself was in driving. He drove once in four hours and a half from Brighton to Carlton House—fifty-six miles. All the young men of that day were fond of that sport. But the fashion of rapid driving deserted England; and, I believe, trotted over to America. Where are the amusements of our youth? I hear of no gambling now but amongst obscure ruffians; of no boxing but amongst the lowest rabble. One solitary four-in-hand still drove round the parks in London last year; but that charioteer must soon disappear. He was very old; he was attired after the fashion of the year 1825. He must drive to the banks of Styx ere long,—where the ferry-boat waits to carry him over to the defunct revellers who boxed and gambled and drank and drove with King George.

The bravery of the Brunswicks, that all the family must have it, that George possessed it, are points which all English writers have agreed to admit; and yet I cannot see how George IV. should have been endowed with this quality. Swaddled in feather-beds all his life, lazy, obese, perpetually eating and drinking, his education was quite unlike that of his tough old progenitors. His grandsires had confronted hardship and war, and ridden up and fired their pistols undaunted into the face of death. His father had conquered luxury and overcome indolence. Here was one who never resisted any temptation; never had a desire but he coddled and pampered it; if ever he had any nerve, frittered it away among cooks, and tailors, and barbers, and furniture-mongers, and opera-dancers. What muscle would not grow flaccid in such a life—a life that was never strung up to any action—an endless Capua without any campaign—all fiddling, and flowers, and feasting, and flattery, and folly? When George III. was pressed by the Catholic Question and the India Bill, he said he would retire to Hanover rather than yield upon either point; and he would have done what he said. But, before yielding, he was determined to fight his Ministers and Parliament; and he did, and he beat them. The time came when George IV. was pressed too upon the Catholic claims; the cautious

Peel had slipped over to that side; the grim old Wellington had joined it; and Peel tells us, in his "Memoirs," what was the conduct of the King. He at first refused to submit; whereupon Peel and the Duke offered their resignations, which their gracious master accepted. He did these two gentlemen the honour, Peel says, to kiss them both when they went away. (Fancy old Arthur's grim countenance and eagle beak as the monarch kisses it!) When they were gone he sent after them, surrendered, and wrote to them a letter begging them to remain in office, and allowing them to have their way. Then his Majesty had a meeting with Eldon, which is related at curious length in the latter's "Memoirs." He told Eldon what was not true about his interview with the new Catholic converts; utterly misled the old ex-Chancellor; cried, whimpered, fell on his neck, and kissed him too. We know old Eldon's own tears were pumped very freely. Did these two fountains gush together? I can't fancy a behaviour more unmanly, imbecile, pitiable. This a defender of the faith! This a chief in the crisis of a great nation! This an inheritor of the courage of the Georges!

Many of my hearers no doubt have journeyed to the pretty old town of Brunswick, in company with that most worthy, prudent, and polite gentleman, the Earl of Malmesbury, and fetched away Princess Caroline, for her longing husband, the Prince of Wales. Old Queen Charlotte would have had her eldest son marry a niece of her own, that famous Louisa of Strelitz, afterwards Queen of Prussia, and who shares with Marie Antoinette in the last age the sad pre-eminence of beauty and misfortune. But George III. had a niece at Brunswick; she was a richer Princess than Her Serene Highness of Strelitz:—in fine, the Princess Caroline was selected to marry the heir to the English throne. We follow my Lord Malmesbury in quest of her; we are introduced to her illustrious father and Royal mother; we witness the balls and fêtes of the old Court; we are presented to the Princess herself, with her fair hair, her blue eyes, and her impertinent shoulders—a lively, bouncing, romping Princess, who takes the advice of her courtly English mentor most generously and kindly. We can be present at her very toilette, if we like; regarding which, and for very good reasons, the British courtier implores her to be particular. What a strange Court! What a queer privacy of morals and manners do we look into! Shall we regard it as preachers and moralists, and cry Woe, against the open vice and selfishness and corruption; or look at it as we do at the king in the pantomime, with his pantomime wife and pantomime courtiers, whose big heads he knocks together, whom he pokes with his pantomime sceptre, whom he orders to prison under the guard of his pantomime beefeaters, as he sits down to dine on his pantomime pudding? It is grave, it is sad: it is theme most curious for moral and political speculation; it is monstrous, grotesque, laughable, with its prodigious littlenesses, etiquettes, ceremonials, sham moralities; it is as serious as a sermon; and as absurd and outrageous as Punch's puppet-show.

Malmesbury tells us of the private life of the Duke, Princess Caroline's father, who was to die, like his warlike son, in arms against the French; presents us to his courtiers, his favourite; his Duchess, George III.'s sister, a grim old Princess, who took the British envoy aside and told him wicked old stories of wicked old dead people and times; who came to England afterwards when her nephew was Regent, and lived in a shabby furnished lodging, old, and dingy, and deserted, and grotesque, but somehow Royal. And we go with him to the Duke to demand the Princess's hand in form, and we hear the Brunswick guns fire their adieux of salute, as H.R.H. the Princess of Wales departs in the frost and snow; and we visit the domains of the Prince Bishop of Osnaburg—the Duke of York of our early time; and we dodge about from the French revolutionists, whose ragged legions are pouring over Holland and Germany and gaily trampling down the old world to the tune of "Ça ira;" and we take shipping at Stade, and we land at Greenwich, where the Princess's ladies and the Prince's ladies are in waiting to receive Her Royal Highness.

What a history follows! Arrived in London, the bridegroom hastened eagerly to receive his bride. When she was first presented to him, Lord Malmesbury says she very properly attempted to kneel. "He raised her gracefully enough, embraced her, and turning round to me, said—

"'Harris, I am not well; pray get me a glass of brandy.'

"I said, 'Sir, had you not better have a glass of water?'

"Upon which, much out of humour, he said, with an oath, 'No; I will go to the Queen.'"

What could be expected from a wedding which had such a beginning—from such a bridegroom and such a bride? I am not going to carry you through the scandal of that story, or follow the poor Princess through all her vagaries; her balls and her dances, her travels to Jerusalem and Naples, her jigs, and her junketings, and her tears. As I read her trial in history, I vote she is not guilty. I don't say it is an impartial verdict; but as one reads her story the heart bleeds for the kindly, generous, outraged creature. If wrong there be, let it lie at his door who wickedly thrust her from it. Spite of her follies, the great hearty people of England loved, and protected, and pitied her. "God bless you! we wiil bring your husband back to you," said a mechanic one day, as she told Lady Charlotte Bury with tears streaming down her cheeks. They could not bring that husband back; they could not cleanse that selfish heart. Was hers the only one he had wounded? Steeped in selfishness, impotent for faithful attachment and manly enduring love, —had it not survived remorse, was it not accustomed to desertion?

Malmesbury gives us the beginning of the marriage story;—how the Prince reeled into chapel to be married; how he hiccupped out his vows of fidelity—you know how he kept them: how he pursued the woman whom he had married; to what a state he brought her; with what blows he struck her; with what malignity he pursued her; what his treatment of his daughter was; and what his own life. *He* the first gentleman of Europe! There is no stronger satire on the proud English society of that day, than that they admired George.

No, thank God, we can tell of better gentlemen; and whilst our eyes turn away, shocked, from this monstrous image of pride, vanity, weakness, they may see in that England over which the last George pretended to reign, some who merit indeed the title of gentlemen, some who make our hearts beat when we hear their names, and whose memory we fondly salute when that of yonder imperial mannikin is tumbled into oblivion. I will take men of my own profession of letters. I will take Walter Scott, who loved the King, and who was his sword and buckler, and championed him like that brave Highlander in his own story, who fights round his craven chief. What a good gentleman! What a friendly soul, what a generous hand, what an amiable life was that of the noble Sir Walter! I will take another man of letters, whose life I admire even more,—an English worthy, doing his duty for fifty noble years of labour, day by day storing up learning, day by day working for scant wages, most charitable out of his small means, bravely faithful to the calling which he had chosen, refusing to turn from his path, for popular praise or princes' favour:—I mean *Robert Southey*. We have left his old political landmarks miles and miles behind; we protest against his dogmatism; nay, we begin to forget it and his politics: but I hope his life will not be forgotten, for it is sublime in its simplicity, its energy, its honour, its affection. In the combat between Time and Thalaba, I suspect the former destroyer has conquered. Kehama's Curse frightens very few readers now; but Southey's private letters are worth piles of epics, and are sure to last among us as long as kind hearts like to sympathise with goodness and purity, and love and upright life.

"If your feelings are like mine," he writes to his wife, "I will not go to Lisbon without you, or I will stay at home, and not part from you. For though not unhappy when away, still without you I am not happy. For your sake, as well as my own and little Edith's, I will not consent to any separation; the growth of a year's love between her and me, if it please God she should live, is a thing too delightful in itself, and too valuable in its consequences, to be given up for any light inconvenience on your part or mine. . . . On these things we will talk at leisure; only, dear, dear Edith, *we must not part!*"

This was a poor literary gentleman. The First Gentleman in Europe had a wife and daughter too. Did he love them so? Was he faithful to them? Did he sacrifice ease for them, or show them the sacred examples of religion and honour? Heaven gave the Great English Prodigal no such good fortune. Peel proposed to make a baronet of Southey; and to this advancement the King agreed. The poet nobly rejected the offered promotion.

"I have," he wrote, "a pension of £200 a year, conferred upon me by the good offices of my old friend C. Wynn, and I have the laureateship. The salary of the latter was immediately appropriated, as far as it went, to a life insurance for £3000, which, with an earlier insurance, is the sole provision I have made for my family. All beyond must be derived from my own industry. Writing for a livelihood, a livelihood is all that I have gained; for, having also something better in view, and never, therefore, having courted popularity, nor written for the mere sake of gain, it has not been possible for me to lay by anything. Last year, for the first time in my life, I was provided with a year's expenditure beforehand. This exposition may show how unbecoming and unwise it would be to accept the rank which, so greatly to my honour, you have solicited for me."

How noble his poverty is, compared to the wealth of his master! His acceptance even of a pension was made the object of his opponents' satire: but think of the merit and modesty of this State pensioner; and that other enormous drawer of public money, who receives £100,000 a year, and comes to Parliament with a request for £650,000 more!

Another true knight of those days was Cuthbert Collingwood; and I think, since Heaven made gentlemen, there is no record of a better one than that. Of brighter deeds, I grant you, we may read performed by others; but where of a nobler, kinder, more beautiful life of duty, of a gentler, truer heart? Beyond dazzle of success and blaze of genius, I fancy shining a hundred and a hundred times higher the sublime purity of Collingwood's gentle glory. His heroism stirs British hearts when we recall it. His love, and goodness, and piety make one thrill with happy emotion. As one

2

reads of him and his great comrade going into the victory with which their names are immortally connected, how the old English word comes up, and that old English feeling of what I should like to call Christian honour! What gentlemen they were, what great hearts they had! "We can, my dear Coll," writes Nelson to him, "have no little jealousies; we have only one great object in view,—that of meeting the enemy, and getting a glorious peace for our country." At Trafalgar, when the *Royal Sovereign* was pressing alone into the midst of the combined fleets, Lord Nelson said to Captain Blackwood: "See how that noble fellow, Collingwood, takes his ship into action! How I envy him!" The very same throb and impulse of heroic generosity was beating in Collingwood's honest bosom. As he led into the fight, he said: "What would Nelson give to be here!"

After the action of the 1st of June, he writes:—

"We cruised for a few days, like disappointed people looking for what they could not find, *until the morning of little Sarah's birthday*, between eight and nine o'clock, when the French fleet, of twenty-five sail of the line, was discovered to windward. We chased them, and they bore down within about five miles of us. The night was spent in watching and preparation for the succeeding day; and many a blessing did I send forth to my Sarah, lest I should never bless her more. At dawn, we made our approach on the enemy, then drew up, dressed our ranks, and it was about eight when the admiral made the signal for each ship to engage her opponent, and bring her to close action; and then down we went under a crowd of sail, and in a manner that would have animated the coldest heart, and struck terror into the most intrepid enemy. The ship we were to engage was two ahead of the French admiral, so we had to go through his fire and that of two ships next to him, and received all their broadsides two or three times before we fired a gun. It was then near ten o'clock. I observed to the admiral that about that time our wives were going to church, but that I thought the peal we should ring about the Frenchman's ear would outdo their parish bells."

There are no words to tell what the heart feels in reading the simple phrases of such a hero. Here is victory and courage, but love sublimer and superior. Here is a Christian soldier spending the night before battle in watching and preparing for the succeeding day, thinking of his dearest home, and sending many blessings forth to his Sarah, "lest he should never bless her more." Who would not say Amen to his supplication? It was a benediction to his country—the prayer of that intrepid loving heart.

We have spoken of a good soldier and good men of letters as

specimens of English gentlemen of the age just past: may we not also—many of my elder hearers, I am sure, have read, and fondly remember, his delightful story—speak of a good divine, and mention Reginald Heber as one of the best of English gentlemen? The charming poet, the happy possessor of all sorts of gifts and accomplishments, birth, wit, fame, high character, competence—he was the beloved parish priest in his own home of Hodnet, "counselling his people in their troubles, advising them in their difficulties, comforting them in distress, kneeling often at their sick-beds at the hazard of his own life; exhorting, encouraging where there was need; where there was strife, the peacemaker; where there was want, the free giver."

When the Indian bishopric was offered to him he refused at first; but after communing with himself (and committing his case to the quarter whither such pious men are wont to carry their doubts), he withdrew his refusal, and prepared himself for his mission and to leave his beloved parish. "Little children, love one another, and forgive one another," were the last sacred words he said to his weeping people. He parted with them, knowing, perhaps, he should see them no more. Like those other good men of whom we have just spoken, love and duty were his life's aim. Happy he, happy they who were so gloriously faithful to both! He writes to his wife those charming lines on his journey:—

"If thou, my love, wert by my side, my babies at my knee,
How gladly would our pinnace glide o'er Gunga's mimic sea!

I miss thee at the dawning grey, when, on our deck reclined,
In careless ease my limbs I lay and woo the cooler wind.

I miss thee when by Gunga's stream my twilight steps I guide;
But most beneath the lamp's pale beam I miss thee by my side.

I spread my books, my pencil try, the lingering noon to cheer;
But miss thy kind approving eye, thy meek attentive ear.

But when of morn and eve the star beholds me on my knee,
I feel, though thou art distant far, thy prayers ascend for me.

Then on! then on! where duty leads my course be onward still—
O'er broad Hindostan's sultry meads, or bleak Almorah's hill.

That course nor Delhi's kingly gates, nor wild Malwah detain,
For sweet the bliss us both awaits by yonder western main.

Thy towers, Bombay, gleam bright, they say, across the dark blue sea:
But ne'er were hearts so blithe and gay as then shall meet in thee!'

Is it not Collingwood and Sarah, and Southey and Edith? His affection is part of his life. What were life without it? Without love, I can fancy no gentleman.

How touching is a remark Heber makes in his "Travels through India," that on inquiring of the natives at a town, which of the governors of India stood highest in the opinion of the people, he found that, though Lord Wellesley and Warren Hastings were honoured as the two greatest men who had ever ruled this part of the world, the people spoke with chief affection of Judge Cleveland, who had died, aged twenty-nine, in 1784. The people have built a monument over him, and still hold a religious feast in his memory. So does his own country still tend with a heart's regard the memory of the gentle Heber.

And Cleveland died in 1784, and is still loved by the heathen, is he? Why, that year 1784 was remarkable in the life of our friend the First Gentleman of Europe. Do you not know that he was twenty-one in that year, and opened Carlton House with a grand ball to the nobility and gentry, and doubtless wore that lovely pink coat which we have described. I was eager to read about the ball, and looked to the old magazines for information. The entertainment took place on the 10th February. In the *European Magazine* of March 1784 I came straightway upon it:—

"The alterations at Carlton House being finished, we lay before our readers a description of the State apartments as they appeared on the 10th instant, when H.R.H. gave a grand ball to the principal nobility and gentry. . . . The entrance to the State room fills the mind with an inexpressible idea of greatness and splendour.

"The State chair is of a gold frame, covered with crimson damask; on each corner of the feet is a lion's head, expressive of fortitude and strength; the feet of the chair have serpents twining round them, to denote wisdom. Facing the throne, appears the helmet of Minerva; and over the windows, glory is represented by Saint George with a superb gloria.

"But the saloon may be styled the *chef d'œuvre*, and in every ornament discovers great invention. It is hung with a figured lemon satin. The window-curtains, sofas, and chairs are of the same colour. The ceiling is ornamented with emblematical paintings, representing the Graces and Muses, together with Jupiter, Mercury, Apollo, and Paris. Two *ormolu* chandeliers are placed here. It is impossible by expression to do justice to the extraordinary workmanship, as well as design, of the ornaments. They each consist of a palm, branching out in five directions for the reception of lights. A beautiful figure of a rural nymph is represented entwining the stems of the tree with wreaths of flowers. In the centre of the room is a rich chandelier. To see this apartment *dans son plus beau jour*, it should be viewed in the glass over the chimney-piece. The range of apartments from the saloon to the ball-room, when the doors are open, formed one of the grandest spectacles that ever was beheld."

In the *Gentleman's Magazine*, for the very same month and year—March 1784—is an account of another festival, in which another great gentleman of English extraction is represented as taking a principal share:—

"According to order, H.E. the Commander-in-Chief was admitted to a public audience of Congress; and, being seated, the President, after a pause, informed him that the United States assembled were ready to receive his communications. Whereupon he arose, and spoke as follows:—

"'Mr. President,—The great events on which my resignation depended having at length taken place, I present myself before Congress to surrender into their hands the trust committed to me, and to claim the indulgence of retiring from the service of my country.

"'Happy in the confirmation of our independence and sovereignty, I resign the appointment I accepted with diffidence; which, however, was superseded by a confidence in the rectitude of our cause, the support of the supreme power of the nation and the patronage of Heaven. I close this last act of my official life by commending the interests of our dearest country to the protection of Almighty God, and those who have the superintendence of them to His holy keeping. Having finished the work assigned me, I retire from the great theatre of action; and, bidding an affectionate farewell to this august body, under whose orders I have so long acted, I here offer my commission and take my leave of the employments of my public life.'

"To which the President replied:—

"'Sir, having defended the standard of liberty in the New World, having taught a lesson useful to those who inflict and those who feel oppression, you retire with the blessings of your fellow-citizens; though the glory of your virtues will not terminate with your military command, but will descend to remotest ages.'"

Which was the most splendid spectacle ever witnessed,—the opening feast of Prince George in London, or the resignation of Washington? Which is the noble character for after ages to admire,—yon fribble dancing in lace and spangles, or yonder hero who sheathes his sword after a life of spotless honour, a purity unreproached, a courage indomitable, and a consummate victory? Which of these is the true gentleman? What is it to be a gentleman? Is it to have lofty aims, to lead a pure life, to keep your honour virgin; to have the esteem of your fellow-citizens, and the love of your fireside; to bear good fortune meekly; to suffer evil with constancy; and through evil or good to maintain truth always? Show me the happy man whose life exhibits these qualities, and him we will salute as gentleman, whatever his rank may be; show me the prince who possesses them, and he may be sure of our love and loyalty. The heart of Britain still beats kindly for George III., —not because he was wise and just, but because he was pure in life, honest in intent, and because according to his lights he worshipped Heaven. I think we acknowledge in the inheritrix of his sceptre a wiser rule and a life as honourable and pure; and I am sure the future painter of our manners will pay a willing allegiance to that good life, and be loyal to the memory of that unsullied virtue

CHARITY AND HUMOUR

CHARITY AND HUMOUR*

SEVERAL charitable ladies of this city, to some of whom I am under great personal obligation, having thought that a Lecture of mine would advance a benevolent end which they had in view, I have preferred, in place of delivering a Discourse, which many of my hearers no doubt know already, upon a subject merely literary or biographical, to put together a few thoughts which may serve as a supplement to the former Lectures, if you like, and which have this at least in common with the kind purpose which assembles you here, that they rise out of the same occasion, and treat of charity.

Besides contributing to our stock of happiness, to our harmless laughter and amusement, to our scorn for falsehood and pretension, to our righteous hatred of hypocrisy, to our education in the perception of truth, our love of honesty, our knowledge of life, and shrewd guidance through the world, have not our humorous writers, our gay and kind weekday preachers, done much in support of that holy cause which has assembled you in this place; and which you are all abetting—the cause of love and charity, the cause of the poor, the weak, and the unhappy; the sweet mission of love and tenderness, and peace and good-will towards men? That same theme which is urged upon you by the eloquence and example of

* This lecture was first delivered in New York on behalf of a charity at the time of Mr. Thackeray's visit to America in 1852, when he had been giving his series of lectures on the English Humourists. It was subsequently repeated with slight variations in London (once under the title of "Weekday Preachers") for the benefit of the families of Angus B. Reach and Douglas Jerrold. The lecture on behalf of the Jerrold Fund was given on July 22, 1857, the day after the declaration of the poll in the Oxford election, when Mr. Thackeray was a candidate for Parliament, and was defeated by Mr. Cardwell. The *Times*, in its account of the lecture, says: "The opening words of the discourse, uttered with a comical solemnity, of which Mr. Thackeray alone is capable, ran thus:—'Walking yesterday in the High Street of a certain ancient city.' So began the lecturer, and was interrupted by a storm of laughter that deferred for some moments the completion of the sentence."

good men to whom you are delighted listeners on Sabbath-days, is taught in his way and according to his power by the humorous writer, the commentator on everyday life and manners.

And as you are here assembled for a charitable purpose, giving your contributions at the door to benefit deserving people who need them, I like to hope and think that the men of our calling have done something in aid of the cause of charity, and have helped, with kind words and kind thoughts at least, to confer happiness and to do good. If the humorous writers claim to be weekday preachers, have they conferred any benefit by their sermons? Are people happier, better, better disposed to their neighbours, more inclined to do works of kindness, to love, forbear, forgive, pity, after reading in Addison, in Steele, in Fielding, in Goldsmith, in Hood, in Dickens? I hope and believe so, and fancy that in writing they are also acting charitably, contributing with the means which Heaven supplies them to forward the end which brings you too together.

A love of the human species is a very vague and indefinite kind of virtue, sitting very easily on a man, not confining his actions at all, shining in print, or exploding in paragraphs, after which efforts of benevolence, the philanthropist is sometimes said to go home, and be no better than his neighbours. Tartuffe and Joseph Surface, Stiggins and Chadband, who are always preaching fine sentiments, and are no more virtuous than hundreds of those whom they denounce and whom they cheat, are fair objects of mistrust and satire; but their hypocrisy, the homage, according to the old saying, which vice pays to virtue, has this of good in it, that its fruits are good: a man may preach good morals, though he may be himself but a lax practitioner; a Pharisee may put pieces of gold into the charity-plate out of mere hypocrisy and ostentation, but the bad man's gold feeds the widow and the fatherless as well as the good man's. The butcher and baker must needs look, not to motives, but to money, in return for their wares.

I am not going to hint that we of the Literary calling resemble Monsieur Tartuffe or Monsieur Stiggins, though there may be such men in our body, as there are in all.

A literary man of the humouristic turn is pretty sure to be of a philanthropic nature, to have a great sensibility, to be easily moved to pain or pleasure, keenly to appreciate the varieties of temper of people round about him, and sympathise in their laughter, love, amusement, tears. Such a man is philanthropic, man-loving by nature, as another is irascible, or red-haired, or six feet high. And so I would arrogate no particular merit to literary men for the possession of this faculty of doing good which some of them enjoy. It costs a gentleman no sacrifice to be benevolent on paper;

and the luxury of indulging in the most beautiful and brilliant sentiments never makes any man a penny the poorer. A literary man is no better than another, as far as my experience goes; and a man writing a book, no better nor no worse than one who keeps accounts in a ledger, or follows any other occupation. Let us, however, give him credit for the good, at least, which he is the means of doing, as we give credit to a man with a million for the hundred which he puts into the plate at a charity-sermon. He never misses them. He has made them in a moment by a lucky speculation, and parts with them, knowing that he has an almost endless balance at his bank, whence he can call for more. But in esteeming the benefaction, we are grateful to the benefactor, too, somewhat; and so of men of genius, richly endowed, and lavish in parting with their mind's wealth, we may view them at least kindly and favourably, and be thankful for the bounty of which Providence has made them the dispensers.

I have said myself somewhere, I do not know with what correctness (for definitions never are complete), that humour is wit and love; I am sure, at any rate, that the best humour is that which contains most humanity, that which is flavoured throughout with tenderness and kindness. This love does not demand constant utterance or actual expression, as a good father, in conversation with his children or wife, is not perpetually embracing them, or making protestations of his love; as a lover in the society of his mistress is not, at least as far as I am led to believe, for ever squeezing her hand, or sighing in her ear, "My soul's darling, I adore you!" He shows his love by his conduct, by his fidelity, by his watchful desire to make the beloved person happy; it lightens from his eyes when she appears, though he may not speak it; it fills his heart when she is present or absent; influences all his words and actions; suffuses his whole being; it sets the father cheerily to work through the long day, supports him through the tedious labour of the weary absence or journey, and sends him happy home again, yearning towards the wife and children. This kind of love is not a spasm, but a life. It fondles and caresses at due seasons, no doubt; but the fond heart is always beating fondly and truly, though the wife is not sitting hand-in-hand with him, or the children hugging at his knee. And so with a loving humour: I think, it is a genial writer's habit of being; it is the kind gentle spirit's way of looking out on the world—that sweet friendliness which fills his heart and his style. You recognise it, even though there may not be a single point of wit, or a single pathetic touch in the page; though you may not be called upon to salute his genius by a laugh or a tear. That collision of ideas, which provokes the one or the other, must be occasional. They must be like papa's embraces which I spoke of anon, who only delivers them now and again, and cannot be expected to go on kissing the children all night. And so the writer's jokes and sentiment, his ebullitions of feeling, his outbreaks of high spirits, must not be too frequent. One tires of a page of which every sentence sparkles with points, of a sentimentalist who is always pumping the tears from his eyes or your own. One suspects the genuineness of the tear, the naturalness of the humour; these ought to be true and manly in a man, as everything else in his life should be manly and true; and he loses his dignity by laughing or weeping out of place, or too often.

When the Reverend Laurence Sterne begins to sentimentalise over the carriage in Monsieur Dessein's courtyard, and pretends to squeeze a tear out of a rickety old shandrydan; when, presently, he encounters the dead donkey on his road to Paris, and snivels over that asinine corpse, I say: "Away, you drivelling quack: do not palm off these grimaces of grief upon simple folks who know no better, and cry misled by your hypocrisy." Tears are sacred. The tributes of kind hearts to misfortune, the mites which gentle souls drop into the collections made for God's poor and unhappy, are not to be tricked out of them by a whimpering hypocrite, handing round a begging-box for your compassion, and asking your pity for a lie. When that same man tells me of Lefevre's illness and Uncle Toby's charity; of the noble at Rennes coming home and reclaiming his sword, I thank him for the generous emotion which, springing genuinely from his own heart, has caused mine to admire benevolence and sympathise with honour; and to feel love, and kindness, and pity.

If I do not love Swift, as, thank God, I do not, however immensely I may admire him, it is because I revolt from the man who placards himself as a professional hater of his own kind; because he chisels his savage indignation on his tombstone, as if to perpetuate his protest against being born of our race—the suffering, the weak, the erring, the wicked, if you will, but still the friendly, the loving children of God our Father: it is because, as I read through Swift's dark volumes, I never find the aspect of nature seems to delight him; the smiles of children to please him; the sight of wedded love to soothe him. I do not remember in any line of his writing a passing allusion to a natural scene of beauty. When he speaks about the families of his comrades and brother clergymen, it is to assail them with gibes and scorn, and to laugh at them brutally for being fathers and for being poor. He does mention in the Journal to Stella a sick child, to be sure—a child of Lady Masham, that was ill of the smallpox—but then it is to confound the brat for being ill, and the mother for attending to it, when she should have been busy about a Court intrigue, in which the Dean was deeply engaged. And he alludes to a suitor of Stella's, and a match she might have made, and would have made, very likely, with an honourable and faithful and attached man, Tisdall, who loved her, and of whom Swift speaks, in a letter to this lady, in language so foul that you would not bear to hear it. In treating of the good the humourists have done, of the love and kindness they have taught and left behind them, it is not of this one I dare speak. Heaven help the lonely misanthrope! be kind to that multitude of sins, with so little charity to cover them!

Of Mr. Congreve's contributions to the English stock of benevolence, I do not speak; for, of any moral legacy to posterity, I doubt whether that brilliant man ever thought at all. He had some money, as I have told; every shilling of which he left to his friend the Duchess of Marlborough, a lady of great fortune and the highest fashion. He gave the gold of his brains to persons of fortune and fashion, too. There is no more feeling in his comedies than in as many books of Euclid. He no more pretends to teach love for the poor, and good-will for the unfortunate, than a dancing-master does; he teaches pirouettes and flic-flacs; and how to bow to a lady, and to walk a minuet. In his private life Congreve was immensely liked—more so than any man of his age, almost; and, to have been so liked, must have been kind and good-natured. His good-nature bore him through extreme bodily ills and pain, with uncommon cheerfulness and courage. Being so gay, so bright, so popular, such a grand seigneur, be sure he was kind to those about him, generous to his dependants, serviceable to his friends. Society does not like a man so long as it liked Congreve, unless he is likeable; it finds out a quack very soon; it scorns a poltroon or a curmudgeon: we may be certain that this man was brave, good-tempered, and liberal; so, very likely, is Monsieur Pirouette, of whom we spoke; he cuts his capers, he grins, bows, and dances to his fiddle. In private he may have a hundred virtues; in public, he teaches dancing. His business is cotillons, not ethics.

As much may be said of those charming and lazy Epicureans, Gay and Prior, sweet lyric singers, comrades of Anacreon, and disciples of love and the bottle. "Is there any moral shut within the bosom of a rose?" sings our great Tennyson. Does a nightingale preach from a bough, or the lark from his cloud? Not knowingly; yet we may be grateful, and love larks and roses, and the flower-crowned minstrels, too, who laugh and who sing.

Of Addison's contributions to the charity of the world I have spoken before, in trying to depict that noble figure; and say now, as then, that we should thank him as one of the greatest benefactors of that vast and immeasurably spreading family which speaks our common tongue. Wherever it is spoken, there is no man that does not feel, and understand, and use the noble English word "gentleman." And there is no man that teaches us to be gentlemen better than Joseph Addison. Gentle in our bearing through life; gentle and courteous to our neighbour; gentle in dealing with his follies and weaknesses; gentle in treating his opposition; deferential to the old; kindly to the poor, and those below us in degree; for people above us and below us we must find, in whatever hemisphere we dwell, whether kings or presidents govern us; and in no republic or monarchy that I know of, is a citizen exempt from the tax of befriending poverty and weakness, of respecting age, and of honouring his father and mother. It has just been whispered to me—I have not been three months in the country, and, of course, cannot venture to express an opinion of my own—that, in regard to paying this latter tax of respect and honour to age, some very few of the Republican youths are occasionally a little remiss. I have heard of young Sons of Freedom publishing their Declaration of Independence before they could well spell it; and cutting the connection with father and mother before they had learned to shave. My own time of life having been stated, by various enlightened organs of public opinion, at almost any figure from forty-five to sixty, I cheerfully own that I belong to the Fogey interest, and ask leave to rank in, and plead for, that respectable class. Now a gentleman can but be a gentleman, in Broadwood or the backwoods, in Pall Mall or California; and where and whenever he lives, thousands of miles away in the wilderness, or hundreds of years hence, I am sure that reading the writings of this true gentleman, this true Christian, this noble Joseph Addison, must do him good. He may take Sir Roger de Coverley to the Diggings with him, and learn to be gentle and good-humoured, and urbane, and friendly in the midst of that struggle in which his life is engaged. I take leave to say that the most brilliant youth of this city may read over this delightful memorial of a bygone age, of fashions long passed away; of manners long since changed and modified; of noble gentlemen, and a great, and a brilliant and polished society; and find in it much to charm and polish, to refine and instruct him, a courteousness, which can be out of place at no time, and under no flag, a politeness and simplicity, a truthful manhood, a gentle respect and deference, which may be kept as the unbought grace of life, and cheap defence of mankind, long after its old artificial distinctions, after periwigs, and small-swords, and ruffles, and red-heeled shoes, and titles, and stars and garters have passed away. I will tell you when I have been put in mind of two of the finest gentlemen books bring us any mention of. I mean *our* books (not books of history, but books of humour). I will tell you when I have been put in mind of the courteous gallantry of the noble knight, Sir Roger de Coverley of Coverley Manor, of the noble Hidalgo Don Quixote of La Mancha: here in your own omnibus-carriages and railway-cars, when I have seen a woman step in, handsome or not, well dressed or not, and a workman in hobnail shoes, or a dandy in the height of the fashion, rise up and give her his place. I think Mr. Spectator, with his short face, if he had seen such a deed of courtesy, would have smiled a sweet smile to the doer of that gentleman-like action, and have made him a low bow from under his great periwig, and have gone home and written a pretty paper about him.

I am sure Dick Steele would have hailed him, were he dandy or mechanic, and asked him to a tavern to share a bottle, or perhaps half-a-dozen. Mind, I do not set down the five last flasks to Dick's score for virtue, and look upon them as works of the most questionable supererogation.

Steele, as a literary benefactor to the world's charity, must rank very high, indeed, not merely from his givings, which were abundant, but because his endowments are prodigiously increased in value since he bequeathed them, as the revenues of the lands, bequeathed to our Foundling Hospital at London, by honest Captain Coram, its founder, are immensely enhanced by the houses since built upon them. Steele was the founder of sentimental writing in English, and how the land has been since occupied, and what hundreds of us have laid out gardens and built up tenements on Steele's ground! Before his time, readers or hearers were never called upon to cry except at a tragedy, and compassion was not expected to express itself otherwise than in blank verse, or for personages much lower in rank than a dethroned monarch, or a widowed or a jilted empress. He stepped off the high-heeled cothurnus, and came down into common life; he held out his great hearty arms, and embraced us all; he had a bow for all women; a kiss for all children; a shake of the hand for all men, high or low; he showed us Heaven's sun shining every day on quiet homes; not gilded palace-roofs only, or Court processions, or heroic warriors fighting for princesses, and pitched battles. He took away comedy from behind the fine ladies' alcove, or the screen where the libertine was watching her. He ended all that wretched business of wives jeering at their husbands, of rakes laughing wives, and husbands too, to scorn. That miserable, rouged, tawdry, sparkling, hollow-hearted comedy of the Restoration fled before him, and, like the wicked spirit in the Fairy-books, shrank, as

Steele let the daylight in, and shrieked, and shuddered, and vanished. The stage of humourists has been common life ever since Steele's and Addison's time; the joys and griefs, the aversions and sympathies, the laughter and tears of nature.

And here, coming off the stage, and throwing aside the motley habit, or satiric disguise, in which he had before entertained you, mingling with the world, and wearing the same coat as his neighbour, the humourist's service became straightway immensely more available; his means of doing good infinitely multiplied; his success, and the esteem in which he was held, proportionately increased. It requires an effort, of which all minds are not capable, to understand "Don Quixote"; children and common people still read "Gulliver" for the story merely. Many more persons are sickened by "Jonathan Wild" than can comprehend the satire of it. Each of the great men who wrote those books was speaking from behind the satiric mask I anon mentioned. Its distortions appal many simple spectators; its settled sneer or laugh is unintelligible to thousands, who have not the wit to interpret the meaning of the vizored satirist preaching from within. Many a man was at fault about Jonathan Wild's greatness, who could feel and relish Allworthy's goodness in "Tom Jones," and Doctor Harrison's in "Amelia," and dear Parson Adams, and Joseph Andrews. We love to read—we may grow ever so old, but we love to read of them still—of love and beauty, of frankness, and bravery, and generosity. We hate hypocrites and cowards; we long to defend oppressed innocence, and to soothe and succour gentle women and children. We are glad when vice is foiled and rascals punished; we lend a foot to kick Blifil downstairs; and as we attend the brave bridegroom to his wedding, on the happy marriage day, we ask the groom's-man's privilege to salute the blushing cheek of Sophia. A lax morality in many a vital point I own in Fielding, but a great hearty sympathy and benevolence; a great kindness for the poor; a great gentleness and pity for the unfortunate; a great love for the pure and good; these are among the contributions to the charity of the world with which this erring but noble creature endowed it.

As for Goldsmith, if the youngest and most unlettered person here has not been happy with the family at Wakefield; has not rejoiced when Olivia returned, and been thankful for her forgiveness and restoration; has not laughed with delighted good-humour over Moses's gross of green spectacles; has not loved with all his heart the good Vicar, and that kind spirit which created these charming figures, and devised the beneficent fiction which speaks to us so tenderly—what call is there for me to speak? In this place, and on this occasion, remembering these men, I claim from you your sympathy for the good they have done, and for the sweet charity which they have bestowed on the world.

When humour joins with rhythm and music, and appears in song, its influence is irresistible, its charities are countless, it stirs the feelings to love, peace, friendship, as scarce any moral agent can. The songs of Béranger are hymns of love and tenderness; I have seen great whiskered Frenchmen warbling the "Bonne Vieille," the "Soldats, au pas, au pas," with tears rolling down their mustachios. At a Burns's Festival I have seen Scotchmen singing Burns, while the drops twinkled on their furrowed cheeks; while each rough hand was flung out to grasp its neighbour's; while early scenes and sacred recollections, and dear and delightful memories of the past came rushing back at the sound of the familiar words and music, and the softened heart was full of love, and friendship, and home. Humour! if tears are the alms of gentle spirits, and may be counted, as sure they may, among the sweetest of life's charities,—of that kindly sensibility, and sweet sudden emotion, which exhibits itself at the eyes, I know no such provocative as humour. It is an irresistible sympathiser; it surprises you into compassion: you are laughing and disarmed, and suddenly forced into tears. I heard a humorous balladist not long since, a minstrel with wool on his head, and an ultra-Ethiopian complexion, who performed a negro ballad that I confess moistened these spectacles in the most unexpected manner. They have gazed at dozens of tragedy-queens, dying on the stage, and expiring in appropriate blank verse, and I never wanted to wipe them. They have looked up, with deep respect be it said, at many scores of clergymen in pulpits, and without being dimmed; and behold a vagabond with a corked face and a banjo sings a little song, strikes a wild note which sets the whole heart thrilling with happy pity. Humour! humour is the mistress of tears; she knows the way to the *fons lachrymarum*, strikes in dry and rugged places with her enchanting wand, and bids the fountain gush and sparkle. She has refreshed myriads more from her natural springs than ever tragedy has watered from her pompous old urn.

Popular humour, and especially modern popular humour, and the writers, its exponents, are always kind and chivalrous, taking the side of the weak against the strong. In our plays, and books, and entertainments for the lower classes in England, I scarce remember a story or theatrical piece in which a wicked aristocrat is not bepummelled by a dashing young champion of the people. There was a book which had an immense popularity in England, and I believe has been greatly read here, in which the Mysteries of the Court of London were said to be unveiled by a gentleman who, I suspect, knows about as much about the Court of London as he does of that of Pekin. Years ago I treated myself to sixpennyworth of this performance at a railway station, and found poor dear George IV., our late most religious and gracious king, occupied in the most flagitious designs against the tradesmen's families in his metropolitan city. A couple of years after, I took sixpennyworth more of the same delectable history: George IV. was still at work, still ruining the peace of tradesmen's families; he had been at it for two whole years, and a bookseller at the Brighton station told me that this book was by many, many times the most popular of all periodical tales then published, because, says he, "it lashes the aristocracy!" Not long since I went to two penny theatres in London; immense eager crowds of people thronged the buildings, and the vast masses thrilled and vibrated with the emotion produced by the piece represented on the stage, and burst into applause or laughter, such as many a polite actor would sign for in vain. In both these pieces there was a wicked Lord kicked out of the window—there is always a wicked Lord kicked out of the window. First piece:—"Domestic drama—Thrilling interest!—Weaver's family in distress!—Fanny gives away her bread to little Jacky, and starves!—Enter wicked Lord: tempts Fanny with offer of Diamond Necklace, Champagne Suppers, and Coach to ride in!—Enter sturdy Blacksmith.—Scuffle between Blacksmith and Aristocratic minion: exit wicked Lord out of the window." Fanny, of course, becomes Mrs. Blacksmith.

The second piece was a nautical drama, also of thrilling interest, consisting chiefly of hornpipes, and acts of most tremendous oppression on the part of certain Earls and Magistrates towards the people. Two wicked Lords were in this piece the atrocious scoundrels: one Aristocrat, a deep-dyed villain, in short duck trousers and Berlin cotton gloves; while the other minion of wealth enjoyed an eyeglass with a blue riband, and whisked about the stage with a penny cane. Having made away with Fanny Forester's lover, Tom Bowling, by means of a pressgang, they meet her all alone on a common, and subject her to the most opprobrious language and behaviour: "Release me, villains!" says Fanny, pulling a brace of pistols out of her pockets, and crossing them over her breast so as to cover wicked Lord to the right, wicked Lord to the left; and they might have remained in that position ever so much longer (for the aristocratic rascals had pistols too), had not Tom Bowling returned from sea at the very nick of time, armed with a great marlinespike, with which—whack! whack! down goes wicked Lord No. 1—wicked Lord No. 2. Fanny rushes into Tom's arms with an hysterical shriek, and I dare say they marry, and are very happy ever after. Popular fun is always kind: it is the champion of the humble against the great. In all popular parables, it is Little Jack that conquers, and the Giant that topples down. I think our popular authors are rather hard upon the great folks. Well, well! their Lordships have all the money, and can afford to be laughed at.

In our days, in England, the importance of the humorous preacher has prodigiously increased; his audiences are enormous; every week or month his happy congregations flock to him; they never tire of such sermons. I believe my friend Mr. Punch is as popular to-day as he has been any day since his birth; I believe that Mr. Dickens's readers are even more numerous than they have ever been since his unrivalled pen commenced to delight the world with its humour. We have among us other literary parties; we have Punch, as I have said, preaching from his booth; we have a Jerrold party very numerous, and faithful to that acute thinker and distinguished wit; and we have also—it must be said, and it is still to be hoped—a Vanity-Fair party, the author of which work has lately been described by the London *Times* newspaper as a writer of considerable parts, but a dreary misanthrope, who sees no good anywhere, who sees the sky above him green, I think, instead of blue, and only miserable sinners round about him. So we are; so is every writer and every reader I ever heard of; so was every being who ever trod this earth, save One. I cannot help telling the truth as I view it, and describing what I see. To describe it otherwise than it seems to me would be falsehood in that calling in which it has pleased Heaven to place me; treason to that conscience which says that men are weak; that truth must be told; that fault must be owned; that pardon must be prayed for; and that love reigns supreme over all.

I look back at the good which of late years the kind English Humourists have done; and if you are pleased to rank the present speaker among that class, I own to an honest pride at thinking what benefits society has derived from men of our calling. That "Song of the Shirt," which *Punch* first published, and the noble, the suffering, the melancholy, the tender Hood sang, may surely rank as a great act of charity to the world, and call from it its thanks and regard for its teacher and benefactor. That astonishing poem, which you all of you know, of the "Bridge of Sighs," who can read it without tenderness, without reverence to Heaven, charity to man, and thanks to the beneficent genius which sang for us nobly?

I never saw the writer but once; but shall always be glad to think that some words of mine, printed in a periodical of that day, and in praise of these amazing verses (which, strange to say, appeared almost unnoticed at first in the magazine in which Mr. Hood published them)—I am proud, I say, to think that some words of appreciation of mine reached him on his deathbed, and pleased and soothed him in that hour of manful resignation and pain.

As for the charities of Mr. Dickens, multiplied kindnesses which he has conferred upon us all; upon our children; upon people educated and uneducated; upon the myriads here and at home, who speak our common tongue; have not you, have not I, all of us reason to be thankful to this kind friend, who soothed and charmed so many hours, brought pleasure and sweet laughter to so many homes; made such multitudes of children happy; endowed us with such a sweet store of gracious thoughts, fair fancies, soft sympathies, hearty enjoyments? There are creations of Mr. Dickens's which seem to me to rank as personal benefits; figures so delightful, that one feels happier and better for knowing them, as one does for being brought into the society of very good men and women. The atmosphere in which these people live is wholesome to breathe in; you feel that to be allowed to speak to them is a personal kindness; you come away better for your contact with them; your hands seem cleaner from having the privilege of shaking theirs. Was there ever a better charity sermon preached in the world than Dickens's "Christmas Carol"? I believe it occasioned immense hospitality throughout England; was the means of lighting up hundreds of kind fires at Christmas-time; caused a wonderful outpouring of Christmas good feeling; of Christmas punch-brewing; an awful slaughter of Christmas turkeys, and roasting and basting of Christmas beef. As for this man's love of children, that amiable organ at the back of his honest head must be perfectly monstrous. All children ought to love him. I know two that do, and read his books ten times for once that they peruse the dismal preachments of their father. I know one who, when she is happy, reads "Nicholas Nickleby"; when she is unhappy, reads "Nicholas Nickleby"; when she is tired, reads "Nicholas Nickleby"; when she is in bed, reads "Nicholas Nickleby"; when she has nothing to do, reads "Nicholas Nickleby"; and when she has finished the book, reads "Nicholas Nickleby" over again. This candid young critic, at ten years of age, said, "I like Mr. Dickens's books much better than your books, papa"; and frequently expressed her desire that the latter author should write a book like one of Mr. Dickens's books. Who can? Every man must say his own thoughts in his own voice, in his own way; lucky is he who has such a charming gift of nature as this, which brings all the children in the world trooping to him, and being fond of him.

I remember, when that famous "Nicholas Nickleby" came out, seeing a letter from a pedagogue in the north of England, which, dismal as it was, was immensely comical. "Mr. Dickens's ill-advised publication," wrote the poor schoolmaster, "has passed like a whirlwind over the schools of the North." He was a proprietor of a cheap school; Dotheboys Hall was a cheap school. There were many such establishments in the northern counties. Parents were ashamed that never were ashamed before until the kind satirist laughed at them; relatives were frightened; scores of little scholars were taken away; poor schoolmasters had to shut their shops up; every pedagogue was voted a Squeers, and many suffered, no doubt unjustly; but afterwards schoolboys' backs were not so much caned; schoolboys' meat was less tough and more plentiful; and schoolboys' milk was not so sky-blue. What a kind light of benevolence it is that plays round Crummles and the Phenomenon, and all those poor theatre people in that charming book! What a humour! and what a good-humour! I coincide with the youthful critic, whose opinion has just been mentioned, and own to a family admiration for "Nicholas Nickleby."

One might go on, though the task would be endless and needless, chronicling the names of kind folks with whom this kind genius has made us familiar. Who does not love the Marchioness, and Mr. Richard Swiveller? Who does not sympathise, not only with Oliver Twist, but his admirable young friend the Artful Dodger? Who has not the inestimable advantage of possessing a Mrs. Nickleby in his own family? Who does not bless Sairey Gamp and wonder at Mrs. Harris. Who does not venerate the chief of that illustrious family who, being stricken by misfortune, wisely and greatly turned his attention to "coals," the accomplished, the Epicurean, the dirty, the delightful Micawber?

I may quarrel with Mr. Dickens's art a thousand and a thousand times, I delight and wonder at his genius; I recognise in it—I speak with awe and reverence—a commission from that Divine Beneficence, whose blessed task we know it will one day be to wipe every tear from every eye. Thankfully I take my share of the feast of love and kindness which this gentle, and generous, and charitable soul has contributed to the happiness of the world. I take and enjoy my share, and say a Benediction for the meal.

THE END